OCEANIC PROCESSES IN MARINE POLLUTION
Volume 5

OCEANIC PROCESSES IN MARINE POLLUTION

Editors: Iver W. Duedall, Florida Institute of Technology, Melbourne, Florida
           Dana R. Kester, University of Rhode Island, Kingston, Rhode Island
           P. Kilho Park, U.S. National Oceanic and Atmospheric Administration, Rockville, Maryland

Volume 1:   Biological Processes and Wastes in the Ocean
  Editors: Judith M. Capuzzo and Dana R. Kester

Volume 2:   Physicochemical Processes and Wastes in the Ocean
  Editors: Thomas P. O'Connor, Wayne V. Burt, and Iver W. Duedall

Volume 3:   Marine Waste Management: Science and Policy
  Editors: Michael A. Champ and P. Kilho Park

Volume 4:   Scientific Monitoring Strategies for Ocean Waste Disposal
  Editors: Donald W. Hood, Amy Schoener, and P. Kilho Park

Volume 5:   Urban Wastes in Coastal Marine Environments
  Editors: Douglas A. Wolfe and Thomas P. O'Connor

Volume 6:   Physical and Chemical Processes: Transport and Transformation
  Editors: Donald J. Baumgartner and Iver W. Duedall

OCEANIC PROCESSES IN MARINE POLLUTION
Volume 5

URBAN WASTES IN COASTAL MARINE ENVIRONMENTS

Edited By

DOUGLAS A. WOLFE
Ocean Assessments Division
U.S. National Oceanic and Atmospheric Administration
Rockville, Maryland

THOMAS P. O'CONNOR
Ocean Assessments Division
U.S. National Oceanic and Atmospheric Administration
Rockville, Maryland

KRIEGER PUBLISHING COMPANY
MALABAR, FLORIDA

Original Edition 1988

Printed and Published by
ROBERT E. KRIEGER PUBLISHING COMPANY, INC.
KRIEGER DRIVE
MALABAR, FL 32950

Library of Congress Cataloging in Publication Data

Urban wastes in coastal marine environments.
  (Oceanic processes in marine pollution; v. 5)

    Bibliography: p.
    Includes indexes.
    1. Waste disposal in the ocean.   2. Marine
pollution. 3. Refuse and refuse disposal.
4. Factory and trade waste. I. Wolfe, Douglas A.
II. O'Connor, Thomas P. III. Series.
TD645.U75   1988   363.7'394   87-22831
ISBN 0-89874-963-8

10 9 8 7 6 5 4 3

CONTRIBUTORS

BAIRD, RODGER, Los Angeles County Sanitation Districts, P.O. Box 4998, Whittier, California 90607

BARRICK, ROBERT C., PTI Environmental Services, 13231 SE 36th Street, Suite 200, Bellevue, Washington 98006

*BECKER, D. SCOTT, PTI Environmental Services, 13231 SE 36th Street, Suite 200, Bellevue, Washington 98006

BERRY, WALTER, U.S. Environmental Protection Agency, Environmental Research Laboratory, Narragansett, Rhode Island 02882

BIERMAN, VICTOR J., JR., Department of Civil Engineering, University of Notre Dame, Notre Dame, Indiana 46556

BLACK, DIANNE, U.S. Environmental Protection Agency, Environmental Research Laboratory, Narragansett, Rhode Island 02882

BLOOM, NICKOLAS, Battelle Marine Research Laboratory, Pacific Northwest Division, 439 West Sequim Bay Road, Sequim, Washington 98382

BRATKOVICH, ALAN, Ocean Physics Group, Department of Geological Sciences, University of Southern California, Los Angeles, California 90089-0741

*CHAPMAN, PETER M., E.V.S. Consultants, 195 Pemberton Avenue, North Vancouver, B.C., Canada V7P 2R4

*CRECELIUS, ERIC A., Battelle Marine Research Laboratory, Pacific Northwest Division, 439 West Sequim Bay Road, Sequim, Washington 98382

*CROSS, JEFFREY N., Southern California Coastal Water Research Project, 646 W. Pacific Coast Highway, Long Beach, California 90806

DAVIS, WAYNE R., U.S. Environmental Protection Agency, Environmental Research Laboratory, Narragansett, Rhode Island 02882

DEACUTIS, CHRISTOPHER, U.S. Environmental Protection Agency, Environmental Research Laboratory, Narragansett, Rhode Island 02882

DICKEY, TOMMY D., Ocean Physics Group, Department of Geological Sciences, University of Southern California, Los Angeles, California 90089-0741

DILLON, THOMAS, M., U.S. Army Corps of Engineers, Environmental Research Laboratory, Waterways Experiment Station, Vicksburg, Mississippi 39180

GALLOWAY, WALTER B., U.S. Environmental Protection Agency, Environmental Research Laboratory, Narragansett, Rhode Island 02882

GARNER, KATHRYN A., Environmental Sciences Program, University of Massachusetts–Boston, Boston, Massachusetts 02125

*GARBER, WILLIAM F., Bureau of Sanitation, Department of Public Works, City of Los Angeles, 200 North Spring Street, Los Angeles, California 90012

*GENTILE, JOHN H., U.S. Environmental Protection Agency, Environmental Research Laboratory, Narragansett, Rhode Island 02882

*GINN, THOMAS C., PTI Environmental Services, 13231 SE 36th Street, Suite 200, Bellevue, Washington 98006

GOSSETT, RICHARD W., Southern California Coastal Water Research Project, 646 W. Pacific Coast Highway, Long Beach, California 90806

GUTJAHR-GOBELL, RUTH, U.S. Environmental Protection Agency, Environmental Research Laboratory, Narragansett, Rhode Island 02882

HAYDOCK, IRWIN, Los Angeles County Sanitation Districts, P.O. Box 4998, Whittier, California 90607

HEBER, MARGARETE, U.S. Environmental Protection Agency, Environmental Research Laboratory, Narragansett, Rhode Island 02882

HEESEN, THEADORE, Los Angeles County Sanitation Districts, P.O. Box 4998, Whittier, California 90607

HELTSCHE, JAMES, U.S. Environmental Protection Agency, Environmental Research Laboratory, Narragansett, Rhode Island 02882

HOFFMAN, GERALD L., U.S. Environmental Protection Agency, Environmental Research Laboratory, Narragansett, Rhode Island 02882

*HOSHIKA, AKIRA, Government Industrial Research Institute, Chougoku, 15,000 Hiromachi, Kure, Hiroshima 737-01, Japan

JACKIM, EUGENE, U.S. Environmental Protection Agency, Environmental Research Laboratory, Narragansett, Rhode Island 02882

JOHNS, D. MICHAEL, U.S. Environmental Protection Agency, Environmental Research Laboratory, Narragansett, Rhode Island 02882

JONES, BURTON H., Allan Hancock Foundation, University of Southern California, Los Angeles, California 90089-0371

KITANO, YASUSHI, Water Research Institute, Nagoya University, Chikusa-ku, Nagoya 464, Japan

KUHN, ANN, U.S. Environmental Protection Agency, Environmental Research Laboratory, Narragansett, Rhode Island 02882

LAKE, JAMES L., U.S. Environmental Protection Agency, Environmental Research Laboratory, Narragansett, Rhode Island 02882

LIU, GUOXIAN, Institute of Marine Environmental Protection, State Oceanic Administration, Dalian, China

LUSSIER, SUZANNE, U.S. Environmental Protection Agency, Environmental Research Laboratory, Narragansett, Rhode Island 02882

MARCY, MARTHA, U.S. Environmental Protection Agency, Environmental Research Laboratory, Narragansett, Rhode Island 02882

*MATSUMOTO, EIJI, Geological Survey of Japan, 1-1-3 Higashi, Yatabe, Ibaraki 305, Japan

MAYER, GARRY F., National Oceanic and Atmospheric Administration, National Sea Grant Program, Rockville, Maryland, 20852

MILLER, DON C., U.S. Environmental Protection Agency, Environmental Research Laboratory, Narragansett, Rhode Island 02882

*MONAHAN, ROSEMARY, K., U.S. Environmental Protection Agency, Region I, Boston, Massachusetts 02125

MUELLER, CORNELIA, U.S. Environmental Protection Agency, Environmental Research Laboratory, Narragansett, Rhode Island 02882

MUNNS, WAYNE R., JR., Science Applications International Corporation, EPA Environmental Research Laboratory, Narragansett, Rhode Island 02882

NELSON, WILLIAM G., U.S. Environmental Protection Agency, Environmental Research Laboratory, Narragansett, Rhode Island 02882

*PAUL, JOHN F., U.S. Environmental Protection Agency, Environmental Research Laboratory, Narragansett, Rhode Island 02882

PESCH, CAROL E., U.S. Environmental Protection Agency, Environmental Research Laboratory, Narragansett, Rhode Island 02882

PESCH, GERALD G., U.S. Environmental Protection Agency, Environmental Research Laboratory, Narragansett, Rhode Island 02882

*PHELPS, DONALD K., U.S. Environmental Protection Agency, Environmental Research Laboratory, Narragansett, Rhode Island 02882

REDMOND, MICHELE, U.S. Environmental Protection Agency, Environmental Research Laboratory, Narragansett, Rhode Island 02882

REYNOLDS, BRUCE H., U.S. Environmental Protection Agency, Environmental Research Laboratory, Narragansett, Rhode Island 02882

ROGERSON, PETER F., U.S. Geological Survey, Analytical Services Branch, Arvada, Colorado 80002

ROSEN, JEFFREY S., U.S. Environmental Protection Agency, Environmental Research Laboratory, Narragansett, Rhode Island 02882

SCHAUER, PAUL S., U.S. Environmental Protection Agency, Environmental Research Laboratory, Narragansett, Rhode Island 02882

SCHIMMEL, STEVEN C., U.S. Environmental Protection Agency, Environmental Research Laboratory, Narragansett, Rhode Island 02882

SCOTT, K. JOHN, U.S. Environmental Protection Agency, Environmental Research Laboratory, Narragansett, Rhode Island 02882

SHIBA, TAKIO, Maritime Safety Agency Research Center, Kitanakadori, Naka-ku, Yokohama-shi, Japan

SHIOZAWA, TAKAYUKI, Government Industrial Research Institute, Chougoku, 15,000 Hiromachi, Kure, Hiroshima 737-01, Japan

*SIEGEL, DAVID A., Ocean Physics Group, Department of Geological Sciences, University of Southern California, Los Angeles, California 90089-0741

STANFORD, HAROLD M., National Oceanic and Atmospheric Administration, Office of Oceanography and Marine Assessment, Rockville, Maryland 20852

*STODDARD, ANDREW, Science Applications International Corporation, 8400 Westpark Drive, McLean, Virginia 22102

*STULL, JANET, Los Angeles County Sanitation Districts, P.O. Box 4998, Whittier, California 90607

WADA, FRANK F., Bureau of Sanitation, Department of Public Works, City of Los Angeles, 200 North Spring Street, Los Angeles, California 90012

WALDICHUK, MICHAEL, Department of Fisheries and Oceans, West Vancouver Laboratory, 4160 Marine Drive, West Vancouver, British Columbia, Canada V7V 1N6

*WALLACE, GORDON T., JR., Environmental Sciences Program, University of Massachusetts–Boston, Boston, Massachusetts 02125

WALSH, JOHN J., Department of Marine Science, University of South Florida, St. Petersburg, Florida 33701

WAN, BANGHE, Institute of Marine Environmental Protection, State Oceanic Administration, Dalian, China

WATANABE, KEIZO, Maritime Safety Agency Research Center, Kitanakadori, Naka-ku, Yokohama-shi, Japan

WAUGH, JEFFREY H., Battelle New England Marine Research Laboratory, Duxbury, Massachusetts 02332

WOLFE, DOUGLAS, A., Ocean Assessments Division, National Oceanic and Atmospheric Administration, Rockville, Maryland 20852

YANG, SONGLIN, Institute of Marine Environmental Protection, State Oceanic Administration, Dalian, China

YEVICH, CAROLYN A., U.S. Environmental Protection Agency, Environmental Research Laboratory, Narragansett, Rhode Island 02882

YEVICH, PAUL P., U.S. Environmental Protection Agency, Environmental Research Laboratory, Narragansett, Rhode Island 02882

*YOSHIMURA, HIROZO, Maritime Safety Agency Research Center, Kitanakadori, Naka-ku, Yokohama-shi, Japan

*YOUNG, DAVID R., U.S. Environmental Protection Agency, Hatfield Marine Science Center, Newport, Oregon 97365

ZAROOGIAN, GERALD E., U.S. Environmental Protection Agency, Environmental Research Laboratory, Narragansett, Rhode Island 02882

ZHOU, YIHUA, Institute of Marine Environmental Protection, State Oceanic Administration, Dalian, China

*indicates first author

Preface To
Oceanic Processes In Marine Pollution

It is becoming increasingly evident that the marine environment—oceans, seas, and estuaries comprising over 70% of the entire earth's surface—are not separate entities but are, instead, parts of a continuum. As such, the impacts dealt to one part of the marine environment must be expected to affect eventually the whole. As the ocean is used increasingly as a reservoir for wastes, it is imperative to ensure that the marine resources be used wisely and efficiently. One important approach to such a global perspective is the exchange of information vital to the health and careful management of the ocean. Many people associated with the marine scientific and technical community worldwide are now working to find solutions to problems of mutual interest. The results of their endeavors can be efficiently used through a common medium, such as *Oceanic Processes in Marine Pollution*.

The *Oceanic Processes in Marine Pollution* series is organized into individual reference books that focus on specifically related topics or themes in order to provide unity throughout. To date, six volumes are scheduled for publication:

Volume 1: *"Biological Processes and Wastes in the Ocean,"*
Volume 2: *"Physicochemical Processes and Wastes in the Ocean,"*
Volume 3: *"Marine Waste Management: Science and Policy,"*
Volume 4: *"Scientific Monitoring Strategies for Ocean Waste Disposal,"*
Volume 5: *"Urban Wastes in Coastal Marine Environments,"* and
Volume 6: *"Physical and Chemical Processes: Transport and Transformation."*

The objective of this series is to bring together selected scientific and technical information about fundamental oceanic processes, marine pollution, and marine waste management. The series will cover a broad range of topics, be interdisciplinary in scope, and be of use to scientists and researchers, environmental managers and engineers, administrative officials and legislative staffers, oceanographers, and students.

The driving force behind this series is our belief that some human activities, such as industrial and wastewater discharges to sea, ocean dumping, and inadvertent discharges from non-point sources, could lead to serious problems of marine pollution. A key element in this thought is the recognition that the combination of many dynamic biological, chemical, and physical processes in the sea sometimes reduce the effects of marine pollution; however, serious problems of marine pollution can and do occur even in the most dynamic system if it is overloaded with contaminants. The marine scientist, aware of the dynamics of this system, must, when called upon, be able to translate available technical findings into something that will be of use to the policy maker, the environmental manager, or the engineer who is given the task of regulating or setting policy for the use of the ocean. With this series we hope to provide a cohesive overview of the state-of-the-art technology and thought in a wide range of marine pollution topics.

The chapters included in this and succeeding volumes of this series have been subjected to both external and editorial reviews. We are especially grateful to the reviewers of these chapters for the time and effort that they devoted to the development of the final manuscripts.

Oceanic Processes in Marine Pollution could not have been produced without the willingness and support of the Ocean Assessments Division of the U.S. National Oceanic and Atmospheric Administration.

Iver W. Duedall
Series Editors   **Dana R. Kester**
P. Kilho Park

PREFACE

In today's world, the coastal margins of all continents are being used increasingly by humans, for industry and commerce, recreation, and residence. The shallow waters of the coastal zone receive a wide variety of wastes directly from industrial and municipal outfalls and from ocean dumping (e.g., of sewage sludge and dredged materials). To these direct inputs are added a number of more diffuse contaminant inputs: riverine flows that contain materials from upland agricultural runoff and from upland discharge, runoff from urban areas, residential communities and farms in the coastal zone, and inputs from the atmosphere (including fallout from local injections such as smokestacks and automobile exhaust and from large-scale atmospheric transport processes). These wastes are mixed in the coastal marine waters of the continental margins (extending from the estuarine zone to the edges of the continental shelves), from which over 90% of the world catch of fishery organisms is drawn.

Many waste-related conflicts arise from the divergent and multiple uses of the coastal marine environment. Resolution of these conflicts requires detailed information on the nature and magnitude of contaminant inputs, the dispersion and persistence of contaminants in the environment, and their bioaccumulation and effects in marine resource organisms. This information is required to predict the consequences of waste disposal in the marine environment and to identify the preferred means of managing that disposal.

The chapters in this volume are concerned with the distribution and effects of contaminants in coastal waters, and with their effective management. The volume begins with a conceptual framework for assessing coastal waste impacts and managing their inputs at an acceptable level. Part II examines the distribution and effects of contaminants in coastal waters of Southern California. Part III presents investigations on waste-related problems of the Northeastern United States and efforts to develop protocols for their assessment and management. Part IV focuses on pollution status and biological effects in Puget Sound and the Pacific Northwest, and Part V illustrates the distribution and effects of metallic contaminants in coastal water and sediments of Japan and China.

We wish to recognize here the far-reaching vision of our good friend and mentor, P. Kilho Park, who ten years ago, as director of the National Oceanic and Atmospheric Administration's Ocean Dumping Program, conceived and initiated the series of International Ocean Disposal Symposia on which this and eleven preceding scientific volumes have been based. Each of these technical volumes has represented a developmental stage in the continuing human quest for understanding and knowledge about the consequences of our many-faceted, waste-generating activities on the processes and the quality of the marine environment. Kilho's contribution to that goal has been enormous, not only through his dedication to, and promotion of, quality research, but also through his encouragement of information exchange and discussion among scientists.

Many members of the scientific community took time from their research, teaching, and administrative responsibilities to review the chapters in this book. Their criticism and helpful suggestions are gratefully acknowledged. We deeply appreciate the assistance of the staff of the Center for Academic Publications at the Florida Institute of

Technology in Melbourne. In particular, we thank Joyce Nuttall for her professional editing skills that were applied to this volume; Barbara J. Struttman, Duane E. De Freese, and Kimberley A. D'Arcy for preparing many of the illustrations; Madge Taylor for preparing the author index; and Mary Ann Nelson for overall coordination and preparation of the manuscript. We also thank Zenobia Neugebauer of NOAA's Ocean Assessments Division for her secretarial support on correspondence with authors and for retyping several manuscripts, and N. Jean Chatfield, also of the Ocean Assessments Division, for expert assistance with proofreading, page checking, and indexing. Finally we acknowledge the tireless efforts of Iver Duedall, chairman of the Department of Oceanography and Ocean Engineering at Florida Institute of Technology, who has served for several years as chairman of the Organizing Committee for the Ocean Disposal Symposia, and who coordinated the production of this series of volumes.

Most of the chapters in this book are based on papers presented at the Fifth International Ocean Disposal Symposium held 10–14 September 1984 at Oregon State University in Corvallis. That symposium and the preparation of this volume were supported in large part by a grant from the U.S. National Oceanic and Atmospheric Administration.

DOUGLAS A. WOLFE
THOMAS P. O'CONNOR

Rockville, Maryland

CONTENTS

GLOSSARY OF ACRONYMS AND INITIALISMS   xv

PART I. INTRODUCTION

1. Urban Wastes in Coastal Waters: Assimilative Capacity
   and Management   3

   Douglas A. Wolfe

**PART II. SEWAGE EFFLUENTS IN THE SOUTHERN CALIFORNIA
BIGHT ECOSYSTEM**

2. Relationship between Declining Discharges of Municipal Wastewater
   Contaminants and Marine Sediment Core Profiles   23

   Janet Stull, Rodger Baird, and Theadore C. Heesen

3. Persistence of Chlorinated Hydrocarbon Contamination in a California
   Marine Ecosystem   33

   David R. Young, Richard W. Gossett, and Theadore C. Heesen

4. Effects of Nearshore Upwelling on Coliform Dispersion near
   the Whites Point Ocean Outfall   43

   *David A. Siegel, Burton H. Jones, Tommy D. Dickey, Irwin Haydock,
   and Alan Bratkovich*

5. Water Quality in Santa Monica Bay, as Indicated by Measurements
   of Total Coliforms   49

   William F. Garber and Frank F. Wada

6. Fin Erosion and Epidermal Tumors in Demersal Fish from Southern
   California   57

   Jeffrey N. Cross

**PART III: WASTE DISPOSAL AND EFFECTS IN NORTHEASTERN U.S.
COASTAL WATERS**

7. Metal Distribution in a Major Urban Estuary (Boston Harbor)
   Impacted by Ocean Disposal   67

   Gordon T. Wallace, Jr., Jeffrey H. Waugh, and Kathryn A Garner

8. Thirty-Five Years of Dumping Titanium Dioxide Wastes in U.S. Waters: What Have We Learned?   79

Rosemary K. Monahan, Garry F. Mayer, and Harold M. Stanford

9. Modeling Oxygen Depletion in the New York Bight: The Water Quality Impact of a Potential Increase of Waste Inputs   91

Andrew Stoddard and John J. Walsh

10. The Acute Toxicity of Sewage Sludge to Marine Fish, Mysids, and Copepods   103

Don C. Miller, Martha Marcy, Walter Berry, Christopher Deacutis, Suzanne Lussier, Ann Kuhn, Margarete Heber, Steven C. Schimmel, and Eugene Jackim

11. The Application of a Hazard Assessment Research Strategy to the Ocean Disposal of a Dredged Material: Overview   115

John H. Gentile, Gerald G. Pesch, and Thomas M. Dillon

12. The Application of a Hazard Assessment Research Strategy to the Ocean Disposal of a Dredged Material: Exposure Assessment Component   123

John F. Paul, Victor J. Bierman, Jr., Wayne R. Davis, Gerald L. Hoffman, Wayne R. Munns, Jr., Carol E. Pesch, Peter F. Rogerson, and Steven C. Schimmel

13. The Application of a Hazard Assessment Research Strategy to the Ocean Disposal of a Dredged Material: Effects Assessment and Monitoring Component   137

Donald K. Phelps, D. Michael Johns, K. John Scott, Walter B. Galloway, Bruce H. Reynolds, William G. Nelson, Jeffrey S. Rosen, Dianne Black, James L. Lake, Ruth Gutjahr-Gobell, Suzanne Lussier, Cornelia Mueller, Michele Redmond, Paul S. Schauer, Carolyn A. Yevich, Paul P. Yevich, Gerald E. Zaroogian, and James Heltsche

PART IV. CONTAMINANT EFFECTS AND STATUS IN PUGET SOUND

14. Temporal Trends of Contamination in Puget Sound   149

Eric A. Crecelius and Nickolas Bloom

15. Bioaccumulation of Toxic Substances in Puget Sound Organisms   157

Thomas C. Ginn and Robert C. Barrick

16. Summary of Biological Effects in Puget Sound—Past and Present   169

Peter M. Chapman

17. Implications of Opportunistic Predation for Predicting the Impacts of Ocean Dumping on Demersal Fish   185

  D. Scott Becker

18. Effects of Solid Wood Wastes on Marine Benthic Organisms and Habitats   193

  Michael Waldichuk

PART V. CONTAMINANT STATUS IN COASTAL WATERS OF JAPAN AND CHINA

19. Residence Times of Trace Metals and Nutrients in Tokyo Bay Water   211

  Eiji Matsumoto

20. Manganese, Iron, Copper, and Zinc in Sediment Cores from Seasonally Stratified Beppu Bay, the Seto Inland Sea, Japan   219

  Akira Hoshika, Takayuki Shiozawa, and Yasushi Kitano

21. Identification of Pollution Sources of Heavy Metals in Marine Coastal Sediments from Patterns of Partitioning and Diagenetic Change   235

  Hirozo Yoshimura, Takio Shiba, and Keizo Watanabe

22. The Pollution History of Jin Zhou Bay, Bohai Sea, China   245

  Liu Guoxian, Yang Songlin, Zhou Yihua, and Wan Banghe

Author Index   257

Subject Index   263

GLOSSARY OF ACRONYMS AND INITIALISMS

AAS	Atomic Absorption Spectrophotometry
AEC	Adenylate Energy Change
ASARCO	American Smelting and Refining Company
BIP	Balanced Indigenous Population
BOD	Biochemical Oxygen Demand
BRH	Black Rock Harbor
BSL	Board Standard Length
CAA	Clean Air Act
CAG	Carcinogen Assessment Group of the U.S. EPA
CBD	Chlorinated Butadiene
CLIS	Central Long Island Sound
COD	Chemical Oxygen Demand
COE	U.S. Army Corps of Engineers
CPAH	Combustion Polynuclear Aromatic Hydrocarbons
CSDLAC	County Sanitation Districts of Los Angeles County
CSO	Combined Sewage Overflow
CWA	Clean Water Act
DDE	2,2-bis(p-chlorophenyl)-1,1-dichloroethylene
DDT	2,2-bis(p-chlorophenyl)-1,1,1-trichloroethane
DNA	Deoxyribonucleic Acid
DO	Dissolved Oxygen
DOC	Dissolved Organic Carbon
EC_{50}	Effective Concentration that produces a specific effect or response in 50% of the test organisms.
EC	Electron Capture
EDTA	Ethylenediaminetetraaretic Acid
EOM	Extractable Organic Matter
EPA	U.S. Environmental Protection Agency
EPR	Electron Paramagnetic Resonance
ERLN	Environmental Research Laboratory, Narragansett (EPA)
FDA	U.S. Food and Drug Administration
FVP	Field Verification Program (EPA, COE)
FWPCA	Federal Water Pollution Control Act (Clean Water Act)
GC/MS	Gas Chromatography/Mass Spectrometry
GESAMP	Joint Group of Experts on the Scientific Aspects of Marine Pollution

HCB	Hexachlorobenzene
HCBD	Hexachlorobutadiene
ICP	Inductive Coupled Plasma (spectrophotometry)
IMO	International Maritime Organization
JWPCP	Joint Water Pollution Control Plant
LACSD	Los Angeles County Sanitation Districts
LC_{50}	Lethal Concentration resulting in death to 50% of the test organisms
LDC	London Dumping Convention
LPC	Limiting Permissible Concentration
MCP	Maximum Permissible Concentration
MERS	Mass Emission Rates
MFO	Mixed Function Oxydase
MPN	Most Probable Number
MPRSA	Marine Protection, Research and Sanctuaries Act
NACOA	National Advisory Committee on Oceans and Atmospheres
NAS	U.S. National Academy of Sciences
NOAA	U.S. National Oceanic and Atmospheric Administration
NPDES	National Pollutant Discharge Elimination System
NYTL	New York Testing Laboratory
PAH	Polynuclear Aromatic Hydrocarbons
PCB	Polychlorinated Biphenyls
PSP	Paralytic Shellfish Poisoning
POC	Particulate Organic Carbon
POTW	Publically Owned Treatment Works
RCRA	Resource Conservation and Recovery Act
SCCWRP	Southern California Coastal Water Resources Project
SCE	Sister Chromatid Exchange
SDWA	Safe Drinking Water Act
SFG	Scope for Growth
STP	Sewage Treatment Plant
TL	Total Length
UCM	Unresolved Complex Mixture
VMCM	Vector-Measuring Current Meter
WDOE	Washington State Department of Energy
WSL	Waste Sulfite Liquor

PART I: INTRODUCTION

Chapter 1

Urban Wastes in Coastal Waters: Assimilative Capacity and Management

Douglas A. Wolfe

Ocean Assessments Division
U.S. National Oceanic and Atmospheric Administration
Rockville, Maryland

Abstract	**3**
1.1. Introduction	**3**
1.2. Assimilative Capacity of Coastal Marine Systems	**6**
1.2.1. Environmental End Points: Criteria of Acceptability	6
1.2.2. Persistence and Problems of Scale	8
1.3. Environmental Assessment and Management	**10**
1.3.1. Multimedia Assessment: Options and Outcomes	10
1.3.2. Unreasonable Environmental Degradation	14
1.3.3. Role of Monitoring	15
1.4. Summary Conclusions	**17**
Acknowledgments	**17**
References	**17**

ABSTRACT

Management decisions on the disposal of wastes are currently based on regulations, criteria, and tests developed separately for different disposal media (i.e., for coastal discharges, ocean dumping, landfill, and incineration). These criteria do not include any provisions for uncertainty in the information, nor do they provide direct estimates either of the risks to human health and the environment or other associated costs of a particular disposal option or strategy. This chapter outlines a general analytical framework for the assessment and management of marine environmental problems related to waste disposal in the coastal zone. The assessment framework is consistent with principles of decision analysis and is structured to guide the selection of optimal disposal alternatives or strategies (i.e., those with the lowest expected overall detriment). Such an approach necessarily involves assignment of values to the outcomes that are predicted for various identified alternatives and the weighing of environmental consequences against human health and economic considerations. Two most critical steps in this process, both often overlooked in traditional assessment approaches, are specifying the outcomes of concern and establishing criteria of acceptability for each outcome. Together these factors represent the end points (1) that determine the assimilative capacity of an environment for a waste, (2) that must be weighed in the consideration of management alternatives, and (3) that must be monitored to assess the adequacy of the selected management approach. The overall program of waste management resembles a controlled environmental experiment in which the expected limits of environmental change are hypothesized (predicted) for certain stipulated disposal conditions, and a multiple-objective monitoring program is implemented to validate the hypotheses and to provide a basis for modifying the stipulations in the event that the predictions prove to have been unsatisfactory.

1.1. INTRODUCTION

Coastal marine waters have been used by humans for many centuries as a transport medium and processor for waste materials. The burgeoning human population in the coastal zone (nearly 80 million people, or about 38% of the U.S.

population, lived in U.S. coastal counties in 1980) has exacerbated the conflicts among the uses of the coastal ocean. These conflicts arise from the traditional uses of the sea for waste disposal and transportation, as well as for recreation and a sustained source of living marine resources that are safe and nutritious.

Coastal marine waters are particularly susceptible to impacts from municipal and industrial wastes from coastal population centers. This volume presents results of recent research on the distribution and effects of such wastes in four separate coastal regions (Southern California Bight, northeastern U.S. coast, Puget Sound and the Pacific Northwest, and coastal Japan and China), each with its own mix of wastes and conflicts in use of resources. A unifying feature among these regions is a common need for regulation and management of waste disposal in a way that is compatible with the other multiple uses of the environment. This introductory chapter focuses on these management aspects and outlines a general analytical framework for the assessment and management of marine environmental problems related to waste disposal in the coastal zone.

The potentially adverse impacts of waste materials on human health and the environment underlie the concerns that have led to substantive U.S. legislation and international conventions that regulate waste disposal. The Clean Water Act (CWA) regulates the discharge of waste materials and effluents into fresh and coastal waters (U.S. Congress, 1977), while the Marine Protection, Research and Sanctuaries Act (MPRSA) regulates the dumping of wastes into ocean waters (U.S. Congress, 1972). The London Dumping Convention (LDC) [International Maritime Organization (IMO), 1982] is a global convention for the prevention of marine pollution from dumping of wastes, with 60 signatory nations participating. In addition, three other U.S. federal laws are directly concerned with the environmental aspects of the management of waste materials: the Safe Drinking Water Act (SDWA) (U.S. Code, 1981a), the Resource Conservation and Recovery Act (RCRA) (U.S. Code, 1981b), and the Clean Air Act (CAA) (U.S. Code, 1981c). These five statutes (along with the Federal Insecticide, Fungicide and Rodenticide Act as amended; the Toxic Substance Control Act; and the Comprehensive Environmental Response, Compensation and Liability Act) constitute the law of toxic substances, which has been described as a complex legal and institutional maze (Garrett, 1979; Levin and Kimball, 1984).

Each of the five U.S. legislative statutes highlighted above regulates waste disposal into a particular type of environment (Erdheim, 1985), as follows: CWA, discharges into freshwa-

ter and coastal waters; MPRSA, ocean dumping; RCRA, onland disposal; SDWA, contamination of drinking water; and CAA, air pollution (Fig. 1.1). Unfortunately, the various acts tend to regulate these media separately, protecting each medium individually from potential misuse and abuse as a waste disposal medium. This situation leads to two interrelated management problems pertaining to waste disposal into the environment:

1. The different criteria and requirements imposed by the various acts lead to logical inconsistencies in waste-management procedures among the media. For example, regulation of dredged-material disposal into the open ocean (under MPRSA) is more stringent than that for disposal of the same materials into water within the three-mile limit (under CWA); and

2. Implementation of the various regulations individually may effectively prohibit (or encourage) disposal of a particular waste in one medium without regard for either the relative economic costs or the environmental effects associated with disposal in the other media. For example, the initial decision (under MPRSA) to phase out sewage-sludge dumping in the New York Bight in 1980 gave little consideration to the environmental impacts or economic costs of alternative disposal practices.

In reviewing this situation, the National Advisory Committee on Oceans and Atmospheres (NACOA) (1981) concluded that ". . .we must manage wastes, not media, and that the medium-by-medium approach of the 1970s is no longer adequate."

A reorientation of management focus from media to wastes has implications not only for policy development and regulatory strategies, but for the scientific and technical approaches taken in environmental assessment and management, as well. Environmental risk assessment and management are inherently difficult (Champ et al., 1988) because of the many competing uses made of the environment and because many different contaminants enter the environment from multiple sources, including industrial and municipal point-source releases, and from diffuse sources such as atmospheric transport and runoff from agricultural lands. Multiple sources and contaminants may exert their influence over different spatial and temporal scales in the environment, and their effects may be cumulative or even synergistic. In addition, however, these various aspects of waste management and environmental protection are the concerns of many different segments of society: policy makers and regulators, engineers, environmental assessment scientists, and the public at large.

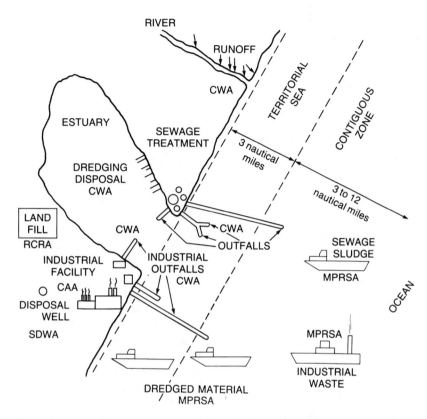

Figure 1.1. Five laws, with different jurisdictional boundaries, govern the disposal of wastes into the coastal waters of the United States: (1) Clean Air Act (CAA); (2) Clean Water Act (CWA); (3) Marine Protection, Research and Sanctuaries Act (MPRSA); (4) Resource Conservation and Recovery Act (RCRA); and (5) Safe Drinking Water Act (SDWA). Redrawn from NACOA (1981).

Within the overall population at risk from a particular strategy for waste management, individual exposures and risks may be quite different for different groups, depending on the specific uses made of the environment and the resultant exposure pathways. The individuals most likely to incur the environmental risks associated with a management decision are rarely those most likely to benefit directly from the decision. Moreover, perceptions of risk vary considerably among individuals. Environmental assessment scientists and managers alike must take into account these important considerations of equity and risk perception in developing, communicating, and applying policies and regulations (Matthews, 1975). Further complications arise because policy development occurs at local, state, and federal levels, and each of these levels has different perspectives on the desired balance among regulation, industrial services, and environmental quality (or risk).

Implementing a multimedium, waste-oriented management in place of the present medium-by-medium approach, as suggested by NACOA (1981), is thus not a trivial exercise; it will require not only refined assessment technology but also improved interaction and coordination among different disciplinary and societal groups. Within this overall scenario, two major scientific and technical problems require special attention and development: (1) estimating for each environmental medium the detailed relationships between the environmental flux of wastes and the resultant hazards to the environment and risks to human health; and (2) devising means for objective comparison of the overall risk potentials associated with alternative waste-management policies and practices involving different environmental media, each with its own composition of hazards, risks, and direct costs.

These two problem areas may be identified as *Assimilative Capacity* and *Multimedia Environmental Assessment*, respectively. They are reviewed and discussed in the succeeding sections of this chapter.

1.2. ASSIMILATIVE CAPACITY OF COASTAL MARINE SYSTEMS

Assimilative capacity (Goldberg, 1979, 1983a) is a concept for waste management in which the waste inputs to an environment are balanced against the natural environmental processes of dilution, dispersion, and degradation to maintain the potentially adverse environmental impacts within acceptable bounds. In its most general form, assimilative capacity may be defined as the flux of materials (wastes) that can be sustained by a receiving environment without producing unacceptable impacts within that environment. Thus, the assimilative capacity of an environment for receiving wastes is determined not only by the nature of the wastes and their effects on the environment, but also by the complement of values placed on the environment. These values in turn are derived from the alternative uses being made of that environment, and the assimilative capacity reflects the extent to which an environment can receive wastes without unacceptable compromise of those alternative uses.

To apply the concept of assimilative capacity effectively in waste management requires (1) the specification of the environmental end points that are not to be exceeded (i.e., the limits of acceptable impact) and (2) the ability to estimate (with specified confidence) the magnitude of environmental impacts as a function of waste flux. "Acceptability" of impact (and of predictive confidence) is clearly a judgment that depends both on the regional values and on the attitudes toward risk that are prevalent within the group(s) deciding on, and affected by, the management decision. Such judgments may be very difficult in public policy issues where jurisdictional responsibilities overlap (e.g., multiple regulations and agencies) at different levels of government (i.e., local, state, and federal), and where multiple groups with diverse values are affected. Approaches for normalizing the train of analytical logic in this judgmental process are discussed in section 1.3 of this chapter.

1.2.1. Environmental End Points: Criteria of Acceptability

Goldberg (1979) likened the determination of assimilative capacity to a chemical titration of the pollutant with the water body, until a specified "end point" was reached. That comparison suggests that the end point chosen is an important determinant of assimilative capacity. Careful specification of end point(s) is also an essential step both in predictive assessment of environmental impact and in design of monitoring programs (Wolfe and O'Connor, 1986). A practical managerial strategy is to begin by answering the question, "What environmental effects do we wish to avoid?" For example, O'Connor and Dewling (1986) identified a selection of indicators that are related directly to marine environmental resource values. These indicators are potentially vulnerable to pollution impacts and, therefore, have potential utility as end points. Multiple end points (or criteria) may be specified for a variety of different environmental characteristics and applied simultaneously in the management of an environment receiving wastes. Different criteria, however, are likely to be approached at different rates and on different geographic scales (Fig. 1.2). For this reason, it is important to define the boundaries of the ecosystem or environment to be impacted and managed [GESAMP (United Nations Joint Group of Experts on the Scientific Aspects of Marine Pollution), 1986]. One must remain cognizant, however, that contaminant effects may occur beyond the defined boundaries of the system being managed. While it is clearly advisable to establish complementary criteria for a variety of environmental resource values, a cost-conscious and effective manager would nonetheless wish to avoid redundant or superfluous end points.

The application of traditional water quality criteria [McKee and Wolf, 1963; U.S. National Academy of Sciences (NAS),

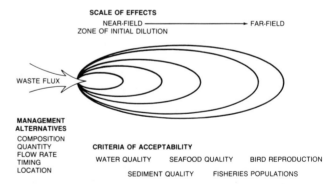

Figure 1.2. Conceptual relationships among management alternatives, criteria of acceptability (or environmental endpoints), and scales of environmental impact. Management criteria focus on short-term impacts in the near field and long-term phenomena in the far field. On any defined environmental scale, the criteria of acceptability (coupled with the dispersiveness of the environment and persistence of the wastes) determine the assimilative capacity of the receiving environment.

1972; U.S. Environmental Protection Agency (EPA), 1976; American Fisheries Society, Water Quality Section, 1979] represents one approach to the concept of assimilative capacity, in that these criteria represent a no-effect prediction (based on results of toxicity bioassays and appropriate application factors). The technical limitations of this approach have been pointed out by others (Ruckelshaus, 1983; White and Champ, 1983), and the search continues for more accurate and effective measures of environmental effects (McIntyre and Pearce, 1980; Widdows, 1983; White, 1984; Ryder and Edwards, 1985; O'Connor and Dewling, 1986; Wolfe and O'Connor, 1986; Spitzer and O'Connor, 1987). For example, a major effort is currently underway to formulate effective criteria for sediment quality (Kadeg et al., 1986; Neff et al., 1986; Poston and Prohammer, 1986).

Water quality standards are applied in management of coastal effluents, as regulated by the EPA under the National Pollutant Discharge Elimination System in compliance with the CWA. Although this approach does not identify in advance the specific environmental values to be maintained, the management aim is generally to use the dispersive character of the environment to minimize the magnitude and scale of environmental effects. This approach was taken, for example, in managing the effluent from the facility for the treatment of ballast water at the trans-Alaska pipeline terminal at Port Valdez (Wolfe, 1988b). The effluent, with a maximum permitted concentration of hydrocarbons, was discharged into a highly dispersive regime, and the discharge permit required that Alaska's water quality standards be met at the boundaries of a specified mixing zone. This approach represented a management decision that the environment within the limited mixing zone would not be unacceptably impacted by the permitted flux of contaminants, and, further, that the environment beyond the mixing zone limits would not be unacceptably impacted at contaminant concentrations below the state water quality standards. To check the adequacy of this management approach using mixing zones and water quality standards, requirements for environmental research and monitoring were included in the discharge permit. These requirements focused on detecting possible biological impacts, especially in the benthos, and on quantifying long-term trends in contaminant distributions outside the mixing zone. While some accumulation of polynuclear aromatic hydrocarbons has been demonstrated (Shaw, 1988), no significant effects have been ascribed to the ballast-water effluent. Rapid expansion of human activities using the Port Valdez marine environment, however, will probably require broader perspectives of its assimilative capacity.

Another section (301h) of the CWA deals with waivers of the requirement for secondary treatment of sewage effluents from publicly owned treatment works (POTW). The waiver conditions include the requirement for maintenance of a balanced indigenous population (BIP) of shellfish, fish, and wildlife outside the zone of initial dilution. The applicant POTW must identify and describe the constituents of such BIPs and demonstrate (through a monitoring system) their continued existence despite the allowed effluent (Harwell, 1984). This requirement represents another explicit criterion of environmental values that establishes the limits of assimilative capacity of a receiving environment for a given discharge.

The foregoing examples (water quality criteria and BIP) represent two types of end points, or criteria, that may be applied in environmental management. Each is subjected to criticism. Water quality criteria are pragmatic extrapolations from the results of laboratory bioassays, made without complete understanding of their accuracy and appropriateness for the field environment; whereas the BIP criterion represents a generally desirable environmental attribute for which the dose–response relationships to pollution are poorly known and easily confounded by other sources of natural fluctuation. Despite these technical and practical limitations, however, both approaches represent the concept of assimilative capacity in the overall management scheme for individual discharges to a receiving environment.

A more difficult management problem arises when multiple pollution loads enter a single environment. Such situations are likely to require determination of assimilative capacity for large systems that support intensive multiple use under different jurisdictional authorities. Under these conditions, the definition of criteria for the limits of acceptability is much more difficult. In the New York Bight, for example, environmental effects cannot be ascribed readily to specific pollutants or sources (Wolfe et al., 1982). Although a 1979 technical assessment of the waste inputs and impacts in the New York Bight (Goldberg, 1979) concluded (albeit without explicit designation of end points) that the assimilative capacity of the bight had not been exceeded, the prolonged regulatory and legislative dispute (Lahey, 1982) over disposal of sewage sludge at the 12-Mile Dumpsite attests to the difficulty of deciding what criteria of acceptability should be applied.

A similar search has been underway for meaningful and useful management objectives for the Great Lakes (Robertson, in press). Water quality criteria and waste-load allocation are in current use (International Joint Commission, Canada and the United States, 1978; Thomas et al., 1980), but desire remains to supplement these practices with ecosystem objectives that would demonstrate more fully the adequacy of the management approach. A target objective has been recommended, therefore, using the lake trout (*Salvelinus namaycush*) as an indicator of ecosystem health in the oligotrophic, cold-water areas of the Great Lakes, and a comparable objective using the walleye (*Stizostedion vitrium*) is being developed for the warmer, mesotrophic areas (Robertson, in press). The recommended criteria also specify minimal productivity rates (at a specified maximal rate of harvest) and maximal allowable contaminant levels in tissue. The designation of these top predators as indicators for management objectives will provide additional assurance of overall ecosystem quality. This recommendation also recognizes explicitly the relationship between management of exploited resources and management of environmental quality. In the marine environment these management functions have been institutionally and conceptually quite distinct. Nonetheless, criteria for the productivity and product quality of desired species may be applicable in the long term to the marine environment as well.

1.2.2. Persistence and Problems of Scale

Pollution effects are a function of contaminant exposure, which depends on concentrations of environmental contaminants, duration of contact, and size of the exposed population. To meet any specified criterion of acceptability, therefore, the environmental loading must stay below the critical levels leading to the effect of concern. The flux of contaminants into the receiving environment must be balanced against the processes (dilution, diffusion, evaporation, sedimentation, and decay) that diminish their concentration.

Upon entering the marine environment, contaminants are cycled and recycled among numerous compartments, including the water, sediments, and biota (Wolfe and Rice, 1972; Wolfe et al., 1973; Wolfe, 1975). While management concern is generally for biological effect, the current understanding of contaminant cycling in natural systems is often insufficient for accurate prediction of effects based on flux information. When multiple criteria or end points are applied simultaneously to the control of waste inputs to an environmental system, only one is likely to be effective, or limiting, at any specified spatial scale. That is, one of the limiting end points will be approached before the others, and that end point becomes the effective control.

The duration and magnitude of the waste flux, coupled with the dispersive nature of the environment and the degradation characteristics of the contaminant, will influence the ultimate geographic scale of contaminant distribution. Different criteria of acceptability may well be effective at different temporal or spatial scales. To determine allowable flux limits for the established criteria of acceptability, a manager must evaluate all significant flows of contaminants within the system to predict the critical (or limiting) pathways of flux and effect. The mechanistic pathway most critical for controlling the release of the waste may not be immediately obvious. For example, important limitations on the release of radioactive wastes from the Windscale processing facility at Sellafield, England, were based on the accumulation of radioisotopes (principally [106]Ru) by the edible seaweed *Porphyra umbilicalis* growing on intertidal rocks near the point of discharge (Howells, 1966). This seaweed was used in making laverbread, a staple food item in the diet of the local coastal population.

When multiple inputs of contaminants enter the same environment, overlapping zones of exposure will result (Fig. 1.3), leading to cumulative effects. Under these circumstances, the sources are likely to require collective management on a regional basis instead of individual management based directly and simply on one or more criteria of acceptability. That is, the boundaries of the area for which assimilative capacity is to be determined and applied must be defined to encompass all or most of the overlapping zones of influence. On such a collective-management basis, the assimilative capacity of a receiving environment may be allocated among several sources. Such source-load allocation has been applied in riverine and lacustrine systems (International Joint Commission, Canada and the United States, 1978; Thomas, et al., 1980) and is under consideration for heavily used estuarine areas such as Chesapeake Bay (Chesapeake Executive Council, 1985). Some types of cumulative effect, however, may defy even collective regional management because of the pervasiveness of the use and distribution of the contaminant. The widespread use of DDT, for example, caused eggshell thinning and reduction in coastal populations of numerous fish-eating bird species, and effective management could be achieved only by banning the use of the pesticide throughout the United States. Analogous problems could develop with other xenobiotics, such as toxaphene (Goldberg, 1983b) or tributyltin (Goldberg, 1986), for which general usage and release could quickly outstrip the assimilative capacity of some critical part of the environment.

Numerous authors have emphasized that environmental changes occur on a continuum of spatial and temporal scales,

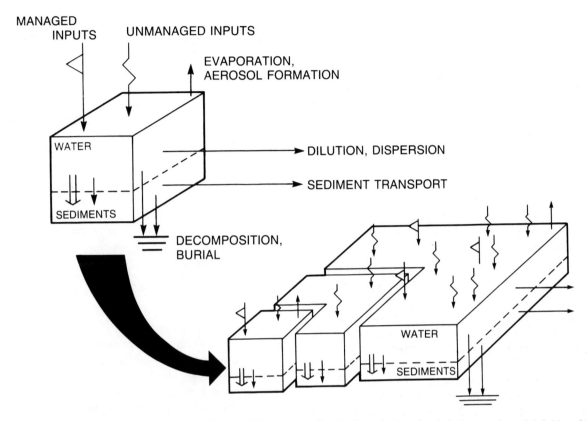

Figure 1.3. Diagram illustrating the succession of embedded spatial scales that affect the determination of assimilative capacity and definition of feasible management units. On any given environmental scale, the cumulative contaminant inputs must be balanced against the cumulative losses so as not to exceed the limits of assimilative capacity that are established by the applicable criteria of acceptability. Assimilative capacity must be evaluated at several different scales to ensure that inputs managed at small scales do not cumulatively exceed the assimilative capacity established by different criteria at larger scales. This possibility is aggravated by the existence of unmanaged and unquantified (non-point source) contaminant sources.

in which systems defined at one scalar level are embedded successively within other larger-scale systems (Allen and Starr, 1982; Holling, 1985; Wolfe and Kjerfve, 1986). Such relationships of scale apply equally to the management of pollution effects and to human societal effects upon climatic change (Clark, 1985). An understanding of such relationships is essential for effective management of human activities with environmental implications.

O'Connor et al. (1987) examined the typical spatial scales associated with marine environmental effects and concluded that the overall problem of marine pollution to date could be viewed as a collection of local problems. For the most part, the observed scales of effect suggested that contaminant concentrations have rarely been large enough to cause effects over scales greater than 400 km^2. Contaminant fluxes and distributions on such scales are amenable to fairly effective modeling (Csanady, 1983; O'Connor et al., 1987), as con-

trasted with larger-scale, long-term processes. The most notable exceptions observed by O'Connor et al. (1987) were reproductive losses in marine birds, which exhibited areal extents of 10^3–10^4 km^2, and hypoxia, which has been observed over scales of 10^3 (Chesapeake Bay) to 10^5 (Baltic Sea) km^2. Hypoxia results from cumulative loading by nutrients and biochemical oxygen demand (BOD) and, therefore, is not representative of typical xenobiotic additions. Waste-load allocation based on the assimilative capacity of the receiving water body for nutrients and/or BOD is nonetheless a plausible management approach, as demonstrated by the control of phosphorous loadings to the Great Lakes (Great Lakes Water Quality Board, 1985).

Assimilative capacity must be considered over a succession of embedded spatial scales (Fig. 1.3). The critical scale for management depends upon the magnitude and duration of individual fluxes entering different parts of the system and upon the potential cumulative effects that may be manifested at different scales. Individual management of the separate fluxes entering the tributaries of a system may not adequately consider either the overall flux or any recycling that occurs within the system. This will be particularly likely if significant unmanaged fluxes exist at some of the scales (e.g., non-point source runoff or atmospheric inputs). Also, chronic inputs from multiple point sources to the same receiving environment can lead to a significant contaminant reservoir in the sediments. Recycling of contaminants from the sediment reservoir, along with non-point-source inputs and continuing point-source inputs, may lead to overload of a system (relative to the applicable criterion of acceptability at that scale), despite control of the individual point sources through water quality standards.

The management criteria that are applied on different scales must be reviewed to ensure that the criteria used on short-term or local scales are adequately protective of those appropriate to larger scales. The appropriate spatial scales for management are determined by the scale of the resource distributions that are the focus of management objectives and by the dynamic rate functions that control contaminant distribution (and effects) at every scale. Thus, the geographic or spatial scales of concern are inseparably intertwined with the temporal scales of decay and dispersion processes in the environment (Wolfe and Kjerfve, 1986). Management perspectives and objectives must be carefully matched to these scales (Wolfe and O'Connor, 1986). Where long time frames are involved, management must take care to anticipate future activities or resource uses that may be compromised by present waste-management decisions.

1.3. ENVIRONMENTAL ASSESSMENT AND MANAGEMENT

Assimilative capacity depends in large part upon the criteria of acceptability that are imposed by the managers (both of the waste-generating activity and of the environment). Specification of these criteria of acceptability is an essential early step in decision making for waste management at the national, state, regional, or local level (Wolfe, 1983; U.S. NAS, 1984; GESAMP, 1986; Wolfe and O'Connor, 1986; Wolfe, 1988a). In practice, however, management or policy objectives are frequently not clearly defined, or they may be inconsistent among waste categories, among disposal media, or among regions. Fragmentation of jurisdictional responsibility among numerous different sectors of society and government is a major contributing cause to the inconsistencies among specified management objectives (U.S. NAS, 1984; Kitsos et al., 1988). The constraints placed on effective policy implementation by the present statutory framework and system of public administration, and by economic factors, were discussed in detail by the National Academy of Sciences' Panel on Sludge Management and Public Policy (Kildow et al., 1984). These considerations lead to the overall conclusion that

> There is a necessity for multimedia and multidisciplinary assessments of waste disposal practices. The scientific, technological, political, and economic information needed to make an optimal choice among land, sea, and air [disposal] sites is today generally available or attainable (U.S. NAS, 1984).

The need for objective comparison of land and sea disposal options is also being recognized increasingly by the International Convention on the Prevention of Marine Pollution by Dumping of Wastes and Other Matter, otherwise known as the London Dumping Convention. Despite the general single-medium and protectionist orientations of the LDC, implementation guidelines for assessment in connection with disposal permits (IMO, 1985) call for comparative assessment of human health risks, environmental costs, hazards, economics, and exclusions of future uses of disposal areas, for all disposal sites and management alternatives. Thus, there is widespread recognition of the need for systematic comparative assessment of waste-management options to identify the least detrimental disposal practices.

The next sections of this chapter introduce and review very briefly some of the approaches to assessment and analysis that have been proposed for effective multimedia waste management.

1.3.1. Multimedia Assessment: Options and Outcomes

The concept of multimedia assessment represents a merging of three technologies with very different disciplinary origins: (1) environmental assessment, (2) risk assessment, and (3) decision analysis. These three activities have been the traditional realms of (1) environmental scientists; (2) design engineers and health scientists; and (3) systems engineers, economists, and policy analysts, respectively, and have addressed the following general questions:

1. What will happen (or, sometimes, has happened) in the environment, given a particular perturbation or activity?

2. What might happen to human health, given a particular activity?

3. What course of action is likely to result in the optimal outcome?

This discipline-based schism is gradually being overcome and the various techniques are presently being integrated to address management issues with simultaneous implications for economic risks, environmental risks, and risks to human health (e.g., Keeney and Raiffa, 1976; North and Merkhofer, 1976; Howard et al, 1977; O'Neill et al., 1982; Leschine and Broadus, 1985; Champ et al., 1988; Gift et al., 1988; Leschine and Quinn, 1988). Such risk or hazard assessments still tend to be restricted, however, to comparisons of alternatives involving a single medium (i.e., either air, land, freshwater, or marine). A pioneering effort to compare cross-media risks and costs was conducted for New York City in relation to the controversial and contested disposal of sewage sludge at the 12-Mile Dumpsite in the New York Bight (New York City Department of Environmental Protection, 1983; Gift et al., 1988). The comparison and selection of alternatives in this approach relied upon a somewhat subjective tiered-matrix elimination procedure, which is briefly described also in a report by the U.S. NAS (1984). This procedure made no use of probabilistic risk-assessment techniques, nor were explicit values associated with the outcomes. Incorporation of these features would greatly increase the realism, accuracy, and computational ease of the overall assessment procedure, and would also create valuable documentation on the distribution of values used in reaching such decisions.

Each of the three general questions listed above implies the prediction of *outcomes* that may be associated with a series of management *options*. The identification of management alternatives and specification of outcomes are two of the first and most important steps in decision analysis (North, 1968; Keeney and Raiffa, 1976; Howard et al., 1977; Matheson and Howard, 1977). These steps are illustrated in Fig. 1.4 as part of an overall assessment and decision process related to waste management. This figure represents the processes of analysis, decision, and regulation through which past and proposed human activities are related to potential environmental consequences and, consequently, are managed or controlled.

The starting point for the overall analytical process is problem perception (step 1, Fig. 1.4), which arises from resource-use conflicts between ocean pollution and other ocean uses. These perceived conflicts may result from proposed human activities, or from the consequences of past human activities. The decision process (steps 2–5) is initiated

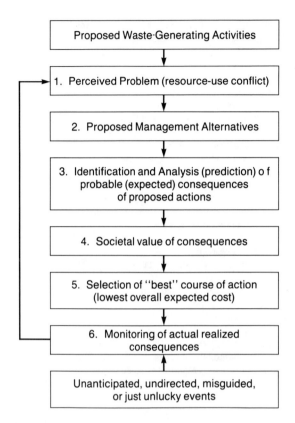

Figure 1.4. Major elements of the decision process related to marine pollution and management.

in response to the perceived problem. First, the alternatives or options that may be taken to reduce or eliminate the problem must be identified (step 2). For each of these alternatives, potential outcomes must be identified and predictively quantified (step 3). This step includes most of the elements of risk or hazard assessment, which are outlined in Chapters 11–13, for ocean disposal of dredged materials.

Prediction of outcomes is difficult because outcomes generally involve multiple attributes (Keeney and Raiffa, 1976), and each outcome variable (see Table 1.1 for examples) must be quantified for every alternative. To the extent possible, outcome variables should be specified in objective terms, as nearly free of implicit values as possible. The measures of outcome used in the decision process should be identical (or directly translatable) to (1) the practical criteria of acceptability applied in determinations of assimilative capacity, and (2) the monitoring parameters selected to ensure suitability of the accepted management alternatives. Conversely, it should be obvious that effective criteria of acceptability and monitor-

Table 1.1. Values at Risk from Waste-Disposal Practices and Potential Measures of Outcome

Human Health
  deaths per year for exposed population
  shortening of life span (days)
  number of "sick days" per year
Fish and Shellfish (Commercial and Sports)
  stock size
  annual marketable production
  reproductive potential
  disease incidence
  age–size composition and mortality
  contaminant levels
  fraction of historical or available range occupied
Birds and Endangered Species
  population size
  reproductive potential
  age–size composition and mortality
  contaminant levels
  fraction of historical or available range occupied
Recreational and Aesthetic Values
  number "floatables" per mile
  sport fishing days per year
  scuba diver days per year
  coastal motel–tourism receipts
Ecological–Aesthetic (Wilderness) Value
  species composition
  diversity
  heterotrophy or feeding-type index

ing parameters must closely represent the values that affect management decisions and policy development for marine resources.

Many outcomes depend in part upon uncertain or stochastic events or processes, and the likelihood of these events must be established and incorporated into a probability density function for the occurrence of each of the outcomes. These density functions may be derived from statistical distribution of variability in actual data, or they may be based on input from recognized technical experts (Spetzler and Staël von Holstein, 1975). The probabilistic assessment approach increases the realism of dealing with uncertain information. Techniques for probabilistic analysis are well established as a component of decision analysis (Howard et al., 1977), and their merits are being recognized increasingly for risk analysis and environmental assessment (GESAMP, 1986).

After establishing the probable outcomes, some measure of value must be ascribed to each outcome variable (step 4) so that the overall costs (environmental, health, and economic) and benefits associated with each alternative can be com-

pared. Once the alternatives have been so evaluated, the identification of the optimal alternative (step 5) is straightforward. The reasonable or rational decisionmaker will select that alternative with the lowest expected overall costs (or the greatest expected overall benefits).

Once a particular decision alternative is implemented, of course, the actual outcomes (step 6) depend upon those numerous stochastic processes and events that were (one hopes) identified and used in the assessment or prediction (step 3). The actual outcome may be perceived as a new problem that may initiate another, subsequent decision process. It must be emphasized that a good decision does not always produce a good outcome. A good decision is one based on a logical treatment of the information, values, and preferences of the decisionmaker(s); whereas, a good outcome is merely one that is favorably regarded by the decisionmaker(s) (Matheson and Howard, 1977). Stochastic processes or events may in fact lead to very unlikely, but highly unfavorable, outcomes. It becomes essential, therefore, that all available and relevant information is considered and used appropriately in the assessment or prediction (step 3), and that meaningful values or preferences are accurately reflected in step 4 for each of the possible outcomes identified and quantified in step 3.

The steps shown in Fig. 1.4 constitute a basic, generic environmental-assessment and pollution-management approach, which can be systematically applied to alternatives involving any environmental medium, and then documented, tested, and improved as new management options come under consideration. The traditional elements of environmental assessment are contained mostly in step 3 of this overall process: defining and predictively quantifying potential pollution-related outcomes for the environment. It is recognized that reliable prediction, even in a probabilistic sense, of many environmental characteristics and outcomes is beyond present state of the art. It is important, therefore, to recognize the entire decision and assessment process as an iterative and adaptive process (Holling, 1978). The iterative nature of the assessment and management process is depicted in Fig. 1.5. After the best-effort predictive assessment is performed, appropriate monitoring programs (Wolfe and O'Connor, 1986) are implemented to verify the adequacy of the predictions and the appropriateness of the management strategy and evolving policy.

Formal and rigorous decision–analytic approaches may be applied to very complex decisions involving multiple alternatives and outcomes (for examples, see Newendorp, 1975;

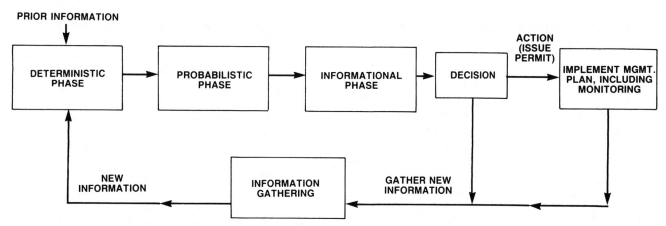

Figure 1.5. The phases of decision analysis as they apply to marine environmental management, showing the iterative nature of the analytical steps, the decision, and the monitoring.

Keeney and Raiffa, 1976; Bell et al., 1977; Howard, 1979). The greatest obstacle to effective application of decision–analytic procedures to problems of multimedia waste management probably lies in the difficulty of equitable assignment of values to the predicted outcome variables, where different outcomes may affect different segments of the population and where decision responsibility for those different constituencies may be fragmented among numerous jurisdictions. Compared to these valuation problems, the actual analytical techniques for predictive environmental assessment and risk or hazard assessment are relatively well developed (O'Neill et al., 1982; Connor, 1988; Cross and Boesch, 1983; Gift et al., 1988; Leschine and Quinn, 1988; Gentile et al., Chapter 11; Paul et al., Chapter 12; Phelps et al., Chapter 13). Such scientific assessments must be integrated, however, along with the value-related judgments, into an overall analytic strategy that can be documented, communicated, and subjected to iterative redesign. Documentation of the entire analysis is important to ensure the equitability of the value assignments and the scientific quality of the assessments (Hammond and Adelman, 1976), and to provide a meaningful basis for subsequent revisions.

Explicit recognition of the overall decision process is also necessary to identify the research programs and information products needed most for the decision(s) at hand. In this informational phase (Fig. 1.5), the prior specification of resource–use conflicts, potential management alternatives, and values associated with outcomes guides the identification of the environmental characteristics and processes most in need of research. Identification of the specific outcomes

relevant to the decision process also guides the specification of the monitoring (or research) programs that will be required to test and validate the predictions used to identify the optimal strategies for pollution control.

Together, the environmental assessment, the waste-disposal strategy or policy that is selected, and the post-decision monitoring constitute an iterative experimental approach (Holling, 1978; Wolfe, 1983; Wolfe, 1988a). In this evolving and adaptive approach, a particular management strategy is selected and implemented as the optimal alternative, based on the best available technical information and the applicable values at the time. This management strategy governs the waste-generating activity. Stipulations in the policy pre-establish the limits of allowable environmental change, and the disposal practices are designed so as not to exceed those limits. The sampling design and analytical requirements of the monitoring program are specified (ahead of time) to determine the changes that actually occur. If the pre-established limits of acceptability are unexpectedly approached, then both the predictive methodology and the disposal practices can be appropriately modified. In a sense, the program for waste management constitutes a large-scale environmental experiment in which the expected limits of environmental change are hypothesized (predicted) for certain stipulated disposal conditions, and a multiple-objective monitoring program (Wolfe and O'Connor, 1986) is implemented to validate the hypotheses and to provide a basis for modifying the stipulations in the event that the predictions prove to have been in error.

1.3.2. Unreasonable Environmental Degradation

In framing the MPRSA to regulate disposal of wastes into the ocean, the U.S. Congress (1977) authorized the Administrator of the EPA to issue permits for ocean dumping in cases for which it was determined "that such dumping will not unreasonably degrade or endanger human health, welfare, or amenities, or the marine environment, ecological systems, or economic potentialities." The MPRSA further instructed the EPA Administrator to consider the following factors in evaluation of permit applications:

(A) The need for the proposed dumping.

(B) The effect of such dumping on human health and welfare, including economic, esthetic, and recreational values.

(C) The effect of such dumping on fisheries resources, plankton, fish, shellfish, wildlife, shore lines and beaches.

(D) The effect of such dumping on marine ecosystems, particularly with respect to—

    (i) the transfer, concentration, and dispersion of such material and its byproducts through biological, physical, and chemical processes,

    (ii) potential changes in marine ecosystem diversity, productivity, and stability, and

    (iii) species and community population dynamics.

(E) The persistence and permanence of the effects of the dumping.

(F) The effect of dumping particular volumes and concentrations of such materials.

(G) Appropriate locations and methods of disposal or recycling, including land-based alternatives and the probable impact of requiring use of such alternative locations or methods upon considerations affecting the public interest.

(H) The effect on alternate uses of oceans, such as scientific study, fishing, and other living resource exploitation, and non-living resource exploitation.

(I) In designating recommended sites, the Administrator shall utilize wherever feasible locations beyond the edge of the Continental Shelf.

Although no formal analytical procedures were prescribed by the MPRSA, it should be noted that many of the elements of the multimedia assessment technology are explicit in requirements A through I. These include the consideration of multiple disposal alternatives and the comparison of probable impacts of these alternatives on public values, including (at least for the marine case) human health, economic, aesthetic, recreational, fisheries resource, and wildlife values.

The U.S. District Court (1981) held that Congress intended for the EPA to balance the environmental, health, and economic costs of disposal alternatives when determining whether a permit applicant's waste would unreasonably degrade the marine environment. Simple failure of waste to pass the operational toxicity and bioaccumulation bioassays used by the EPA could not be conclusively presumed to indicate unacceptable degradation of the marine environment. The legislative events leading to this decision and its ramifications have been discussed in much greater detail (Lahey, 1982; Bakalian, 1984; Erdheim, 1985), but its implications seem clear.

"Unreasonable degradation" assumes real meaning only in the context of a comprehensive weighing of management options and decision outcomes, as outlined in this chapter and elsewhere (Keeney and Raiffa, 1976; Howard et al., 1977; Wolfe, 1983, 1988a). "Unreasonable" clearly implies a judgment in which environmental outcome variables and their associated values must be considered and weighed against other values (e.g., health, economic, natural resources). For any given decision reached through such a carefully considered analysis, the composite consequences of the optimal alternative are (by definition) the most reasonable among all alternatives analyzed, and the subset of environmental consequences associated with that optimal alternative must also be the most reasonable. Thus, the determination of unreasonable degradation depends upon the alternatives available and the values assigned to the outcome variables in the decision process. In this context, unreasonable degradation may be defined as follows: *Unreasonable degradation* is any degree of environmental degradation that results from the selection and implementation of any management or disposal approach other than that alternative determined to be optimal through a process of weighing and balancing the environmental, health, economic, and other significant outcomes associated with the available options. This definition suggests the need for careful documentation of alternatives, outcomes and assessment procedures, explicit assignment of values to outcome variables, and consistent recognition and treatment of uncertainty in an overall decision–analytic framework. Iterative application and review of this structured, analytical approach is essential for scientifically sound, objective, and logical treatment of the environment in multimedia waste-management issues.

1.3.3. Role of Monitoring

The assignment of explicit values to outcome variables in a structured decision analysis permits the analyst (or the manager) to determine the value of new information that may be required to reduce the uncertainty associated with any aspect of the analysis (Matheson and Howard, 1977; Wolfe, 1983). This "informational phase" of the analysis (Fig. 1.5) serves to identify that body of new information that, if available, would increase the expected cumulative value of the decision outcomes by an amount greater than the costs of acquiring the information. The value of information is normally determined prior to the decision (Matheson and Howard, 1977) to ensure cost-effective identification of the optimal alternative. Some environmental assessment data may be difficult or impossible to obtain, however, prior to the actual decision. For example, information on long-term population effects of contaminants under specified field conditions may be unavailable. Such information may not be extrapolated reliably from laboratory results and modeling studies, and generation of such information may be prohibitively expensive in the absence of a long-term waste flux into the environment of concern. When the environmental management and decision process are recognized as iterative (Holling, 1978), however, appropriate information can be generated quite economically through environmental monitoring (after an "interim" disposal decision is reached).

Monitoring thus should be considered a normal extension of the usual analytical phases (Fig. 1.5) carried out in decision analysis (Wolfe, 1988a). In this decision analytic context, however, (1) the management objectives for the monitoring program must be clearly specified, (2) specific courses of management action should be defined for different potential monitoring outcomes, and (3) the costs of the program should be commensurate with the expected value of the information to future decisions. Too often effective implementation of monitoring has been hindered by inadequate specification of objectives; by inconsistent choices of monitoring parameters, sampling strategies, or analytical procedures; and by uncertainty about the benefits to be gained from the (typically expensive) program (Wolfe and O'Connor, 1986).

Three categories of monitoring objectives (and associated sampling strategies) are pertinent:

1. *Compliance*: to ensure that activities are carried out in accordance with regulations or permit requirements.
2. *Hypothesis Testing–Model Verification*: to check the validity of assumptions and predictions used at the permitting stage.
3. *Trend Monitoring or Surveillance*: to identify and quantify large-scale environmental changes anticipated (hypothesized) as possible consequences of multiple activities.

A fourth monitoring objective, that of *early warning*, is often cited for detection of potentially harmful environmental impacts in early stages of development. Early warning will be provided by all three of the other design objectives, but only to the extent that the potential effects are hypothesized and addressed by sampling strategies. The effectiveness of the warning will depend strictly on the extent of management's anticipation (prediction) of the effects associated with a particular activity (or management option) and on the conformity between the design (sampling intensity, frequency, and replication) of the monitoring program used to verify the expected impacts and the actual severity and scale of the realized impacts.

Elements of monitoring design both for compliance and for hypothesis testing depend strongly upon the details of the permitting process and disposal activity, the local and regional characteristics of the environment, the regional values attached to alternate or conflicting uses of resources, and the reliability of information used in permitting. The intent of compliance monitoring is to ensure that the materials to be disposed of meet the conditions of the permit and that the disposal operation is conducted in accord with the permit. Compliance monitoring should be required for the duration of each permitted activity and would be performed either continuously or intermittently, depending on the nature of the discharge or disposal operation.

Monitoring design for hypothesis testing, or "scientific monitoring" (Hood et al., 1988), is specific to activities at specified locations. It is usually directed at confirming the rates and extents of contaminant distribution and the magnitudes of environmental impact as a further check on the appropriateness both of the permitting decision(s) and of the regional pollutant loading. Near-field hypothesis testing may address such issues as dispersion under different meteorological conditions (e.g., Siegel et al., Chapter 4); bioaccumulation, toxicity, and recovery in biological populations (e.g., Cross, Chapter 6; Waldichuk, Chapter 18); and chemical transformations of contaminants in the water column. As information is gained on these processes, both the regulatory stipulations and the associated monitoring requirements should be reviewed and appropriately revised.

On a larger scale, hypothesis testing might also determine the distribution patterns, persistence (e.g., Garber and Wada, Chapter 5; Wallace et al., Chapter 7; Crecelius and Bloom, Chapter 14), bioaccumulation (Ginn and Barrick, Chapter 15), and effects (Cross, Chapter 6) of waste materials disposed of in the ocean to verify the accuracy of transport models and calculations used to estimate the potential impacts of the disposal activity. This class of monitoring may continue through the life of the activity, focusing at first on short-term processes and concerns and slowly shifting, as information is gained, toward long-term concerns. Intensive sampling may be required, therefore, during the initial phases, with only infrequent sampling in later stages. Hypothesis testing may also extend beyond the life of the activity to verify the persistence of contaminants (e.g., Stull et al., Chapter 2; Young et al., Chapter 3; Crecelius and Bloom, Chapter 14; Matsumoto, Chapter 19) or the recoverability of an impacted resource (e.g., Waldichuk, Chapter 18).

Management must also be concerned with subtle, far-field effects of cumulative loading from ocean dumping, coastal discharges and runoff, and atmospheric inputs. Research and near-field monitoring programs seldom provide much reassurance about longer term, large-scale effects; confident predictions are precluded by the complexities of multiple pollutant sources, of atmospheric and oceanic pollutant transport, and of the mechanisms of contaminant effects in marine ecosystems. Trend-monitoring programs are required on these large scales (Wolfe and O'Connor, 1986) to determine if there are progressive long-term environmental changes that should require changes in pollution-management practices (e.g., discontinuation of disposal of certain waste types, revision of disposal techniques, or imposition of alternative source controls at some other stage in the manufacture or use of a contaminant). In many cases, mere detection of pollution-caused trends may be difficult because of the natural variability of many ecosystem properties. Major changes in contaminant inputs over extended periods, however, will generally be reflected in subsequent monitoring data (e.g., Stull et al., Chapter 2; Garber and Wada, Chapter 5; Crecelius and Bloom, Chapter 14; Hoshika et al., Chapter 20; Liu et al., Chapter 22). Natural variability must be evaluated carefully

in the selection of indicators and in the design of sampling strategies for all categories of monitoring objectives.

Because of the multiplicity of contaminant sources and effects upon resource populations, clear indications of source-specific causality may be difficult or impossible in trend-monitoring programs, and additional research may be required to strengthen implied causal relationships. Furthermore, the most effective, corrective management approach will seldom be evident. The costs of the trend-monitoring program must be evaluated in this context against the value of information about large-scale and long-term environmental change.

One effective means of establishing the management usefulness of monitoring information is to identify in advance the courses of management action to be taken in response both to the expected results and to other, unexpected (but possible) outcomes. Cost-effective sampling design will also be greatly facilitated if target criteria are specified in advance for acceptable levels of environmental quality. Thus, the importance of clearly defined management objectives and end points (Wolfe and O'Connor, 1986) is again re-emphasized. The outcome variables of concern to management provide a direct basis for specifying criteria of acceptability and for selecting monitoring parameters. The detailed design of a monitoring program depends upon the management objectives and the particular management alternatives chosen for implementation. Monitoring design also depends upon the spatial scale of the management problem. If, for example, a waste flux is being controlled at or near the near-field assimilative capacity of the receiving environment, then frequent, high-density sampling may be required in order to make adjustments in the waste flux in response to natural changes in climate or successional state of indigenous populations. If, on the other hand, environmental inputs are managed significantly below the near-field assimilative capacity, then it may be necessary to check only periodically for environmental trends relative to large-scale or far-field assimilative capacity, as a potential basis for changes in policy or regulation. In either case, however, the objectives of the monitoring observations must be clearly defined, along with the levels of concern and the courses of action to be taken if those levels are approached. These elements are necessary to guide the design of temporally and spatially stratified sampling for the monitoring program to ensure (1) that adequate statistical resolution is achieved in areas where criteria are being approached (i.e., where important changes are occurring) and (2) that excessive effort is not placed on over-defining trivial changes well below the criterion levels (Morgan, 1986).

1.4. Summary Conclusions

Waste-management practices and regulatory policies should be chosen (1) to avoid significant risk of harm to human health and to living and non-living resources, including amenities, in any environmental medium (land, freshwater, groundwater, oceans, and air); and (2) to minimize the probable overall cost (including detriment to human health, environmental harm, direct economic burden, and other "costs") of the accepted practice. At the present time the policy for waste disposal in the United States still focuses on the management and protection of individual environmental media. This encourages jurisdictional and disciplinary fractionation of responsibilities and inconsistencies among the criteria and procedures applied to different media.

From a broad policy perspective, requirements for a prescribed and documented optimization process for multimedia analyses and decisions, accompanied by appropriate environmental monitoring, on applicable local and/or regional scales may be preferable to the present approach of prescribing detailed technical procedures or standards for individual media or wastes. Optimal strategies for waste disposal depend greatly upon local and regional considerations: waste composition and fluxes; environmental characteristics, including resource use patterns and dispersion regimes; populations at risk; and risk perceptions. Regional and local strategies for waste management can be formulated to reflect and take advantage of these regional differences more effectively than can uniform policies applied over broad geographic scales.

The limits to the assimilative capacity of an environment (for introduced wastes) depend upon the waste form and effects, the dispersive regime within the environment, the degradation rates of the waste, the duration and flux of the waste input, and the criteria of acceptability imposed by management at the environmental boundaries. Different criteria of acceptability may be imposed simultaneously at different levels in a hierarchy of embedded spatial scales—i.e., allowing small, restricted zones (near-field) to become more severely degraded, while rigorously protecting broad standards for multiple use over larger environmental scales (far-field).

Consistent measures of potential outcome should be used in comparing and determining the relative merits of different disposal practices and media. These outcome measures should be the basis for the criteria or standards to be applied, on any spatial scale, in environmental protection. Threshold standards may be necessary for individual media (according to categories of potential use), to preclude significant risk of harm either directly to the medium, or perpetrated through the medium (e.g., to human health). To the extent practicable, any such broad standards should reflect uniform risk levels across media (e.g., to humans or native organisms). The measures of outcome useful in decision making should be the basis both for the criteria of acceptability in determinations of assimilative capacity and for selection of monitoring parameters. Monitoring parameters, in both near- and far-field situations, should be selected to test directly the adequacy of accepted management practices and policies for meeting the specified criteria of acceptability.

Prescriptive decision–analytical techniques are available that can provide logical and consistent treatment of uncertainty and values in the weighing and balancing of potential outcomes from prospective management or policy alternatives. Such an analysis documents the specific values assigned to different outcomes (including health, environmental, and economic consequences), and provides a management-oriented basis for identifying and evaluating research and monitoring programs. Perhaps more importantly, the analysis establishes a documented point of reference for the assessment of revised alternatives and outcomes as they are developed or become known.

ACKNOWLEDGMENTS

I wish to express my appreciation to Ronald A. Howard, James Matheson, and Sam Holtzman, all of the Engineering–Economics Systems Department of Stanford University for introducing me to the concepts and practice of decision analysis. P. Kilho Park and Iver W. Duedall provided encouragement and advice during the writing of this chapter, and Thomas P. O'Connor, Joel S. O'Connor, and Andrew Robertson reviewed the manuscript. Joyce Nuttall provided expert editorial assistance and Zenobia Neugebauer typed the manuscript through numerous revisions. The Ocean Assessments Division of the U.S. National Oceanic and Atmospheric Administration provided support for this work. Opinions expressed are those of the author and do not necessarily reflect U.S. government policy.

REFERENCES

Allen, T. F. H., and T. B. Starr. 1982. Hierarchy Perspectives for Ecological Complexity. University of Chicago Press, Chicago, Illinois. 310 pp.

American Fisheries Society, Water Quality Section. 1979. A Review of the EPA Red Book: Quality Criteria for Water. American Fisheries Society, Bethesda, Maryland. 313 pp.

Bakalian, A. 1984. Regulation and control of United States ocean dumping: a decade of progress, and appraisal for the future. *Harvard Environmental Law Review*, **8**, 193–256.

Bell, D. E., R. L. Keeney, and H. Raiffa (Eds.). 1977. Conflicting Objectives in Decisions. John Wiley & Sons, New York, 442 pp.

Champ, M. A., M. A. Conti, and P. K. Park. 1988. The use of multimedia risk assessment for ocean waste management. *In*: Oceanic Processes in Marine Pollution, Vol. 3: Marine Waste Management Science and Policy, M. A. Champ and P. K. Park (Eds.). R. E. Krieger Publishing Co., Malabar, Florida, pp. 3–24.

Chesapeake Executive Council. 1985. Chesapeake Bay Restoration and Protection Plan. Published by the U.S. Environmental Protection Agency in cooperation with the State of Maryland, Commonwealth of Virginia, District of Columbia, and Commonwealth of Pennsylvania. U.S. Environmental Protection Agency, Chesapeake Bay Liaison Office, Annapolis, Maryland, 4 sections, paginated separately.

Clark, W. C. 1985. Scales of climatic impacts. *Climatic Change*, **7**, 5–27.

Connor, M. S. 1988. Estimating the public health risk of organic carcinogens in fish. *In*: Oceanic Processes in Marine Pollution Vol. 3: Marine Waste Management: Science and Policy, M. A. Champ and P. K. Park (Eds.). R. E. Krieger Publishing Co., Malabar, Florida, pp. 221–229.

Cross, F. A., and D. F. Boesch. 1983. Assessment Technologies. Paper No. 38. *In*: Ocean Waste Management: Policy and Strategies. Background Papers for an International Ocean Disposal Symposium. National Oceanic and Atmospheric Administration, Rockville, Maryland. 12 pp.

Csanady, G. T. 1983. Models of assimilative capacity. *In*: Assimilative Capacity of the Oceans for Man's Wastes, Jong-Ching Su and Tsu-Chang Hung (Eds.). Proceedings of a Pacific Regional Workshop on Assimilative Capacity of the Oceans for Man's Wastes (26–30 April 1982), Taipai, Republic of China. Tah-Jinn Printing Co., Taipai, pp. 1–7.

Erdheim, E. 1985. United States marine waste disposal policy. *In*: Wastes in the Ocean, Vol 6: Nearshore Waste Disposal, B. H. Ketchum, J. M. Capuzzo, W. V. Burt, I. W. Duedall, P. K. Park, and D. R. Kester (Eds.). Wiley-Interscience, New York, pp. 421–460.

GESAMP (Joint Group of Experts on Scientific Aspects of Marine Pollution). 1986. Environmental Capacity. An Approach to Marine Pollution Prevention. Reports and Studies No. 30, Food and Agriculture Organization of the United Nations, Rome, 49 pp.

Garrett, T. L. 1979. The law of toxic substances. *Environmental Health Perspectives*, **32**, 279–284.

Gift, J. J., H. Plugge, W. J. Rue, B. L. Rubin, J. A. Fava, S. E. Storms, D. A. Segar, and E. Stamman. 1988. Incineration versus ocean disposal of sewage sludge: A multimedia assessment of New York City management options. *In*: Oceanic Processes in Marine Pollution Vol. 3: Marine Waste Management: Science and Policy, M. A. Champ and P. K. Park (Eds.). R. E. Krieger Publishing Co., Malabar, Florida, pp. 297–313.

Goldberg, E. D. 1979. Proceedings of a Workshop on Assimilative Capacity of U.S. Coastal Waters for Pollutants. (29 July–4 August 1979), Crystal Mountain, Washington. U.S. National Oceanic and Atmospheric Administration, Boulder, Colorado, 284 pp.

Goldberg, E. D. 1981. The Crystal Mountain Report: An approach to defining ocean assimilative capacity. *In*: Use of the Ocean for Man's Wastes. Engineering and Scientific Aspects. Proceedings of a Symposium (23–24 June 1981), Lewes, Delaware. U.S. National Research Council, National Academy Press, Washington, D.C., pp. 1–10.

Goldberg, E. D. 1983a. The oceans as a waste receptable. *In*: Assimilative Capacity of the Oceans for Man's Wastes, Jong-Ching Su and Tsu-

Chang Hungs (Eds.). Proceedings of a Pacific Regional Workshop on Assimilative Capacity of the Oceans for Man's Wastes (26–30 April 1982), Taipai, Republic of China. Tah-Jinn Printing Co., Taipai, pp. 1–7.

Goldberg, E. D. 1983b. Can the oceans be protected? *Canadian Journal of Fisheries and Aquatic Sciences*, **40**(Supplement 2), 349–353.

Goldberg, E. D. 1986. TBT: An environmental dilemma. *Environment*, **28**, 17-22.

Great Lakes Water Quality Board. 1985. 1985 Report on Great Lakes Water Quality. Report to the International Joint Commission, Canada and the United States, Presented June 1985, Kingston, Ontario. International Joint Commission, Windsor, Ontario, and Detroit, Michigan, 212 pp.

Hammond, K. R., and L. Adelman. 1976. Science, values and human judgment. *Science*, **194**, 389–396.

Harwell, C. C. 1984. Regulatory Framework of Clean Water Act Section 301(h). Ecosystems Research Center Report No. 29, Ecosystems Research Center, Cornell University, Ithaca, New York, 21 pp. + appendices.

Holling, C. S. (Ed.). 1978. Adaptive Environmental Assessment and Management. John Wiley & Sons, New York, 377 pp.

Holling, C. S. 1985. Resilience of ecosystems: local surprise and global change. *In*: Global Change: The Proceedings of a Symposium Sponsored by the International Council of Scientific Unions (ICSU) during its 20th General Assembly in Ottawa, Canada on September 25, 1985, T. F. Malone and J. G. Roederer (Eds.). Cambridge University Press, Cambridge, England, pp. 228–269.

Hood, D. W., A. Schoener, and P. K. Park. 1988. Evolution of at-sea scientific monitoring strategies. *In*: Oceanic Processes in Marine Pollution Vol. 4: Scientific Monitoring Strategies for Ocean Waste Disposal, D. W. Hood, A. Schoener, and P. K. Park (Eds.). R. E. Krieger Publishing Co., Malabar, Florida, pp. 3–28.

Howard, R. A. 1979. Life and Death Decision Analysis. Research Report No. EES DA-79-2, Department of Engineering–Economic Systems, Stanford University, Stanford, 145 pp.

Howard, R. A., J. E. Matheson, and K. L. Miller (Eds.). 1977. Readings in Decision Analysis, 2nd edition. Stanford Research Institute, Menlo Park, California, 613 pp.

Howells, H. 1966. Discharges of low-activity radioactive effluent from the Windscale Works into the Irish Sea. *In*: Disposal of Radioactive Wastes into Seas, Oceans and Surface Waters, International Atomic Energy Agency Proceedings Series. International Atomic Energy Agency, Vienna, Austria, pp. 769–785.

International Joint Commission, Canada and the United States. 1978. Great Lakes Water Quality Agreement of 1978, with Annexes and Terms of Reference. Signed at Ottawa, 22 November 1978, 52 pp.

International Maritime Organization (IMO). 1982. Intergovernmental Conference on the Convention on the Dumping of Wastes at Sea (30 October–13 November 1972), London. Convention on the Prevention of Marine Pollution by Dumping of Wastes and Other Matter, 1982 Edition. International Maritime Organization, London, 32 pp.

IMO. 1985. Draft Resolution LDC.17(8): Guidance for the Application of Annex III. *In*: The Provisions of the London Dumping Convention, 1972, and Decisions Made by the Consultative Meetings of Contracting Parties, 28 May 1985. Document No. LDC 9/INF.2. International Maritime Organization, London, 60 pp. + 15 appendices.

Kadeg, R. D., S. P. Pavlou, and A. S. Duxbury. 1986. Sediment criteria methodology validation: Elaboration of sediment normalization theory for nonpolar hydropholic organic chemicals. Report prepared for U.S. Environmental Protection Agency Criteria and Standards Division, Washington, D.C., 44 pp. + appendices.

Keeney, R. L., and H. Raiffa. 1976. Decisions with Multiple Objectives: Preferences and Value Tradeoffs. John Wiley & Sons, New York, 569 pp.

Kildow, J. T., D. J. Basta, R. K. Bastian, D. Brown, M. S. Connor, A. M. Freeman III, P. M. Fye, E. D. Goldberg, P. S. Jessup, K. S. Kamlet, R. G. Kasper, T. M. Leschine, J. S. Mattson, W. R. Muir, J. P. Murray, T. P. O'Connor, A. Robertson, W. Robertson IV, E. D. Schneider, and D. A. Segar. 1984. Report of the Panel on Sludge Management and Public Policy. *In*: Disposal of Industrial and Domestic Wastes: Land and Sea Alternatives. National Academy Press, Washington, D.C., pp. 8–38.

Kitsos, T. R., W. W. Stelle, Jr., and S. O. Wate. 1988. The Congressional struggle for an ocean dumping policy in the United States. *In*: Oceanic Processes in Marine Pollution Vol. 3: Marine Waste Management: Science and Policy, M. A. Champ and P. K. Park (Eds.). R. E. Krieger Publishing Co., Malabar, Florida, pp. 102–110.

Lahey, W. L. 1982. Ocean dumping of sewage sludge: The tide turns from protection to management. *Harvard Environmental Law Review,* **6**, 395–431.

Leschine, T. M., and J. M. Broadus. 1985. Economic and operational considerations of offshore disposal of sewage sludge. *In*: Wastes in the Ocean, Vol. 5: Deep-Sea Waste Disposal, D. R. Kester, W. V. Burt, J. M. Capuzzo, P. K. Park, B. H. Ketchum, and I. W. Duedall (Eds.). Wiley-Interscience, New York, pp. 287–315.

Leschine, T. M., and R. J. Quinn. 1988. Decision analysis as an aid to future waste management decisions. *In*: Oceanic Processes in Marine Pollution Vol. 3: Marine Waste Management Science and Policy, M. A. Champ and P. K. Park (Eds.). R. E. Krieger Publishing Co., Malabar, Florida, pp. 187–197.

Levin, S. A., and K. D. Kimball (Eds.). 1984. New perspectives in ecotoxicology. *Environmental Management*, **8**(5), 375–442.

Matheson, J. E., and R. A. Howard. 1977. An introduction to decision analysis. *In*: Readings in Decision Analysis, 2nd edition, R. A. Howard, J. E. Matheson, K. L. Miller (eds.). Stanford Research Institute, Menlo Park, California, pp. 5–43.

Matthews, W. H. 1975. Objective and subjective judgments in environmental impact analysis. *Environmental Conservation*, **2**, 121–131.

McIntyre, A. D., and J. B. Pearce. 1980. Biological Effects of Marine Pollution and the Problems of Monitoring. *Rapports et Procès-Verbaux des Réunions*, **179**, 1–346.

McKee, J. E., and H. W. Wolf. 1963. Water Quality Criteria, 2nd edition. Publication 3-A, State Water Quality Control Board, State of California, Sacramento, 548 pp.

Morgan, M. G. 1986. Risk research: When should we say "Enough"? *Science*, **232**, 197.

National Advisory Committee on Oceans and Atmosphere (NACOA). 1981. The Role of the Ocean in a Waste Management Strategy. A Special Report to the President and the Congress. National Advisory Committee on Oceans and Atmosphere, Washington, D.C., 103 pp + appendices.

Neff, J. M., D. J. Bean, B. W. Cornsby, R. M. Vaga, T. C. Gulbransen, and J. A. Scanlon. 1986. Sediment quality criteria methodology validation: Calculation of screening level concentrations from field data. Report prepared for U.S. Environmental Protection Agency Criteria and Standards Division, Washington, D.C., 60 pp + appendix.

Newendorp, P. D. 1975. Decision Analysis for Petroleum Exploration. Petroleum Publishing Co., Tulsa, Oklahoma, 668 pp.

New York City Department of Environmental Protection. 1983. A Special Permit Application for the Disposal of Sewage Sludge from Twelve New York City Water Pollution Control Plants at the 12-Mile Site. Prepared by Ecological Analysts, Sparks, Maryland, and SEAMOcean, Wheaton, Maryland, 512 pp. + appendices.

North, D. W. 1968. A tutorial introduction to decision theory, *IEEE Transactions on Systems Science and Cybernetics*, **SSC-4**(3), 200–210.

North, D. W., and M. W. Merkhofer. 1976. A methodology for analyzing emission control strategies. *Computer and Operations Research*, **3**, 185–207.

O'Connor, J. S., and R. T. Dewling. 1986. Indices of marine degradation: their utility. *Environmental Management*, **10**(3), 335–343.

O'Connor, T. P., M. G. Norton, A. J. Mearns, D. A. Wolfe, and I. W. Duedall. 1987. Scales of biological effects. *In*: Oceanic Processes in Marine Pollution Vol. 2: Physicochemical Processes and Wastes in the Ocean, T. P. O'Connor, W. V. Burt, and I. W. Duedall (Eds.). R. E. Krieger Publishing Co., Malabar, Florida, pp. 1–7.

O'Neill, R. V., R. H. Gardner, L. W. Barnthouse, G. W. Suter, S. G. Hildebrand, and C. W. Gehrs. 1982. Ecosystem risk analysis: A new methodology. *Environmental Toxicology and Chemistry*, **1**, 167–177.

Poston, T. M., and L. A. Prohammer. 1986. Sediment criteria methodology validation: Protocol for sediment toxicity testing of nonpolar organic compounds. Report prepared for U.S. Environmental Protection Agency Criteria and Standards Division, Washington, D.C., 31 pp.

Robertson, A. In Press. Development of ecosystem objectives for the Great Lakes. *In*: Great Lakes Ecosystem Health: Effects of Toxic Substances, M. S. Evans (Ed.). Wiley-Interscience, New York.

Ruckelshaus, W. D. 1983. Science, risk and public policy. *Science*, **221**, 1026–1028.

Ryder, R. A., and C. J. Edwards (Eds.). 1985. A Conceptual Approach for the Application of Biological Indicators of Ecosystem Quality in the Great Lakes Basin. International Joint Commission, Windsor, Ontario, and Detroit, Michigan, 169 pp.

Shaw, D. G. 1988. Hydrocarbon accumulations. *In*: Port Valdez, Alaska: Environmental Science and Management, D. G. Shaw and M. J. Hameedi (Eds.). Springer-Verlag, New York, pp. 243–265.

Spetzler, C., and C. A. S. Staël von Holstein. 1975. Probability encoding in decision analysis. *Management Science*, **22**(3), 340–358.

Spitzer, P. R., and J. S. O'Connor. 1987. Index of Reproductive Success in Marine Birds. NOAA Special Report, U.S. National Oceanic and Atmospheric Administration, Rockville, Maryland.

Thomas, N. A., A. Robertson, and W. C. Sonzogni. 1980. Review of control objectives: New target loads and input controls. *In*: Phosphorus Management Strategies for Lakes, R. C. Loehr, C. S. Martin, and W. Rost (Eds.). Ann Arbor Science Publishers, Ann Arbor, Michigan, pp. 61–90.

U.S. Code. 1981a. Safe Drinking Water Act. *In*: U.S. Code, 1976 Edition and Supplement IV (1980), Government Printing Office, Washington, D.C. Title *42*, Sections 300f-300j-10.

U.S. Code. 1981b. Resource Convention and Recovery Act. *In*: U.S. Code, 1976 Edition and Supplement IV (1980), Government Printing Office, Washington, D.C. Title *42*, Sections 6901–6987.

U.S. Code. 1981c. Clean Air Act. *In*: U.S. Code, 1976 Edition and Supplement IV (1980), Government Printing Office, Washington, D.C. Title 42, Sections 7401–7642.

U.S. Congress. 1972. Marine Protection, Research and Sanctuaries Act of 1972. Public Law 92-532, 86 Stat, Washington, D.C.

U.S. Congress. 1977. The Clean Water Act of 1977. Public Law 95-217, 91 Stat. 1566, Washington, D.C.

U.S. District Court. 1981. *New York City vs. Environmental Protection Agency*. Federal Supplement, West Publishing Co., St. Paul, Minnesota, 543 pp. 1084–1115.

U.S. Environmental Protection Agency (EPA). 1976. Quality Criteria for Water. U.S. Environmental Protection Agency, Washington, D.C., 256 pp.

U.S. National Academy of Sciences (NAS). 1972. Water Quality Criteria 1972. U.S. National Academy of Sciences, Washington, D.C., 594 pp.

U.S. NAS. 1984. Disposal of Industrial and Domestic Wastes: Land and Sea Alternatives. National Academy Press, Washington, D.C., 210 pp.

White, H. H. (Ed.). 1984. Concepts in Marine Pollution Measurements. Maryland Sea Grant Publication No. UM-SG-TS-84-03, University of Maryland, College Park, 743 pp.

White, H. H., and M. A. Champ. 1983. The great bioassay hoax, and alternatives. American Society for Testing and Materials, Philadelphia, Pennsylvania, Special Technical Publication 805, pp. 299–312.

Widdows, J. 1983. Field measurement of the biological impacts of pollutants. *In*: Assimilative Capacity of the Oceans for Man's Wastes, Jong-Ching Su and Tsu-Chang Hung (Eds.). Proceedings of a Pacific Regional Workshop on Assimilative Capacity of the Oceans for Man's Wastes (26–30 April 1982), Taipai, Republic of China. Tah-Jinn Printing Co., Taipai, pp. 111–129.

Wolfe, D. A. 1975. Modeling the distribution and cycling of metallic elements in estuarine ecosystems. *In*: Estuarine Research, Vol 1: Chemistry, Biology, and the Estuarine System, E. Cronin (Ed.). Academic Press, New York, pp. 645–671.

Wolfe, D. A. 1983. Needs for modeling in marine pollution assessment. *In*: Marine Ecosystem Modeling: Proceedings from a Workshop Held April 6–8, 1982, Frederick, Maryland, K. W. Turgeon (Ed.). U.S. National Oceanic and Atmospheric Administration, National Environmental Satellite, Data, and Information Service, Washington, D.C., pp. 1–20

Wolfe, D. A. 1988a. A decision–analytic approach for development of optimal waste management strategies. *In*: Oceanic Processes in Marine Pollution, Vol. 3: Marine Waste Management: Science and Policy, M. A. Champ and P. K. Park (Eds.). R. E. Krieger Publishing Co., Malabar, Florida, pp. 315–325.

Wolfe, D. A. 1988b. Management use of scientific information. *In*: Port Valdez, Alaska: Environmental Science and Management, D. G. Shaw and M. J. Hameedi (Eds.). Springer-Verlag, New York, pp. 345–374.

Wolfe, D. A., and B. Kjerfve. 1986. Estuarine variability: An overview. *In*: Estuarine Variability, D. A. Wolfe (Ed.). Academic Press, New York, pp. 3–17.

Wolfe, D. A., and J. S. O'Connor. 1986. Some limitations of indicators and their place in monitoring schemes. *In*: Oceans '86 Proceedings, Vol. 3: Monitoring Strategies Symposium. Marine Technology Society No. 86CH2363-0, Washington, D.C., pp. 878–884.

Wolfe, D. A., and T. R. Rice. 1972. Cycling of elements in estuaries. *Fishery Bulletin*, **70**(3), 959–972.

Wolfe, D. A., F. A. Cross, and C. D. Jennings. 1973. The flux of Mn, Fe, and Zn in an estuarine ecosystem. *In*: Radioactive Contamination of the Marine Environment. International Atomic Energy Agency, Vienna, Austria, pp. 159–175.

Wolfe, D. A., D. F. Boesch, A. Calabrese, J. F. Lee, C. D. Litchfield, R. J. Livingston, A. D. Michael, J. M. O'Connor, M. Pilson, and L. Sick. 1982. Effects of toxic substances on communities and ecosystems. *In*: Ecological Stress and the New York Bight: Science and Management, G. F. Mayer (Ed.). Estuarine Research Federation, Columbia, South Carolina, pp. 67–86.

PART II: SEWAGE EFFLUENTS IN THE SOUTHERN CALIFORNIA BIGHT ECOSYSTEM

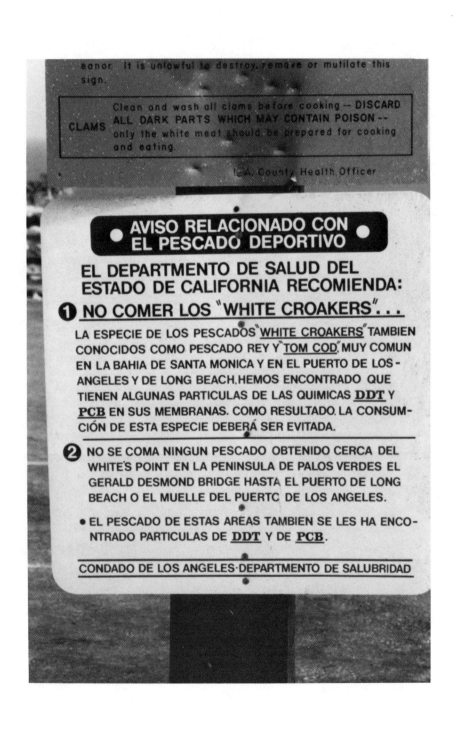

Chapter 2

Relationship between Declining Discharges of Municipal Wastewater Contaminants and Marine Sediment Core Profiles

Janet Stull, Rodger Baird, and Theadore Heesen

Los Angeles County Sanitation Districts
Whittier, California

Abstract	23
2.1. Introduction	23
2.2. Experimental Methods	25
2.2.1. Field	25
2.2.2. Laboratory	26
2.3. Results	26
2.4. Discussion	28
2.5. Conclusions	31
Acknowledgments	31
References	32

ABSTRACT

Sediment cores were collected at 17 sites in the vicinity of the submarine wastewater discharges of the Los Angeles County Sanitation Districts (California, U.S.A.) in 1981. Trace metals and chlorinated hydrocarbons were analyzed to describe geographic and temporal distributions in these sediments from the Palos Verdes Peninsula. The stratigraphy of the wastewater constituents is clearly related to the chronology of discharge mass emissions. A reservoir of historically discharged sewage constituents lies buried beneath progressively less contaminated sediments. At a 60-m water depth, the magnitude of peak concentrations and the depth of burial were inversely related to distance from the outfalls. At greater and shallower water depths, peak concentrations were typically nearer the sediment surface. Zinc, Cu, Cr, Pb, DDT, and polychlorinated biphenyls (PCB) profiles were most similar to the mass emission patterns, and approximate dates were assigned to core strata based on these distributions. Cadmium levels decreased more rapidly in the sediment than in the wastewater, perhaps as a result of chemical or biochemical mobility. In the outfall region, levels of organic N declined more slowly than did emissions of suspended solids, possibly because of hypoxia and slower biodegradation. Emissions and sediment concentrations of Ni decreased slightly.

2.1 INTRODUCTION

The Los Angeles County Sanitation Districts (California, U.S.A.) serve the wastewater treatment needs of 3.5 million people, including 70,000 industrial and commercial establishments. Approximately 1.4×10^9 liters d^{-1} (360 million gallons) of advanced primary treated domestic and industrial wastewaters were discharged into the Pacific Ocean off the Palos Verdes Peninsula in Southern California during the 1970s. Discharge is via two submarine outfalls that extend 2.5 km across the ocean bottom to terminate, at a water depth of 60 m, in multiport diffuser structures designed to maximize initial dilution (Fig. 2.1).

Effluent quality improved significantly during the decade 1971–1980 (Table 2.1) as a result of greater source control of industrial wastes (Eason et al., 1978) and modifications of treatment plant processes, including additional digestion and removal of solids (Moshiri et al., 1982). Reductions were well over 90% for DDT and polychlorinated biphenyls (PCB); nearly 80% for Zn; 55–65% for Cr, Cu, and Pb; and 45% for suspended solids.

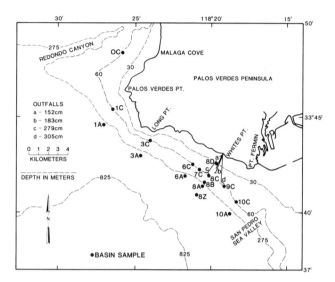

Figure 2.1. Sampling locations for sediment cores, offshore from the Palos Verdes Peninsula. Outfalls C and D have been active since 1956 and 1966, respectively; outfalls A and B are standby.

Table 2.1. Annual Mass Emission Rates of Wastewater Constituents from Los Angeles County Sanitation Districts Outfalls to the Ocean off Palos Verdes Peninsula, 1971 and 1980

Effluent Parameter	Year	
	1971	1980
Flow [liters d⁻¹ (× 10⁶)]	1,404	1,416
General Constituents (t y⁻¹)		
total suspended solids	167,000	91,000
5-d biochemical oxygen demand	168,000	107,500
oil and grease	38,000	16,600
NH₃-N	41,000	20,500
Trace Metals (t y⁻¹)		
As	—[a]	2.58
Cd	15.4	10.3
Cr	462	160
Cu	267	98
Pb	144	62
Hg	0.72	0.41
Ni	144	103
Se	8.21	5.17
Zn	1,400	310
Chlorinated Hydrocarbons (t y⁻¹)		
Total DDT	21.5	0.54
Total PCB	5.20	0.34

[a]Dash indicates no data.

It has long been understood that a substantial mass of wastewater contaminants occurs in sediments on the Palos Verdes Shelf (Galloway, 1972; Bruland et al., 1974; Myers, 1974; Morel et al., 1975; Hershelman et al., 1977; Sweeney et al., 1980; Katz and Kaplan, 1981; Kettenring, 1981). The flux of effluent particulate material has produced a sediment burden of organically rich solids and associated trace constituents. Since prevailing subsurface currents are toward the northwest through most of the year, often oriented along depth contours, maximum deposition of effluent particulate material occurs northwest of the outfall region at the discharge depth of 60 m. In this area the large loading rate of particulate material results in a negative porewater oxidation–reduction potential, H_2S generation, and elevated contaminant levels. The deposition rate tends to decrease with distance from the outfall and with other factors, such as offshore wastefield movement and sediment transport via erosion mechanisms (e.g., resuspension from currents, storms, and bioturbation), that also modify contaminant distributions. The net result is that sewage constituents in the surface sediment generally are distributed in an oblong pattern with the longitudinal axis oriented along depth contours (Fig. 2.2).

Improvements in effluent quality in the 1970s were reflected in surface sediments in the discharge region. For example, Cu emissions between 1973 and 1979 diminished 52%, from 638 to 307 kg d⁻¹. Surveys in January 1974 and 1980 (Stull and Baird, 1985) revealed parallel reductions in Cu concentrations among the nearshore, top 5 cm of sediments on the shelf (Fig. 2.2). The area supporting the greatest metal burdens in the surficial sediment also gradually shifted further offshore.

Changes in levels of organic N in surface sediments also reflect emissions of suspended solids in effluent (Fig. 2.3). Reductions in mass emission rates of suspended solids between 1971 and 1981 are paralleled in decreasing N concentrations at two Palos Verdes 60-m-depth sites (stations 6C and 3C); organic N at the "reference" site (station 0C) in southern Santa Monica Bay is essentially unchanged. Background levels are <0.1% dry weight (Word and Mearns, 1978).

Even with more than a decade of studies of surficial sediment, no comprehensive picture has ever been made of the distribution of trace constituents remaining in the sediment column on the shelf. A clearer understanding of the sediment reservoir was needed in view of the effects of sediment-borne contaminants on the marine biota, both infaunal (Stull et al., 1985) and water column (Young et al., 1976b, Smokler et al., 1979); the known association between contaminants in wastewater particulate material and sedi-

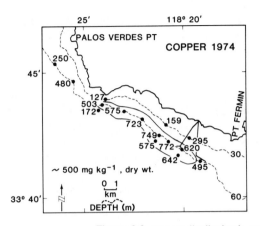
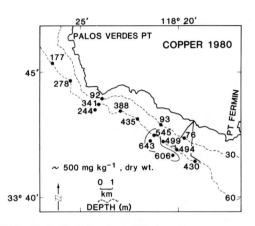

Figure 2.2. Copper distribution in surface sediments of Palos Verdes Shelf (top 5 cm, Shipek grab).

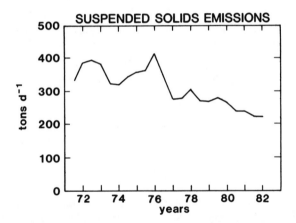
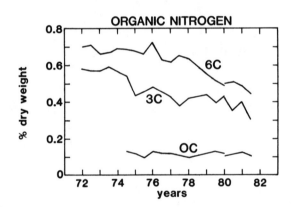

Figure 2.3. Sediment response to improved wastewater treatment: organic N levels in the surface sediment versus mass emissions of suspended solids into the ocean. (Refer to Fig. 2.1 for sediment sampling sites.)

ments; and the proposed improvements in waste treatment processes. A substantial sediment-monitoring program was therefore conducted to obtain a comprehensive database on spatial and temporal distributions of wastewater-derived materials in the sediments. This chapter reports the results of chemical analysis of sediment cores from the Palos Verdes region and relates historical patterns of wastewater emission to sediment characteristics.

2.2. EXPERIMENTAL METHODS

2.2.1. Field

Sediment cores were collected during the months February–April 1981, at 17 sampling sites (Fig. 2.1) that were chosen based both on historical information and on the projected value for tracing the fate of effluent materials and for modeling sediment quality. Depths sampled range from 30 to 870 m; the most distant site (station 0C) was in Santa Monica Bay, 22 km from the outfalls. Sampling effort was focused along the 60-m isobath, since greatest sedimentation and biological and chemical impacts were historically observed at this discharge depth. Additional sample sites were also concentrated in the outfall region and on the 305-m isobath.

A light (~150 kg), large-bore (~12 cm) coring device (Bascom et al., 1982) was employed in gathering the sediment cores; these ranged from 21 to 84 cm in length depending on the nature of the sediments. Navigation was via LORAN C, and sampler deployment was monitored by a recording sonar fathometer. The ship was anchored on station in waters up to 60 m deep, but had to be held on station by ship's power in deeper waters. Each core was collected and stored in a 0.25-mm-thick acetate tube, which lined the steel core barrel. Liquid nitrogen was used to freeze and seal the sediment–air interface, and the core was immediately surrounded with dry ice; frozen cores were stored at −20°C after being returned to the laboratory.

2.2.2. Laboratory

Frozen cores were sectioned at 2-cm intervals by using a stationary cutoff wheel with cleaned steel blades. The outer 2 cm of the 12-cm diameter slices was removed to minimize vertical cross-contamination, which might have occurred during sampling, and slices were stored in the freezer in acid-washed jars with Teflon® (E.I. DuPont de Nemours and Co., Wilmington, Delaware) cap liners. Analytical procedures were as follows:

To detect organic N and volatile solids, samples were ignited at 550°C and analyzed according to Standard Methods (American Public Health Association et al., 1980).

To detect metals, homogenized samples were lyophilized at −60°C, 10^{-6} torr for 24 h, pulverized, and digested with a mixture of concentrated HNO_3 and 30% H_2O_2 in a Parr Bomb (Parr Instruments Co., Moline, Illinois). Digestates were filtered, diluted, and analyzed by flame atomic absorption spectrometry (AAS) (model IL951 aa, Instrumentation Laboratories, Lexington, Massachusetts) for all metals except As, which was analyzed by flameless AAS on an IL555 graphite furnace (Stull and Baird, 1985).

To determine wet density, a portion of each wet sample was placed in a tared glass tube [50.8 mm × 6.95 mm inside diameter (ID)] and weighed; the density was determined by dividing by the volume of the glass tube (1.926 ml).

To detect chlorinated hydrocarbons, aliquots of wet sediment were prepared according to a U.S. Environmental Protection Agency (EPA) method (U.S. EPA, 1979). A portion of the hexane concentrate was dehydrohalogenated in alcoholic KOH for analysis for PCB. Analysis of DDT and PCB was by dual packed-glass column (2 mm × 4 mm ID 1.5% OV-17 + 1.95% QF-1 on Gas Chrom Q, 80/100, and 3% OV-17 on Gas Chrom Q, 80/100 mesh) gas chromatography (model 5755B, Hewlett Packard, Fullerton, California) with electron capture detection.

Moisture content and compaction of the sediments varied with sampling location and depth within the sediments. Upper sediments near the outfall were least dense; compaction increased with depth. In comparisons of historic mass emissions of effluent constituents with sediment core profiles, it was necessary to convert data on sediment depth to units of dry mass, using data on percent moisture and sediment density. Depth, in units of cumulative g cm^{-2}, was calculated from the sediment surface downward.

2.3. RESULTS

Representative sediment profiles are summarized in three series of transects that traverse the Palos Verdes Shelf: the 60-m and 305-m longshore transects and a transect seaward from the Y-shaped ocean outfall (Fig. 2.1).

Figures 2.4–6 illustrate the stratigraphy and geographic distribution of organic N, chlorinated hydrocarbons, and metals at six sites on the 60-m isobath extending 0–22 km northwest from the Y outfall. At this water depth the sediment patterns were as follows:

Peak concentrations of organic N were greatest in the outfall region (Fig. 2.4). Maximum burial of peak concentrations was at the site 1 km northwest of the Y outfall pipe (7C) and decreased progressively with increasing distance from the outfall. The depth of burial was greater at sites 1–2 km distant from, than immediately adjacent to, the Y outfall. Upper sediments in the cores from this area were successively less enriched by organic matter.

The stratigraphy of total DDT (Fig. 2.5) is similar to that of organic N except that concentration peaks are considerably sharper and narrower, and levels in surficial and deepest

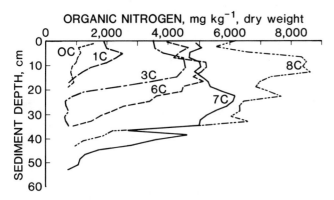

Figure 2.4. Organic N profiles in sediment cores along the 60-m isobath.

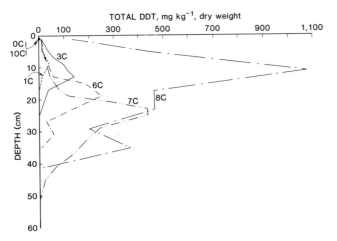

Figure 2.5. Total DDT distribution in sediment cores from the 60-m isobath.

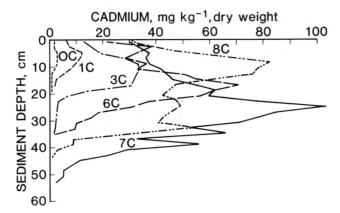

Figure 2.6. Vertical distribution of Cd in sediments from the 60-m isobath.

sediments are low relative to these peaks. A buried but persistent reservoir of DDT from discharges that were terminated in the early 1970s clearly exists (see section 2.4).

Cadmium exhibited a similar profile (Fig. 2.6); however, greatest concentrations were found at station 7C, 1 km northwest of the Y diffuser.

A complementary display of Cr distribution among shelf sediments, which includes eight sites both northwest and southeast of the pipes (Fig. 2.7), illustrates the presence of a subsurface deposit centered just northwest of the Y outfall. The generalized distributions for organic N, DDT, and all other monitored metals were similar to that shown for Cr. Rapid declines both in concentrations and in sedimentation were typical of stations 9C and 10C to the southeast (currents and flux of effluent particulate material were stronger to the northwest). Maximum metal enrichments (over "background," estimated from the average metal concentration in the deepest sediment slice from the two outlying stations, 0C and 10C) were as follows: ~10 for Ni, 40–50 for Cr and Zn, 110–120 for Pb and Cu, and 300 for Cd.

The northwesterly transport of effluent-associated material was also evident at 305-m water depth; however, net sedimentation rates and contaminant concentrations were considerably lower than observed at 60 m. Greatest concentrations were often still exposed in surficial sediments at this water depth, as shown for Cd in Fig. 2.8.

The sampling transect extending offshore from the Y outfall shows the effects both of depth and of distance on contaminant distributions (Fig. 2.9). Greatest concentrations of Cd were measured near the diffuser, as expected, at 60-m depth (station 8C). Smaller peaks were less buried at 150 (station 8B) and 480 m (station 8Z); however, the 330-m site (station 8A) was anomalous because of its short core length; dense, compact sediments; and small unburied Cd peak.

At station 7C, a 60-m site 1 km northwest of the outfalls, concentrations in the surface sediment represented the following percentages of subsurface maximum concentrations: 70–80% for Ni and organic N; 40% for Cr, Cu, and Pb; 30% for Zn and Cd; and 2 and 5% for DDT and PCB, respectively. Corresponding mass emissions (1980 versus maximum for 1971–1980) were as follows: 66 and 54% for Ni and suspended solids; 35, 34, and 43% for Cr, Cu, and Pb, respectively; 22 and 53% for Zn and Cd; and 2.5 and 6.5% for DDT and PCB.

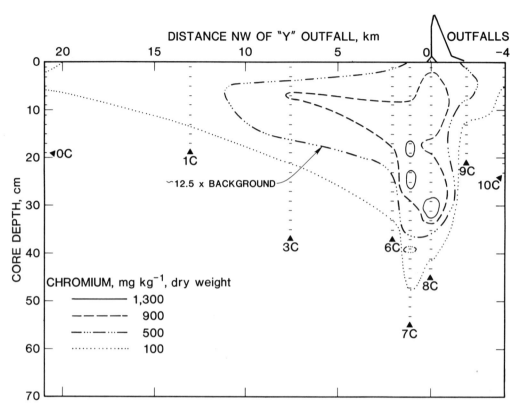

Figure 2.7. Chromium stratigraphy in sediments from the 60-m isobath across the Palos Verdes Shelf.

2.4. DISCUSSION

The study of these sediment cores clearly documents both significant improvements in recent sediment quality and the existence of a subsurface contaminant reservoir in the sediments of the Palos Verdes Shelf. Relative improvements and the magnitude of the reservoir were greatest within a few kilometers of the discharge.

Although the relationship varies with the effluent parameter, an overall similarity between sediment character and wastewater emissions seems to exist. In general, as wastewater quality improved, levels of trace constituents and organic N in the sediments decreased (Figs. 2.4–9). Geographic (spatial) distributions of trace constituents and organic matter were related primarily to longshore distance from the outfalls and hydrodynamics of the region (the greatest particulate flux and peak organic concentrations were nearest the diffusers and to the northwest due to prevailing currents). Vertical

(temporal) profiles may be a function of emissions rates of effluent solids and biodegradation of organic material in the sediment.

Relationships between the sediment and the effluent are examined in a series of paired graphs that compare semi-annual records of effluent emissions (1971–1980) to sediment core stratigraphies (Figs. 2.10–12). A sediment core from station 7C was selected for closer examination of the relationship between the sediment and the effluent because it originated from the zone of greatest net sedimentation [as described by Hendricks (1982) and as supported by our findings], and its longer core had the potential to provide a more detailed history. Based on DDT concentrations (since primary emission termination date is known to be 1971), wastewater emissions from the decade 1971–1980 were represented in the top 26 cm of sediment from station 7C. Since solid material in this core ranged from 30% in upper strata to 70% at the bottom, depths were converted to dry mass. The

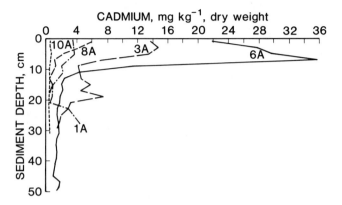

Figure 2.8. Cadmium profiles in sediment cores from the 305-m isobath.

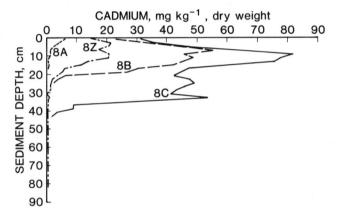

Figure 2.9. Cadmium distribution in sediments at and offshore of the Y ocean outfall. Sample depths: 8C = 62 m, 8B = 153 m, 8A = 332 m, and 8Z = 482 m.

correction for moisture:density leads to a calculated cumulative dry mass of 10.5 g cm^{-2} deposition of solid material from sediment surface to peak DDT depth (26 cm).

Although the fluctuations in the emission patterns for different constituents are generally damped in the sediment profiles, the overall patterns in the paired graphs are very similar (Figs. 2.10–2.12). Best relationships between effluent discharges and station 7C sediment profiles were found for Cu, Cr, Pb (Fig. 2.10), Zn, DDT, and PCB (Fig. 2.11). Matching prominent portions in the paired profiles allows rough age dating of different sediment depths and approximation of net sedimentation rates at this site. For example, on the average, the upper 3.3 g cm^{-2} appears equivalent to 1979–1980; 5.3–7.1 g cm^{-2} parallels flux from 1975–1976; and 8.3–10.5 g cm^{-2} is estimated to represent 1971–1972.

Annual sediment accumulation rates are thus estimated to range from ~0.6 g cm^{-2} in 1973–1974 to 1.7 g cm^{-2} in 1979–1980. The latter is the most recent and probably least decomposed material; 1971–1972 accumulations of 1.1 g cm^{-2} are attributed to higher emissions of solid material (Fig. 2.3). The similarities between effluent emissions and sediment concentration profiles suggest that bioturbation and other physical mixing processes do not play a major role in overall sediment stratigraphy patterns near the outfall, although localized surface effects have been reported (Stull et al., 1985).

The DDT profiles (Fig. 2.5) exhibit a steep rate of decline in more recent sediments, a result of the abrupt removal of the pesticide manufacturer from the wastewater treatment system (Young et al., Chapter 3). Although discharges into the sewer system were terminated in 1971, DDT-laden sediments in the sewer pipes provided a continuous but decreasing source of release into the sea for several years after termination (Mac-Gregor, 1974; Young et al., 1976a), explaining, at least in part, the continued detection of DDT and its metabolites in upper sediments.

Profiles of metal concentrations are generally similar to one another in that the greatest concentrations and burial are observed within 1 km of the outfall and at the discharge depth (Figs. 2.6–2.9); however, strata with the greatest concentrations vary with the trace constituent, suggesting differences in emission, sedimentation, and/or mobilization rates. For example, peak concentrations decreased from stations 8C > 7C > 6C for Cu, Pb, Ni, organic N, and Cr, and from 7C > 6C > 8C for Cd and Zn. Depth of peak burial varied but decreased 7C > 6C > 8C for Cu, Pb, Ni, organic N, Cd, and Zn, and 8C > 7C > 6C for Cr.

The most common pattern was of a maximum contaminant concentration at station 8C, but greatest sedimentation at station 7C, 1 km to the northwest. A likely explanation is that with improvements in treatment over the decade (Moshiri et al., 1982), coarser particles with a higher settling velocity have been removed from the effluent stream. A larger proportion of less-dense particles are entrained in the wastewater plume and transported away from the outfalls. Sedimentation of fine particles then decreases with increasing distance from the pipes.

The sediment parameter distributions for Cd, organic N, and Ni at station 7C did not clearly reflect effluent emission rates. Mass emission rates for all three of these constituents fluctuated widely between 1971 and 1981, although the average emissions both for total suspended solids and for Ni

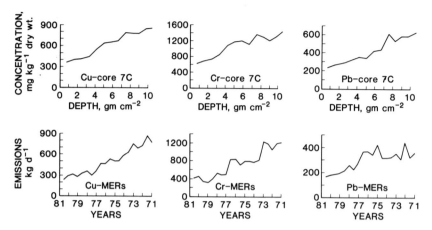

Figure 2.10. Effluent mass emission rates (MERs), 1971–1980, and concentration profiles in sediments from station 7C for Cr, Cu, and Pb. Semiannual effluent records reversed onto *x*-axis correspond with sediment core stratigraphy. Sediment depths were converted to units of dry mass to normalize for moisture and compaction.

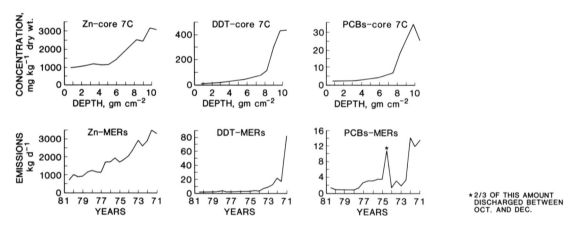

Figure 2.11. Effluent MERs, 1971–1980, and concentration profile in sediments from station 7C for Zn, DDT, and PCB (see Fig. 2.10).

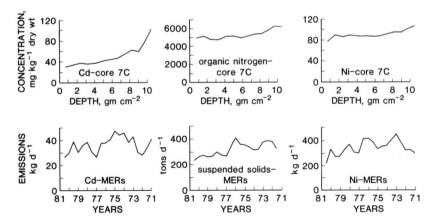

Figure 2.12. Effluent MERs, 1971–1980, and concentration profiles in sediments from station 7C for Cd, organic N, and Ni. The variability of the MERS is not reflected in the sediment profiles (see Figs. 2.10–11).

declined during that period (Fig. 2.12). The sediment levels of Ni and organic N declined in approximate proportion to the average rate of decline for emissions. Despite variable discharge rates for Cd, however, the sediment levels decreased steadily. Although there are no simple explanations for the decrease in Cd, several potential factors may be involved; these include release into the water column during effluent dilution with seawater (Rohatgi and Chen, 1975), possible association with effluent bacteria (Hays and Theis, 1978), mobilization from the sediments (Lu and Chen, 1977) under oxidizing conditions (observed in Stull et al., 1985), microbial activity, or biological uptake from the sediments (U.S. EPA, 1983).

Other wastewater tracers have been examined by using these sediment cores. Long-chain alkylbenzenes (LABs) from detergents used since 1965 are useful source-specific tracers (Eganhouse et al., 1983), although transport distances are limited (there were strong correlations at station 3C, but San Pedro Basin LABs were somewhat degraded). Vitamin E acetate (α-tocopheryl acetate) may be another useful tracer (Eganhouse and Kaplan, 1985).

Hendricks (1982, 1983) used distributions of DDT and organic matter from this core study for numerical modeling of sedimentation of natural and effluent particulate material, and the subsequent bottom processes affecting sediment composition. He estimates that 15–20% of the discharged particulate material settles to the sediments within a 16-km distance along the coast, and the remainder of the material is advected out of the shelf region.

As more recent "cleaner" particulate material has covered historical deposits, ecological improvements (both chemical and biological) have become apparent at the discharge depth of 60 m (Stull and Baird, 1985; Stull et al., 1986). Such improvements are not as evident at greater water depths, where contaminants lie exposed (and more available to the biota) at or near the sediment surface.

The anomalous distribution at station 8A (Fig. 2.9) probably resulted from historical or continuing erosional mechanisms that transport the sewage-derived materials further offshore, across the steep shelf break. This interpretation is supported by topographic studies (Emery and Terry, 1956) and acoustic reflections of a thin to absent sediment cover on this steep slope (Moore, 1960).

In summary, a direct temporal correlation appears to exist between effluent emissions and sediment quality. Several important questions remain: (1) Is the historical contaminant reservoir a source of concern? This question relates not only to buried peak concentrations near the outfall but also to contaminants that are closer to the sediment surface (e.g., at greater isobath depths). (2) Is re-emergence of high concentrations of trace constituents possible if emissions of suspended solid material in the effluent are substantially reduced? (3) Can large storms resurface buried contaminants? (4) Can modeling adequately project sediment quality under different treatment scenarios? Some of these questions could be addressed with this database, but others are controversial and require further knowledge of the behavior both of sewage-derived trace contaminants and of organic material in the sea.

2.5. CONCLUSIONS

The sediment cores from the Palos Verdes Shelf show spatial and temporal patterns in metal, chlorinated hydrocarbon, and organic matter distributions that are clearly related to wastewater discharge. A substantial reservoir of contaminants lies buried near the submarine outfalls.

At a site 1 km northwest of the Y outfall, the distributions of Cr, Cu, Zn, DDT, and PCB in the sediment strata correspond well to the chronological record of waste flow. The patterns reflect the increasing urbanization and industrialization of Los Angeles County from 1937 to the 1960s, followed by reduced emissions of solids and trace contaminants in the 1970s. Cadmium levels, however, decreased more rapidly in sediments from the outfall region than the emission pattern for Cd would suggest.

Over much of the study area, the quality of surface sediments has improved in direct relation to effluent quality. As wastewater particulate material that is less contaminated with industrial materials is deposited and compacted on the shelf, the historical sediment reservoir of this particulate material should become less available to biota in this area.

ACKNOWLEDGMENTS

Irwin Haydock, Supervisor of Ocean Monitoring, guided the coring study: the authors appreciate his continuing support. The technical assistance of Harold Stubbs (Southern California Coastal Water Research Project) and Elly Gabrielian, Tsam Wong, and Tsu Kai Jan (Sanitation Districts) is gratefully acknowledged.

REFERENCES

American Public Health Association, American Water Works Association, and Water Pollution Control Federation. 1980. Standard Methods for Examination of Water and Wastewater, 15th edition. American Public Health Association, Washington, D.C., 1134 pp.

Bascom, W., J. Mardesich, and H. Stubbs. 1982. An improved corer for soft sediments. *In*: Biennial Report, 1981–1982, Coastal Water Research Project, Long Beach, California, pp. 266–271.

Bruland, K. W., K. Bertine, M. Koide, and E. D. Goldberg. 1974. History of metal pollution in Southern California coastal zone. *Environmental Science and Technology*, **8**, 425–432.

Eason, J. E., J. G. Kremer, and F. D. Dryden. 1978. Industrial waste control in Los Angeles County. *Journal Water Pollution Control Federation*, **50**, 672–677.

Eganhouse, R. P., and I. R. Kaplan. 1985. α-tocopheryl acetate as an indicator of municipal waste contamination in the environment. *Environmental Science and Technology*, **19**, 282–285.

Eganhouse, R. P., D. L. Blumfield, and I. R. Kaplan. 1983. Long-chain alkylbenzenes as molecular tracers of domestic wastes in the marine environment. *Environmental Science and Technology*, **17**, 523–530.

Emery, K. O. 1960. The Sea off Southern California. John Wiley & Sons, New York, 366 pp.

Emery, K. O., and R. D. Terry. 1956. A submarine slope off Southern California. *Journal of Geology*, **64**, 271–280.

Galloway, J. N. 1972. Man's Alteration of the Natural Geochemical Cycle of Selected Trace Metals. Ph.D. Dissertation, University of California, San Diego, 143 pp.

Hayes, T. D., and T. L. Theis. 1978. The distribution of heavy metals in anaerobic digestion. *Journal Water Pollution Control Federation*, **50**, 61–72.

Hendricks, T. J. 1982. An advanced sediment quality model. *In*: Biennial Report, 1981–1982. Coastal Water Research Project, Long Beach, California, pp. 247–257.

Hendricks, T. J. 1983. Numerical Model of Sediment Quality Near an Ocean Outfall. Report submitted to National Oceanic and Atmospheric Administration Pacific Marine Environmental Laboratory, Seattle, Washington, 97 pp + figures and appendices.

Hershelman, G. P., T. K. Jan, and H. A. Schafer. 1977. Pollutants in sediments off Palos Verdes. *In*: Annual Report, 1977, Coastal Water Research Project, Long Beach, California, pp. 63–68.

Katz, A., and I. R. Kaplan. 1981. Heavy metals behavior in coastal sediments of Southern California: a critical review and synthesis. *Marine Chemistry*, **10**, 261–299.

Kettenring, K. N. 1981. The Trace Metal Stratigraphy and Recent Sedimentary History of Anthrogenous Particulates on the San Pedro Shelf, California. Ph.D. Dissertation, University of California, Los Angeles, 156 pp.

Lu, J. C. S., and K. Y. Chen. 1977. Migration of trace metals in interfaces of seawater and polluted surficial sediments. *Environmental Science and Technology*, **11**, 174–182.

MacGregor, J. S. 1974. Changes in the amount and proportions of DDT and its metabolites, DDE and DDD, in the marine environment off Southern California. *Fishery Bulletin*, **72**, 275–293.

Moore, D. G. 1960. Acoustic-reflection studies of the continental shelf and slope off Southern California. *Geological Society of America Bulletin*, **71**, 1121–1136.

Morel, F. M. M., J. C. Westall, C. R. O'Melia, and J. J. Morgan. 1975. Fate of trace metals in Los Angeles County wastewater discharge. *Environmental Science and Technology*, **9**, 756–761.

Moshiri, M., R. F. Luthy, Jr., and B. E. Hansen. 1982. Upgrading a large treatment plant—problems and solutions. *Journal Water Pollution Control Federation*, **54**, 1270–1280.

Myers, E. P. 1974. The Concentration and Isotopic Composition of Carbon in Marine Sediments Affected by a Sewage Discharge. Ph.D. Dissertation, California Institute of Technology, Pasadena, 178 pp.

Rohatgi, N., and K. Y. Chen. 1975. Transport of trace metals by suspended particulates on mixing with seawater. *Journal Water Pollution Control Federation*, **47**, 2298–2316.

Smokler, P. E., D. R. Young, and K. L. Gard. 1979. DDTs in marine fishes following termination of dominant California input: 1970–1977. *Marine Pollution Bulletin*, **10**, 331–334.

Stull, J. K., and R. B. Baird. 1985. Trace metals in marine surface sediments of the Palos Verdes Shelf, 1974 to 1980. *Journal Water Pollution Control Federation*, **57**, 833–840.

Stull, J. K., C. I. Haydock, and D. E. Montagne. (1986). Effects of *Listriolobus pelodes* (Echiura) on coastal shelf benthic communities and sediments modified by a major California wastewater discharge. *Estuarine, Coastal and Shelf Science*, **22**, 1–17

Sweeney, R. E., E. K. Kalil, and I. R. Kaplan. 1980. Characterization of domestic and industrial sewage in Southern California coastal sediments using nitrogen, carbon, sulfur and uranium tracers. *Marine Environmental Research*, **3**, 225–243.

U.S. Environmental Protection Agency (EPA). 1979. Chlorinated hydrocarbons methods: Organochlorine and organophosphorus insecticides in bottom sediments, Section II. *In*: Manual of Analytical Methods for the Analysis of Pesticides in Human and Environmental Samples, U.S. Environmental Protection Agency, Washington, D.C., pp. 1–5.

U.S. EPA. 1983. Revised Section B of Ambient Water Quality Criteria for Cadmium. U.S. Environmental Protection Agency, Washington, D.C., 89 pp.

Word, J. Q., and A. J. Mearns. 1978. The 60-meter control survey. *In*: Annual Report, 1978, Coastal Water Research Project, Long Beach, California, pp. 41–56.

Young, D. R., D. J. McDermott, and T. C. Heesen. 1976a. DDT in sediments and organisms around southern California outfalls. *Journal Water Pollution Control Federation*, **48**, 1919–1928.

Young, D. R., T. C. Heesen, and D. J. McDermott. 1976b. An offshore biomonitoring system for chlorinated hydrocarbons. *Marine Pollution Bulletin*, **7**, 156–159.

Chapter 3

Persistence of Chlorinated Hydrocarbon Contamination in a California Marine Ecosystem

David R. Young

Ocean Assessments Division
U.S. National Oceanic and Atmospheric Administration
State University of New York
Stony Brook, New York

Richard W. Gossett

Southern California Coastal Water Research Project
Long Beach, California

Theadore C. Heesen

Los Angeles County Sanitation Districts
Whittier, California

Abstract	33
3.1. Introduction	34
3.2. Study Area	34
3.3. Methods	35
3.4. Results and Discussion	35
Acknowledgments	40
References	40

ABSTRACT

Despite major reductions in the dominant DDT and polychlorinated biphenyls (PCB) input off Los Angeles (California, U.S.A.) in the early 1970s, the levels of these pollutants decreased only slightly from 1972 to 1975 both in surficial bottom sediments and in a flatfish bioindicator (Dover sole, *Microstomus pacificus*) collected near the submarine outfall. In contrast, the DDT and PCB concentrations in surficial sediment, Dover sole, and various sportfish species from the outfall area decreased by about an order of magnitude between 1977 and 1981, when the input rate was relatively low and essentially constant. The total DDT:total PCB ratio in the fish species collected between 1972 and 1981 more closely resembled those in the bottom sediments than those in the wastewater input. Concentrations of these pollutants in the soft tissues of the mussel *Mytilus californianus*, collected intertidally well inshore of the highly contaminated bottom sediments, followed much more closely the decreases in the outfall discharges. These observations suggest that contaminated sediments on the seafloor were the principal (although

Dr. Young's present address: U.S. Environmental Protection Agency, Hatfield Marine Science Center, Newport, Oregon.

not necessarily direct) cause of the relatively high and persistent concentrations of DDT and PCB residues in tissues of seafood fishes and invertebrates from the study area 5–7 y after control of the dominant wastewater input. Five of 11 fish species averaged >5 mg kg^{-1} total DDT in their edible tissue, the U.S. Food and Drug Administration (FDA) action guideline for interstate commerce. The highest value, 39 mg kg^{-1}, was found in the muscle of white croaker (*Genyonemus lineatus*), the most popular sportfish caught in southern California. The average concentration of total PCB in this species, 2.8 mg kg^{-1}, also exceeded the 2 mg kg^{-1} FDA action guideline for PCB. In 1980, concentrations in the muscle tissue of white croaker from the outfall study area still averaged 7.6 mg kg^{-1}. The study indicated that residues of the higher-molecular-weight chlorinated hydrocarbons, such as DDT and PCB, can be highly persistent once released to coastal marine ecosystems and that their accumulation in surficial bottom sediments is the most likely cause of this persistence observed in the biota of the discharge zone.

3.1. INTRODUCTION

Chlorinated hydrocarbons, such as the pesticide DDT and the industrially important polychlorinated biphenyls (PCB), are probably the most serious environmental contaminants studied over the past several decades (Risebrough, 1969; DeLong et al., 1973; U.S. National Academy of Sciences, 1975; Young et al., 1983). Concern over the unrestricted release of these higher-molecular-weight synthetic organic compounds increased in the late 1960s, and programs were developed to reduce their emissions and to monitor ecosystems exposed to such discharges. One benefit of the long-term monitoring programs has been an increased understanding of the rates at which different components of particular ecosystems will recover chemically or biologically from a major environmental stress after that stress has been removed or greatly reduced. This chapter presents results obtained from a 10-y study of chlorinated hydrocarbons in the vicinity of one of the nation's largest submarine outfall systems, which has been a principal source of DDT and PCB residues to the coastal waters of southern California.

3.2. STUDY AREA

The Joint Water Pollution Control Plant (JWPCP) of the Los Angeles County Sanitation Districts (LACSD) releases municipal wastewater through a submarine outfall system at a

depth of ~60 m off Whites Point, Palos Verdes Peninsula, in the Southern California Bight (Fig. 3.1). Industrial discharges to the JWPCP sewer have been a major source of metals and synthetic and petroleum hydrocarbons to the coastal waters, causing high concentrations of these materials in the bottom sediments (Young et al., 1975a; Young et al., 1978). Although PCB are ubiquitous contaminants with numerous individual sources, the predominant input of DDT to the wastewater system arose from one of the world's largest manufacturers of the pesticide, Montrose Chemical Co., in Los Angeles County (Carry and Redner, 1970; Anderson, 1983; Young and Heesen, 1978).

Large quantities of DDT residues were released for two decades, and a survey in 1972 (Young et al., 1976) revealed that ~200 metric tons (t) of these residues had accumulated in the upper 30 cm of bottom sediments in a 50-km^2 area off the Palos Verdes Peninsula (Fig. 3.1). Gradients of 2–4 orders of magnitude existed between the boundaries of the bight and the JWPCP discharge zone for total DDT concentrations in bottom sediments, intertidal mussels, flatfish, and other benthic organisms (Risebrough, 1969; Burnett, 1971; Duke and Wilson, 1971; DeLong et al., 1973; McGregor, 1974; Risebrough et al., 1974; Young et al., 1975b; McDermott et al., 1976; Young et al., 1978). The pesticide was also accumulated by pelagic organisms, leading to at least one seizure of a commercial fish shipment (white croaker, *Genyonemus linea-*

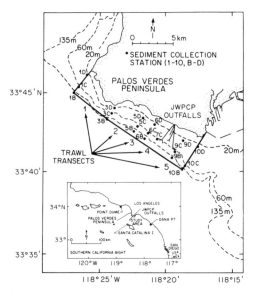

Figure 3.1. The study area (bordered by solid line) within the JWPCP outfall monitoring zone. Royal Palm Beach is located at the base of the outfall system.

tus) for tissue residues above the U.S. Food and Drug Admin-istration's (FDA) action guideline of 5 mg kg⁻¹ (wet wt). Reproduction of the brown pelican (*Pelicanus occidentalis*) off southern California was severely reduced owing to egg-shell thinning caused by excessive levels in tissue of total DDT (DDT plus the primary metabolites DDE and DDD), which were accumulated through the plankton–anchovy–marine–bird food web (Anderson et al., 1975).

Release of DDT wastes from the Montrose Chemical Co. to the JWPCP sewer was terminated in the spring of 1970 (Anderson, 1973). Nevertheless, ~22 t of DDT residues were discharged in 1971 through the JWPCP submarine outfall system (Young and Heesen, 1978). In 1971, a survey by the LACSD revealed ~60 t of total DDT in sediments that had settled in a 200-m section of a wastewater main downstream from the pesticide manufacturer. These highly contaminated sewer sediments appear to account for the large discharge of DDT residues monitored by the LACSD during 1971.

3.3. METHODS

In 1971, a long-term monitoring program was initiated for chlorinated hydrocarbons in wastewater, bottom sediments, flatfish, and intertidal mussels from the JWPCP outfall study area off the Palos Verdes Peninsula (Fig. 3.1). Duplicate sets of flow-weighted, composite week-long samples of JWPCP effluent were collected during summer and winter of each year, preserved without filtration by addition of pesticide-grade hexane, and analyzed in the laboratories of both the LACSD and the Southern California Coastal Water Research Project (SCCWRP). The major constituents measured were *total DDT* (expressed as the sum of the *p,p'* and *o,p'* isomers of DDT, DDE, and DDD) and *total PCB* (expressed as the sum of PCB 1242 and PCB 1254). Very satisfactory agree-ment (generally within 20%) was obtained between the two laboratories for concentrations of total DDT in the JWPCP effluent (Young et al., 1976); the monthly DDT values from the LACSD's monitoring program were adopted for this study. Consistent agreement was not obtained for PCB anal-yses by the two programs, and the values for PCB concentra-tions reported here are the average of the four values per year obtained in the SCCWRP laboratory.

Bottom sediments were collected by a Phleger gravity corer or Shipek grab sampler from 19 benthic stations (Fig. 3.1) within the JWPCP outfall study area during the summer of 1972 and the summer of 1975. The sediments were then analyzed at SCCWRP for DDT and PCB residues in the top

5-cm layer (Young et al., 1977). The top 2-cm layer of sediment from several of these same stations was sampled during the summer of 1977 and the spring of 1981 by using a modified Van Veen grab sampler (Word, 1976). The variations in sediment samplers and layer thicknesses used in this study resulted from modifications made in the monitoring pro-grams. Although systematic differences caused by the changes in sampling methods were not observed, to minimize bias the 5-cm layer results (for 1972 and 1975) and the 2-cm layer re-sults (for 1977 and 1981) were compared independently. Stull et al. (Chapter 2) described in detail the vertical distributions of chlorinated hydrocarbons and other contaminants, which were measured in sediment core samples, and corresponding estimated sedimentation rates, which were obtained from several stations in the JWPCP outfall study area.

Tissues from a number of different species of organisms collected from various sites near the outfall were analyzed for DDT and PCB residues during this same period. Specimens of Dover sole (*Microstomus pacificus*), with standard lengths generally ranging from 130 mm to 200 mm, were analyzed for DDT and PCB residues in the muscle tissue (Young et al., 1977). Composite samples of the undepurated soft tissues from five specimens of the intertidal mussel *Mytilus califor-nianus* which were 4–6 cm in length, were obtained quarterly (February, May, August, and November) most years during 1971–1981 from Royal Palm Beach at the base of the JWPCP outfalls (Fig. 3.1). Because of the extended period of freezer storage for some of these samples, all were freeze-dried before analysis, and the concentrations were converted to a wet-weight basis by using an average value of 83% moisture determined for fresh specimens. (Tests on wet and freeze-dried aliquots of fresh mussel samples showed no detectable differences in total DDT or total PCB concentrations.) Fi-nally, 17 species of seafood fishes and invertebrates, collected between the spring of 1975 and the spring of 1977 from the outfall study area and at southern California island (Santa Catalina) or coastal (Dana Point) control stations (Fig. 3.1), were analyzed similarly. Sample preparation and analytical procedures used at SCCWRP have been described by Young et al. (1976) and Hu et al. (1980).

3.4. RESULTS AND DISCUSSION

The controls placed on the release of chlorinated hydrocar-bons into the JWPCP wastewater collection system during the early 1970s caused a large reduction in the annual discharges of DDT and PCB residues via the submarine outfall system off Palos Verdes Peninsula. Between 1972 and 1975, the estimated emissions of total DDT and total PCB were reduced by approximate factors of 6 and more than 18, respectively (Table 3.1). However, the median concentrations of total DDT and PCB 1254 (the only PCB residue measured) in the surficial sediments only decreased over this period by factors of 1.6 and 1.2, respectively (Table 3.2). The corresponding 1972–1975 decrease factors for the Dover sole that were trawled from the study area were 1.5 and 1.9 (Table 3.3), respectively. By 1977, the major reductions in the JWPCP discharges of DDT and PCB residues had already occurred, and over the next 4 y the decrease factors for these contaminants were only 1.8 and 0.8, respectively (Table 3.1). In contrast, the 1977–1981 decrease factors obtained for the median concentrations of total DDT and total PCB measured in surficial sediments from three stations in the JWPCP study area in 1977 and 1981 were ~9 and 12, respectively (Table 3.2). The corresponding decrease factors for these residues in the Dover sole collected from this area were 9 and 15, respectively (Table 3.3).

Thus, over the study period the concentrations of total DDT and total PCB in muscle tissue of Dover sole collected from the JWPCP outfall study area appear to have more closely followed the levels of contaminants measured in the surficial sediments than the levels of contaminants measured in the effluent discharges (Fig. 3.2 and 3.3; Table 3.4). In contrast, the concentrations of these chlorinated hydrocarbons in the soft tissue of the intertidal California mussel more closely followed the annual discharges from the outfalls (Fig. 3.2; Fig. 3.3). This filter-feeding organism occupies a hard

Table 3.2. Median and Mean Concentrations of Measurable DDT and PCB Residues in Surficial Sediments from the JWPCP Outfall Study Area from 1972 to 1975 and 1977 to 1981[a]

Period	Total DDT (mg kg^{-1} ±1 standard error)		PCB Residue[b] (mg kg^{-1} ±1 standard error)	
	Median	Mean	Median	Mean
Monitoring Grid[c]				
1972	19	66 ± 16	1.0	4.0 ± 1.0
1975	12	41 ± 9.6	0.81	2.4 ± 0.64
1972:1975	1.6	1.6	1.2	1.7
Diffuser Transect[d]				
1977	49	86 ± 45	3.8	5.8 ± 2.6
1981	5.6	6.5 ± 1.1	0.33	0.34 ± 0.14
1977:1981	8.8	13	12	17

[a]Surficial sediment samples were 0–5 cm from 1972 to 1975 and 0–2 cm from 1977 to 1981.
[b]From 1972 to 1975 PCB 1254 was analyzed. From 1977 to 1981 total PCB were analyzed.
[c]The monitoring grid is 17–19 stations around discharge in 30–150 m water depth.
[d]The diffuser transect was three stations (3C, 5C, and 7C) downcurrent of the discharge in 60 m water depth.

substrate in a high-energy, non-depositional environment; thus, it is much more likely to be exposed to recently released effluent particulate material than to the historical deposits of the more highly contaminated particulate material that had been incorporated into the fine-grained bottom sediments inhabited by the Dover sole.

The specimens of Dover sole analyzed during this study generally fell within the size range of 130–200 mm standard length, corresponding approximately to age classes II–IV (Mearns and Harris, 1975). In particular, the standard length of the specimens collected in May 1977 (whose contamination levels were similar to those collected in May 1972) averaged ~140 mm (with an average whole-body weight of ~40 g) and thus probably had inhabited the outfall study area for no more than 2 y. These specimens, therefore, must have entered the outfall study area several years after the major reduction in the outfall loading of DDT and PCB residues; they could not have accumulated their high levels of contaminants during the high discharge period and simply retained the residues in their tissues. The June 1980 and June 1981 specimens were somewhat smaller than were the May 1977 specimens (average standard length of ~130 mm and whole-body weight of ~30 g). We have not observed significant relationships between fish size and age and tissue concentra-

Table 3.1. Annual Emissions of JWPCP Municipal Wastewater, Total DDT, and Total PCB Discharged off Palos Verdes Peninsula from 1971 to 1981

Year	Flow (10^{11} liter y^{-1})	Total DDT (kg y^{-1})	Total PCB (kg y^{-1})
1971	5.13	21,600	—[a]
1972	4.84	6,300	≥11,600
1973	4.96	3,720	2,670
1974	4.78	1,440	1,270
1975	4.71	1,080	650
1976	4.88	850	1,320
1977	4.63	730	310
1978	4.78	970	150
1979	5.07	640	640
1980	5.17	540	390
1981	5.03	420	270

[a]Dash indicates no data.

Table 3.3. Median and Mean Concentrations of Total DDT and Total PCB in Muscle Tissue of Dover Sole (*Microstomus pacificus*) Trawled from the JWPCP Outfall Monitoring Zone from 1972 to 1981

Period	n	Total DDT [mg kg^{-1} (wet wt) ±1 standard error]		Total PCB [mg kg^{-1} (wet wt) ±1 standard error]	
		Median	Mean	Median	Mean
May 1972	21	17	26 ± 5.3	2.1	2.3 ± 0.36
Dec 1973	9	18	16 ± 2.4	1.9	2.0 ± 0.23
May 1974	20	13	15 ± 2.4	1.5	1.5 ± 0.19
Feb 1975	10	11	25 ± 10	1.1	1.9 ± 0.67
Nov 1976	24	16	17 ± 2.2	1.2	1.1 ± 0.14
May 1977	25	20	26 ± 5.2	1.4	1.8 ± 0.4
Jun 1980	17	2.7	3.6 ± 0.77	0.093	0.14 ± 0.03
Jun 1981	4[a]	2.3	2.5 ± 0.06	0.093	0.13 ± 0.03

[a]Composite samples of 18 ± 2 individuals each.

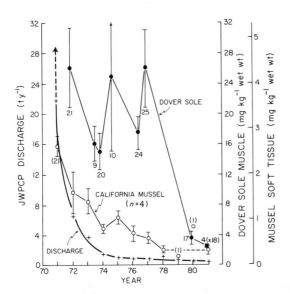

Figure 3.2. Annual discharge of total DDT via the JWPCP outfalls (t), compared with average concentrations (±1 standard error) of total DDT in muscle tissue of Dover sole (*Microstomus pacificus*) (solid circle) and whole soft tissues of the California mussel (*Mytilus californianus*) (hollow circle; *n* = 4) from the outfall study area, 1971–1981.

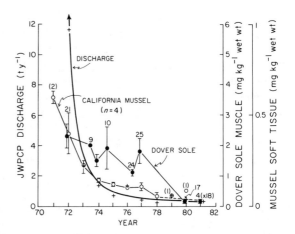

Figure 3.3. Annual discharge of total PCB via the JWPCP outfalls (t), compared with average concentrations (± 1 standard error) of total PCB in muscle tissue of Dover sole (*Microstomus pacificus*) (solid circle) and in soft tissues of the California mussel (*Mytilus californianus*) (hollow circle; *n* = 4) from the outfall study area, 1971–1981.

tion of DDT or PCB residues, however, that could account for the order-of-magnitude concentration reductions from 1977 to 1980–1981.

The foregoing observations suggest that the lag in decline of DDT and PCB in Dover sole after the significant loading reductions in the early 1970s can be attributed to the persistence of chlorinated hydrocarbon contamination in the surficial sediment environment (sediment, interstitial water,

and/or infaunal prey). The most likely routes of such hypothesized uptake from this environment are direct partitioning from contaminated interstitial water and/or consumption of contaminated benthic organisms.

The large reservoir of DDT and PCB residues contained in the bottom sediments off Palos Verdes Peninsula during the mid-1970s was probably at least indirectly responsible also for the relatively high concentrations of these synthetic or-

Table 3.4. Median and Mean Concentrations of Total DDT and Total PCB in Whole Soft Tissue of California Mussels (*Mytilus californianus*) Collected Quarterly from Royal Palm Beach at the Base of the JWPCP Outfalls, 1971–1981[a]

Period	n	Total DDT		Total PCB	
		Median	Mean	Median	Mean
1971	2	2.7	2.7 ± 0.22	0.61	0.61 ± 0.034
1972	4	1.2	1.6 ± 0.48	0.31	0.41 ± 0.12
1973	4	1.5	1.4 ± 0.29	0.27	0.22 ± 0.034
1974	4	0.75	0.82 ± 0.10	0.15	0.15 ± 0.008
1975	4	1.0	1.1 ± 0.15	0.12	0.12 ± 0.012
1976	4	0.73	0.71 ± 0.19	0.11	0.11 ± 0.019
1977	4	0.60	0.61 ± 0.12	0.10	0.11 ± 0.022
1978	4	0.36	0.34 ± 0.05	0.054	0.054 ± 0.012
1979	1	0.20	0.20	0.060	0.060
1980	1	0.87	0.87	0.087	0.087
1981	4	0.32	0.34 ± 0.10	0.034	0.037 ± 0.003

[a]Concentrations expressed as mg kg^{-1} wet wt ±1 standard error. Converted from a freeze-dry weight basis using an average value of 83% moisture determined for fresh specimens.

ganic compounds measured in the edible tissue of other seafood organisms collected during 1975–1977 from the JWPCP study area (Table 3.5). Average levels of DDT residues in 5 of the 11 fish species that were investigated exceeded the FDA action guideline (5 mg kg^{-1}). White croaker exhibited the highest mean total DDT concentration (39 mg kg^{-1}) and the highest mean total PCB concentration (2.8 mg kg^{-1}) which exceeded the 2 mg kg^{-1} limit for polychlorinated biphenyls in seafood (U.S. FDA, 1977, 1984). According to a 1978 sportfishing survey by the California Department of Fish and Game, one in three fish caught in southern California was a white croaker, making it the most popular sportfish there (Gossett et al., 1983). Of the 17 seafood species collected off the Palos Verdes Peninsula, 11 averaged >1 mg kg^{-1} total DDT in their edible tissue (Table 3.5). These observations are consistent with those reported previously for total DDT in muscle tissue of Dover sole, black perch, and kelp bass collected off the peninsula between 1970 and 1977 (Smokler et al., 1979).

Liver samples from five fish species were also analyzed, and all contained much higher concentrations of chlorinated hydrocarbons than did the corresponding muscle samples (Table 3.5). Average concentrations (± standard error) of total DDT in the livers of Pacific sanddab (*n* = 2), white croaker (*n* = 10), scorpionfish (*n* = 2), sablefish (*n* = 6), and Bocaccio (*n* = 7) from the outfall zone were 930 ± 170, 130 ± 48, 115 ± 2, 63 ± 10, and 32 ± 17 mg kg^{-1}, respectively; corresponding values for total PCB were 51 ± 5, 7.6 ± 2.0, 12 ± 7, 0.28 ± 0.08, and 4.1 ± 1.3 mg kg^{-1}. In comparison, multiple analyses (*n* = 6) of a homogenate of liver tissue from

six Dover sole collected during November 1976 from the study area yielded averages of 240 ± 34 mg kg^{-1} total DDT and 18 ± 3 mg kg^{-1} total PCB (Young and Heesen, 1978).

Five sportfishes (white croaker, scorpionfish, kelp bass, Bocaccio, and bonito) were collected from the JWPCP outfall study area during 1980 as part of a seafood contamination survey (H. Puffer, personal communication), and samples were analyzed at SCCWRP. The average contaminant concentrations in these muscle tissue samples collected in 1980 were lower by factors of ~5 and 7 for total DDT and PCB, respectively, than were the corresponding values obtained in the 1975–1977 seafood survey (Table 3.5). These values are of the same order as the 1977–1981 decrease factors for total DDT (9) and total PCB (12) in sediments (Table 3.2). This observation supports the hypothesis that the DDT and PCB contamination of the seafood fishes from the study area during 1975–1980 was maintained by the chlorinated hydrocarbon contamination of the surficial sediment environment there.

Despite the major reductions in levels of chlorinated hydrocarbons in the sediments, Dover sole, and sportfishes collected off the Palos Verdes Peninsula after 1977, very high levels of DDT residues (>5 mg kg^{-1}) remained in muscle tissue of the white croaker collected off the peninsula in 1980. The mean and standard error values for total DDT were 7.6 ± 1.6 mg kg^{-1}; corresponding values for total PCB were 0.38 ± 0.05 mg kg^{-1} (Gossett et al., 1983). Thus, more than 10 y after the predominant industrial source was removed from the JWPCP wastewater collection system, levels of DDT and its

Table 3.5. Mean Concentration (± standard error) of Total DDT and Total PCB in Muscle Tissue of Seafood Organisms from the JWPCP Outfall Study Area and Southern California Control Regions from 1975 to 1977[a]

| Organism | n | Outfall Zone | | n | Island Control Zone | |
		Total DDT [mg kg^{-1} (wet wt)]	Total PCB [mg kg^{-1} (wet wt)]		Total DDT [mg kg^{-1} (wet wt)]	Total PCB [mg kg^{-1} (wet wt)]
Fishes						
White croaker (*Genyonemus lineatus*)	10	39 ± 18	2.8 ± 1.0	—	—	—
Dover sole (*Microstomus pacificus*)[b]	35	26 ± 5	1.8 ± 0.3	11	0.029 ± 0.003	0.011 ± 0.002
Pacific sanddab (*Citharichthys sordidus*)[b]	13	6.2 ± 0.7	0.53 ± 0.07	10	0.17 ± 0.03	0.026 ± 0.006
Sablefish (*Anoplopoma fimbria*)[c]	6	5.6 ± 1.7	0.28 ± 0.08	—	—	—
Black perch (*Embiotoca jacksoni*)[d]	26	5.4 ± 0.6	0.89 ± 0.12	8	0.04 ± 0.02	—
Scorpionfish (*Scorpaena guttata*)	4	3.6 ± 0.7	0.57 ± 0.14	3	0.097 ± 0.033	0.043 ± 0.017
Queenfish (*Seriphus politus*)[e]	6	3.3 ± 0.9	0.72 ± 0.16	—	—	—
Kelp bass (*Paralabrax clathratus*)	6	1.6 ± 0.3	0.30 ± 0.10	3	0.030 ± 0.014	0.033 ± 0.010
Bocaccio (*Sebastes paucispinis*)	7	1.1 ± 0.5	0.15 ± 0.04	—	—	—
Bonito (*Sarde chilinesis*)[b]	3	0.83 ± 0.27	0.31 ± 0.10	3	1.1 ± 0.4	0.39 ± 0.12
Anchovy (*Engraulis mordax*)	5	0.30 ± 0.05	0.07 ± 0.02	3	0.24 ± 0.15	0.036 ± 0.010
Invertebrates						
Sea urchin (*Strongylocentrotus franciscanus*)[f]	35	4.5 ± 0.6	1.2 ± 0.3	—	—	—
Crab (*Cancer anthonyi*)[b]	5	1.5 ± 0.2	0.37 ± 0.16	3	0.004 ± 0.002	0.032 ± 0.006
Mussel (*Mytilus californianus*)[g]	4	0.84 ± 0.16	0.15 ± 0.02	4	0.12 ± 0.007	0.056 ± 0.006
Lobster (*Panulirus interruptus*)	5	0.56 ± 0.26	0.10 ± 0.05	3	0.003 ± 0.001	0.010 ± 0.004
Scallop (*Hinnites giganteus*)	9	0.15 ± 0.01	0.014 ± 0.001	10	0.040 ± 0.017	0.004 ± 0.002
Abalone (*Haliotis cracherodii*)	5	0.001 ± 0.0003	0.08 ± 0.06	3	0.0001 ± 0.0001	0.023 ± 0.011

[a]Dash indicates no data.
[b]Control specimens from Dana Point.
[c]Collected March 1978.
[d]D. Hotchkiss (personal communication).
[e]Based on a measured muscle:whole body ratio of mean concentrations (±1 standard error) of 0.8 ± 0.2.
[f]Gonadal tissue of samples collected March 1979. J. Meistrell (personal communication).
[g]Based on analysis of duplicate composites of fresh soft tissue obtained June 1974 and January 1976 (both outfall and control zones).

residues still exceeded the FDA action guideline in one popular sportfish collected from the JWPCP outfall study area.

The correlation coefficients listed in Table 3.6 show that, during this study, the mean concentrations of total DDT and total PCB were strongly associated in every medium analyzed. However, the average ratios (±1 standard error) of mean total DDT to mean total PCB concentrations are significantly different for the JWPCP final effluent (2.0 ± 0.6) and

surficial sediments (16.9 ± 0.9). The similarity of the average for surficial sediments to that obtained for muscle tissue from Dover sole (14.7 ± 2.0) provides further evidence that concentrations of DDT and PCB residues in the Dover sole were controlled principally by contaminant concentrations in the surficial sediments rather than in the discharged wastewater. A laboratory study of chlorinated hydrocarbon uptake by Dover sole that were fed an uncontaminated diet and maintained in sediment both from the outfall zone and from a

Table 3.6. Median and Average Ratio of Mean Total DDT and Mean Total PCB Values and Corresponding Correlation Coefficient (*r*) Obtained for the Various Types of Samples Collected During 1971–1981 from the JWPCP Outfall Study Area

Sample Type	*n*	DDT and PCB		*r*	Significance[b]
		Median	Average[a]		
Wastewater (effluent)	9	1.4	2.0 ± 0.6	0.903	p < 0.001
Sediment (surficial)	4	16.8	16.9 ± 0.9	0.996	p < 0.01
Dover sole (muscle)	8	13.8	14.7 ± 2.0	0.912	p < 0.01
Seafood fishes (muscle)	11	6.3	8.8 ± 1.6	0.973	p < 0.001
Seafood invertebrates (edible tissue)	6	4.8	5.0 ± 1.4	0.993	p < 0.001
Mussels (soft tissues)	11	6.2	6.6 ± 0.6	0.965	p < 0.001

[a]Average ±1 standard error.
[b]$p < 0.01$: very significant; $p < 0.001$: highly significant.

control zone supports this hypothesis (Sherwood, 1976; Sherwood and Mearns, 1977). The average DDT:PCB ratio in muscle tissue of the 11 fishes collected in the 1975–1977 seafood survey was substantially smaller (8.8 ± 1.6) but still agreed more closely with that for the surficial sediment than for the wastewater. The average DDT:PCB ratio for the six seafood invertebrate species, which were hand collected well inshore of the most highly contaminated bottom sediments, was 5.0 ± 1.4 (Table 3.6).

Examination of the DDT:PCB ratios obtained from the mean concentrations (Table 3.5) from the seafood survey provides further insight on this topic. Considering the six fishes for which specimens were obtained from both the outfall and island control zones, the average ratio for the outfall zone specimens was 7.4 (±2.0), twice the value of 3.6 (±1.1) obtained for the control zone specimens. A similar result is obtained for the five seafood invertebrates collected from both zones, where the respective average DDT:PCB ratios were 5.2 (±1.7) and 2.5 (±1.9). These observations are consistent with the fact that discharges from the JWPCP outfall system have been the predominant source of DDT wastes to the southern California Bight, while PCB inputs are distributed more generally throughout this region (Young and Heesen, 1978). Thus, the DDT:PCB ratio would be expected to decrease in environmental samples with increasing distance from the outfall plume.

ACKNOWLEDGMENTS

The studies reported here were conducted by the Southern California Coastal Water Research Project while the senior author was associated with the project, with the help of Project Scientists Michael Moore, Patrick Hershelman, Henry Schafer, David Brown, and Director Willard Bascom. Partial support for this research was provided to the project by the U.S. Environmental Protection Agency (Grant No. R803707) and the U.S. National Oceanic and Atmospheric Administration (NOAA) (Grant No. NA80RAD00040); we thank the respective grant officers, Donald Baumgartner and Alan Mearns, for their technical advice. Initial preparation of this manuscript was supported by Dames & Moore (Los Angeles, California) while the senior author was associated with that firm, and completion of the manuscript was supported by NOAA's Ocean Assessments Division. The assistance of Thomas Scanland and Harold Stanford of these two groups, respectively, is gratefully acknowledged.

REFERENCES

Anderson, B. P. 1983. Trace Constituents Monitoring. Technical Services Department Monthly Report, January, Los Angeles County Sanitation Districts, Los Angeles, pp. 51–62.

Anderson, D. W., J. R. Jehl, Jr., R. W. Risebrough, L. A. Woods, Jr., L. R. Deweese, and W. G. Edgecomb. 1975. Brown pelicans: improved reproduction off the southern California coast. *Science*, **198**, 806–808.

Burnett, R. 1971. DDT residues: distribution of concentrations in *Emerita analoga* (Stimpson) along coastal California. *Science*, **174**, 606–608.

Carry, C. W., and J. A. Redner. 1970. Pesticides and Heavy Metals. Progress Report, December, Los Angeles County Sanitation Districts, Whittier, California, 51 p.

DeLong, R. L., W. G. Gilmartin, and J. G. Simpson. 1973. Premature births in California sea lions: association with high organochlorine pollutant residue levels. *Science*, **181**, 1168–1170.

Duke, T. W., and A. J. Wilson, Jr. 1971. Chlorinated hydrocarbons in livers of fishes from the northeastern Pacific Ocean. *Pesticide Monitoring Journal*, **5**, 228–232.

Gossett, R. W., H. W. Puffer, R. H. Arthur, Jr., and D. R. Young. 1983. DDT, PCB and benzo(*a*)pyrene levels in white croaker (*Genyonemus lineatus*) from southern California. *Marine Pollution Bulletin*, **14**, 60–65.

Hu, T. C. L., R. Gossett, and D. Young. 1980. Mass spectrometry confirmation of PCB and DDT analyses of fish. *In*: Biennial Report for the Years 1979–1980. Southern California Coastal Water Research Project, Long Beach, California, pp. 131–138.

McDermott, D. J., D. R. Young, and T. C. Heesen. 1976. PCB contamination of southern California marine organisms. *In*: Proceedings of the National Conference on Polychlorinated Biphenyls, 19–21 November 1975, Chicago, Illinois. U.S. Environmental Protection Agency Report No. 560/6-75-004, U.S. Environmental Protection Agency, Washington, D.C., pp. 209–217.

McGregor, J. S. 1974. Changes in the amount and proportions of DDT and its metabolites, DDE and DDD, in the marine environment off southern California, 1949–1972. *Fisheries Bulletin* **72**, 275–293.

Mearns, A. J., and L. Harris. 1975. Chapter I, Overview. *In*: Age, Length, and Weight Relationships in Southern California Populations of Dover Sole. Technical Memorandum 219, Southern California Coastal Water Research Project, El Segundo, California, 17 pp.

Risebrough, R. W. 1969. Chlorinated hydrocarbons in marine ecosystems. *In*: Chemical Fallout, M. W. Miller and G. C. Berg (Eds.). Charles C. Thomas, Springfield, Illinois, pp. 5–23.

Risebrough, R. W., D. R. Young, T. Munson, M. Goodwin, and R. Parrish. 1974. Contamination of marine resources for human consumption—synthetic organic compounds. *In*: Marine Bioassays Workshop Proceedings. Marine Technological Society, Washington, D.C., pp. 94–108.

Sherwood, M. J. 1976. Fin erosion disease induced in the laboratory. *In*: Annual Report for the Year 1976. Southern California Coastal Water Research Project, El Segundo, California, pp. 149–153.

Sherwood, M. J., and A. J. Mearns. 1977. Environmental significance of fin erosion in southern California demersal fishes. *Annals of the New York Academy of Science*, **298**, 177–189.

Smokler, P. E., D. R. Young, and K. L. Gard. 1979. DDTs in marine fishes following termination of dominant California input: 1970–77. *Marine Pollution Bulletin* **10**, 331–334.

U.S. Food and Drug Administration (FDA). 1977. Polychlorinated biphenyls (PCBs): unavoidable contaminants in food and food packaging materials; reduction of temporary tolerances. *Federal Register* **42** (63), 17487–17494.

U.S. FDA. 1984. Polychlorinated biphenyls (PCBs) in fish and shellfish; reductions of tolerances; final decision. *Federal Register* **49** (100), 21514–21520.

U.S. National Academy of Sciences. 1975. Assessing Potential Ocean Pollutants. U.S. National Academy of Sciences, Washington, D.C., pp. 3–13.

Word, J. Q. 1976. Biological comparison of grab sampling devices. *In*: Annual Report for the Year 1976. Southern California Coastal Water Research Project, El Segundo, California, pp. 189–194.

Young, D. R., and T. C. Heesen. 1978. DDTs, PCBs, and chlorinated benzenes in the marine ecosystem off southern California. *In*: Water Chlorination: Environmental Impact and Health Effects, Vol. 2, R. L. Jolley, H. Gorchev, and D. H. Hamilton, Jr. (Eds.). Ann Arbor Science, Ann Arbor, Michigan, pp. 267–290.

Young, D. R., D. J. McDermott, T. C. Heesen, and T. K. Jan. 1975a. Pollutant inputs and distributions off southern California. *In*: Marine Chemistry in the Coastal Environment, T. M. Church (Ed.). American Chemical Society, Washington, D.C., pp. 424–439.

Young, D. R., D. J. McDermott, T. C. Heesen, and D. A. Hotchkiss. 1975b. DDT residues in bottom sediments, crabs, and flatfish off southern California submarine outfalls. *California Water Pollution Control Association Bulletin*, **12**, 62–66.

Young, D. R., D. J. McDermott, and T. C. Heesen. 1976. DDT in sediments and organisms around southern California outfalls. *Journal Water Pollution Control Federation*, **49**, 1919–1928.

Young, D. R., D. McDermott-Ehrlich, and T. C. Heesen. 1977. Sediments as sources of DDT and PCB. *Marine Pollution Bulletin*, **8**, 254–257.

Young, D. R., T. K. Jan, and T. C. Heesen. 1978. Cycling of trace metal and chlorinated hydrocarbon wastes in the Southern California Bight. *In*: Estuarine Interactions, M. L. Wiley (Ed.). Academic Press, New York, pp. 481–496.

Young, D. R., R. W. Gossett, R. B. Baird, D. A. Brown, P. A. Taylor, and M. J. Miille. 1983. Wastewater inputs and marine bioaccumulation of priority pollutant organics off southern California. *In*: Vol. 4, Water Chlorination: Environmental Impact and Health Effects. R. L. Jolley (Ed.). Ann Arbor Science Publishers, Ann Arbor, Michigan. pp. 871–884.

Chapter 4

Effects of Nearshore Upwelling on Coliform Dispersion near the Whites Point Outfall

David A. Siegel

Ocean Physics Group
Department of Geological Sciences
University of Southern California
Los Angeles, California

Burton H. Jones

Allan Hancock Foundation
University of Southern California
Los Angeles, California

Tommy D. Dickey

Ocean Physics Group
Department of Geological Sciences
University of Southern California
Los Angeles, California

Irwin Haydock

Los Angeles County Sanitation Districts
Whittier, California

Alan Bratkovich

Ocean Physics Group
Department of Geological Sciences
University of Southern California
Los Angeles, California

Abstract	44	4.4. Discussion and Conclusions	47
4.1. Introduction	44	Acknowledgments	47
4.2. Experimental Methods	44	References	48
4.3. Results	45		

ABSTRACT

The relationships between nearshore physical processes and outfall effluent distributions were studied during the period 5 May to 15 June 1982 at the Whites Point outfall of the Los Angeles County Sanitation Districts (California, U.S.A.). Physical parameters were sampled from a mooring located near the end of one of the two outfall diffusers (~2.5 km offshore, 60-m depth). Moored instrumentation included a wind anemometer, vector-measuring current meters at 7- and 44-m depths, and 18 thermistors spaced uniformly throughout the water column. Total coliform bacterial counts were sampled at nearby beach stations. During the 40-d period, two cooling (upwelling) events and one warming (relaxation) event were observed. The upwelling episodes were characterized by southeastward longshore winds of from 3 to ~5 m s^{-1}, offshore surface flow, near-surface water temperatures of 14°C or less, and cooling rates of ~1°C d^{-1}. A cessation of the upwelling response was induced by a weak northwestward wind event. The relaxation response was strongest in the longshore current field, which showed an energetic northwestward pulse of several days' duration. The associated temperature response was strongest near the surface (the total increase in temperature was ~2°C). The beach coliform bacterial counts generally increased during the upwelling and decreased during the non-upwelling events. Evidence is presented that supports the hypothesis that upwelling was the major process contributing to transport of bottom-discharged effluent toward the beaches during this observational period.

4.1. INTRODUCTION

Oceanic wastewater outfall flows may be characterized as turbulent buoyant plumes. Koh and Brooks (1975) described three stages in the dispersal of a turbulent buoyant plume into a stratified fluid: (1) the plume rises and entrains the ambient fluid until the buoyancy of the effluent stream has been dissipated; (2) the plume spreads horizontally along its newly found constant density surface; and (3) the effluent becomes dynamically passive and is advected by the far-field flow.

The time scales of the mixing and advective processes relative to the lifetime of the pollutant give some estimate of the suitability of using an ocean outfall for the disposal of a pollutant. Koh and Brooks (1975) concluded that the first two stages of dispersion generally occur on time scales of <3 h. Since coliform bacteria in seawater have lifetimes on the order of several days (Chamberlain and Mitchell, 1978), most

of the lifetime of these bacteria is spent being advected and mixed by the ambient physical oceanographic processes. In other words, the third step (listed above) of the conceptual dispersal process is of primary importance in determining the ultimate dispersion of water-borne wastes. The objective here is to illustrate how these far-field processes contribute to the dispersal of a wastewater effluent plume, using the Whites Point ocean outfall near Los Angeles, California, as a case study.

Nearshore upwelling is the primary far-field oceanographic dispersive process examined in this chapter. Nearshore upwelling has been described by many authors [see Brink (1983) for a review] and is commonly observed along the California coast (Sverdrup, 1938; Huyer, 1983; Jones et al., 1983) where upwelling is characterized by longshore southward winds creating offshore Ekman transport in the surface layers. Conservation of mass requires that the near-surface waters be replaced by denser (colder) waters that are advected from depth. The wind-induced vertical velocity in the subsurface region is referred to as the upwelling velocity. The onshore flow of denser (colder) water caused by the offshore surface transport also leads to upward sloping (as the coastline is approached), isopycnal (isothermal) surfaces. It is hypothesized that, because of the wind-driven upwelling, the subsurface effluent stream is advected preferentially toward the coast. It will be demonstrated that the dynamics of the system are dominated by wind-driven upwelling, and further, that the concentrations of effluent observed at beach locations correlate well with upwelling-dominated flows.

4.2. EXPERIMENTAL METHODS

The Whites Point outfall of the Los Angeles County Sanitation Districts (LACSD) is located on the south side of the Palos Verdes Peninsula near Los Angeles, California (Fig. 4.1). The outfall terminates in 60 m of water, and ~30% of its length is the diffuser; hence, the source of the effluent cannot be described as a point source. The LACSD installed a physical oceanographic buoy with a surface float near the end of the outfall. The buoy instrumentation included 18 thermistors with a vertical spacing of ~3 m (one failed). The LACSD also deployed two vector-measuring current meters (VMCMs) located at 7- and 44-m depths and a wind anemometer located 3 m above the mean sea surface. The data were transmitted by telemetry to shore every 30 min. Forty days (5 May 1982 through 15 June 1982 or Julian days 125–165) of the entire record had complete enough data (nearly continuous) for thorough analysis. Subinertial variance ellipses (similar to

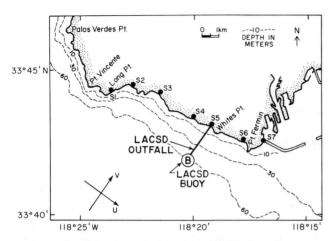

Figure 4.1. Geometry and bathymetry of the Whites Point outfall region. S1–S7 refer to the beach collection stations. The U and V axes refer to the coordinate system used in this analysis. Dashed lines indicate depth in meters.

tidal ellipses) indicated a directional ambiguity ($\pm 90°$) in the data recorded by the bottom (44-m) VMCM. Hence, these data were of limited utility for the analysis.

A coordinate system was established (Fig. 4.1) to describe the longshore and onshore components of horizontal velocity. The U component of velocity is defined to be longshore with the positive direction pointed approximately toward the southeast, and the V component is defined to be in the cross-shelf direction with positive onshore or approximately toward the northeast. Previous work indicates that this region may be characterized by subsurface cross-shelf flows at subinertial frequencies (Stevenson and Gorsline, 1956; Whitledge and Bishop, 1972). The local bathymetry is generally parallel to the coast with a cross-shelf slope of ~ 0.03 (30 m km^{-1}).

Total coliform bacterial counts were monitored at seven beach stations (Fig. 4.1, S1–S7) as part of the LACSD monitoring program. The beach stations spanned 12 km of coastline and were sampled daily at ~ 1000 Pacific Standard Time. Bacterial counts were determined by using a standard filtration technique. The coliform bacterial counts were logarithmically transformed ($\log_{10}(n + 1)$) and then smoothed by a 3-point (3-d) running mean. Buoy data were averaged by using 12-h bins and smoothed with a 5-point (2.5-d) running mean. These procedures were used to remove variability associated with surface tides, internal gravity waves, surface waves, internal tides, and diurnal sea breeze effects. Thus, frequencies between 0.05 cycle d^{-1} and 0.4 cycle d^{-1} were

analyzed. The time scale of this frequency band is often termed the synoptic scale (Jones et al., 1983). Additional data from an LACSD hydrographic survey cruise were also used.

4.3. RESULTS

A cross-shelf temperature section (day 148, or 28 May) indicated relatively cool water nearshore with no surface mixed layer (Fig. 4.2). A general characteristic of the vertical temperature profile was an intense thermocline seen in the upper 30 m. The vertical temperature gradient in the thermocline was $\sim 0.2°C$ m^{-1}. The isotherms generally sloped upward toward the beach; the slope of the 13°C isotherm was ~ 3 m km^{-1}. This suggests that upwelling was occurring during this survey.

The buoy measurements provide time series of wind speed and direction, horizontal currents at 7 m, and temperature at 17 depths (Fig. 4.3a,b,c). The interrelationships among these variables will be examined in the context of a wind-forced upwelling event.

The winds (Fig. 4.3a) were predominantly downcoast (trending toward the southeast) with the exception of the period from day 136 to 140. These prevailing (longshore) winds are considered to be favorable for upwelling (i.e., capable of producing offshore Ekman transport in the near-

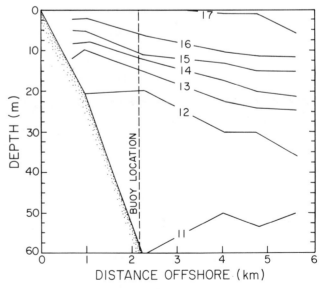

Figure 4.2. Cross-shelf temperature section (°C) from a LACSD hydrographic survey on 28 May 1982. The dashed line indicates the buoy location.

LACSD BUOY TIME SERIES

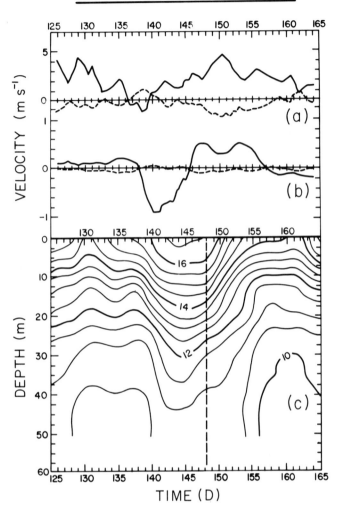

Figure 4.3. The 40-d time series of the low-pass buoy records of (a) winds, (b) horizontal currents at 7-m depth, and (c) vertical temperature profile. For (a) and (b) the units are m s⁻¹, the solid lines are the U component (downcoast), and the dashed lines are the V component (onshore). For (c) the units are °C.

surface layer). The two periods of upwelling-favorable winds (prior to day 136 and after day 140) were separated by a 4-d wind-reversal episode when the wind was onshore and up-coast. The maximum upwelling-favorable winds (>3 m s⁻¹) occurred between days 125 and 132 and between days 148 and 156. The unsmoothed wind data indicate a large diurnal sea breeze component, which will not be discussed in this chapter.

The temporal evolution of the subsurface temperature structure (Fig. 4.3c) is the primary indicator of upwelling. The most obvious features are the warming event (between days 138 and 144) and the cooling event (between days 144 and 156). During the warming event, the temperature increased ~2°C in the upper layer, but during the cooling event it decreased ~3°C. The upwelling velocity during the cooling event is estimated from isotherm displacements to be ~3.5 m d⁻¹. The temperature record also indicated a net cooling at depth (i.e., the 12°C isotherm rose ~10 m). Similar observations of nearshore cooling at depth during the spring and summer seasons have been reported by Winant and Bratkovich (1981) off Del Mar, California. This effect is consistent with onshelf transport of cooler deep water (i.e., upwelling). The unsmoothed temperature record from the buoy showed a high degree of variability at semi-diurnal frequencies. The isotherm displacement associated with these motions was 5–10 m. These large near-tidal motions will obviously contribute to the variability of a tracer (i.e., the coliform bacteria) observed in the natural system.

Winds favorable to upwelling were associated with decreasing water temperatures. The wind reversal appears to be well correlated (at a 2-d lag) with the warming event observed in the buoy temperature record. As seen in the measured isotherm displacements (about day 144–156), upwelling returned ~4–5 d after the start of wind intensification (on about day 140). The warming event represents the relaxation portion of the upwelling event cycle. This episodic upwelling cycle is common to the California coast and has a typical period of 3–10 d (Huyer, 1983).

Data from the upper VMCM (7-m depth) indicate down-coast, slightly offshore flow approximately coincident with (though lagging) upwelling-favorable winds (Fig. 4.3b). The upper-ocean response to upwelling-favorable winds described here is generally consistent with the classical description of nearshore upwelling (e.g., Brink, 1983). On day 138 (the onset of extreme warming), an intense upcoast and slightly onshore flow was indicated by the upper VMCM record. This flow coincided with the relaxation of the upwelling (onset of warming) observed in the temperature record but again lagged the wind by about 2 d. The flow direction reversed on day 145 and again returned to the upwelling state. This flow reversal lagged the wind reversal but was nearly coincident with the apparent onset of ascending isotherms. Due to the relative weakness of the surface wind forcing, several processes may be associated with coastal cooling (such as longshore advection), which may account for the relatively large time lag observed. The maximum upwelling-favorable currents correlate reasonably well (after phase shifting) with the maximum upwelling-favorable winds.

The beach coliform bacterial count (C) time series is shown in Fig. 4.4. Large inter-station variability was obvious; however, the overall station average showed several distinct periods. Periods of higher counts ($\log_{10} C > 1$) were noted for days 126–131 and 155–164; and periods of lower counts ($\log_{10} C < 0.5$) for days 133–140 and 147–154. In a qualitative sense, the periods with high bacterial counts coincided with upwelling (cooling), and the periods with low bacterial counts were associated with the warming trend (up to about day 140). However, this simple relationship, based upon ocean temperature alone, is invalid for days 140–147. This particular episode lags the only period of onshore–upcoast surface flow by ~2 d. One may speculate that the high coliform bacterial counts are associated with the surface onshore flow of the buoyant organic component of the effluent stream (Word et al., 1986). Unfortunately, based upon these data, a conclusive statement cannot be made. A major transi-

tion in the average coliform counts was observed on day 154. This transition is nearly coincident with the most pronounced upwelling as observed from the buoy measurements.

4.4. DISCUSSION AND CONCLUSIONS

The use of coliform bacteria as tracers of effluent dispersion has several obvious problems. First, the concentration of coliform bacteria is not a simple function of mixing and advection. Coliform bacterial growth and decay rates are functions of variables such as temperature, nutrients, dissolved organic carbon, solar radiation (particularly ultraviolet), and predation. These variables change by several orders of magnitude in a nearshore environment, especially in the vicinity of a wastewater outfall. Furthermore, the determination of coliform bacterial counts is subject to measurement errors, and standard deviations of measured values are, at times, of the same order as the mean values.

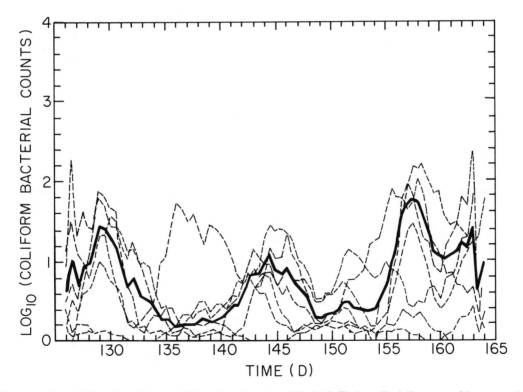

Figure 4.4. Time series of total coliform bacterial counts. Units are $\log_{10}$ (counts per 100 ml + 1). The heavy line is the average of the seven station values shown.

Other factors also contribute to the variability of the results. The shoreline and local bathymetry are irregular, and, as mentioned earlier, the diffuser is a non-uniform line source rather than a point source of effluent. These irregularities in coastal and diffuser geometries make models of effluent advection difficult to construct and interpret. The effects both of tidal and of solar cycles could also contribute to the sample variability. Despite these difficulties, there is reasonable evidence that upwelling was a major process contributing to beachward transport of effluent. Wind-driven upwelling was observed at the LACSD Whites Point wastewater outfall during May and June 1982. The average coliform bacterial counts appear to be generally well correlated with these upwelling events.

ACKNOWLEDGMENTS

This project was funded by the Los Angeles County Sanitation Districts. Support for this work was also obtained from the University of Southern California–Sea Grant Program. D. Siegel would also like to acknowledge support from the Graduate Research Fellowship Program of the Office of Naval Research, administered by American Society for Engineering Education. Discussions with Gary Kleppel and Rodolfo Iturriaga were most useful. Hermawan Indrapradja and Edward Hurst assisted with the preliminary data analysis. Sue Turnbow expeditiously typed the manuscript and Janet Dodds expertly drafted the figures.

REFERENCES

Brink, K. H. 1983. The near surface dynamics of coastal upwelling. *Progress in Oceanography*, **12**, 233–257.

Chamberlain, C. E., and R. Mitchell. 1978. A decay model for enteric bacteria in natural waters. *In*: Water Pollution Microbiology, Vol 2, R. Mitchell (Ed.). John Wiley and Sons, New York, pp. 325–348.

Huyer, A. 1983. Coastal upwelling in the California current system. *Progress in Oceanography*, **12**, 259–284.

Jones, B. H., K. H. Brink, R. C. Dugdale, D. W. Stuart, J. C. Van Leer, D. Blasco, and J. C. Kelley. 1983. Observations of a persistent upwelling center off Point Conception, California. *In*: Coastal Upwelling Part A, E. Suess and J. Thiede (Eds.). Plenum Press, New York, pp. 37–60.

Koh, R. C. Y., and N. H. Brooks. 1975. Fluid mechanics of waste-water disposal in the ocean. *Annual Review of Fluid Mechanics*, **7**, 187–211.

Stevenson, R. E., and D. S. Gorsline. 1956. A shoreward movement of cool subsurface water. *Transactions of the American Geophysical Union*, **32**, 180–184.

Sverdrup, H. V. 1938. On the process of upwelling. *Journal of Marine Research*, **2**, 155–164.

Whitledge, T. E., and D. Bishop. 1972. Data Report: *R/V T. G. Thompson* Cruise 67 (MESCAL I-OUTFALL I), Part II: Outfall I, Hydrography and Productivity. Special Report 51, University of Washington, Seattle, 391 pp.

Winant, C. D., and A. W. Bratkovich. 1981. Temperature and currents of the Southern California shelf: a description of the variability. *Journal of Physical Oceanography*, **11**, 71–86.

Word, J. Q., C. D. Boatman, C. C. Ebbesmeyer, R. E. Singer, S. Fischnaller, and Q. J. Stober. In press. Vertical transport of freon extractable and non-extractable material and bacteria (fecal coliforms and Enterococci) to the surface of marine waters: some experimental results using secondary sewage effluent. *In*: Oceanic Processes in Marine Pollution, Vol. 6: Physical and Chemical Transport and Transformation, D. Baumgartner and I. W. Duedall (Eds.). R. E. Krieger Publishing Company, Malabar, Florida, in press.

Chapter 5

Water Quality in Santa Monica Bay, as Indicated by Measurements of Total Coliforms

William F. Garber and Frank F. Wada

Bureau of Sanitation
Department of Public Works, City of Los Angeles
Los Angeles, California

Abstract	49
5.1. Introduction	49
5.2. Historical Account of Outfalls and Wastewater Treatment in the City of Los Angeles	50
5.3. Review of Coliform Group Concentrations and Distributions	51
5.4. Summary and Conclusions	54
References	55

ABSTRACT

Data are presented to show the changes from 1947 through 1984 in the bacteriological quality, as indicated by the Most Probable Number (MPN) Coliform Index, in the littoral waters of Santa Monica Bay, California (U.S.A.), which receives treated wastewater from the major sewage treatment plant of the city of Los Angeles. State of California discharge standards permit a coliform MPN of 1000 per 100 ml, with no more than 20% of the samples greater than this figure over each designated sampling period. Samples were collected daily over 37.5 km of shoreline and weekly at 28 stations reaching up to ~20 km offshore. The standards were met during the full 37-y period. From 1947 to 1984, flows increased from 0.61×10^6 to $>1.55 \times 10^6$ m^3 d^{-1}. Treatment varied from fine screening and chlorination with incineration of removed solids to mixed primary–secondary treatment with the digested and screened solids discharged 11 km out into the ocean. Discharge pipes were changed in length from 1.6 km offshore with the outfall at 13.7 m deep to 8 km offshore and 70 m deep for effluent and 11 km offshore and ~100 m deep for the processed solids. When the chlorinated effluent was being discharged at 1.6 km offshore and at a depth of 13.7 m, the arithmetic mean coliform MPN, based on the annual geometric means of the 17 shoreline sampling stations, averaged 500 per 100 ml. When the discharge point for the effluent was changed to 8 km offshore and to a depth of 70 m, the annual average coliform MPN for these 17 shore stations decreased to <40 per 100 ml, giving an excellent margin of safety, relative to the State Discharge Standard. Over the 37-y period no negative epidemiology was evident in records from California and Los Angeles County Department of Health Services. The MPN Coliform Index thus apparently successfully indicated water quality based on bacterial counts during a period of very great change.

5.1. INTRODUCTION

For wastewater facilities that diffuse treated effluents into open-ocean waters, the prime measure of the adequacy of outfall and diffuser design and of the success of process operations in treatment plants has been the degree to which the concentration of the coliform group of bacteria is controlled in the nearby littoral waters and along the adjacent shoreline.

The city of Los Angeles has diffused wastewaters into the Pacific Ocean at the site of its Hyperion Treatment Plant since 1894. During this period the effluent has varied from totally untreated to a modified secondary treatment; the discharge point has varied from shoreline to 8 km offshore; and the discharge depth has varied from the surface to ~70 m.

Disinfection by chlorine has or has not been practiced at different times. Since 1957, a separate outfall has diffused solid residuals from the wastewater treatment processes after anaerobic digestion and screening for removal of floatables. This outfall for residual solids is located ~11 km offshore in water ~100 m deep and ~3500 m north–northwest of the Y-shaped diffusion structure of the present 8-km effluent outfall described above (Fig. 5.1). The outfall for residual solids undoubtedly has had some effect upon the coliform content of the waters in the area examined, but the present principal impact is from the diffusion of ~1.6 × 10⁶ m³ d⁻¹ of mixed primary–secondary effluent into the ocean.

Because of the wide range of conditions that have been present at Hyperion and because of the additional impact of the digested and screened residual solids diffused in an area nearby, it was believed that a review and discussion of the historical record of public health protection at Hyperion as indicated by the coliform group of organisms would be of value. Scientists, operators, and designers must consider public health protection as part of their evaluation of the engineering "trade-offs" among possible ocean discharge, degree of treatment, outfall location, and degree of diffusion. This chapter describes the distribution of coliform bacteria in marine waters near the Hyperion outfalls for the period from 1943 to 1984, for which excellent bacteriological data are available.

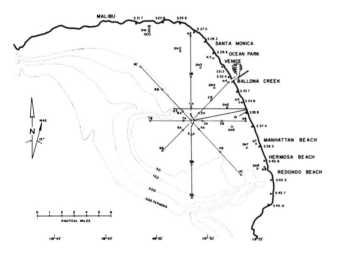

Figure 5.1. Sampling stations for total coliform bacteria in Santa Monica Bay, California, showing the radial distribution of transects around the end of the Y-shaped outfall and the locations of the beach stations.

5.2. HISTORICAL ACCOUNT OF OUTFALLS AND WASTEWATER TREATMENT IN THE CITY OF LOS ANGELES

The city of Los Angeles was founded in 1781, and the first public sewers were constructed in about 1873, when the population was 7000. By 1883 the population was ~15,000, and the wastewaters were handled by farmland irrigation. By 1894 the population had increased to ~70,000, so the city found it necessary to construct a 17-km land outfall sewer to Hyperion and to start the discharge of untreated wastewater into the ocean through a 61-cm diameter cast-iron pipe terminating 200 m from shore; however, farmland irrigation with untreated wastewaters also continued for a substantial amount of the city flow.

In 1904 a steel ocean outfall ~310 m long and 76 cm in diameter was constructed to replace the original cast-iron pipe. In addition, a trestle 280 m in length carrying an 86-cm diameter wooden stave pipe was constructed to carry the untreated wastewater from another newly constructed land outfall (City of Los Angeles Bureau of Engineering, 1982).

In 1924 a land outfall capable of carrying a flow of >10⁶ m³ d⁻¹ was put into service with the only treatment being rotary "fine" screens with openings of 0.16 × 5 cm. Discharge was through a 1524-m underwater outfall 2.13 m in diameter discharging at a depth of 13.7 m. This underwater outfall developed leaks, and the screens soon did not have sufficient capacity for the flow received so that gross onshore pollution effects were noticed (State of California Department of Public Health, 1943).

By 1949 the flow received at Hyperion had increased to 761 × 10³ m³ d⁻¹, a new 1524-m underwater outfall ~4-m inside diameter and discharging at a depth of 13.7 m had been constructed, and chlorination of the screened wastewater was begun. Water quality based on bacterial counts did not meet California coliform standards, however, until 1951 when full secondary treatment plus chlorination was instituted.

During the period 1949–1957, primary and secondary treatment, digestion of solids, and fertilizer production were added, although the new 1524-m underwater outfall continued to be used and chlorination was necessary. In 1957 an 11-km outfall was placed in service to diffuse residual solids at a depth of 100 m, and fertilizer production ceased. On 20 December 1959 the present 8-km long effluent outfall terminating in 70-m-deep water was also placed in service. The effluent in this line was a mix of 67% primary- and 33% secondary-treated water. Chlorination was no longer required.

Population growth and effluent flow from these outfalls have increased very sharply in the last several years, with average dry-weather flow during weekdays in excess of 1.63 $\times$ 10^6 m^3 d^{-1} and the annual average Hyperion–Glendale system flow in excess of 1.55 $\times$ 10^6 m^3 d^{-1} (Fig. 5.2). Initial dilution at the effluent diffuser section (Fig. 5.1) in 1984, therefore, was only ~80% of what it was in 1974. These historical factors, along with rapid population growth along the coast, heavy recreational use along the canyons and watercourses leading to the coast, more commercial boating as well as sharp increases in pleasure boat marinas, and increased beach use, have led to many changes in the average quality of the littoral waters as measured by the Coliform Index.

5.3. REVIEW OF COLIFORM GROUP CONCENTRATIONS AND DISTRIBUTIONS

The locations of the sampling grid for coliform determinations in shoreline and littoral water are along a series of transects around the underwater outfalls and along some 37.5 km of shoreline in Santa Monica Bay (Fig. 5.1). The shoreline stations are occupied daily, while the littoral water stations are visited weekly. Coliform determinations are by the multiple-tube technique described in Standard Methods (American Public Health Association et al., 1985). The statistically derived Most Probable Number (MPN) is used as the actual numerical index. California requires that waters in which body contact can occur have an MPN Coliform Index <1000

per 100 ml except that 20% of the samples can exceed this number, provided that a repeat sample taken within 48 h does not exceed 10,000 per 100 ml (State of California Department of Public Health, 1943). During rainfall, bacterial distributions are influenced primarily by storm-drain runoff, and data obtained on the day of a rainstorm and the day after are exempted from the state discharge standards. The standard coliform test was applied against the California limits throughout the 37-y period reported here.

Figure 5.3 summarizes the coliform information over 37.5 km of shoreline extending ~16.1 km south and 21.4 km north of the treatment plant. Beyond the 16.1-km point to the south the shoreline may be influenced by the discharge of another large treatment facility. The ordinate of Fig. 5.3 displays the arithmetic mean of the separate annual geometric means for 17 shoreline stations. Data are shown for the years of record over which excellent data on coliform groups were available. Table 5.1 provides additional detail on the operational conditions prevailing at the various stages mentioned in Fig. 5.3.

Figure 5.4 complements Fig. 5.3 and Table 5.1 by showing the actual geometric mean counts for selected years at each of the shoreline stations. Operationally, under the present configuration of the effluent outfall with no chlorination, the geometric mean at any station must be less than ~250 per 100 ml to meet the California State Coliform Standard. Since 1957 the microbiological quality along the shoreline of Santa Monica Bay has been excellent, including the year 1977, which, with high flows and the greatest recorded diffusion of residual solids, was one of the best on record. As already noted, the period since 1977 has been one of great growth (Fig. 5.2). Overall water quality has suffered, but treatment and diffusion changes to be made in the future are expected to help in alleviating this situation.

The recent increases shown in shore counts from stations 33.7 to 27.5 (Fig. 5.4) arose primarily from storm sewers, which have large upstream drainage areas and reach the coast at these points. Los Angeles has separate sanitary and storm sewers, and responsibility rests with the city Sewage Treatment Division only for the treated outflow from the sanitary sewers. Outflow from both types of sewers can obviously affect microbiological water quality since storm sewers drain the streets and the land areas of the city. Use of the beaches for bathing and other land-based activities are also believed to be major reasons for the more recent variances in the coliform counts. The data shown in Figs. 5.3 and 5.4 suggest, however, that the outfall discharge is of great importance to the quality of the receiving waters based on quantity of microorganisms.

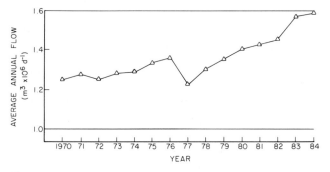

Figure 5.2. Average annual flow of sewage from the Hyperion–Glendale system, January 1970 to June 1984.

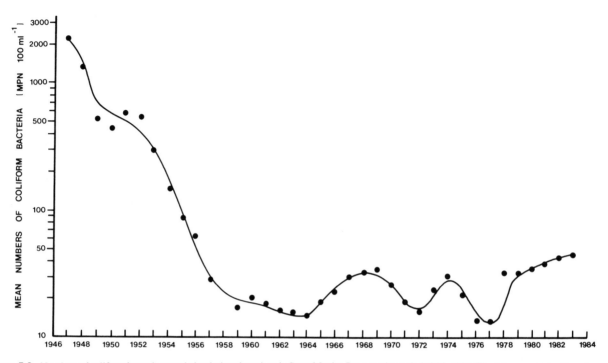

Figure 5.3. Numbers of coliform bacteria recorded at the beach stations in Santa Monica Bay over the period 1946–1983. The data represent arithmetic means of the separate annual geometric means for each of the 17 shoreline stations.

During the winter, when the temperature is essentially isothermal from the surface to the 70-m depth, viable coliform bacteria are observed in the water directly over the diffusers 8 km out into the ocean. These counts are generally below the 1000 per 100 ml standard required by California and do not in any event affect the bacteriological quality of the shore or the littoral waters within 100 m of the shore where body contact and shellfish harvests occur. The horizontal diffusion of water carrying viable coliform organisms is in fact less under isothermal conditions since the total water column is well mixed from the 70-m depth to the surface. Under summer conditions, when a strong thermocline is present, the water column available for dilution extends only from the bottom to the base of the thermocline at a depth of ~25 m. The horizontal scale of distribution for viable coliform bacteria is thus increased during the summer months.

By reviewing Fig. 5.3 more closely in terms of the operational changes that occurred during the 37-y period, certain general observations can be made. For example, prior to 1951 when chlorination was practiced with the 1.6-km outfall, the California State Coliform Standard was met operationally when the arithmetic average of the geometric averages of 17 individual shore stations was <500 per 100 ml. Without chlorination and with increased outfall length (8 and 11 km), the coliform bacterial average operationally meeting the standards dropped to <250 per 100 ml. The longer outfalls avoid chlorination and are considered to the more suitable from an environmental standpoint.

In the period 1951 through 1957, when an intermediate (high rate) type of full secondary treatment was used, coliform standards could be met by using chlorination and the 1.6-km outfall. This was true in spite of the fact that initial dilution was only ~9:1 and ~115 metric tons (t) d^{-1} of elutriated, digested, and effluent solids was also being discharged through this facility.

In the period 1957–1962 the intermediate type of full

Table 5.1. Average Coliform Content and Operational Changes over 40 y at the Hyperion Treatment Plant, Los Angeles, California

Time Period	Coliform Mean (100 ml⁻¹)	Submarine Outfall Effluent	Submarine Outfall Residual Solids	Effluent Chlorination Treatment	Effluent Chlorination (kg d⁻¹)	Treatment of Removed Solids (t d⁻¹)	Total Flow (m d⁻¹)
1943–1947	2000	Old 1524 m	None	Fine screening (0.16 × 5 cm slots)	None	Incinerated 10	613,000
1948	1300	Old 1524 m	None	Fine screening (0.16 × 5 cm slots)	16,400	Incinerated 11.9	726,700
1949	510	New 1524 m	None	Fine screening (0.16 × 5 cm slots)	16,400	Digestion 13	760,600
1950	420	New 1524 m	None	Primary sediment	16,400	Digestion Filtration drying 114	745,400
1951–1957	26–580	New 1524 m	None	High rate secondary	16,400	Digestion filtration drying 142	946,000
1958–1959	20	New 1524 m	11-km offshore, 100 m deep	High rate secondary	16,400	Digestion 100	999,000
1960–1962	16–20	New 8 km, 70 m deep	11-km offshore, 100 m deep	38% secondary 62% primary	None	Digestion 118	1,142,800 (estimated)
1963–1978	13–35	New 8 km, 70 m deep	11-km offshore, 100 m deep	29% secondary 74% primary	None	Digestion 132	1,286,500
1979–1983	33–45	New 8 km, 70 m deep	11-km offshore, 100 m deep	26% secondary 74% primary	None	Digestion 127	1,393,000

secondary treatment with effluent chlorination and diffusion through the 1.6-km outfall and accompanying diffusion of residual and digested solids through the 11-km solids outfall resulted in coliform counts at stations along the shore near background for a large metropolitan area (Fig. 5.3). Approximately 65 t d⁻¹ of effluent solids reached the 1.6-km outfall, and 100 t d⁻¹ of residual and digested solids was diffused through the 11-km outfall.

In 1962 a mixed 2:1 primary:secondary (standard rate) effluent was diffused 8 km at sea at a depth of 70 m with a minimum of 100:1 initial dilution and no chlorination. The residual and digested solids were screened and then diffused 11 km at sea into 100-m-deep water. Coliform bacterial values were near the lowest ever measured (overall annual mean ~15 per 100 ml). These values are believed to be near background for the Los Angeles metropolitan area (Fig. 5.3). Approximately 80 t d⁻¹ of effluent solids were diffused through the 8-km outfall, while 118 t d⁻¹ of screened, digested solids were diffused through the 11-km outfall.

By 1984, flows had increased to $\sim 1.6 \times 10^6$ m³ d⁻¹ and the primary to secondary effluent mix changed to ~3:1 with no chlorination. Control of coliform bacteria was still maintained, although ~158 t d⁻¹ of effluent solids reached the 8-km outfall and 115 t d⁻¹ of screened, digested solids was diffused through the 11-km outfall. Average coliform bacterial indexes were above the levels recorded in 1962 (Fig. 5.3).

Present flows are still increasing. No problems with coliform bacteria have been observed at the shore or in the littoral waters up to 100 m from shore, where body contact is of concern. What the flows could be, assuming a lesser and lesser percentage of secondary treatment, before concentrations of coliform bacteria would increase to a point of public health concern is not now known. Steps are now being taken, however, to increase secondary treatment to ~50% of the effluent mix. This modification should again produce a decrease in the mean curve of Fig. 5.3.

Recent work (Cabelli, 1980; Cabelli et al., 1982) has

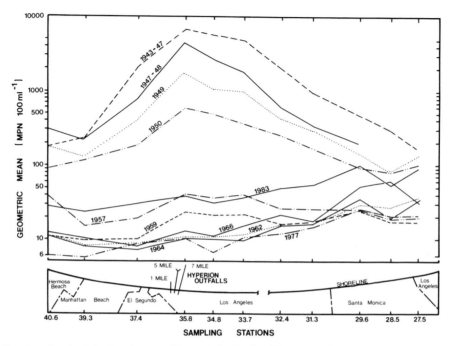

Figure 5.4. Distribution of coliform bacteria along the coast of Santa Monica Bay for different years. Data shown represent the geometric means of all samples taken at each station in any given year.

indicated that the Coliform Index might not be a suitable indicator of microbiological water quality. Although total coliform bacterial counts do not provide a direct measure of hazard from pathogenic microorganisms, their presence is an indication of the possible presence of treated or untreated sewage. The authors recognize the need for more accurate microbiological indexes of quality, but would urge that for an interim period the Coliform Index and any recognized new index be run in parallel. The data included in this chapter show ~37 y of apparently successful microbiological protection based upon the Coliform Index. No other index at this time has the same type of database. The Coliform Index should not be discarded, therefore, until a better index has been demonstrated through long-term parallel testing.

In addition, those responsible for the operation of wastewater treatment plants need to have goals and indexes of attainment clearly designated so that the public health can be protected and the ultimate goal of overall environmental improvement approached. The Clean Water Act (U.S. Congress, 1977) calls for the abatement of certain named pollutants, not improvement of microbiological water quality. Improved microbiological water quality and named pollutant abatement are not necessarily compatible (U.S. District

Court, 1980; U.S. National Advisory Committee on Oceans and Atmosphere, 1981). Any successor to the Coliform Index should provide operators of treatment plants with similarly clear management objectives to facilitate the continued maintenance of environmental quality to protect the public health.

5.4. SUMMARY AND CONCLUSIONS

The city of Los Angeles has been using the ocean waters in Santa Monica Bay for the diffusion of treated wastewater throughout 90 y of growth and change. During a substantial portion of this time, the measurements of the coliform group of organisms have been used as an index of water and environmental quality. Daily monitoring of the shoreline and weekly testing of nearshore water for total coliform bacteria have been very useful for gauging water quality and for quickly identifying onshore activities that affect water quality, such as runoff from the storm sewers located along the shores of Santa Monica Bay. The coliform bacterial data also suggest that the shore areas in the vicinity of the outfalls are of high water quality despite increasing flows and waste loads to the Hyperion Plant. The Coliform Index has been useful for evaluation of the various changes in flow, treatment, and disposal location for the Hyperion wastes. The present mode of operation (i.e., discharging a mix of primary and secondary treatment effluents 8 km out into the ocean at a depth of 70 m) appears to be effective for safeguarding the quality of the receiving waters.

REFERENCES

American Public Health Association, American Water Works Association, and Water Pollution Control Federation. 1985. Multiple-tube fermentation technique for members of the coliform group. *In*: Standard Methods for the Examination of Water and Wastewater, 16th edition. American Public Health Association, Washington, D.C., pp. 870–878.

Cabelli, V. J. 1980. Health Effects Criteria for Marine Recreational Water. U.S. Environmental Protection Agency Report No. EPA-600/1-80-081, U.S. Environmental Protection Agency, Washington, D.C., 132 pp.

Cabelli, V. J., A. P. Dufour, L. J. McCabe, and M. A. Levin. 1982. Swimming-associated gastro-enteritis and water quality. *American Journal of Epidemiology*, **115**, 606–615.

City of Los Angeles Bureau of Engineering. 1982. City of Los Angeles Wastewater Facilities Plan. Final Report, Part I. The Department of Public Works, Los Angeles, California, pp. 7–9.

State of California Department of Public Health. 1943. Report on a Pollution Survey of Santa Monica Bay Beaches in 1942. California State Printing Office, Sacramento, pp. 9–17.

U.S. Congress. 1977. Clean Water Act of 1977. Public Law 95–217, 91 Stat. 1566, Washington, D.C.

U.S. District Court, Central District of California. 1980. *United States of America v. City of Los Angeles and the State of California*. Consent Decree, June 19, 1980. No. CV77-3047-HP.

U.S. National Advisory Committee on Oceans and Atmosphere. 1981. The Role of the Ocean in a Waste Management Strategy. U.S. Government Printing Office, Washington, D.C., 103 pp + appendices.

Chapter 6

Fin Erosion and Epidermal Tumors in Demersal Fish from Southern California

Jeffrey N. Cross

Southern California Coastal Water Research Project
Long Beach, California

Abstract	57
6.1. Introduction	57
6.2. Methods	58
6.3. Results and Discussion	59
6.3.1. Characteristics of the Diseases in Dover Sole	59
6.3.2. Relationship to Municipal Wastewater Discharge	60
6.4. Conclusions	63
Acknowledgments	63
References	64

ABSTRACT

The relationship between municipal wastewater discharge and the two most prevalent external diseases of demersal fish collected near the outfalls in the coastal waters off Los Angeles, California (U.S.A.), was examined using monitoring data collected from 1971 through 1983. Fin erosion occurred in 8.5% of all individuals and in 23% of all species collected. Epidermal tumors occurred in 0.3% of all individuals and in 12% of all species collected. Dover sole (*Microstomus pacificus*) accounted for 89% of the fish with fin erosion, 93% of the fish with tumors, and 23% of all fish collected. Thirty-two percent of the Dover sole had fin erosion and 1.2% had epidermal tumors. Both diseases developed some time after the fish recruited to the area around the outfalls. Fin erosion occurred in all size classes examined; epidermal tumors occurred primarily in smaller individuals. Fin erosion did not appear to affect the nutritional condition or seasonal migratory behavior of juvenile Dover sole but did lower survival. Epidermal tumors, however, appeared to alter the seasonal migratory behavior of Dover sole. During the study period, the number of species with both diseases declined, and the prevalence of fin erosion declined in two of the three most affected species. The declines were directly correlated with decreased mass emission of contaminants in the effluent, decreased contamination of surface sediment, and decreased body burdens of contaminants in fish. The prevalence of epidermal tumors in Dover sole did not decline during the study period; however, the prevalence was significantly higher at stations closer to the outfalls than at those farther away.

6.1. INTRODUCTION

The most prevalent and visible external abnormalities observed in fish collected near the municipal wastewater outfalls in the coastal waters off Los Angeles (California, U.S.A.) are fin erosion and epidermal tumors (Mearns and Sherwood, 1974, 1977; Sherwood and Mearns, 1977). Both conditions occur in marine fish, especially pleuronectid flatfishes, in coastal waters off urban and industrialized areas in other parts of the world (Stich et al., 1976; Möller, 1979; Dethlefsen, 1980; Murchelano and Ziskowski, 1982). The role that pollution plays in these conditions remains controversial and elusive (Möller, 1979; Sindermann, 1983; Patton and Couch, 1984). In this chapter, the relationship between municipal wastewater discharge and fin erosion and epidermal tumors in fish is examined through the use of data collected over more than a decade of monitoring in the coastal waters off Los Angeles.

6.2. METHODS

The data analyzed in this study were collected by County Sanitation Districts of Los Angeles County (CSDLAC) during regular monitoring cruises. The station numbers used herein are the CSDLAC designations.

The data consisted of catch records of fishes and the frequency of fin erosion and epidermal tumors by species along seven transects sampled by otter trawl on the Palos Verdes shelf (Fig. 6.1). At each transect, 10-min daytime trawls were made along depth isobaths at 23, 61, and 137 m twice a year (spring and fall) from 1971 through 1978 and quarterly after 1979. Additional trawls at irregular intervals were also included in the analyses. Fishes were sorted from the catch by species and measured to the nearest cm board standard length (BSL). As each fish was measured, it was examined externally for fin erosion and epidermal tumors by trained biologists.

Time trends in the diseases were determined with linear regressions of the prevalence [proportion (p) of diseased fish per trawl transformed to arcsin $\sqrt{p}$] against time in months (numbered consecutively from 1971). The null hypothesis of slope $= 0$ was tested with a t-test.

Seasonal trends in the quarterly trawl data (1979–1983) were estimated from a multiplicative decomposition model (Bowerman and O'Connell, 1979), using numbers of fish per trawl and prevalence data after the appropriate transformations:

$$Y_t = T_t \times S_t + e_t \qquad 1$$

where Y_t is the number of fish per trawl (or proportion with the disease) at time t, T_t is the trend component at time t, S_t is the seasonal component at time t, and e_t are the remaining components (cyclical and aperiodic) at time t. Regressions were fitted to the catch and to the prevalence data to estimate T (regression coefficient) for each quarter. The trend was eliminated by dividing the quarterly Y values by T. The value for S was then estimated for each quarter (assuming e was small), normalized to four (the number of quarters in one year), and multiplied by 100. The seasonal index is a correction factor (in percent) that adjusts for seasonality in the time series. Values > 100 indicate that Y_t is greater than that predicted by

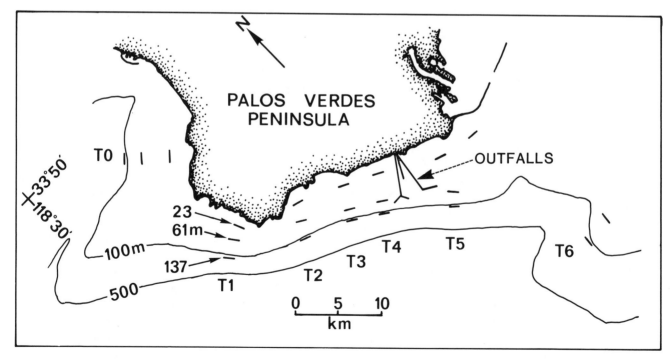

Figure 6.1. Map of the study transects (T0, T1, . . . , T6) on the Palos Verdes shelf. Three depths were sampled at each transect.

the trend; likewise, values < 100 indicate that Y_t is less than that predicted by the trend.

6.3. RESULTS AND DISCUSSION

From 1971 through 1983, 672 otter trawls produced 15,670 individuals with fin erosion, representing 8.5% of all fishes collected, distributed among 29 species (23% of all collected). The trawls also produced 539 individuals with epidermal tumors, representing 0.3% of all fishes collected, distributed among 15 species (12% of all collected). It is not known whether the etiology of the epidermal tumors was the same in all affected species. Dover sole (*Microstomus pacificus*) accounted for 89% of the fish with fin erosion, 93% of the fish with epidermal tumors, and 23% of the fish collected.

6.3.1. Characteristics of the Diseases in Dover Sole

Of the Dover sole collected from 1971 through 1983, 32% had fin erosion, and 1.2% had epidermal tumors. Most Dover sole recruited to the study area when they were 40–50 mm BSL. Fin erosion was rarely observed in fish <80 mm BSL, and epidermal tumors were rarely observed in fish <60 mm BSL (Fig. 6.2).

The prevalence of fin erosion increased with fish size up to 120–129 mm BSL and then declined slowly to <1% in fish >270 mm BSL (Fig. 6.3). The prevalence of epidermal

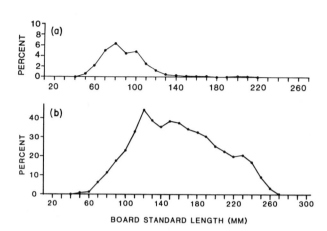

Figure 6.3. Prevalence of (a) epidermal tumors and (b) fin erosion by size class in Dover sole (*Microstomus pacificus*) collected on the Palos Verdes shelf from 1971 through 1983.

tumors peaked in fish 80–90 mm BSL and then declined rapidly to <0.1% in fish >150 mm BSL (Fig. 6.3).

Among Dover sole <120 mm BSL (the average size of individuals ~1 y after recruiting to the Palos Verdes shelf), 16.9% had fin erosion, 3.4% had epidermal tumors, and 1.1% had both diseases. The two diseases were not independent; significantly more individuals were afflicted with both diseases than predicted ($\chi^2 = 45.4$, $p < .001$).

The weight–length relationships for Dover sole were not significantly different either for males or for females with and without fin erosion (Cross, 1985). Comparable data are not available for Dover sole with epidermal tumors; however, Campana (1983) showed that starry flounder (*Platichthys stellatus*) with similar epidermal tumors had lower growth rates than did individuals without tumors.

Time series analyses of the quarterly trawl data for Dover sole showed consistent seasonal peaks in total catch, number of individuals with fin erosion (but not proportion), and proportion of individuals with epidermal tumors (but not number) (Fig. 6.4). Total catch and number of fish with fin erosion were highest in the spring and summer, and lowest in the fall and winter. These trends are probably the result of seasonal onshore–offshore migrations. Dover sole migrate in the winter into deeper water to reproduce and return in the summer to shallow water to feed (Hagerman, 1952). Apparently the juveniles also participate in the offshore migration in the winter.

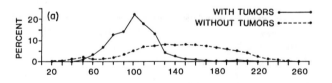

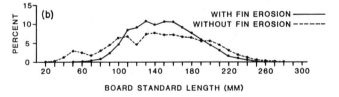

Figure 6.2. Size distribution of Dover sole (*Microstomus pacificus*) collected on the Palos Verdes shelf from 1971 through 1983 (a) with and without epidermal tumors and (b) with and without fin erosion.

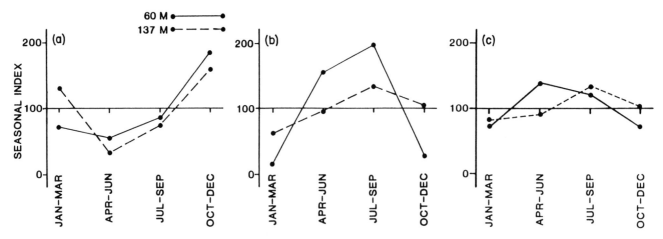

Figure 6.4. Seasonal trends in (a) the proportion of Dover sole (*Microstomus pacificus*) with epidermal tumors per trawl, (b) the number of Dover sole caught per trawl, and (c) the number of Dover sole with fin erosion per trawl from 1979 through 1983.

The high proportion of tumorous Dover sole that were collected during the fall and winter suggests that these individuals do not participate in the offshore movement to the same extent as do fish without tumors. Stich et al. (1976) suggested that the emigration of juvenile English sole (*Parophrys vetulus*) from shallow nursery areas to deeper water may be slower in individuals with epidermal tumors.

Cross (1985) estimated the survival rates of Dover sole that were collected on the Palos Verdes shelf between 1972 and 1975 from age–length data. The survival rates of fish with and without fin erosion were not significantly different from ages 1–3 y; thereafter, however, the survival rates of fish with the disease were significantly lower. Comparable data are not available for Dover sole with epidermal tumors; however, Campana (1983) showed that starry flounder with epidermal tumors were more susceptible to stress and had much higher mortality rates than did individuals without tumors.

The two diseases possess important similarities and differences. Both diseases develop some time after the fish recruit to the area around the outfalls. Epidermal tumors affect far fewer individuals than does fin erosion but reach peak prevalence earlier and decline more rapidly. Over 90% of Dover sole with tumors were estimated to be <2 y of age. The tumor prevalence of <0.1% in fish between 150 and 220 mm BSL suggests, however, that some individuals either survive several years with tumors or develop them later in life. Fin erosion is a more chronic disease that takes longer than tumors to reach peak prevalence and declines more slowly

with increasing fish size. It occurred in all size classes of Dover sole examined.

6.3.2. Relationship to Municipal Wastewater Discharge

The number of species affected by fin erosion declined from a high of 18 in 1971 to a low of 3 in 1981 and rose slightly through 1983 (Fig. 6.5). The number of species affected by epidermal tumors declined from 6 in 1971 to 1 in 1976 and remained at 1 or 2 through 1983 (Fig. 6.5). The negative Spearman rank correlations (r_s) between the number of species with fin erosion and year ($r_s = -0.626$), and between the number of species with epidermal tumors and year ($r_s = -0.706$) were significant ($p < .05$), while the correlation between the total number of species collected and year ($r_s = -0.080$) was not significant ($p > .50$).

The number of species affected by either disease declined most rapidly from 1971 to 1976 (Fig. 6.5). As discussed by Stull et al. (Chapter 2) and Young et al. (Chapter 3), the modifications to the wastewater treatment made by CSDLAC in the early 1970s greatly reduced the mass emission of many contaminants during this period (Table 6.1). This was reflected in decreased concentrations of DDT in surface sediments and in the muscle tissue of Dover sole around the outfalls (Fig. 6.6). The decline of DDT was exponential for effluent and sediment and linear for muscle.

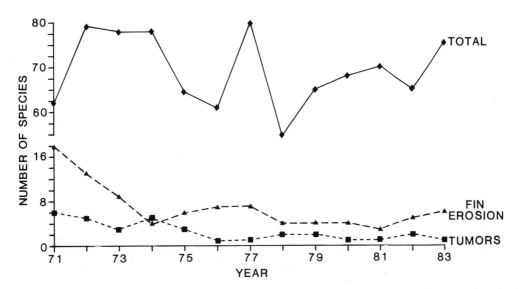

Figure 6.5. Total annual number of species, number of species with fin erosion, and number of species with epidermal tumors collected on the Palos Verdes shelf from 1971 through 1983.

Table 6.1. Mass Emission of 15 Contaminants from Los Angeles County Outfalls (t y^{-1})^a

| Contaminant | Concentration in 1971 (t y^{-1}) | Maximum Emission | | Concentration in 1983 (t y^{-1}) | r_s | p |
		Concentration (t y^{-1})	Year			
Oil and grease	38,000	38,000	1971	13,640	−0.934	**
Cyanide	62	205	1974	19	−0.681	*
Phenols	1,640	1,945	1975	1,260	−0.500	
Ag	10.8	10.8	1971	5.1	−0.533	
As	—^{b}	11.3	1974	3.1	−0.385	
Cd	15.4	19.6	1974	7.4	−0.731	**
Cr	462	462	1971	70	−0.951	**
Cu	267	286	1974	62	−0.951	**
Hg	0.7	0.7	1971	0.4	−0.486	
Ni	144	157	1976	75	−0.848	**
Pb	144	144	1971	41	−0.956	**
Se	8.2	14.5	1981	6.5	0.286	
Zn	1,400	1,400	1971	254	−0.967	**
DDT	21.5	21.5	1971	0.2	−0.984	**
PCB	5.2	5.2	1971	0.2	−0.967	**

^{a}Data presented for years 1971, 1983, and the year of maximum mass emission (Schafer, 1984). Spearman rank correlation (r_s) between year and mass emission is for the years 1971–1983; p = probability that r_s = 0 (two-tailed); * = significant at 0.05, ** = significant at 0.01.
^{b}Not measured in 1971.

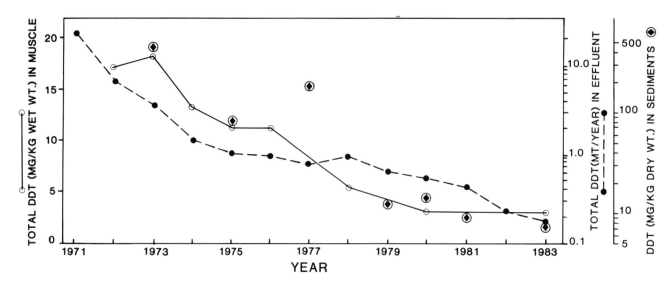

Figure 6.6. Median total DDT concentration (mg kg^{-1} wet wt) in muscle of Dover sole (*Microstomus pacificus*) collected between transects T1 and T5 on the Palos Verdes shelf during regular monitoring cruises (sample sizes were $n = 21$, 1972; $n = 9$, 1973; $n = 20$, 1974; $n = 10$, 1975; $n = 6$, 1976; $n = 10$, 1978; $n = 10$, 1980; $n = 7$, 1983) (County Sanitation Districts of Los Angeles County, 1983), mass emission [metric tons (t) y^{-1}] of total DDT in effluent (Schafer, 1984), and total DDT concentration (mg kg^{-1} dry wt) in surface sediments (0–2 cm) at 61 m on transect T4 by year (Cross, 1985).

The prevalence of fin erosion in Dover sole declined during the study period (Fig. 6.7). The slopes of the trend lines were significantly ($p < .05$) negative at stations T1, T4, and T5; the slope of the trend line for station T0 was not significantly different from zero. The prevalence of epidermal tumors in Dover sole that were <120 mm BSL did not show a significant decline during the study period. Tumor prevalence in these smaller fishes was, however, significantly ($\chi^2 = 25.4$, $p < .001$) greater at stations closer to the outfalls (station T1, 4.4% prevalence in all individuals that were collected from 1971 through 1983 and were <120 mm BSL; T4, 4.4%; T5, 3.5%) than at the farthest station (T0, 1.2%).

While the prevalence of fin erosion declined in Dover sole and in rex sole (*Glyptocephalus zachirus*), which were the third most frequently affected species on the Palos Verdes shelf (Cross, 1985), the prevalence increased in calico rockfish (*Sebastes dallii*), the second most frequently affected species (Fig. 6.7). This increase was significant ($p < .05$) at stations T4 and T5.

Calico rockfish were rarely collected before 1975 (only 0.8% of the individuals collected during the study were caught before 1975). None of the 1485 calico rockfish collected in 1975 and 1976 had fin erosion, while 26% of the 1947 individuals collected in 1977 and 1978 had the disease. Most of the calico rockfish collected were adults. Since the

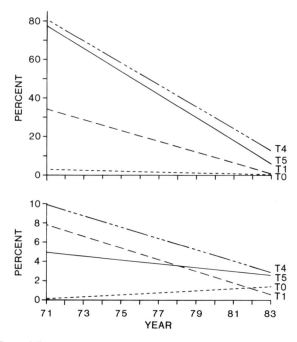

Figure 6.7. Trends as determined by linear regression in the prevalence of fin erosion (a) in Dover sole (*Microstomus pacificus*) and (b) in calico rockfish (*Sebastes dallii*) collected at four transects on the Palos Verdes shelf (1971–1983 for sole; 1975–1983 for rockfish). Closed circles are actual data for T4.

presence and severity of fin erosion appear to be directly related to the magnitude of body burdens of chlorinated hydrocarbon (McDermott-Ehrlich et al., 1977; Sherwood and Mearns, 1977; Sherwood, 1982), several years may be necessary for newly exposed adult fish to accumulate the contaminants that directly or indirectly contribute to the disease. In a laboratory experiment, juvenile Dover sole that were collected from relatively uncontaminated sites off southern California were exposed to contaminated sediments from the Palos Verdes shelf and developed fin erosion in 13 months. Control fish held on clean sediments did not develop the lesions (Sherwood and Mearns, 1977).

The spatial patterns of disease prevalence in fish collected on the Palos Verdes shelf are closely related to the spatial patterns of sediment contamination (Fig. 6.8). The prevalence of both diseases was highest at T4 and T5, the stations flanking the outfalls; lowest at T0, the station farthest from the outfalls; and intermediate at station T1 (Fig. 6.9).

6.4 CONCLUSIONS

The spatial patterns of fin erosion and tumors in demersal fish on the Palos Verdes shelf show enhancement of both diseases near the municipal wastewater outfalls. The spatial patterns of contaminants in surface sediments suggest that the magni-

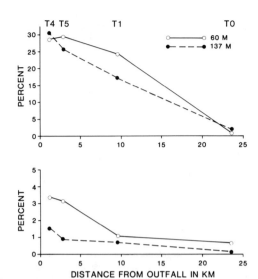

Figure 6.9. Overall (1971–1983) prevalence (a) of fin erosion and (b) of epidermal tumors in Dover sole (*Microstomus pacificus*) collected on the Palos Verdes shelf as a function of distance from the outfalls. Station transects labeled across the top.

tude of disease prevalence is directly related to the magnitude of sediment contamination. The temporal patterns in disease prevalence, body burdens of contaminants in fish, mass emission of contaminants, and contamination of surface sediment further suggest that both diseases are directly related to the environmental contaminants that emanated from the outfalls.

While there are strong correlations between the presence and magnitude of both diseases and degraded environments, the etiologies of the lesions are either unknown (fin erosion) or controversial (epidermal tumors). Sindermann (1979) described fin erosion as "the best known but least understood disease of fish from polluted waters" and attributed it to a combination of environmental stress, facultative pathogens, host resistance, and latent infections. Recent evidence suggests that epidermal tumors are caused by a unicellular protozoan parasite resembling a parasitic amoeba (Dawe et al., 1979; Dawe, 1981; Watermann and Dethlefsen, 1982). Peters et al. (1981, 1983), however, suggest that the tumor cells are virus-transformed fish cells.

ACKNOWLEDGMENTS

The Los Angeles County Sanitation District kindly provided access to the monitoring data. A. J. Mearns encouraged me to

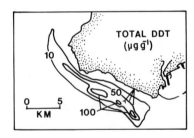

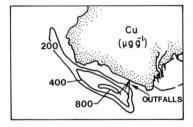

Figure 6.8. Distribution of total DDT (mg kg^{-1} dry wt) and Cu (mg kg^{-1} dry wt) in surface sediments (0–2 cm) on the Palos Verdes shelf in 1975 (after Hershelman et al., 1977).

undertake the project; his conversations were informative and stimulating. The comments of D. A. Wolfe and an anonymous reviewer improved the quality of the manuscript.

REFERENCES

Bowerman, B. L., and R. T. O'Connell. 1979. Time Series and Forecasting. Duxbury Press, North Scituate, Massachusetts, 481 pp.

Campana, S. E. 1983. Mortality of starry flounders (*Platichthys stellatus*) with skin tumors. *Canadian Journal of Fisheries and Aquatic Sciences*, **40**, 200–207.

County Sanitation Districts of Los Angeles County (CSDLAC). 1983. Joint Water Pollution Control Plant Revised Application for Modification of Secondary Treatment Requirements for Discharges into Marine Waters. Unpublished 301 (h) waiver application, County Sanitation Districts of Los Angeles County, submitted to U.S. Environmental Protection Agency, Washington, D.C., 14 sections (paginated separately) + 7 appendices.

Cross, J. N. 1985. Fin erosion among fishes collected near a southern California municipal wastewater outfall (1971–1982). *Fishery Bulletin*, **83**, 195–206.

Dawe, C. J., J. Bagshaw, and C. M. Poore. 1979. Amoebic pseudotumors in pseudobranchs of Pacific cod, *Gadus macrocephalus*. *Proceedings of the American Association of Cancer Research*, **20**, 245.

Dawe, C. J. 1981. Polyoma tumors in mice and X-cell tumors in fish, viewed through telescope and microscope. *In*: Phyletic Approaches to Cancer, C. J. Dawe, J. C. Harshbarger, S. Kondo, T. Sugimura, and S. Takayama (Eds.). Japan Scientific Society Press, Tokyo, pp. 19–49.

Dethlefsen, V. 1980. Observations on fish diseases in the German Bight and their possible relation to pollution. *Rapports et Procès-Verbaux des Réunions Conseil International pour l'Exploration de la Mer*, **179**, 110–117.

Hagerman, F. B. 1952. The biology of the Dover sole, *Microstomus pacificus* (Lockington). *California Department of Fish and Game, Fish Bulletin* **85**, 48 pp.

Hershelman, G. P., T.-K. Jan, and H. A. Schafer. 1977. Pollutants in sediments off Palos Verdes. *In*: Coastal Water Research Project Annual Report, W. Bascom (Ed.). Southern California Coastal Water Research Project, El Segundo, California, pp. 63–68.

McDermott-Ehrlich, D. J., M. J. Sherwood, T. C. Heesen, D. R. Young, and A. J. Mearns. 1977. Chlorinated hydrocarbons in Dover sole, *Microstomus pacificus*: local migrations and fin erosion. *Fishery Bulletin*, **75**, 513–517.

Mearns, A. J., and M. J. Sherwood. 1974. Environmental aspects of fin erosion and tumors in southern California Dover sole. *Transactions of the American Fisheries Society*, **103**, 799–810.

Mearns, A. J., and M. J. Sherwood. 1977. Distribution of neoplasms and other diseases in marine fishes relative to the discharge of wastewater. *Annals of the New York Academy of Sciences*, **298**, 210–224.

Möller, H. 1979. Geographical distribution of fish diseases in the NE Atlantic. *Meeresforschung*, **27**, 217–235.

Murchelano, R. A., and J. Ziskowski. 1982. Fin rot disease in the New York Bight (1973–1977). *In*: Ecological Stress and the New York Bight: Science and Management, G. F. Mayer (Ed.). Estuarine Research Foundation, Columbia, South Carolina, pp. 347–358.

Patton, J. S., and J. A. Couch. 1984. Can tissue anomalies that occur in marine fish implicate specific pollutant chemicals? *In*: Concepts in Marine Pollution Measurements, H. H. White (Ed.). Maryland Sea Grant, University of Maryland, University Park, pp. 511–538.

Peters, N., H. Stich, and H. Kranz. 1981. The relationship between lymphocystis disease and X-cell papillomatosis in flatfish. *In*: Phyletic Approaches to Cancer, C. J. Dawe, J. C. Harshbarger, S. Kondo, T. Sugimura, and S. Takayama (Eds.). Japan Scientific Society Press, Tokyo, pp. 111–121.

Peters, N., W. Schmidt, H. Kranz, and H. F. Stich. 1983. Nuclear inclusions in the X-cells of skin papillomas of Pacific flatfish. *Journal of Fish Diseases*, **6**, 533–536.

Schafer, H. 1984. Characteristics of municipal wastewater. *In*: Coastal Water Research Project Biennial Report, 1983–1984. Southern California Coastal Water Research Project, Long Beach, California, pp. 11–19.

Sherwood, M. J. 1982. Fin erosion, liver condition, and trace contaminant exposure in fishes from three coastal regions. *In*: Ecological Stress and the New York Bight: Science and Management, G. F. Mayer (Ed.). Estuarine Research Foundation, Columbia, South Carolina, pp. 359–377.

Sherwood, M., and A. J. Mearns. 1977. Environmental significance of fin erosion in southern California demersal fishes. *Annals of the New York Academy of Sciences*, **298**, 177–189.

Sindermann, C. J. 1979. Pollution-associated diseases and abnormalities of fish and shellfish: A review. *Fishery Bulletin*, **76**, 717–749.

Sindermann, C. J. 1983. An examination of some relationships between pollution and disease. *Rapports et Procès-Verbaux des Réunions Conseil International pour l'Exploration de la Mer*, **182**, 37–43.

Stich, H. F., A. B. Acton, and C. R. Forrester. 1976. Fish tumors and sublethal effects of pollutants. *Journal of the Fisheries Research Board of Canada*, **33**, 1993–2001.

Watermann, B., and V. Dethlefsen. 1982. Histology of pseudobranchial tumors in Atlantic cod (*Gadus morhua*) from the North Sea and the Baltic Sea. *Helgoländer Wissenschaftliche Meeresuntersuchungen*, **35**, 231–242.

PART III: WASTE DISPOSAL AND EFFECTS IN NORTHEASTERN U.S. COASTAL WATERS

Chapter 7

Metal Distribution in a Major Urban Estuary (Boston Harbor) Impacted by Ocean Disposal

Gordon T. Wallace, Jr., Jeffrey H. Waugh, and Kathryn A. Garner

Environmental Sciences Program
University of Massachusetts–Boston
Boston, Massachusetts

Abstract	67
7.1. Introduction	67
7.2. Experimental Methods	69
7.2.1. Sample Collection	69
7.2.2. Sample Analysis	69
7.3. Results	70
7.3.1. Boston's Inner Harbor	70
7.3.2. Northern Section of Boston's Outer Harbor	71
7.3.3. Southern Section of Boston's Outer Harbor	72
7.4. Discussion	74
7.4.1. General Distribution Patterns	74
7.4.2. Tidal Flushing	74
7.4.3. Tidal Variations of Cu in the Southern Section of the Harbor	75
7.5. Conclusions	77
Acknowledgments	77
References	77

Jeffrey Waugh's current address: Battelle New England Marine Research Laboratory, Duxbury, Massachusetts 02332. Kathryn Garner's current address: 4240 Village Parkway Circle, Indianapolis, Indiana 46219.

ABSTRACT

Boston Harbor (Massachusetts, U.S.A.) receives large anthropogenic inputs of metals from industrial and sewage wastes that are introduced directly into harbor waters. Over half of the freshwater input into the harbor is in the form of primary-treated sewage effluent. The distribution of selected metals was determined at high and low tides in a preliminary effort to identify the influence of tidal flushing under weakly stratified conditions that occur in the summer months. Concentrations of Cd, Cu, Ni, Pb, and Zn were generally one to four orders of magnitude greater than currently accepted values for concentrations in surface water of the open ocean and one to two orders of magnitude greater than concentrations in adjacent coastal water. Elevated concentrations of metals were particularly prevalent in the marginal shallow regions of the harbor due to poor horizontal exchange and the possible influence of remobilization from sediments. Evidence for the rapid remobilization of Cu is particularly strong, and hypothetical processes supporting this benthic flux are discussed.

7.1. INTRODUCTION

Estuaries located adjacent to or near major population centers receive, and are frequently impacted by, both domestic and industrial anthropogenic inputs from their associated population centers. The net results of these inputs include loss of economically important fisheries, diminished recreational utility because of associated hazards to human health, loss of marine habitat, alteration of the structure of the marine community, and a general assault on the public's aesthetic senses of sight and smell. Boston Harbor, located on the eastern coast of Massachusetts in the northeastern part of the United States, is no exception to the above and is probably one of the most severely impacted marine estuaries on the North American continent, if not in the world.

Boston Harbor is best classified as a marine estuary according to the definition developed by Fairbridge (1980). The geomorphology of the harbor has been recently described by Fitzgerald (1980). Covering an area of 114 km², the topography of the harbor is dominated by the presence of two major channels, President Roads to the north and Nantasket Roads to the south. The northern channel extends well into what is generally referred to as the inner harbor, which is defined here as the area of the harbor north of the dotted line indicated in Fig. 7.1. Areas outside of the inner harbor and adjacent to the main channels are generally shallow, with mean depths at low tide of <5 m. Sediment types range from muds and fine-grained sands to coarse-grained sands and gravel. Fitzgerald (1980) describes the sediments and underlying geological strata for most areas of the estuary.

Flow of fresh water into the harbor is limited and dominated by inputs from the Mystic, Charles, and Neponset

rivers and the sewage outfalls from the Nut Island and Deer Island treatment facilities (Fig. 7.1). Mean flow in the river is ~22 m³s⁻¹, while the combined mean flow of primary-treated sewage effluent from the two outfalls is ~20 m³s⁻¹, or 46% of the total freshwater input.

Tidal amplitudes in Boston Harbor are ~3 m, and tidal flushing is the dominant means of renewal of Boston Harbor waters via exchange with waters in adjacent Massachusetts Bay. Accurate knowledge of the residence time of water in the harbor is lacking, but it is clear that the residence time of pollutants introduced with fresh water into Boston Harbor may be long compared to that of pollutants introduced near the mouth of the harbor. Ketchum (1951) estimated a residence time of ~42 d for fresh water introduced into the inner harbor.

Hydrographic data acquired by Fitzgerald (1980) over 2–4 tidal periods at different seasons in Boston Harbor show an increased tendency toward mixing in the colder months, but significant haloclines and thermoclines were almost always present. Detailed knowledge of the hydrographic properties of the estuary is still lacking, however. For that matter, there has been no systematic, comprehensive description of the elementary chemistry, physics, and biology of Boston Harbor. Such data that are available have been generated during site-specific studies of existing or anticipated anthropogenic alteration of some section of the harbor, none of which have been published in the open literature.

This lack of comprehensive data prevails despite the dramatic alteration of Boston Harbor over the last century, especially in the inner harbor. Landfill practices beginning in the early 1800s have reduced the area of the inner harbor by >50%. Boston Harbor received untreated sewage from its adjacent communities until the primary-treatment plants at Nut Island and Deer Island became functional in the early 1950s and the late 1960s, respectively. Discharges of raw sewage into Boston Harbor continue to occur, however, due to limited capacity and malfunctions at the two treatment plants and the existence of combined sewer overflows that discharge untreated sewage directly into harbor waters, especially in the inner harbor. Sludge generated by both primary-treatment plants is discharged on the outgoing tide from outfalls located in President Roads. Under average weather conditions, about half the fresh water entering the estuary is in the form of primary-treated sewage discharges. The mean flow of sewage effluent of 20 m³s⁻¹ from the Deer Island and Nut Island outfalls, which are located ~4 km apart, represents the largest single discharge of sewage into a nearshore coastal zone in the United States. The flow of sewage discharged into Boston Harbor is almost twice that entering Puget Sound

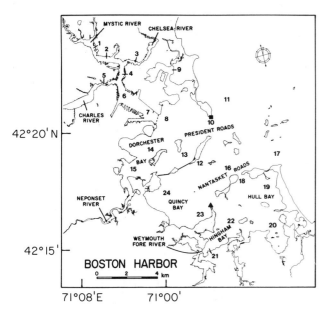

Figure 7.1. Sampling locations in Boston Harbor. The dotted line between stations 7 and 8 marks the arbitrary boundary between the inner and outer harbor. Primary effluent outfalls are located at Deer Island (square) and Nut Island (triangle).

from the Seattle–Tacoma area and greater than either of the effluent discharges entering the coastal ocean from the individual Los Angeles county (16 m³s⁻¹) and city (18 m³s⁻¹) outfalls. In contrast to the Boston Harbor outfalls, the Los Angeles outfalls are located 3 km (Los Angeles county) to 11 km (Los Angeles city) offshore, ~20 km apart, and at depths of 60 and 100 m, respectively. Because of the much smaller size of Boston Harbor in terms of both area and depth, its restricted water circulation, and the location of the outfalls within the harbor itself, the magnitude of the discharge to Boston Harbor and its influence on water quality take on added significance, making it probably the worst-case example of the use of the nearshore zone as a disposal site. Other anthropogenic inputs in the form of industrial and non-point sources to the estuary are known to exist but are not well characterized either qualitatively or quantitatively.

The existence of these discharges has been well recorded in the sediments where metal concentrations often exceed "clean" coastal sediment values by several orders of magnitude (White, 1972; Fitzgerald, 1980). Profiles of trace metals in ²¹⁰Pb-dated cores obtained in the harbor clearly indicate the anthropogenic nature of these increases (Fitzgerald, 1980). Exact definition of the relative significance of different sources (sewage, industrial, and non-point) is impossible because of incomplete data about the concentration and magnitude of these sources. The existing pattern of metal concentration in the sediments cannot be used to determine the relative importance of these sources because of the potential for sediment transport and redistribution within the harbor (Aller et al., 1980; Fitzgerald, 1980).

We undertook an initial survey of selected metals in the water column of Boston Harbor: (1) to provide an accurate database by using currently accepted clean sampling and analytical techniques, (2) to identify the most heavily impacted areas of the harbor, and (3) to gain a preliminary estimate of the flushing characteristics of the harbor with respect to metals. To accomplish these objectives, we conducted a moderate-density sampling program at both high and low tide in the summer of 1983.

7.2. EXPERIMENTAL METHODS

7.2.1. Sample Collection

Sampling locations are given in Fig. 7.1. Collection of samples was made at low tide on 17 and 18 August and at high tide 6 d later on 23 and 24 August. The stations were visited in order of ascending station number, beginning ~2 h before and ending ~2 h after slack low or high tide. Stations 1–15 were sampled on 17 August, stations 12 and 16–24 on 18 August, stations 1–11 again on 23 August, and stations 12–24 on 24 August.

Temperature and salinity profiles at each station were determined by using a Beckman® (Beckman Instruments, Fullerton, California) RS-5 portable inductive salinometer and temperature probe. Only surface samples (~10 cm) were collected at low tide, while surface and deep samples were obtained at high tide at stations having appreciable pycnoclines.

Surface samples were collected directly into 500-ml polyethylene bottles submerged by hand from the bow of a small boat while slowly underway. Care was taken to avoid sampling water through which the sampling vessel or nearby boats had just passed. On several occasions there were distinct differences in the appearance of the surface water at the same station. When this was observed, samples were collected in the two adjacent water masses that differed greatly in apparent turbidity or content of floating debris. Subsurface samples were collected at depths up to 20 m by using a peristaltic pump and silicone-rubber tubing with a Teflon® (E. I. DuPont de Nemours and Co., Wilmington, Delaware) intake designed to face into the current when sampling.

Samples were returned to the laboratory for prompt pressure filtration through a 0.4-μm Nuclepore® filter (Nuclepore Corp., Pleasanton, California) in an all-Teflon® and polycarbonate filtration system. Cleaning procedures used in the preparation of the sampling and filtration apparatus have been described elsewhere (Wallace et al., 1977; Wallace et al., 1983). The procedures have been shown to be adequate for the collection of open-ocean samples with metal concentrations that are 1–4 orders of magnitude lower than those reported here.

7.2.2. Sample Analysis

Filters containing the suspended matter were ashed in a low-temperature asher (LFE Model 504, LFE Corporation, Clinton, Massachusetts) as described by Wallace and Duce (1975) for the analysis of Al, Cd, Cu, Fe, Mn, Ni, Pb, and Zn by flameless atomic absorption spectrophotometry. Sample filtrates were acidified to ~pH 2 until analysis for "dissolved" metals. Analysis of Cd, Cu, Fe, Ni, Pb, and Zn in these filtrates was by a modification of the carbamate extraction procedures of Danielsson et al. (1978) and Bruland et al.

(1979) as described by Wallace et al. (1983) with the exception that back extraction of the metal carbamates from the freon phase was as described by Magnusson and Westerlund (1981). Manganese was analyzed by direct injection into the furnace using standards prepared in surface water from the Sargasso Sea.

All flameless atomic absorption analyses were performed on a Zeeman 5000 Perkin Elmer® (Perkin Elmer Corporation, Norwalk, Connecticut) Atomic Absorption Spectrophotometer equipped with an HGA 400 furnace, and an AS-40 autosampler. Data were received and processed by using a Model 3600 microcomputer and a PR-100 printer. All samples were analyzed by using grooved Ringsdorff tubes with L'vov platforms (Manning and Slavin, 1983). Appropriate matrix modifiers were used in the analyses of all metals except Cu.

The above procedure was adopted upon careful inspection of the peak shapes of samples and standards for each metal. Irregularities in peak shape (shoulders, broadening of peak width, and time of appearance) were noted in a significant number of samples. Use of matrix modifiers as recommended by Manning and Slavin (1983) and adjustment of the furnace program were used to eliminate these irregularities, which we suspect were due to the high organic content of water from Boston Harbor.

7.3. RESULTS

7.3.1. Boston's Inner Harbor

Data obtained for stations sampled within the inner harbor (stations 1–7) are presented in Tables 7.1–7.3. Concentrations of dissolved metals in samples collected in the inner harbor at low tide (Table 7.1) were generally the highest observed in Boston Harbor. Exceptions were anomalously high Cu concentrations (see section 3.3) observed at low tide in southern sections of the outer harbor and high concentrations of some metals in samples from the Deer Island plume. With the exception of Cu, metal concentrations in samples from the uppermost station in the Mystic River (station 1) were significantly higher than those in the remainder of the samples from the inner harbor.

Concentrations of dissolved metals in surface samples collected in the inner harbor at high tide (Table 7.2) were again, with few exceptions, also higher than those observed in samples from the outer harbor. Deeper samples collected at stations 2, 4, 6, and 7 indicated the presence of colder, more saline water that extended as far as station 2 and contained distinctly lower concentrations of dissolved Cd, Mn, Ni, and Zn except at station 2.

Concentrations of particulate metals in the inner harbor (Table 7.3) were similar to those in samples collected in the outer harbor. Particulate forms of Pb and Fe were equivalent to (Pb) or exceeded (Fe) the concentration of these metals in their dissolved form in the inner harbor. Substantially lower but significant proportions of the other metals were also present in particulate form. Within the inner harbor, concentrations of trace metals in particulate form in the deep samples collected at stations 4, 6, and 7 were substantially higher than in respective samples of surface water collected at these stations. This probably reflects resuspension of fine-grained sediments, as indicated by higher concentrations of particulate Al in the deep samples.

Concentrations of dissolved metals in the single station (5) located in the Charles River, just upstream of the Charles

Table 7.1. Concentrations of Dissolved Trace Metals in Boston's Inner Harbor—Low Tide, August 1983

| | | | Metal Concentrations | | | | | | |
Station	Salinity (‰)	Temperature (°C)	Zn (nM liter^{-1})	Pb (nM liter^{-1})	Cd (pM liter^{-1})	Cu (nM liter^{-1})	Ni (nM liter^{-1})	Fe (nM liter^{-1})	Mn (nM liter^{-1})
1	28.9	18.7	191	2.69	935	146	368.0	1520	715
2	29.1	19.5	90	1.38	720	108	28.4	270	250
3	28.9	18.8	111	1.42	738	146	29.7	223	278
4	27.9	18.9	112	1.05	718	81	27.6	218	284
5	1.8	24.5	29	1.88	558	101	50.0	195	40
6	28.2	19.0	144	1.71	549	65	26.2	274	278
7	28.5	19.0	101	1.30	674	67	26.8	175	216

Table 7.2. Concentrations of Dissolved Trace Metals in Boston's Inner Harbor—High Tide, August 1983

Station	Salinity (‰)	Temperature (°C)	Metal Concentrations						
			Zn (nM liter^{-1})	Pb (nM liter^{-1})	Cd (pM liter^{-1})	Cu (nM liter^{-1})	Ni (nM liter^{-1})	Fe (nM liter^{-1})	Mn (nM liter^{-1})
1	26.7	20.2	63	1.97	469	206	38.9	561	502
2	29.6	21.4	86	1.61	707	199	20.4	263	212
2(13)[a]	29.8	17.2	61	1.97	661	176	46.2	316	200
3	29.2	19.3	124	1.74	661	129	22.0	308	290
4	29.2	19.6	107	1.23	725	189	26.8	237	242
4(13)	29.7	17.7	39	1.18	545	94	14.3	179	128
6	29.2	18.9	65	1.10	637	98	18.2	149	202
6(13)	30.0	16.8	38	1.39	574	101	14.5	192	117
7	29.2	19.3	80	0.90	622	51	17.8	146	186
7(13)	30.0	17.1	36	1.06	501	62	12.1	230	131

[a]Number in parentheses following station number is depth of sample in meters. Otherwise samples were collected at a depth of ~10 cm.

Table 7.3. Particulate Trace Metal Concentrations in Boston's Inner Harbor—High Tide, August 1983

Station[a]	Metal Concentrations							
	Zn (nM liter^{-1})	Pb (nM liter^{-1})	Cd (pM liter^{-1})	Cu (nM liter^{-1})	Ni (nM liter^{-1})	Fe (μM liter^{-1})	Mn (nM liter^{-1})	Al (μM liter^{-1})
1	16.2	3.07	82.4	14.4	2.26	2.29	19.4	2.22
2	11.2	2.27	10.7	7.2	1.10	1.51	14.0	2.26
2(13)[b]	8.4	1.98	29.1	6.2	1.24	2.00	16.9	3.08
3	8.0	2.49	29.5	6.8	.73	1.43	11.6	1.08
4	5.3	1.57	8.8	4.6	.65	.95	11.6	.76
4(13)	11.6	2.20	29.4	9.0	1.49	2.02	30.9	3.44
6	5.7	1.38	10.7	6.9	.72	.94	32.2	1.14
6(13)	10.1	1.50	30.2	8.3	1.44	1.90	31.0	2.95
7	6.4	1.20	13.1	5.9	.77	.88	25.4	.99
7(13)	15.0	1.88	63.6	15.5	1.01	2.61	33.2	3.07

[a]Number in parentheses following station number is depth of sample in meters. Otherwise, samples were collected at a depth of ~10 cm.

River Dam, were equivalent to or below those in adjacent samples from the inner harbor collected at low tide except for Cu and Ni (Table 7.1).

7.3.2. Northern Section of Boston's Outer Harbor

Data for the northern part of the outer harbor, including Dorchester Bay (stations 13, 14, and 15), are given in Tables 7.4–7.6.

At these stations, Cu and Ni, and to a lesser extent Cd, concentrations were lower in the samples collected at high

tide but there was little difference in the concentrations of other metals in samples collected either at low or high tide.

Metal concentrations in the sample collected in the Deer Island outfall plume (station 10) at low tide were substantially greater than those at adjacent stations (Table 7.4). Particularly notable were the high concentrations of Cd and Zn in this sample. Metal concentrations in water samples collected in the plume at high tide (Table 7.5) were also higher than those observed in samples from adjacent stations, but the exceptionally higher concentrations of Cd and Zn found at low tide were not observed.

Concentrations of most metals in the samples collected at low and high tide just outside of the northern entrance to Boston Harbor (station 11) were generally lower than those

Table 7.4. Concentrations of Dissolved Metals in the Northern Section of Boston's Outer Harbor—Low Tide, August 1983

Station	Salinity (‰)	Temperature (°C)	Metal Concentrations						
			Zn (nM liter^{-1})	Pb (nM liter^{-1})	Cd (pM liter^{-1})	Cu (nM liter^{-1})	Ni (nM liter^{-1})	Fe (nM liter^{-1})	Mn (nM liter^{-1})
8	28.8	18.6	87	0.92	668	78	32.7	151	210
9	29.3	19.3	62	1.10	680	79	21.4	332	204
10[a]	28.8	17.9	240	1.58	5090	102	38.6	239	284
11	29.5	16.7	39	0.92	675	32	20.6	153	138
13	29.2	19.3	66	1.55	769	47	16.5	144	219
14	28.9	18.6	75	1.29	861	46	16.4	118	281
15	28.7	19.0	76	1.77	835	52	18.5	137	293

[a]Sample taken within Deer Island Outfall plume.

Table 7.5. Concentrations of Dissolved Metals in the Northern Section of Boston's Outer Harbor—High Tide, August 1983

Station	Salinity (‰)	Temperature (°C)	Metal Concentrations						
			Zn (nM liter^{-1})	Pb (nM liter^{-1})	Cd (pM liter^{-1})	Cu (nM liter^{-1})	Ni (nM liter^{-1})	Fe (nM liter^{-1})	Mn (nM liter^{-1})
8	30.0	16.4	30	0.66	620	49	11.7	77	101
8[a]	30.0	18.0	29	0.76	565	59	9.7	82	114
9	30.0	19.6	60	0.98	625	60	16.2	212	178
10	29.8	17.3	30	0.84	616	44	12.2	76	102
10(15)[b]	30.0	16.0	24	0.77	497	64	8.8	78	77
PLUME[c]	30.0	16.8	59	1.23	422	98	30.7	247	206
11	30.0	17.1	31	0.64	620	67	23.8	56	58
11(15)	30.3	14.0	12	0.44	359	6	10.7	112	66
13	29.6	18.9	56	1.29	799	26	14.4	141	155
13	29.6	18.9	52	1.72	768	19	13.9	106	157
14	29.5	18.8	52	1.20	725	31	17.9	117	138
14(8)	29.6	18.2	60	1.61	729	23	13.8	442	138
15	29.3	19.2	50	1.60	731	20	11.2	271	179

[a]A second surface sample was taken nearly but in a visually more turbid zone.
[b]Number in parentheses following station number is the depth of sample in meters. Otherwise, samples were collected at a depth of ~10 cm.
[c]Sample was collected near station 10 but directly in the plume from the Deer Island Outfall. Otherwise, samples were collected at a depth of ~10 cm.

observed in the harbor. Of particular note is the low concentration of metals observed in the colder, more saline water in the 15-m sample collected at this station at high tide.

Concentrations of particulate metals in samples collected from the outfall plume (Table 7.6) were much higher than those observed at adjacent stations. Particulate forms of Cd, Fe, Pb, and Zn represented the major fraction of these metals in this sample. At the remaining stations, the proportion of total metal represented by particulate forms was similar to that observed in samples from the inner harbor. Higher absolute concentrations of particulate metals tended to be associated with high concentrations of particulate Al, which was

probably derived from resuspension of fine-grained sediment.

7.3.3. Southern Section of Boston's Outer Harbor

Concentrations of Cd, Fe, Mn, and Zn in samples collected at low tide from the southern section of Boston's outer harbor (Table 7.7) tended to be somewhat lower than those from the northern section. Lead and Ni concentrations were compara-

Table 7.6. Concentrations of Trace Metals in Particulate Form in the Northern Section of Boston's Outer Harbor—High Tide, August 1983

Station	Metal Concentrations							
	Zn (nM liter^{-1})	Pb (nM liter^{-1})	Cd (pM liter^{-1})	Cu (nM liter^{-1})	Ni (nM liter^{-1})	Fe (μM liter^{-1})	Mn (nM liter^{-1})	Al (μM liter^{-1})
8	4.2	0.61	23.6	5.8	0.72	0.62	13.6	1.18
8[a]	6.1	1.29	20.3	9.3	0.82	0.97	19.4	2.15
9	9.5	1.38	8.7	4.4	1.79	1.87	24.1	4.62
10	7.1	1.16	16.2	6.8	0.28	0.93	21.6	1.88
10(15)[b]	6.3	0.84	36.9	6.7	0.27	0.78	21.2	1.74
Plume[c]	131.0	3.89	614.0	48.9	4.34	1.93	29.3	3.05
11	6.9	0.88	22.4	4.3	0.72	0.51	20.8	0.79
11(15)	6.3	0.85	17.5	9.1	1.37	1.32	22.8	3.10
13	13.3	2.76	39.8	6.0	1.32	1.21	17.8	2.57
13[a]	10.1	2.43	33.1	5.3	1.00	1.06	15.3	2.23
14	12.8	1.74	29.9	5.1	3.57	1.11	20.9	2.19
14(8)	12.6	2.17	35.1	9.3	1.69	1.78	24.0	4.09
15	18.7	3.19	50.8	15.9	2.48	2.82	29.2	5.78

[a]A second surface sample was taken nearby but in a visually more turbid zone.
[b]Number in parentheses following station number is depth of sample in meters. Otherwise, samples were collected at a depth of ~10 cm.
[c]Sample was collected near station 10 but directly in the plume from Deer Island Outfall.

Table 7.7. Concentrations of Dissolved Metals in the Southern Section of Boston's Outer Harbor—Low Tide, August 1983

Station	Salinity (‰)	Temperature (°C)	Metal Concentrations						
			Zn (nM liter^{-1})	Pb (nM liter^{-1})	Cd (pM liter^{-1})	Cu (nM liter^{-1})	Ni (nM liter^{-1})	Fe (nM liter^{-1})	Mn (nM liter^{-1})
12	29.6	17.7	58	1.78	774	26	15.6	130	139
12[a]	29.5	18.5	49	2.08	709	32	14.0	101	135
16	29.5	18.0	47	1.14	658	62	15.1	88	228
17	29.8	17.3	28	0.88	498	49	10.8	92	108
18	29.7	17.7	31	1.16	503	53	10.6	93	126
19	29.9	18.2	41	0.93	541	44	10.0	67	126
20	29.7	18.8	34	1.39	504	195	22.0	137	132
21	29.2	18.3	70	1.78	580	291	15.6	187	299
22	29.8	17.8	44	1.45	622	232	15.0	96	144
23	29.5	18.9	39	1.26	476	189	14.0	68	174
24	29.7	18.5	48	1.88	634	220	24.2	79	138

[a]Station 12 reoccupied on second day of low tide sampling.

ble, but Cu concentrations from stations 20–24 were higher than observed in any other samples except some of those collected in the inner harbor. There were no distinct regional differences in metal concentrations observed at high tide between the northern and southern sections of the outer harbor.

The lowest concentrations of metals in samples collected at both low and high tide (Table 7.8) were generally associated with samples collected in Nantasket Roads and vicinity (stations 16, 17, and 18). Higher concentrations were observed at the shallower stations in Quincy, Hull, and Hingham bays (stations 19–24) under both tidal regimes. The Cu concentration in the sample of surface water collected at high tide at station 17 was almost four times that of the sample of surface water from station 16 but similar to that in the sample of surface water collected at station 18. Copper concentrations in samples collected at 15 m at station 17 and 20 m at station 18 were also similar, which suggests that differences

Table 7.8. Concentrations of Dissolved Metals in the Southern Section of Boston's Outer Harbor—High Tide, August 1983

Station	Salinity (‰)	Temperature (°C)	Metal Concentrations						
			Zn (nM liter^{-1})	Pb (nM liter^{-1})	Cd (pM liter^{-1})	Cu (nM liter^{-1})	Ni (nM liter^{-1})	Fe (nM liter^{-1})	Mn (nM liter^{-1})
12	29.8	18.7	75	1.31	783	31	13.8	126	120
16	30.0	16.9	22	0.67	534	14	27.8	32	76
16[a]	30.0	16.9	32	0.88	518	16	10.0	68	90
17	30.0	17.5	22	0.54	460	58	10.5	34	71
17(15)[b]	30.4	13.2	13	0.46	336	38	9.3	76	32
18	29.9	18.2	43	1.38	536	56	10.6	121	174
18(20)	30.4	17.7	22	0.64	453	42	9.3	81	90
19	29.8	18.3	44	1.66	567	48	13.4	120	154
20	29.8	19.5	36	1.19	517	64	11.5	152	141
21	29.7	20.1	70	1.66	558	35	13.4	151	309
22	30.0	18.8	50	2.75	600	37	13.4	115	154
23	29.9	20.8	38	1.51	498	41	12.5	178	116
24	29.9	19.7	60	4.98	741	41	12.5	135	103

[a]A second surface sample was taken nearby but in a visually more turbid zone.
[b]Number in parentheses following station number is depth of sample in meters. Otherwise, samples were collected at a depth of ~10 cm.

between the Cu concentrations in surface water at stations 16 and 17 may reflect differences in the recent history of the water sampled at each location.

The range and magnitude of concentrations of trace metals in particulate form in the southern section of the outer harbor (Table 7.9) were similar to those observed both in the inner harbor and in the northern section of the outer harbor, excluding the Deer Island plume sample. Within the southern section, samples obtained in the shallower peripheral stations tended to have higher concentrations of trace metals in particulate form than those observed in the samples from Nantasket Roads.

7.4. DISCUSSION

7.4.1. General Distribution Patterns

The concentrations of the metals examined in water from Boston Harbor and from just outside of the harbor are substantially higher (by a factor of one to two orders of magnitude) than those in seawater off the northeastern coast of the United States, based on the few reliable data available (Boyle et al., 1981; Boyle and Huested, 1983; Bruland and Franks, 1983; Hanson and Quinn, 1983). In general, concentrations of all metals were greater at stations located in the innermost peripheral sections of the harbor [i.e., the inner harbor (sta-

tions 1–7); Dorchester Bay (stations 13–15); and southern sections of Quincy, Hingham, and Hull bays (stations 20–24)]. Metal concentrations at low tide were usually greater than those observed at high tide except in stations 1–4 in the inner harbor.

The concentration pattern of Cd, Ni, Pb, and Zn in the water column generally follows that of the concentration of those same metals found in sediment from Boston Harbor (White, 1972; Fitzgerald, 1980). Remobilization from the sediments and restricted tidal exchange of water in these regions may, therefore, be important parameters governing this distribution. Neither of these processes has been examined in detail in Boston Harbor.

The distribution patterns show clearly two predominant sources of metals in Boston Harbor: the sewage outfalls from the Deer Island and Nut Island plants and generalized nearshore inputs from a variety of sources. These sources are ill-defined at present, but undoubtedly include contributions from the combined sewer overflows, urban runoff, and the heavily contaminated underlying sediments.

7.4.2. Tidal Flushing

It is of course impossible to offer a comprehensive picture of the efficiency of the flushing of metals from Boston Harbor given the spatial and temporal nature and limited number of

Table 7.9. Concentrations of Trace Metals in Particulate Form in the Southern Section of Boston's Outer Harbor—High Tide, August 1983

	Metal Concentrations							
Station	Zn (nM liter⁻¹)	Pb (nM liter⁻¹)	Cd (pM liter⁻¹)	Cu (nM liter⁻¹)	Ni (nM liter⁻¹)	Fe (μM liter⁻¹)	Mn (nM liter⁻¹)	Al (μM liter⁻¹)
12	6.3	1.62	20.9	4.1	0.93	0.89	13.4	2.09
16	9.2	0.59	11.3	2.5	0.53	0.53	17.6	1.34
16[a]	13.1	0.74	7.7	2.8	0.55	0.51	20.0	1.19
17	6.6	0.44	6.7	1.5	0.38	0.24	21.3	0.28
17(15)[b]	4.9	0.42	1.4	1.6	0.44	0.40	18.5	1.07
18	7.6	1.45	5.5	5.2	0.94	0.89	24.9	2.47
18(20)	5.2	0.63	5.5	1.8	0.58	0.48	18.0	1.24
19	5.8	1.00	12.3	3.2	0.80	0.77	22.9	2.06
20	6.6	1.02	6.2	3.7	0.75	0.84	18.2	1.92
21	10.5	2.31	12.4	4.7	0.99	1.20	18.2	2.59
22	9.3	1.60	23.6	6.7	1.22	1.05	28.3	2.83
23	12.2	2.40	31.2	5.2	1.13	1.06	39.7	2.58
24	20.1	3.12	40.1	13.4	2.40	2.23	41.2	5.98

[a]A second surface sample was taken nearby but in a visually more turbid zone.
[b]Number in parentheses following station number is depth of sample in meters. Otherwise, samples were collected at a depth of ~10 cm.

samples analyzed in this work. Nevertheless some first-order estimates may be made based on the observed differences between the metal concentrations in surface water collected at both low and high tide. The most efficiently flushed area of the harbor is apparently restricted to the northern channel (President Roads) and its extension up to station 6 in the inner harbor. Flushing of the southern part of the harbor is apparently less efficient and limited to the outer reaches of the southern channel (Nantasket Roads). These are very crude approximations that are likely to be sensitive to seasonal variations (wind forcing, runoff, and degree of vertical stratification) and to short-term episodic events associated with storms.

7.4.3. Tidal Variations of Cu in the Southern Section of the Harbor

The elevated Cu concentrations at low tide in the southern part of the harbor, which were the highest observed at low tide anywhere in the harbor, were unanticipated. While it is well established that the toxicity of Cu to some marine organisms is a function of its speciation (free-ion activity) and not necessarily its total concentration, available observations suggest that these concentrations are in a range capable of exerting biological effects on marine biota in coastal ecosystems (Hodson et al., 1979).

We considered two possible explanations for the increase in Cu concentration observed over the 6-d interval between samplings. The first was mass transport of Cu in the water from one or more potential sources. Initially we suspected a source of this Cu might be the Weymouth Fore River because of the high Cu concentrations there (station 21, Table 7.7); however the magnitude and areal extent made it unlikely that the Weymouth Fore River could be the only source. The local sewage outfalls associated with the Nut Island treatment works (Fig. 7.1) also could have contributed to the high Cu concentrations observed at low tide at stations 20–24; however, the following calculations suggest that the Nut Island discharge was not a direct cause for the dramatic increase in Cu at low tide. The average volume discharge of effluent from the Nut Island plant during August 1983 was 4.6×10^5 m³d⁻¹, with a mean soluble Cu concentration of 1.26 mmol m⁻³ (Jean Haggerty, personal communication). The total volume of discharge of an ebb-tide (6-h) cycle would be ~1.2 $\times 10^5$ m³. From the morphometric data from Jerome et al. (1966) for Quincy Bay we calculate a volume of 2.69×10^7 m³ for the part of Quincy Bay having a depth range of 0–4 m at mean low water. This part (generally the southern part of Quincy Bay) coincides with the area in which our samples were collected during low and high tide. If all of the Nut Island effluent discharged during ebb tide were mixed only into this section of Quincy Bay, the maximum increase in Cu concentration can be calculated to be on the order of 5.4 μmol m⁻³. The observed difference between high and low tides was 158 and 179 μmol m^{-3} (Tables 7.7 and 7.8, stations 23 and 24). In fact, the contribution of the Nut Island discharge must be much lower considering the assumptions made above.

Furthermore, if sewage inputs from Nut Island were the major source and if Cu were to behave conservatively upon mixing, a decrease of $\sim 2 \times 10^{-3}$ in salinity would be expected to accompany the observed increase in Cu concentration. This was not observed. Concurrent increases in other metals present in higher levels in sewage effluent were also not observed, including those, such as Cd, not expected to be rapidly removed on particles (Santschi et al., 1983). In view of the above arguments, we concluded that another source must be responsible for the observed increase in Cu concentrations at low tide. We then explored the possibility of a significant benthic source of Cu to the water.

If the increase were to occur during a single ebb tide, the benthic flux of Cu would have to be on the order of 1300 μmol m^{-2} d^{-1} [mean low water depth of 2 m and a mean increase in Cu concentration of 168 μmol m^{-3} during ebb tide (6 h)]. Hunt and Smith (1983) observed a net export of 840 μmol m^{-2} of Cu over the period of 1 y from contaminated sediments collected from the Providence River, Rhode Island, and placed in 5-m^3 mesocosms. Most (60%) of the observed export occurred during the summer. This difference of almost three orders of magnitude between our estimated flux in Quincy Bay and that observed by Hunt and Smith (1983) may arise in part from our initial assumption that the increase occurred over a single ebb tide, the lower temporal resolution of Hunt and Smith's (1983) observations (samples collected every 2–3 weeks), and substantial differences in sediment chemistry and biology.

We next examined the potential sources of the Cu released to the water column. Total Cu concentrations in five sediment samples collected in Quincy Bay by White (1972) ranged from 0.3 to 1.4 μmol g^{-1}. Assuming a mean Cu concentration in the sediment of 1 μmol g^{-1} and density of 2.5 g cm^{-3}, the depth to which Cu would have to be released to supply the maximum calculated flux of 1300 μmol m^{-2} d^{-1} would be on the order of 500 μm. The observed increase in the concentration of Cu in the water column could thus result from processes within a very thin layer at the sediment–water interface, especially if we allow for a layer of Cu-enriched detritus (from sewage and plankton) on the sediment surface.

We also hypothesize that this release phenomenon may be short term and restricted to the summer months (Crill and Martens, 1983; Hunt and Smith, 1983; Hines et al., 1984)

when microbial and benthic activities in the sediments are at a maximum. During other periods of the year, organic-rich suspended matter, whose source may be the Nut Island sewage outfalls, and fine-grained sediment imported from other areas of the harbor may accumulate in the shallower, quiescent southern parts of Quincy, Hingham, and Hull bays. With increasing temperatures, biological activity in the sediments results in the destruction of accumulated organic matter and subsequent release of associated Cu into the water column (Lu and Chen, 1977; Klinkhammer, 1980; Klinkhammer et al., 1982; Sawlan and Murray, 1983). We hypothesize that most of this release occurs at the sediment–water interface and is not primarily a diffusive flux driven by pore-water concentration gradients or by the activity of benthic organisms. Remobilization of Cu from the pelagic sediment–water interface has been documented, although its importance in estuarine and coastal settings has been questioned (Klinkhammer, 1983). Remobilization from shelf sediments has been suggested also as a source of elevated Cu concentrations in coastal water, although precise definition of the processes leading to the remobilization has not been made (Boyle et al., 1981).

Based on profiles of pore-water chemistry, Elderfield et al. (1981a,b) suggested that remobilization of Cu from sediment from Narragansett Bay was unlikely to be important due to the rapid removal of Cu to solid phases in anoxic pore water; however, Elderfield et al. (1981b) found a rapid release of Cu upon oxygenation of anoxic sediments. They suggested that oxygenation of sediments by benthic organisms may have caused erratically high concentrations of Cu in their profiles of sediment pore water, although they could not rule out contamination as a possibility. Rapid oxygenation of sediments by storm-induced mixing might, therefore, cause rapid release of Cu into the water column; however, this process cannot account for our observations because of the lack of significant winds in the interval of sampling between low and high tide. A rapid increase in benthic activity and subsequent oxygenation of subsurface sediments might explain this release, but whether the temporal nature of these changes is of the appropriate dimension remains to be shown.

We believe that the evidence described in this chapter supports our hypothesis that the probable cause of the increased concentrations of Cu observed in the southern reaches of Boston Harbor is the short-term rapid remobilization of Cu from recently deposited material at the sediment–water interface, as opposed to being from the underlying sediments. As we noted above, the magnitude of this release is apparently sufficient to raise Cu concentrations in the water column above those known to be detrimental to a variety of marine organisms in coastal marine environments (Hodson et al., 1979). Considering the importance of the local recreational flounder fishery in this region (Jerome et al., 1966), and the potential impact to the marine ecosystem in the region as a whole, this phenomenon may be of considerable importance. We believe the potential importance of such rapid release warrants examining the benthic exchange of Cu in Boston Harbor and other estuaries on a time scale not generally attempted.

7.5. CONCLUSIONS

Metal concentrations in Boston Harbor were substantially higher than those of ambient New England coastal water in cases for which comparable data are available. Within the harbor, most metal concentrations were highest in the inner harbor and in waters overlying sediments with the highest metal concentrations. High concentrations in the inner harbor are attributed to local sources coupled with poor tidal flushing and not to the sewage outfalls at the entrance to the harbor. The Charles River does not appear to be a significant source of dissolved metals in the inner harbor. Metal concentrations outside of the inner harbor reflect exchange with inner harbor water, discharge from the two sewage effluent outfalls, and either remobilization from heavily contaminated sediments or poor tidal flushing.

Order of magnitude increases in Cd and Zn were observed in the outfall plume under conditions of slack tide. Particulate forms of Cd, Cu, Fe, Pb, and Zn dominated in the plume and were the major form of Fe and Pb at most stations in the harbor. Elevated concentrations of suspended Al in the deep samples obtained suggest active resuspension and transport of fine-grained sediment in Boston Harbor.

Copper concentrations reached potentially toxic concentrations at low tide in the shallow southernmost stations in the harbor. This increase has been tentatively ascribed to short-term episodic remobilization from recently deposited material at the sediment–water interface.

ACKNOWLEDGMENTS

We thank Michael Shiaris, Michael Larson, and Patricia Schuerch for assistance in collection of the samples and Jan Underwood for preparation of the manuscript.

REFERENCES

Aller, R. C., L. K. Benninger, and J. K. Cochran. 1980. Tracking particle-associated processes in nearshore environments by use of $^{234}Th/^{238}U$ disequilibrium. *Earth and Planetary Science Letters*, **47**, 161–175.

Boyle, E. A., and S. Huested. 1983. Aspects of the surface distributions of copper, nickel, cadmium and lead in the North Atlantic and North Pacific. *In*: Trace Metals in Sea Water, C. S. Wong, E. Boyle, K. W. Bruland, J. D. Burton, and E. D. Goldberg (Eds.). Plenum Press, New York, pp. 379–394.

Boyle, E. A., S. S. Huested, and S. P. Jones. 1981. On the distribution of copper, nickel and cadmium in the surface waters of the North Atlantic and North Pacific Oceans. *Journal Geophysical Research*, **86**, 8048–8066.

Bruland, K. W., and R. P. Franks. 1983. Mn, Ni, Cu, Zn, and Cd in the western North Atlantic. *In*: Trace Metals in Sea Water, C. S. Wong, E. Boyle, K. W. Bruland, J. D. Burton, and E. D. Goldberg (Eds.). Plenum Press, New York, pp. 395–414.

Bruland, K. W., R. P. Franks, G. A. Knauer, and J. H. Martin. 1979. Sampling and analytical methods for the determination of copper, cadmium, zinc, and nickel at the nanogram per liter level in seawater. *Analytica Chimica Acta*, **105**, 233–245.

Crill, P. M., and C. S. Martens. 1983. Spatial and temporal fluctuations of methane production in anoxic coastal marine sediments. *Limnology and Oceanography*, **28**, 1117–1130.

Danielsson, L. G., B. Magnusson, and S. Westerland. 1978. An improved metal extraction procedure for the determination of trace metals in seawater by atomic absorption spectrometry with electrothermal atomization. *Analytica Chimica Acta*, **98**, 47–57.

Elderfield, H., N. Luedtke, R. J. McCaffrey, and M. Bender. 1981a. Benthic flux studies in Narragansett Bay. *American Journal of Science*, **281**, 768–787.

Elderfield, H., R. J. McCaffrey, N. Luedtke, M. Bender, and V. W. Truesdale. 1981b. Chemical diagenesis in Narragansett Bay sediments. *American Journal of Science*, **281**, 1021–1055.

Fairbridge, R. W. 1980. The estuary: its definition and geodynamic cycle. *In*: Chemistry and Biogeochemistry of Estuaries, E. Olavsson, and I. Cato (Eds.). Wiley-Interscience, New York, pp. 1–35.

Fitzgerald, M. G. 1980. Anthropogenic Influence of the Sedimentary Regime of an Urban Estuary—Boston Harbor. Ph.D. Dissertation, Massachusetts Institute of Technology/Woods Hole Oceanographic Institution, Woods Hole, Massachusetts. 297 pp.

Hanson, A. K., Jr., and J. G. Quinn. 1983. The distribution of dissolved and organically complexed copper and nickel in the Middle Atlantic Bight. *Canadian Journal of Fisheries and Aquatic Sciences*, **40** (Supplement 2), 151–161.

Hines, M. E., W. B. Lyons, P. B. Armstrong, W. H. Orem, M. J. Spencer, H. E. Gaudette, and G. E. Jones. 1984. Seasonal metal remobilization in the sediments of Great Bay, New Hampshire. *Marine Chemistry*, **15**, 173–187.

Hodson, P. V., U. Borgmann, and H. Shear. 1979. Toxicity of copper to aquatic biota. *In*: Copper in the Environment, Part II: Health Effects, J. O. Nriagu, (Ed.). Wiley-Interscience, New York, pp. 307–372.

Hunt, C. D., and D. L. Smith. 1983. Remobilization of metals from polluted marine sediments. *Canadian Journal of Fisheries and Aquatic Sciences*, **40**, (Supplement 2) 132–142.

Jerome, W. C., Jr., A. P. Chesmore, and C. O. Anderson, Jr. 1966. A Study of the Marine Resources of Quincy Bay. Monograph Series No. 2, Department of Natural Resources, Boston, Massachusetts, 62 pp.

Ketchum, B. H. 1951. The Dispersion and Fate of Pollution Discharged into Tidal Waters, and the Viability of Enteric Bacteria in the Sea. Woods

Hole Oceanographic Institution Report No. 51-11, Woods Hole, Massachusetts, 46 pp.

Klinkhammer, G. P. 1980. Early diagenesis in sediments from the eastern equatorial Pacific, II: pore water metal results. *Earth and Planetary Science Letters*, **49**, 81–101.

Klinkhammer, G. P. 1983. Separation of copper and nickel by low temperature processes. *In*: Trace Metals in Sea Water, C. S. Wong, E. Boyle, K. W. Bruland, J. D. Burton, and E. D. Goldberg (Eds.). Plenum Press, New York, pp. 317–329.

Klinkhammer, G. P., D. T. Heggie, and D. W. Graham. 1982. Metal diagenesis in toxic marine sediments. *Earth and Planetary Science Letters*, **61**, 211–219.

Lu, J. C. S., and K. Y. Chen. 1977. Migration of trace metals in interfaces of seawater and polluted surficial sediments. *Environmental Science and Technology*, **11**, 174–182.

Magnusson, B., and S. Westerlund. 1981. Solvent extraction procedures combined with back-extraction for trace metal determinations by atomic absorbtion spectrometry. *Analytica Chimica Acta*, **131**, 63–72.

Manning, D. C., and W. Slavin. 1983. The determination of trace elements in natural waters using the stabilized temperature platform furnace. *Applied Spectroscopy*, **37**, 1–11.

Santschi, P. H., D. M. Adler, and M. Amdurer. 1983. The fate of particles and particle-reactive trace metals in coastal waters: radioisotope studies in microcosms. *In*: Trace Metals in Sea Water, C. S. Wong., E. Boyle, K. W. Bruland, J. D. Burton, and E. D. Goldberg (Eds.). Plenum Press, New York, pp. 331–349.

Sawlan, J. J., and J. W. Murray. 1983. Trace metal remobilization in the interstitial waters of red clay and hemipelagic marine sediments. *Earth and Planetary Science Letters*, **64**, 213–230.

Wallace, G. T., and R. A. Duce. 1975. Concentration of particulate trace metals and particulate organic carbon in marine surface waters by a bubble flotation mechanism. *Marine Chemistry*, **3**, 157–181.

Wallace, G. T., G. L. Hoffman, and R. A. Duce. 1977. The influence of organic matter and atmospheric deposition on the particulate trace metal concentration of northwest Atlantic surface seawater. *Marine Chemistry*, **5**, 143–170.

Wallace, G. T., N. Dudek, R. Dulmage, and O. Mahoney. 1983. Trace element distributions in the Gulf Stream adjacent to the southeastern Atlantic continental shelf—influence of atmospheric and shelf water inputs. *Canadian Journal of Fisheries and Aquatic Sciences*, **40** (Supplement 2), 183–191.

White, R. J. 1972. The Distribution and Concentrations of Selected Metals in Boston Harbor Sediments. M.S. Thesis, Northeastern University, Boston, Massachusetts, 103 pp.

Chapter 8

Thirty-Five Years of Dumping Titanium Dioxide Wastes in U.S. Waters: What Have We Learned?

Rosemary K. Monahan, Garry F. Mayer, Harold M. Stanford

Ocean Assessments Division
U.S. National Oceanic and Atmospheric Administration
Stony Brook, New York

Abstract	79
8.1. Introduction	80
8.2. Titanium Dioxide Industry	80
8.3. History of Dumping in the Middle Atlantic Bight	81
8.3.1. New York Bight Acid Wastes Dumpsite	81
8.3.2. DuPont Acid Wastes Dumpsite	83
8.3.3. Deepwater Industrial Waste Dumpsite	83
8.4. Permitting and Regulation of Disposal in U.S. Waters	84
8.5. Effects of Titanium Dioxide Wastes upon the Environment	84
8.5.1. Chemical Effects	84
8.5.2. Physical Effects	85
8.5.3. Biological Effects	86
8.5.3a. Phytoplankton	86
8.5.3b. Zooplankton	87
8.5.3c. Fish	88
8.5.3d. Benthos	88
8.6. Conclusions	88
Acknowledgments	89
References	89

R. K. Monahan's current address: U.S. Environmental Protection Agency, Region I, Boston, Massachusetts 02125.

G. F. Mayer's current address: National Sea Grant College Program, U.S. National Oceanic and Atmospheric Administration, Rockville, Maryland 20852.

H. M. Stanford's current address: Office of Oceanography and Marine Assessment, U.S. National Oceanic and Atmospheric Administration, Rockville, Maryland 20852.

ABSTRACT

Titanium dioxide wastes have been dumped into marine waters of the United States for more than 35 y. This dumping has occurred at three sites in the Middle Atlantic Bight: the New York Bight Acid Wastes Dumpsite, the Deepwater Industrial Waste Dumpsite (formerly Deepwater Dumpsite-106), and the DuPont Acid Wastes Dumpsite. The New York Bight Acid Wastes Dumpsite has the longest and most intensive history of titanium dioxide dumping. Most studies of dumping, even at this heavily used site, have indicated that the contribution of titanium dioxide wastes to adverse environmental effects is minimal. In contrast, some laboratory studies and field work undertaken elsewhere have indicated that titanium dioxide wastes can have substantial impacts upon the fauna. Similar impacts rarely have been seen in the Middle Atlantic Bight, most likely because waste dilution and dispersion have been extensive. Within the New York Bight, the detection of impacts related to the disposal of titanium dioxide waste may have been made more difficult by multiple anthropogenic inputs entering area waters. This chapter summarizes the history of the disposal of titanium waste at sites in the Middle Atlantic Bight and explores the effects of these wastes upon the environment.

8.1. INTRODUCTION

The disposal of titanium dioxide wastes into U.S. oceanic waters began in 1948, but has declined substantially in recent years. Of the three dumpsites for titanium dioxide waste in the Middle Atlantic Bight (the only ones used in the United States), only one continues to receive such wastes. There has been continuing concern over the potential effects of titanium dioxide wastes (also called acid wastes or acid-iron wastes) upon the marine environment. The bases for this concern and the history of such dumping in the Middle Atlantic Bight are the subjects of this review.

8.2. TITANIUM DIOXIDE INDUSTRY

Review of possible adverse effects of titanium dioxide wastes is ironic, because manufacture of titanium dioxide began largely in response to a need for a non-toxic alternative to lead-based pigments. Titanium dioxide has the desirable properties of extreme whiteness and brightness, so it is used extensively as a pigment in paints, papers, plastics, cosmetics, and numerous other products. Titanium dioxide pigment is refined by either a sulfate or a chloride process from ores that vary from ~40% titanium dioxide (ilmenite) to ~95% titanium dioxide (rutile). Iron (as an oxide) is the major contaminant in these ores, but other metals, such as Mn

and V, generally are present in small quantities. The amount of waste generated by the extraction process varies inversely with the purity of the ore.

Disposal of titanium dioxide wastes has long been a problem. Prior to 1948, wastes often were released into nearby freshwaters; however, the low pH of the wastes proved a problem because of the limited buffering capacity of freshwater. In addition, the receiving waters tended to be of relatively small volume, so the wastes were not diluted significantly or rapidly. It soon was recognized that disposal of the wastes into the ocean represented a practical alternative to disposal into freshwater, especially if the wastes were barged offshore to deeper waters. Since 1948, dumping has been the mode of disposal for acid-iron waste in the Middle Atlantic Bight.

The sulfate process has been the more widely used of the two titanium refining methods (both of which are outlined in Fig. 8.1). To extract titanium dioxide, ores are treated with sulfuric acid. This results in large volumes of wastes, because large quantities of acid and low grade ores typically are used. About 10 tons of waste are produced for every ton of titanium dioxide. The volume of acid wastes generated by the sulfate method can be reduced substantially by recycling the sulfuric acid. In addition, iron sulfate, a waste product, can be marketed as a flocculant for wastewater treatment and other uses.

The chloride process for refining titanium-rich ores was developed by DuPont in the 1950s. Typically, a high-grade

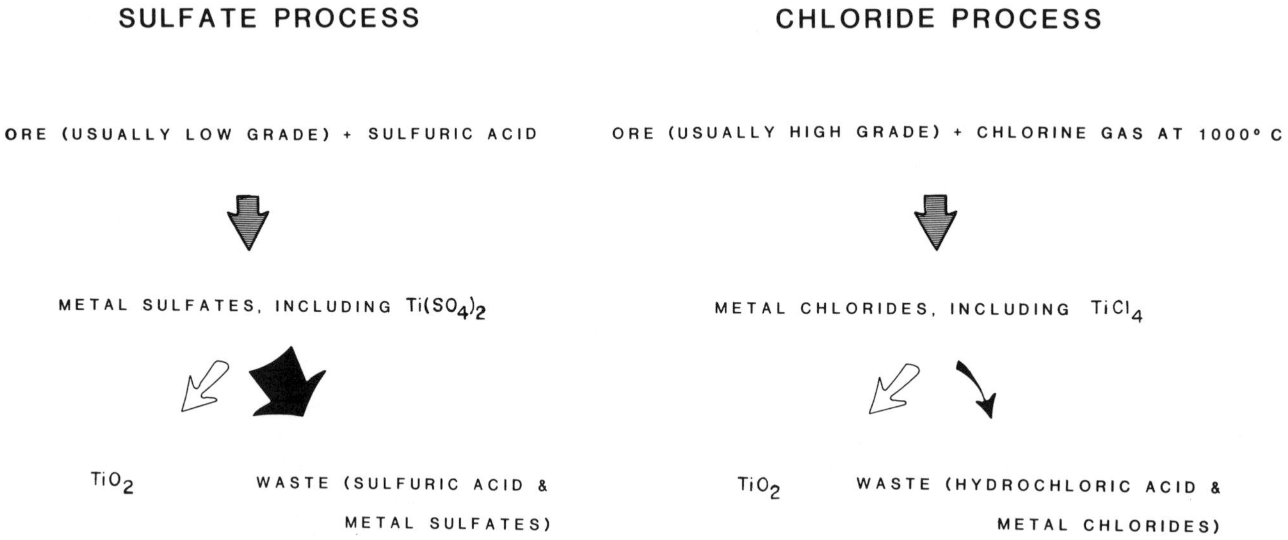

Figure 8.1. Alternative process methodologies for refining titanium dioxide from ore. The chloride process generates much lower quantities of waste per ton of TiO_2 produced.

ore is treated with chlorine gas to purify the titanium dioxide (Fig. 8.1). The chloride process generally results in a smaller volume of wastes than does the sulfate process. As in the sulfate process, the resulting acid wastes can be recycled, and waste iron chloride can be marketed as a flocculant. Representative characteristics of wastes both from a sulfate process and from a chloride process are shown in Table 8.1.

Titanium dioxide refineries are located in a number of countries other than the United States, including England, the Federal Republic of Germany, Finland, and Italy. The annual volume of wastes produced by these plants has varied directly with the economic health and production levels of the titanium dioxide industry. For example, during the end of 1979 and the beginning of 1980, the price and demand for titanium dioxide pigments increased relative to previous years. This period was followed by a world-wide recession, during which time most producers were working well below capacity (Fuller, 1981).

To reduce disposal requirements, environmental agencies in many countries have encouraged industries to convert to the chloride process and to recycle wastes. The European Economic Commission in 1978 directed industries in member countries to gradually reduce titanium dioxide pollution (Pickaver, 1982). In 1980, the U.S. Environmental Protection Agency (EPA) directed NL Industries (the largest disposer of titanium dioxide wastes in U.S. waters) to phase out dumping of titanium dioxide wastes into oceanic waters, and to cease dumping by 1989 (U.S. EPA, 1982). These actions reflect increasing regulatory concern over possible adverse environmental effects from ocean disposal of titanium dioxide wastes. Such effects are most likely to result from the low pH, metal contaminants, or suspended particulate material produced during mixing of wastes and seawater.

8.3. HISTORY OF DUMPING IN THE MIDDLE ATLANTIC BIGHT

Three dumpsites have been used for the disposal of titanium dioxide wastes in the Middle Atlantic Bight (Fig. 8.2). These sites differ in a number of physical characteristics, some of which affect the dispersal of wastes. Of the three dumpsites, the New York Bight (NYB) Acid Wastes Dumpsite has by far the longest and most intensive history of dumping.

8.3.1. New York Bight Acid Wastes Dumpsite

This 41-km^2 site is located in the New York Bight apex on the continental shelf, 27 km from the New Jersey and Long Island shorelines. The site abuts the Hudson Shelf Valley and is

Table 8.1. Characteristics for Acid-Iron Wastes from a Sulfate Process and a Chloride Process[a]

	NL Industries[a]		DuPont Edge Moor[b]	
	Range (mg liter^{-1})	Mean (mg liter^{-1})	1977 (mg liter^{-1})	1979 (mg liter^{-1})
Suspended solids	2.0–20,500	3760	208	844
Organic material	0.19–50.6	5.44		
Total organic carbon			59	100
Cd	0.01–0.5	0.20	0.3	0.4
Cr	2.0–18.9	10.9	205	77
Cu	0.123–140.2	4.1	3.1	1.3
Hg	0.0005–0.008	0.0047	0.01	0.01
Pb	0.27–0.88	1.67	40	23
Zn	0.48–36.1	2.03	73	62
pH	0.10–1.09		0.1	0.1
Specific gravity	1.082–1.197	1.132	1.14	1.09

[a]Sulfate process waste from NL Industries (U.S. EPA, 1980a).
[b]Chloride process waste from DuPont Edge Moor from averaging two years (O'Connor, 1983).

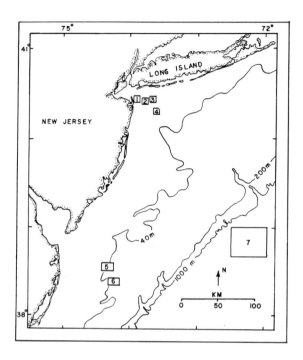

MIDDLE ATLANTIC BIGHT DISPOSAL SITES

Figure 8.2. Location of disposal sites in the Middle Atlantic Bight. Arrows indicate acid waste dumpsites (shaded). 1. Dredged Materials dumpsite. 2. Cellar Dirt dumpsite. 3. Sewage Sludge dumpsite. 4. New York Bight Acid Wastes dumpsite. 5. DuPont Acid Wastes dumpsite. 6. Philadelphia Sewage Sludge dumpsite. 7. Deepwater Industrial Waste dumpsite.

lute hydrochloric acid (Allied Chemical) and sodium sulfate (DuPont-Grasselli), plus trace constituents, such as metals. Beginning in 1975, disposal of Grasselli wastes was shifted from the NYB Dumpsite to the Deepwater Industrial Waste Dumpsite [then known as the Deepwater Dumpsite 106 (DWD-106)] (U.S. EPA, 1980a).

Wastes from NL Industries were barged to the NYB Dumpsite generally once, and sometimes twice a day. From 1960 through 1974, annual disposal quantities fluctuated between 2×10^6 metric tons (t) and 3×10^6 t (Fig. 8.3). Production declined in 1977 during a strike at the plant, and again in 1982 during a slump in the pigment market. Environmental regulations in the late 1970s and early 1980s also affected production at NL Industries. Regulations concerning phase-out of dumping stipulated reduction of two specific components of titanium dioxide wastes: gangue solids (mostly residual ore) and free sulfuric acid. To comply with EPA directives, NL Industries installed a liquid-phase digestion system to reduce waste volume (U.S. EPA, 1982). Because of economic conditions, however, plant production shut down in 1982.

Substantial quantities of acid-iron wastes have been dumped at the NYB Dumpsite; however, the relative contribution of these wastes to the loadings of toxic metals in the bight has been low. Of wastes barged to disposal sites in the

southeast of other disposal sites, including a sewage-sludge dumpsite and a dredged-material dumpsite serving the New York–New Jersey metropolitan area. Water depths range from 23 m to 28 m; sediments are predominantly sandy. Sediments of the nearby Hudson Canyon, dominated by silts and clays, serve as a sink for many of the anthropogenic inputs to the bight apex that are derived from dumping activities as well as from the Hudson–Raritan Estuary.

Ocean dumping of acid-iron wastes began at this site in 1948 after NL Industries (then National Lead) of Sayreville, New Jersey, encountered resistance from the New Jersey Department of Health over continued discharge of the wastes into Raritan Bay, New Jersey. Ninety-five percent of all wastes dumped at the offshore site were generated by NL Industries. The remaining 5% were industrial wastes dumped by two other New Jersey companies not involved in titanium dioxide processing: Allied Chemical Corporation of Elizabeth and DuPont-Grasselli of Linden (U.S. EPA, 1980a). Wastes from these two facilities consisted principally of di-

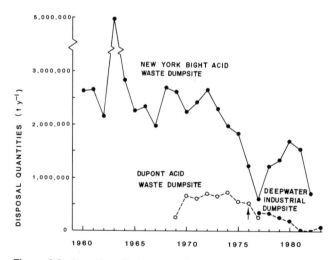

Figure 8.3. Quantities of acid wastes disposed at Middle Atlantic Bight dumpsites from 1960 to 1983. Arrow indicates completed conversion at the DuPont Edge Moor plant from a sulfate to a chloride process. Data from U.S. EPA (1980a,b, 1984), Muir (1983), and O'Connor (1983). Data from 1960 to 1972 at the New York Bight site were converted from cubic meters to metric tons by assuming an average specific gravity of 1.132 (U.S. EPA, 1980a).

New York Bight, dredged materials and sewage sludge far overshadowed acid-iron wastes as sources of most metals. Acid wastes constituted ~19% (by vol) of the barged discharges (including dredged materials, sewage sludge, chemical wastes, and rubble) entering the New York Bight apex from 1960 to 1974, but contributed only ~2% of the combined total inputs of Cd, Cr, Cu, Hg, Pb, and Zn from these sources (Fig. 8.4). The fraction originating from acid wastes ranged from ~0.04% for Hg to 4% for Cr (Mueller et al., 1976).

8.3.2. DuPont Acid Wastes Dumpsite

This 138-km^2 site is located on the continental shelf, 65 km east of the Maryland–Delaware border, and 9 km northwest of a sewage-sludge dumpsite that served the cities of Philadelphia, Pennsylvania, and Camden, New Jersey, from 1973 through 1980. Water depths at the DuPont Acid Wastes Dumpsite range from 45 m to 55 m; the site overlies a primarily sandy bottom with a ridge and swale topography.

Wastes were disposed of at this site periodically from November 1968 through March 1977 by a single permittee, the Edge Moor, Delaware, facility of E. I. DuPont de Nemours and Co. Prior to process changes that were begun in the early 1970s, the wastes were produced as byproducts of a sulfate-refining process. By 1976, conversion to a chloride process was complete. In addition to large amounts of Fe, the

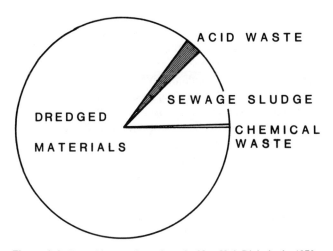

Figure 8.4. Barged inputs of metals to the New York Bight in the 1970s. Percent input by source for the combined total loadings of six metals (Cd, Cr, Cu, Hg, Pb, and Zn) in each waste type. Adapted from Mueller et al. (1976).

wastes contained other metals, especially V and Ti (Lear et al., 1982). Quantities of DuPont wastes dumped at the site varied between 250,000 t y^{-1} and 750,000 t y^{-1} (Fig. 8.3). Dumping at the DuPont site ceased when the company relocated its disposal activities to the Deepwater Industrial Waste Dumpsite.

8.3.3. Deepwater Industrial Waste Dumpsite

This site is located on the continental slope and rise, 196 km southeast of Ambrose Light, New York, and 233 km east of Cape May, New Jersey. Water depths range from 2250 m to 2750 m and overlie a mostly silty, partially sandy bottom. The site has been used for controlled disposal of toxic wastes since 1972, and was used for dumping of munitions and radioactive wastes prior to that (U.S. EPA, 1984a). The Deepwater Industrial Waste Dumpsite is located within the previously interim-designated 2500-km^2 DWD-106. The U.S. EPA (1984b) has issued a final designation of the site for industrial wastes. (A second site, the Deepwater Municipal Sludge Site, has also been designated within the DWD-106 boundaries.)

Wastes dumped at the Deepwater Industrial Waste Dumpsite have been produced primarily by three companies: DuPont Edge Moor, DuPont-Grasselli, and American Cyanamid (located in Linden, New Jersey). Acid-iron wastes were first dumped at this dumpsite in 1977, when the DuPont Edge Moor plant began disposal operations there. Volumes of acid-iron wastes dumped from 1977 to 1983 ranged from 379,000 t in 1977 to 93,000 t in 1983 (Fig. 8.3).

Along with converting to a chloride process, DuPont has sought to market ferric chloride waste as a flocculant and to recycle the acid. By 1980, DuPont had developed a recycling program that significantly reduced ocean disposal (U.S. EPA, 1984c). The low volume of waste dumped in 1981 (Fig. 8.3) indicates success in marketing the iron chloride waste (O'Connor, 1983). As of mid-1987, however, DuPont Edge Moor wastes were still being dumped at sea.

Extensive studies have been made of the physical and biological oceanography of the Deepwater Industrial Waste Dumpsite as well as of observed or potential effects of wastes dumped there (U.S. National Oceanic and Atmospheric Administration, 1981; Pearce et al., 1983). The area is physically dynamic and well flushed. The average residence time for wastes at the site is less than one week (O'Connor and Park,

1982). Wastes are unlikely to reach the bottom in any quantities near the site because of the great depth. Seasonal and permanent thermoclines limit vertical mixing of the wastes. Horizontal dispersion, however, is considered to be extensive (Pearce et al., 1983).

8.4. PERMITTING AND REGULATION OF DISPOSAL IN U.S. WATERS

Prior to 1973, the U.S. Army Corps of Engineers was responsible for authorizing the disposal of titanium dioxide wastes in the Middle Atlantic Bight. Following enactment of the Marine Protection, Research and Sanctuaries Act of 1972 (MPRSA), responsibility was assumed by the EPA. Environmental guidelines for ocean dumping were established by this act, and the EPA was empowered to develop and apply criteria for evaluating dumping permit applications.

Final regulations and criteria for ocean dumping of titanium dioxide wastes were promulgated in January 1977 (U.S. EPA, 1977). Concern over effects of titanium dioxide wastes have focused on the following problems: acidity and metal content of the wastes, the potential for mutagenicity and for anoxia, and possible impacts on fish and coastal beaches. All of these potential problems served as the motivation for regulations outlined in the final revision of the MPRSA (U.S. EPA, 1977). These dumping regulations provide for issuance of temporary dumping permits when human health and the environment will not be unreasonably endangered, with the eventual goal of terminating ocean dumping. The regulations governing dumping further dictate that it be done in a manner that minimizes impacts.

These disposal regulations (U.S. EPA, 1977) stipulate what changes in receiving waters are permissible following dumping. If disposal of wastes cannot be done in such a way as to meet these criteria, dumping is prohibited. Certain substances cannot be dumped at all unless they are present in wastes only as trace constituents. This prohibition applies to Cd and Hg, and to known carcinogens, mutagens, or teratogens. Nor can wastes be dumped into the ocean if they present serious hazards to fishing, navigation, shorelines, or beaches. Certain limited changes in receiving waters are permissible, however. For example, after a dumping operation, total acidity of dumpsite waters cannot change by more than 10%, after allowing for initial mixing. (Initial mixing is defined as a 4-h period following a dumping operation.) Dissolved oxygen (DO) levels are not allowed to drop more than 25% below normal after initial mixing.

It is further stipulated that wastes must be disposed of at a rate that does not exceed the limiting permissible concentrations for the waste constituents. Dumping protocols for titanium dioxide wastes have required disposal rates of 378,500 liter min^{-1} or less, and generally have resulted in waste dilutions of at least 1:90,000 4 h after waste release (U.S. EPA, 1980a).

8.5. EFFECTS OF TITANIUM DIOXIDE WASTES UPON THE ENVIRONMENT

The significance and extent of the adverse environmental effects of titanium dioxide wastes have been debated extensively (e.g., Rose, 1981; Pickaver, 1982). One principal concern is that the acid wastes may introduce heavy metals, such as Cd and Cu, in an uncomplexed, free ionic form, a form known to be most toxic to marine organisms (Engel et al., 1981). If the waste discharge were adequately regulated, however, the low pH of the wastes would be buffered by the receiving water, and the metal ions could complex with organic materials, sorb onto suspended particulate material, or flocculate with $Fe(OH)_3$ from the iron-rich wastes. At a minimum, it is clear that the wastes modify receiving waters, at least temporarily, and influence some resident organisms. The U.S. EPA (1980a) has not been able to demonstrate any unreasonable effects of the wastes, however.

8.5.1. Chemical Effects

Two chemical changes occur upon mixing of acid-iron wastes and seawater: declines in ambient DO levels and declines in pH. The decline in DO levels results from the rapid conversion of ferrous iron (contained in the liquid waste) to ferric iron. The amount of oxygen required for conversion is small relative to the normal amount available in the water column and is therefore not likely to cause a problem (Vaccaro et al., 1972). If ferrous iron should reach the sediments, however, and conversion were to take place there, the potential would exist for a large relative decline in DO for bottom waters with low levels of oxygen.

Conversion from ferrous to ferric iron results in hydrous ferric oxide flakes that form visible and persistent flocculent clouds in the water. Other metals and organic substances from the waste and from seawater appear to be sorbed onto this particulate material and disperse with it (Kester et al., 1981).

Iron can be used as a tracer for the waste and also to estimate mixing and dilution in the wake of a discharge (Fig. 8.5).

The decline in pH immediately following dumping can be substantial for short periods of time. The pH of oceanic waters ranges between 7.2 and 8.5, whereas the pH of wastes may be ~0.01 (Kester et al., 1981). Ketchum and Ford (1952) measured a pH of 3 in surface waters immediately following dumping, but <5 min after passage of the barge the pH returned nearly to its original value. Substantial changes have been found in pH following discharges at the DuPont Dumpsite (M. Champ, personal communication). Under protocols stipulated by dumping regulations (U.S. EPA, 1977), however, the U.S. EPA (1980a) only occasionally found pH changes in the wake of barges. Observed pH depressions rarely exceeded 0.2 pH unit below ambient after initial mixing, largely because of the high buffering capacity of seawater. It is clear that even when pH declines markedly following dumping, it returns to ambient levels quickly if discharge is sufficiently slow (e.g., 378,500 liter min^{-1} or less, as stipulated in EPA permits).

8.5.2. Physical Effects

Wastes entering the marine environment are dispersed by local winds, waves, and currents. Depending upon their nature, wastes may be dispersed over great distances. Much of the suspended particulate floc resulting from acid-iron waste disposal is transported extensively before reaching the bottom. Thermoclines can act as partial barriers to the wastes (which are slightly denser than seawater), thereby reducing the rate at which waste components reach the bottom (Vaccaro et al., 1972).

An August 1977 study of dispersion of wastes from NL Industries at the NYB Dumpsite showed that mixing was dominated by barge-generated turbulence during the first 15 min, and subsequently by meteorologic and oceanographic conditions (EG&G, 1977). Vertical mixing was limited by a seasonal thermocline, but horizontal dispersion was extensive and rapid. Four hours after the dumping operation, waste concentrations in the plume were diluted by a factor of 90,000 (Fig. 8.5), and the waste plume was 2 km wide.

Acid waste plumes are visible for long periods of time following a dumping operation (Fig. 8.6). Using satellite photographs and other remote-sensing techniques, Klemas and Philpot (1981) followed the surface drift of wastes from 16 dumping operations at the DuPont Dumpsite between October 1972 and March 1976. They found that direction of transport depends upon season, and that average drift of the plumes was 0.59 km h^{-1}. When the seasonal thermocline was present, the plume tended to be confined above it. In its absence, vertical mixing was more extensive.

Kester et al. (1981) studied mixing of wastes for 30 h following dumping of acid-iron wastes at the Deepwater Industrial Waste Dumpsite. Dilution appeared to be a two-stage process: rapid initial mixing to a dilution of 10^4 (1:10,000) during the first half hour, followed by dilution to 10^5 (1:100,000) by 27 h. This dilution pattern is similar to that at the NYB Dumpsite (EG&G, 1977; Fig. 8.5). The two processes that appeared to control distribution of the wastes were dilution with seawater and settling of particles (Kester et al., 1981). Metals, such as Cd and Cu, that remained primarily in the dissolved phase were most affected by dilution; whereas, those associated with particulate material, such as Fe and Pb, were affected both by dilution and by settling at the Deepwater Industrial Waste Dumpsite.

In shallower waters, particulate material is more likely to reach the bottom near a dumpsite. Harris and Waschitz (1982) studied the distribution of metals in sediments in the New

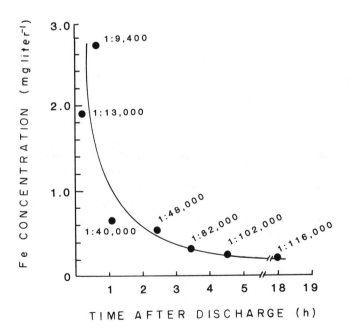

Figure 8.5. Dilution of acid-iron wastes in a plume, using Fe concentrations as a tracer. Equivalent dilutions (V = V) are presented adjacent to data points. Adapted from EG&G (1977).

Figure 8.6. Aerial photograph of an acid waste dump in progress. A signature of a previous dump (10–15 h old) is visible in the upper portion of the figure.

York Bight apex. Using patterns of metal ratios, they deduced the origin and direction of transport of individual metals. Acid-iron wastes contain substantial amounts of Ti; e.g., wastes from NL Industries contain 1.5–2.0 g Ti liter^{-1} waste (U.S. EPA, 1980a). Thus, high levels of Ti were proposed as a tracer for acid-iron wastes. Harris and Waschitz (1982) found that Ti was very widely distributed throughout the bight apex, with highest concentrations in sediments from the vicinity of the NYB Dumpsite. This distribution suggests extensive mixing and transport of dumped wastes within the bight apex.

Biscaye and Olsen (1976) also found evidence for extensive mixing and distribution of particulate material in the New York Bight apex. They found that Fe and, frequently, Ti coat much of the suspended matter in the apex, and that discrete titanium dioxide particles also occur throughout the bight apex. The abundance of both of these materials in the water column decreases with increasing distance from the apex.

Pesch et al. (1977) found elevated concentrations of certain metals in sea scallops (*Placopecten magellanicus*) from the vicinity of the DuPont Dumpsite. The metals they chose as indicators of acid wastes were Fe, Mg, Ti, and V. These metals entered the region in substantial quantities only via waste inputs. The pattern of metal concentrations in scallops up to 25 km south of the dumpsite suggests substantial waste dispersal by the prevailing southerly currents. Mean concentrations of V in scallops south of the dumpsite ranged from 31.3 to 45.7 μg g^{-1} dry wt, whereas concentrations north and east of the dumpsite ranged from 11.4 to 24.4 μg g^{-1} dry wt (Pesch et al., 1977).

8.5.3. Biological Effects

8.5.3a. Phytoplankton

Studies of the effects of pollutants upon phytoplankton communities are complicated by the patchy manner in which individuals and species are distributed. Vaccaro et al. (1972) measured chlorophyll *a* distributions in the vicinity of the NYB Dumpsite and found no distributional patterns that they associated with acid-iron waste dumping.

Laboratory studies have shown clear responses of phytoplankton to industrial wastes, including acid-iron wastes. Murphy et al. (1983) found that growth rates of four clones of the diatom *Thalassiosira pseudonana* were slightly enhanced (relative to controls) in concentrations of 100 mg liter^{-1} waste from DuPont Edge Moor, but growth rates were significantly depressed in waste concentrations of 1000 mg liter^{-1}. O'Connor (1983) has reviewed studies of waste dispersion at the Deepwater Industrial Waste Dumpsite, none of which estimated concentrations of wastes in the plume to be higher than 20 mg liter^{-1} 10 h after a dumping operation. On the basis of this dilution and from results of laboratory toxicity tests, O'Connor (1983) has suggested that wastes dumped at the Deepwater Industrial Waste Dumpsite have not affected phytoplankton. He noted that the absence of observed effects may be attributable to low rates of waste input relative to flushing rates, which would prevent waste concentrations from reaching levels that affect organisms.

8.5.3b. Zooplankton

Vaccaro et al. (1972) found the average zooplankton abundance near the NYB Dumpsite to be 30% lower than at nearby control stations. They attributed this pattern to transitory, large-scale patchiness typical of plankton populations rather than to the effects of acid-iron wastes. Wiebe et al. (1973) also studied the distribution and abundance of zooplankton species at the NYB Dumpsite and at a nearby control site, and reached a similar conclusion. Most species were markedly aggregated, but did not follow any pattern that suggested a response to acid-iron wastes. To supplement field studies, Grice et al. (1973) conducted laboratory experiments on copepod species that occur in the vicinity of the NYB Dumpsite. Copepods were exposed to various waste concentrations in long-term and short-term experiments. Copepods also were transferred through a series of increasing dilutions of acid wastes to simulate declining waste concentrations in the wake of a discharge. No mortality was observed in the latter simulation. In long-term exposures (18 d) to acid wastes, mortality and inhibition of reproduction occurred only when waste concentrations were significantly higher for longer periods of time than those found at the dumpsite.

Grice et al. (1973) also investigated whether titanium dioxide wastes are toxic to copepods because of their acidity

or because of some other toxic component. They found that copepods maintained in buffered acid wastes showed no mortality, but those cultured in water containing sulfuric acid instead of acid wastes showed high mortality at high concentrations (pH 5.5 or less). They concluded that the pH of acid wastes may be the primary cause of mortality in laboratory studies.

Capuzzo and Lancaster (1985) exposed three species of copepods for 96 h to wastes from DuPont Edge Moor and found that in concentrations >5 mg liter^{-1}, 15–30% died (depending both on temperature and species). At concentrations of 100 mg liter^{-1}, 45–65% died, and at 1000 mg liter^{-1} essentially all died. The 96-h LC$_{50}$ (LC$_{50}$ is the lethal concentration at which 50% of the test organisms die) values at 10°C ranged from 104 mg liter^{-1} (for *Centropages typicus*) to 171 mg liter^{-1} (for *Acartia*); at 20°C, LC$_{50}$ values ranged from 91 mg liter^{-1} (for *Pseudocalanus*) to 97 mg liter^{-1} (for *Centropages*).

Capuzzo and Lancaster (1985) also found that 96-h exposures of *Centropages* and *Pseudocalanus* to waste from DuPont Edge Moor at 10 mg liter^{-1} caused egg production rates to decline to 55% and 64% of control values, respectively. During the week following exposure, neither species produced eggs, and high mortality occurred relative to control groups. Energy budgets from *Centropages* and *Pseudocalanus*, developed in association with the laboratory waste exposures, suggested that exposure to waste from DuPont Edge Moor at 10 mg liter^{-1} reduced scope for growth for both species by ~55%. Because concentrations in the waste plume normally are on the order of 10 mg liter^{-1} for several hours, such effects might be realized at the dumpsite.

The acute toxicity of acid-iron wastes to the copepod *Acartia tonsa* was also investigated by C. Rose (personal communication). Animals were exposed both to filtered wastes and to unfiltered wastes that contained hydrous ferric oxide floc. Interestingly, 96-h LC$_{50}$ results were consistently higher in floc-containing medium than in filtered medium (e.g., 220 mg liter^{-1} versus 150 mg liter^{-1} waste, respectively, at 20°C). Thus, toxicity of the wastes was lower when unfiltered. This may have resulted from scavenging of metals by particulate flocs, which might have rendered certain metals biologically unavailable to the test organisms, even if consumed.

Capuzzo (1983) investigated the extent to which copepods accumulated metals contained in waste from DuPont Edge Moor. Copepods in the laboratory actively ingested particulate material from the waste, and levels of trace metals in the copepods exposed to wastes were 10–55% above control levels at the end of the exposure period. Fecal pellets also contained high concentrations of metals. With the exception of Cd, most metals taken up from the waste were effectively depurated through defecation. Because fecal pellets sink more rapidly than the waste floc, ingestion and defecation by copepods may accelerate the transport of waste materials out of the surface mixed layer.

8.5.3c. Fish

Members of the commercial and recreational fishing industries have registered their concern over effects of acid-iron waste floc on fishing at the NYB Dumpsite (U.S. EPA, 1982). In particular, some have suggested that fish tend to avoid areas containing clouds of particulate material. No studies of the behavioral response of fish to acid waste flocs have been done to substantiate this; however, there have been studies of physiological responses of fish to acid wastes. O'Connor (1983) has summarized EG&G's laboratory studies of responses of sheepshead minnow (*Cyprinodon variegatus*) to wastes dumped at the Deepwater Dumpsite. Exposure to 100 mg liter^{-1} or less of wastes from DuPont Edge Moor did not result in changes in hatching success, growth, or survival, but it did result in depressed egg production. Concentrations of 200 mg liter^{-1}, however, produced significant fry mortality and decreased hatching success.

Longwell (1981) collected eggs from the Deepwater Dumpsite and from nearby control sites, and found a higher percentage of cytologically damaged fish eggs in an acid-iron plume. She stated, however, that the numbers of eggs collected were low, and that the data should be considered only suggestive of possible adverse effects.

There has been much study in Europe of the potential responses of fishes to titanium dioxide wastes. For example, epidermal papillomas and other diseases occur with much higher frequency in dab (*Limanda limanda*) and other species in the vicinity of acid waste and sewage-sludge dumpsites in the German Bight (Dethlefsen and Watermann, 1980). Flounder (*Platichthys flesus*) caged in the vicinity of an acid waste outfall in the Humber estuary (England) suffered increased mortality with increased proximity to the effluent pipe (Wilson and White, 1974). In a Finnish study, Lehtinen (1980) found that perch (*Perca fluviatilis*) exposed to titanium dioxide waste in the laboratory manifest clear signs of stress (e.g., impaired swimming ability and brown precipitate on the gills) that were correlated with waste concentration. In another laboratory study, flounder (*Platichthys flesus*) showed changes in ion balance, carbohydrate metabolism, and blood chemistry in association with exposure to titanium dioxide wastes (Larsson et al., 1980). Gills of these fish became coated with a brown precipitate that consisted mainly of an iron–titanium complex. Larsson et al. (1980) speculated that the physiological changes resulted either from gill impairment (from the physical presence of the precipitate) or from a biochemical response to the toxic metals associated with the precipitate. Similar precipitates also have been found on gill epithelia of fish collected from the vicinity of Finnish dumping grounds for titanium dioxide waste (Lehtinen, 1980).

8.5.3d. Benthos

Studies of the impacts of acid wastes on benthos have been largely inconclusive. At the NYB Dumpsite, Vaccaro et al. (1972) found fewer benthic animals at the dumpsite than at a nearby control site, but neither biomass nor species diversity differed significantly between the two sites. The authors did not believe that acid waste dumping had altered the benthos. Studies of the benthos underlying the Deepwater Dumpsite have not shown any detectable impacts of dumping (Steimle and McNulty, 1983).

Kapp (1980) found high percentages of recently dead ocean quahogs (*Arctica islandica*) in the vicinity of two oceanic dumpsites (acid wastes and sewage sludge) off the Maryland–Delaware border. Although data were limited, it was suggested that dumping had caused the mortalities. Thompson and Psuty (1984) further investigated the connection between ocean dumping and ocean quahog mortality, and tentatively concluded that dumping was unlikely to have killed the organisms; however, data were too sparse to be definitive.

8.6. CONCLUSIONS

In the Middle Atlantic Bight, the dumping of titanium dioxide wastes, now reduced in volume, has not caused measurable significant harm to the resident biota. There is no evidence of extensive impacts upon the biota at the NYB Dumpsite, which has received the greatest volume of wastes of the three U.S. dumpsites. Laboratory studies and some field studies in the United States and Europe have suggested that the wastes can affect resident organisms, but these adverse effects have been observed under conditions different from those predominating in the Middle Atlantic Bight. In laboratory studies, for example, effects have been detected at concentrations much higher than those encountered in the field, or those detected near discharge pipes or in restricted coastal areas. The EPA regulations governing discharge of acid-iron wastes in the Middle Atlantic Bight appear to have been effective at maintaining contaminant additions at or below acceptable or safe limits.

For the NYB Dumpsite, it is possible, however, that some effects of acid-iron waste disposal have been masked by the effects of other anthropogenic inputs. Contaminant loadings from acid-iron wastes have been small relative to contributions from Hudson–Raritan Estuary outflow and from barged disposal of dredged materials and sewage sludge. The bight is a physically dynamic region, and mixing of wastes is extensive. It is unlikely that slight ecological changes caused by this minor waste source could be detected in the face of natural variability of concomitant effects of other sources.

Laboratory studies related to the effects of waste disposal at the Deepwater Dumpsite have shown that, at certain levels of exposure, acid-iron wastes can have an adverse impact upon some pelagic biota. However, effects have not been detected at the community level (given natural variability in resident populations) at the volumes of wastes dumped to date. Rapid dilution and dispersion of wastes probably have minimized potential effects.

That significant adverse effects of titanium dioxide wastes have not been observed is attributable, at least in part, to the relatively low volumes dumped and to the well-flushed nature of the disposal sites. Were either of these two variables to differ, the probability of biota being affected could change considerably. This projection is supported by the presence of biotically degraded areas around pipes that discharge acid-iron waste where dilution generally is less rapid than with barge disposal. Surrounding a titanium dioxide waste-effluent pipe in Finland there is a degraded area ~2 km in diameter; a correlation exists between distance from the discharge pipe and number and biomass of benthic fauna (Lehtonen, 1975). Only a limited comparison can be made between conditions in Finland and in the Middle Atlantic Bight, however, since waters surrounding the Finnish discharge pipe are less saline and less capable of buffering the acid relative to the higher salinity oceanic waters.

Large amounts of acid-iron wastes are unlikely to be disposed at sea in the future, because recycling and marketing of wastes have greatly reduced the volume generated. Unfortunately, such acceptable alternatives do not exist for many of the other materials disposed into the ocean.

ACKNOWLEDGMENTS

The authors thank Michael Champ for supplying information on his work at the DuPont site, and for providing many papers on disposal in European waters. The late Peter Anderson kindly provided information on disposal in the New York Bight, as did Frank Csulak, and Curt Rose shared some of his unpublished data. We also thank Joel O'Connor for reviewing the manuscript.

REFERENCES

Biscaye, P. E., and C. R. Olsen. 1976. Suspended particulate concentrations and compositions in the New York Bight. *American Society of Limnology and Oceanography Special Symposium*, **2**, 124–137.

Capuzzo, J. M. 1983. The role of zooplankton in the accumulation and deposition of DuPont Edge Moor waste (an acid-iron waste) at a deepwater dumpsite in the northwest Atlantic. *Canadian Journal of Fisheries and Aquatic Science*, **40(2)**, 242–247.

Capuzzo, J. M., and B. A. Lancaster. 1985. Zooplankton population responses to industrial wastes discharged at Deepwater Dumpsite-106. *In*: Wastes in the Ocean, Vol. 5: Deep-Sea Waste Disposal, D. R. Kester, W. V. Burt, J. M. Capuzzo, P. K. Park, B. H. Ketchum, and I. W. Duedall (Eds.). Wiley-Interscience, New York, pp. 209–226.

Dethlefsen, V., and B. Watermann. 1980. Epidermal papilloma of North Sea dab (*Limanda limanda*); histology, epidemiology and relation to dumping of wastes from TiO$_2$ industry. Paper No. 8. *In*: International Council for the Exploration of the Sea, Special Meeting on Diseases of Commercially Important Marine Fish and Shellfish. pp. 1–30.

EG&G. 1977. Dispersion in Waters of the New York Bight Acid Dump Grounds of Acid-Iron Wastes Discharged from a Towed Barge. Prepared by EG&G, Environmental Consultants, Waltham, Massachusetts. Submitted to Environmental Control Department, NL Industries, Sayreville, New Jersey, 81 pp. + appendix.

Engel, D. W., W. G. Sunda, and B. A. Fowler. 1981. Factors affecting trace metal uptake and toxicity to estuarine organisms. I. Environmental parameters. *In*: Biological Monitoring of Marine Pollutants, F. J. Vernberg, A. Calabrese, F. P. Thurberg, and W. B. Vernberg (Eds.). Academic Press, New York, pp. 127–144.

Fuller, R. H. 1981. Titanium. *Mining Annual Review*, 64–67.

Grice, G. D., P. H. Wiebe, and E. Hoagland. 1973. Acid-iron waste as a factor affecting the distribution and abundance of zooplankton in the New York Bight. I. Laboratory studies on the effects of acid waste on copepods. *Estuarine and Coastal Marine Science*, **1**, 45–50.

Harris, W. H., and M. Waschitz. 1982. Bulk organic geochemistry and trace metals in sewage-derived bottom sediments from the New York Bight apex. *Northeastern Environmental Science*, **1**, 19–32.

Kapp, R. H. 1980. Distribution of Recent Mortalities of the Ocean Quahog, *Arctica islandica*, at Two Middle Atlantic Ocean Dumpsites. Master's Thesis, The American University, Washington, D.C., 43 pp.

Kester, D. R., R. C. Hittinger, and P. Mukherji. 1981. Transition and heavy metals associated with acid-iron waste disposal at Deep Water Dumpsite 106. *In*: Ocean Dumping of Industrial Wastes, B. H. Ketchum, D. R. Kester, and P. K. Park (Eds.). Plenum Press, New York, pp. 215–232.

Ketchum, B. H., and W. L. Ford. 1952. Rate of dispersion in the wake of a barge at sea. *Transactions of the American Geophysical Union*, **33**, 680–684.

Klemas, V., and W. D. Philpot. 1981. Remote sensing of ocean-dumped waste drift and dispersion. *In*: Ocean Dumping of Industrial Wastes, B. H. Ketchum, D. R. Kester, and P. K. Park (Eds.). Plenum Press, New York, pp. 193–211.

Larsson, A., K.-J. Lehtinen, and C. Haux. 1980. Biochemical and hematological effects of a titanium dioxide industrial effluent on fish. *Bulletin of Environmental Contamination and Toxicology*, **25**, 427–435.

Lear, D. W., M. L. O'Malley, W. C. Muir, and G. Pence. 1982. Environmental effects of sewage sludge at the Philadelphia Dumping Site. *In*: Ecological Stress and the New York Bight: Science and Management, G. F. Mayer (Ed.). Estuarine Research Federation, Columbia, South Carolina, pp. 481–493.

Lehtinen, K.-J. 1980. Effects on fish exposed to effluent from a titanium dioxide industry and tested with rotary-flow technique. *Ambio*, **1**, 31–33.

Lehtonen, H. 1975. The biological effects of the titanium dioxide industry in Finland. International Council for the Exploration of the Sea. CM 1975/ E:26, pp. 1–7.

Longwell, A. C. 1981. Cytological examination of fish eggs collected at and near 106-Mile Site. *In*: Assessment Report on the Effects of Waste Dumping in 106-Mile Ocean Waste Disposal Site: Dumpsite Evaluation Report 81-1. U.S. National Oceanic and Atmospheric Administration, Boulder, Colorado, pp. 257–276.

Mueller, J. A., J. S. Jeris, A. R. Anderson, and C. F. Hughes. 1976. Contaminant Inputs to the New York Bight. Technical memorandum, U.S. National Oceanic and Atmospheric Administration, Boulder, Colorado, 347 pp.

Muir, W. C. 1983. History of ocean disposal in the Mid-Atlantic Bight. *In*: Wastes in the Ocean, Vol. 1: Industrial and Sewage Wastes in the Ocean, I. W. Duedall, B. H. Ketchum, P. K. Park, D. R. Kester (Eds.). Wiley-Interscience, New York, pp. 273–291.

Murphy, L. S., E. M. Haugen, and J. F. Brown. 1983. Phytoplankton: Comparison of laboratory bioassay and field measurements. *In*: Wastes in the Ocean, Vol. 1: Industrial and Sewage Wastes in the Ocean, I. W. Duedall, B. H. Ketchum, P. K. Park, and D. R. Kester (Eds.). Wiley-Interscience, New York, pp. 219–233.

O'Connor, T. P. 1983. Contaminant inputs, fate and effects. *In*: Northeast Monitoring Program 106-Mile Site Characterization Update, J. B. Pearce, D. C. Miller, and C. Berman (Eds.). Technical memorandum NMFS-F/NEC-26, U.S. National Oceanic and Atmospheric Administration, Woods Hole, Massachusetts, pp. 12-1–12-61.

O'Connor, T. P., and P. K. Park. 1982. Consequences of industrial waste disposal at the 106-mile ocean waste disposal site. *In*: Ecological Stress and the New York Bight: Science and Management, G. F. Mayer (Ed.). Estuarine Research Federation, Columbia, South Carolina, pp. 675–697.

Pearce, J. B., D. C. Miller, and C. Berman, Eds. 1983. Northeast Monitoring Program 106-Mile Site Characterization Update. Technical memorandum NMFS-F/NEC-26, U.S. National Oceanic and Atmospheric Administration, Woods Hole, Massachusetts, 12 sections (paginated separately).

Pesch, G., B. Reynolds, and P. Rogerson. 1977. Trace metals in scallops from within and around two ocean disposal sites. *Marine Pollution Bulletin*, **8**, 224–228.

Pickaver, A. H. 1982. Titanium dioxide waste dumping at sea. Time to call a halt. *Marine Pollution Bulletin*, **13**, 375–379.

Rose, C. D. 1981. Review of the Biological Effects of Acid-Iron Waste Disposal in Marine Waters off the United States and Germany. Prepared by Energy Resources Co. Inc., Cambridge, Massachusetts. Submitted to Environmental Control Department, NL Industries, Sayreville, New Jersey, 47 pp. + appendixes.

Steimle, F. W., and J. K. McNulty. 1983. Benthic fauna. *In*: Northeast Monitoring Program 106-Mile Site Characterization Update, J. B. Pearce, D. C. Miller, and C. Berman (Eds.). Technical memorandum NMFS-F/NEC-26, U.S. National Oceanic and Atmospheric Administration, Woods Hole, Massachusetts, pp. 8-1–8-27.

Thompson, I., and N. P. Psuty. 1984. Growth of the Ocean Quahog, *Arctica islandica*, in the Area of the Philadelphia Dumpsites. Prepared by Center for Coastal and Environmental Studies, Rutgers University, New Brunswick, New Jersey. Submitted to U.S. National Oceanic and Atmospheric Administration, Rockville, Maryland, 27 pp.

U.S. Environmental Protection Agency (EPA). 1977. Ocean Dumping: Final Revision of Regulations and Criteria. *Federal Register* (11 January), **42**, 2462–2490.

U.S. EPA. 1980a. Final Environmental Impact Statement (EIS) for New York Bight Acid Waste Disposal Site Designation. Contract 68-01-4610, Marine Protection Branch, Washington, D.C., 6 sections (paginated separately) + appendixes.

U.S. EPA. 1980b. Annual Report to Congress January–December 1980. Office of Water and Waste Management, Washington, D.C., 33 pp.

U.S. EPA. 1982. Basis for Final Determination, Ocean Dumping Permit Application, NL Industries, Inc., Region II, New York, 19 pp.

U.S. EPA. 1984a. Report to Congress January 1981–December 1983. Office of Water Regulations and Standards, Washington, D.C., 35 pp.

U.S. EPA. 1984b. Ocean Dumping: Final Designation of Site. 40CFR Part 228, Washington, D.C., 37 pp.

U.S. EPA. 1984c. Ocean Dumping Permit Program, Public Announcement of Complete Application and Scheduling of Public Hearing. Public Notice No. 84-16, Region II, New York, 6 pp.

U.S. National Oceanic and Atmospheric Administration. 1981. Assessment Report on the Effects of Waste Dumping in 106-Mile Ocean Waste Disposal Site: Dumpsite Evaluation Report 81-1. Office of Marine Pollution Assessment, Boulder, Colorado, 319 pp.

Vaccaro, R. F., G. D. Grice, G. T. Rowe, and P. H. Wiebe. 1972. Acid-iron waste disposal and the summer distribution of standing crops in the New York Bight. *Water Research*, **6**, 231–256.

Wiebe, P. H., G. D. Grice, and E. Hoagland. 1973. Acid-iron waste as a factor affecting the distribution and abundance of zooplankton in the New York Bight. II. Spatial variations in the field and implications for monitoring studies. *Estuarine and Coastal Marine Science*, **1**, 51–64.

Wilson, K. W., and I. C. White. 1974. A review of the biological effects of acid-iron wastes from titanium dioxide production in the United Kingdom. International Council for the Exploration of the Sea, C. M. 1974/ E:40 5 pp.

Chapter 9

Modeling Oxygen Depletion in the New York Bight: The Water Quality Impact of a Potential Increase of Waste Inputs

Andrew Stoddard

Science Applications International Corporation
McLean, Virginia

John J. Walsh

Department of Marine Science
University of South Florida
St. Petersburg, Florida

Abstract   91
9.1. Introduction   92
9.2. Methods   93
   9.2.1. State Variables   93
   9.2.2. Forcing Functions   94
   9.2.3. Boundary Conditions and Assumptions   94
9.3. Results   95
   9.3.1. Nitrogen   95
   9.3.2. Carbon   96
   9.3.3. Phytoplankton   97
   9.3.4. Dissolved Oxygen   98
9.4. Discussion   99
9.5. Summary and Conclusions   100
Acknowledgments   101
References   101

ABSTRACT

A two-layered ecosystem model of the New York Bight Apex, developed to analyze the causes of the anoxic episode in 1976, is used to compare the potential impact on water quality of a tenfold increase in carbon and nitrogen waste inputs to the apex ocean dumpsites during summer with the impact under existing waste loads. Distributions of nitrogen, chlorophyll, particulate organic carbon (POC), light penetration, primary production, dissolved oxygen, and oxygen consumption in the water column from the model agreed with observations made during late summer within the apex in 1974 and 1979. The simulated tenfold increase in waste inputs resulted in subpycnocline anoxia and a reduction in primary productivity within a radius of 30 km of the apex ocean dumpsites and the Hudson River estuary. The simulated POC content of this numerical experiment is similar to observed estimates of POC within the apex and the New Jersey midshelf (80–125 g C m^{-2}) during the *Ceratium* bloom in June 1976. The simulation suggested that a detrital carbon loading to the apex water column of 50–100 g C m^{-2} would be sufficient to initiate anoxic events. This estimate is useful as a possible criterion for regulatory decision making regarding site designations for the disposal of wastes into the New York Bight.

9.1. INTRODUCTION

The increasing use of coastal waters for disposal of urban waste requires an understanding of the ecological impacts of nutrients, organic wastes, and toxic substances discharged into the ocean. Significant problems with water quality often occur as a result of changes in climatological conditions or circulation patterns, inputs of urban waste, or shifts in species composition of algae. During the summer, nearshore areas within the New York Bight have been subject to occasional episodes of oxygen depletion in bottom water that have resulted in localized fish kills (Swanson and Sindermann, 1979).

In the summer of 1976, however, mass mortalities of shellfish resulted from the onset of anoxic conditions over an 8600-km² area of the continental shelf off New Jersey (Fig. 9.1). Sewage sludge and other waste materials discharged into the apex of the New York Bight were initially thought to be responsible for the anoxia and the loss of commercially important shellfish (U.S. Court of Appeals, 1979). Subsequent investigations, however, demonstrated that this anoxic episode was related to the decomposition of a detrital carbon pool that resulted from the accumulation of a subsurface bloom of the slow-growing dinoflagellate *Ceratium tripos* (Falkowski and Howe, 1976; Malone et al., 1979; Swanson and Sindermann, 1979; Falkowski et al., 1980; Stoddard, 1983). In contrast to the biologically forced cross-shelf export of phytoplankton production via plankton food webs during summer, particulate carbon derived from *Ceratium* did not enter the pelagic food web because of the inability of the dominant herbivores to ingest this large organism. Coupled with anomalous onshore subsurface transport, *Ceratium* biomass was thus retained within the coastal shelf, where it settled and decomposed within the bottom layer (Malone et al., 1983; Malone, 1984).

Ocean dumping in the apex has been regulated since 1973 by the U.S. Environmental Protection Agency (EPA) under the authority of the Marine Protection, Research and Sanctuaries Act of 1972 (also known as the Ocean Dumping Act). During the past three decades, concern over the potential ecological effects of the disposal of wastes into the ocean has generated numerous research studies (e.g., Ketchum et al., 1951; Redfield and Walford, 1951; Ketchum et al., 1981; Mayer, 1982) and intense public controversy [e.g., U.S. Court of Appeals, 1979; U.S. National Advisory Committee on Oceans and Atmosphere (NACOA), 1981; U.S. EPA, 1985]. The cessation of ocean disposal of sewage sludge in the apex by 31 December 1981 was required by the EPA under

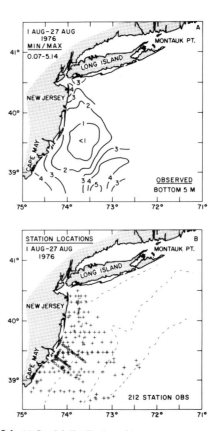

Figure 9.1. (a) Spatial distribution of bottom concentrations of dissolved oxygen (ml liter⁻¹) (0.07 ml liter⁻¹ minimum–5.14 ml liter⁻¹ maximum) within the New York Bight on 1–27 August 1976 and (b) 212 station locations occupied to obtain the data shown in Fig. 9.1a.

the 1977 amendments to the Ocean Dumping Act. This requirement was, however, successfully challenged by the City of New York, and the practice continues (Swanson and Devine, 1982).

With the renewed controversy over recent proposals by the EPA to shift ocean dumping of sewage sludge from 12-Mile Dumpsite in the apex to Deepwater Dumpsite-106, 106 miles (196 km) off the coast (Anon., 1984; U.S. EPA, 1985), a reevaluation of the assimilative capacity of the New York Bight Apex for anthropogenic waste loading is particularly significant. Preliminary estimates of the assimilative capacity for carbon loading (37 g C m⁻²) suggest that existing waste inputs of carbon and nitrogen could account for 10–25% of the loading capacity of the New York Bight with respect to oxygen depletion over the shelf (Goldberg, 1979).

Since the onset of the industrial revolution in about 1850, the nitrogen loading to the coastal zone has increased approximately tenfold as a result of deforestation, sewage disposal, and agricultural fertilizers (Walsh, 1984). If the present urban carbon and nitrogen loading to the New York Bight were increased tenfold and if the photosynthetic supply of oxygen were reduced even further by light limitation from increased turbidity within a stratified water column, then anoxic episodes could presumably occur more frequently in the New York Bight.

In this chapter, we evaluate the potential impact on water quality of a tenfold increase in carbon and nitrogen inputs to the apex with a two-layered, time-dependent ecosystem model of the New York Bight, which was originally developed for an analysis of the 1976 anoxic episode (Stoddard, 1983). The response of water quality in the apex during the summer to a further increase in loading of urban waste is first evaluated by comparison of model output with observed spatial distributions of nitrogen, chlorophyll, particulate organic carbon (POC), light penetration, primary production, dissolved oxygen, and oxygen consumption in the water column. The simulated distributions of these variables, calculated on the basis of inputs of urban waste, which were estimated in 1974 (Mueller et al., 1976) (base run), and a tenfold increase of carbon and nitrogen inputs (10×), are then discussed in relation to hypotheses concerning the impact of increased waste loading on eutrophication and oxygen depletion in the New York Bight (Garside et al., 1976; Malone, 1976; Segar and Berberian, 1976; Officer and Ryther, 1977; Garside and Malone, 1978; Walsh et al., 1981; Malone, 1984; Walsh, 1984).

9.2. METHODS

With a framework similar to other phytoplankton–nutrient–oxygen models (e.g., Walsh, 1975; DiToro and Connolly, 1980) involving numerical integration of non-linear, partial differential equations ($\Delta t = 0.5$ d), our model focuses on the period of the stratified conditions of the water column during May–October over a two-layered grid of the New York Bight from Montauk Point, Long Island, to Cape May, New Jersey (Fig. 9.2). Results presented in this chapter are only for the model segments in the bight apex. The theory, rationale, and documentation of all of the components of the model are presented elsewhere (Stoddard, 1983). The model assumptions that are most relevant to the determination of the assimilative capacity of the New York Bight Apex for carbon and nitrogen inputs are summarized in the following sections.

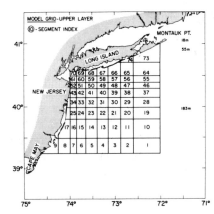

Figure 9.2. Spatial segmentation grid used in the New York Bight model. Numbers in the grid segments are identifying index numbers.

9.2.1. State Variables

The state variables of the model include dissolved nitrogen (ammonia and nitrate), dissolved organic carbon, and dissolved oxygen, as well as POC, phytoplankton, and zooplankton, above and beneath the pycnocline over the continental shelf of the New York Bight. Sources of ammonia nitrogen include remineralization of organic nitrogen, benthic regeneration of ammonia, waste inputs, and zooplankton excretion. Loss terms for nitrogen include nitrification and nutrient uptake by phytoplankton. The sinks of dissolved organic carbon and POC include consumption by bacterial decomposition and settling of POC. The sources of carbon include photosynthetic excretion of dissolved organic carbon (DOC) and loading from waste discharges. In the model, simulated POC is the sum of phytoplankton carbon and detrital sewage or sludge carbon.

Simulated interactions of the dissolved oxygen pool reflect oxidation of POC and DOC, nitrification, respiration of phytoplankton and zooplankton, seabed oxygen demand, atmospheric reaeration, and photosynthetic oxygen production. Photosynthesis is the source term for phytoplankton biomass, and the sink terms include respiration, grazing by zooplankton, settling, and excretion of DOC. The temperature-dependent growth rate of phytoplankton is regulated both by light and by nitrogen limitation with the extinction coefficient calculated as a function of total POC (Walsh and Howe, 1976).

9.2.2. Forcing Functions

Physical forcing functions in the model include water temperature, incident solar radiation and photoperiod, depth of the pycnocline, and seasonal stratification of the water column. The model also considers parameterization of advection and symmetrical dispersion processes both in the horizontal and in the vertical dimensions. A velocity field was obtained from a steady-state diagnostic model of circulation within the New York Bight (Han et al., 1979, 1980) with discharge from the Hudson River included as a boundary condition.

We used an 18–23 May 1976 circulation field (Fig. 9.3) under wind forcing from the west of 1.22 dynes cm^{-2} (Han et al., 1979) to explore the fate of particulate carbon within a "best case" flow regime (i.e., representative of those summer conditions when the Hudson River plume does not hug the New Jersey coast and residence times are ~5–10 d). For

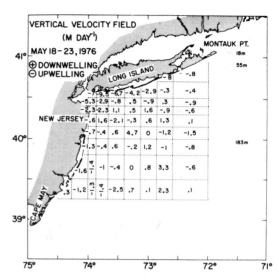

Figure 9.4. Verticle velocity field during 18–23 May 1976. Units are m d^{-1}; + indicates downwelling and − indicates upwelling.

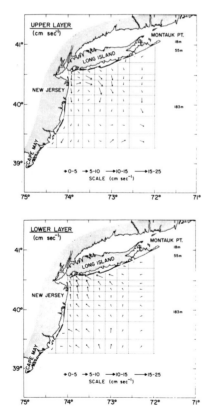

Figure 9.3. Circulation sub-model velocity field for (a) upper and (b) lower layer during 18–23 May 1976.

example, above the pycnocline, southerly flow (~10 cm s^{-1}) still defined the Hudson plume along the inner New Jersey coast, but southeasterly flow occurred off western Long Island. Within the Hudson Shelf Valley, an anti-cyclonic (clockwise) gyre was characterized by weaker flow of ~2–4 cm s^{-1}. Below the pycnocline, onshore flow was dominant with speeds of ~6–15 cm s^{-1} up the Hudson Shelf Valley toward the estuary. Such a two-layer transport regime was balanced by continuity to allow upwelling, which has been observed during the summer off New Jersey and Long Island (Walsh et al., 1978), over all but two of the apex segments (Fig. 9.4).

9.2.3. Boundary Conditions and Assumptions

With respect to initial and boundary conditions, the typical summer nanoplankton dominance of algal species (Malone, 1977) was assumed, with the netplankton (i.e., *Ceratium*) set to zero. Urban waste loading was first estimated from the "existing" (about 1974) discharges at the sewage sludge and dredged material dumpsites in the apex (80,000 kg N d^{-1}; 650,000 kg C d^{-1}) and from the coastal outfalls (Mueller et al., 1976). Simulation of increased wastewater inputs was then represented with a tenfold increment of (1) the boundary flux of both ammonia nitrogen and carbon of sewage or sludge origin across the Sandy Hook–Rockaway transect (Table 9.1), (2) existing loading at the apex dumpsites, and (3) existing loading from coastal sewage outfalls.

9.3. RESULTS

9.3.1. Nitrogen

The computed distribution of dissolved nitrogen for the base run was characterized by a decreasing seaward gradient over the Hudson Shelf Valley and within the coastal plume of the Hudson River off New Jersey (Fig. 9.5). Above the pycnocline, total inorganic nitrogen for the base run ranged from 1.7 to 7.9 µg-atoms N liter^{-1}, with ammonia accounting for 65–90% of the pool of inorganic nitrogen in the apex, similar to previous field observations (Malone, 1976) when ammonia accounted for as much as 60–80% of total inorganic nitrogen. Nitrogen in the upper layer of the model remained nonlimiting (>1 µg-atom N liter^{-1}) within 50–90 km of the Hudson River estuary, while below the pycnocline, base run nitrogen ranged from 4.3 to 12.5 µg-atoms N liter^{-1} within the apex.

A tenfold increase in ammonia nitrogen loading from the estuary (130,000 kg N d^{-1}) and the apex dumpsites (800,000 kg N d^{-1}) resulted in substantial increases of inorganic nitrogen content within the apex (Fig. 9.5). Very high gradients of total nitrogen were found near the Hudson estuary with maximum surface concentrations of 44 µg-atoms N liter^{-1}, decreasing to 4 µg-atoms N liter^{-1} within 60 km of the estuary, and remaining above 1 µg-atom N liter^{-1} for a radius of 100–200 km over the Long Island and New Jersey midshelf areas. Based on the second simulation experiment, the area bounded by the 1.0 µg-atom N liter^{-1} isopleth increased by a factor of ~2.5 over the areal extent of the base run. Assuming a constant relationship for nitrogen uptake and primary production, the model results are in agreement with the 3.2-fold increase in area of nonlimiting nitrogen growth of phytoplankton estimated to result from a tenfold increase in nitrogen inputs to the apex (Garside et al., 1976; Malone, 1976).

Table 9.1. Sandy Hook–Rockaway Transect Boundary Conditions

State Variable	Above Pycnocline		Below Pycnocline	
	Base Run	10×	Base Run	10×
Ammonia[a] (µg-atoms N liter^{-1})	5.0	50.0	5.0	50.0
Sewage carbon[a] (mg C liter^{-1})	0.5	5.0	0	0
Phytoplankton[a] (µg chl liter^{-1})	1.0	1.0	0.1	0.1
Nitrate[b,c] (µg-atoms N liter^{-1})	20.5, 25.5	20.5, 25.5	13.6, 14.6	13.6, 14.6
Oxygen[b,c] (ml O$_2$ liter^{-1})	4.7, 6.1	4.7, 6.1	4.9, 5.1	4.9, 5.1
Net transport[a] (m^3 s^{-1})	1500 (into apex)	1500	300 (into harbor)	300

[a]Segments 61, 70 (see Fig. 9.2).
[b]Segment 61.
[c]Segment 70.

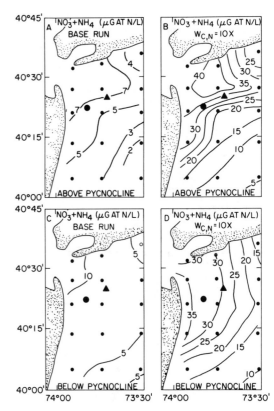

Figure 9.5. Spatial distribution during August of inorganic nitrogen (µg atom N liter^{-1}) above and below the pycnocline in the apex for (a) base run, (b) 10×, (c) base run, and (d) 10× cases. Circles indicate dredged material; triangles indicate sewage sludge.

9.3.2. Carbon

Base run distributions of POC above the pycnocline (Fig. 9.6) were characterized by maximum concentrations (0.75–1.0 mg C liter^{-1}) near the source terms of the estuary and the apex dumpsites in the model. Previous observations of total POC ranged from 1–2 mg C liter^{-1} within the upper 5 m near the dumpsites and 0.5–0.8 mg C liter^{-1} near the estuary compared to typical oceanic concentrations of 0.25 mg C liter^{-1} in the outer apex (Malone, 1976; Malone et al., 1985). Estuarine inputs and ocean dumping within the model resulted in concentrations in sewage of 0.5 mg C liter^{-1}, accounting for the maximum (60–80%) proportion of non-algal carbon in the base run POC pool near the apex dumpsites, similar to observed estimates in the same area of 56–86% during August 1974 (Malone, 1976).

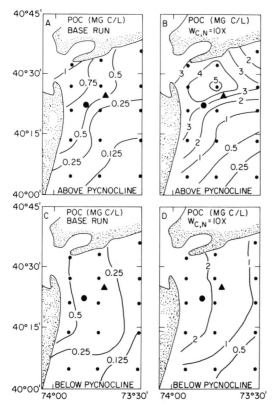

Figure 9.6. Spatial distribution during August of POC (mg liter^{-1}) above and below the pycnocline in the apex for (a) base run, (b) 10×, (c) base run, and (d) 10× cases. Circles indicate dredged material; triangles indicate sewage sludge.

Beneath the pycnocline, maximum base run concentrations of sewage carbon (0.28 mg C liter^{-1}) and total POC (0.54 mg C liter^{-1}) occurred within segments of the inner New Jersey coast south of the estuary. This distribution resulted from seaward transport in the surface layer, settling, and subsurface shoreward transport up the Hudson Shelf Valley toward the estuary. About 60–70% of the model's total POC content in the water column was below the pycnocline over the Hudson Shelf Valley, corresponding closely with observations (60–88%) in September 1969 (Corwin, 1970) and August–September 1976 (Thomas et al., 1979). Furthermore, on a depth-integrated basis, the simulated mean POC content (10.3 g C m^{-2}) of the base run over the whole apex matched the observed July–September POC range of 8–12 g C m^{-2} during 1969 (Corwin, 1970), 1973–1975 (Malone et al., 1979), 1977 (Malone et al., 1985), and 1980 (Behrens and von Bock, 1983) (Table 9.2).

The impact on water quality of a tenfold increase in present sewage carbon loading from the estuary (650,000 kg C d^{-1}) and the apex dumpsites (650,000 kg C d^{-1}) was significant. Maximum concentrations of sewage carbon of 3.1–5.2 mg C liter^{-1} would then account for >90% of the simulated total POC pool (Fig. 9.6) above the pycnocline in the inner apex. Away from the inner apex, mixing and advection reduced concentrations of sewage carbon in the surface layer to 0.1 mg C liter^{-1} (50% of total POC) within a radius of ~60 km. On a depth-integrated basis, such an increased carbon loading resulted in a simulated content of sewage carbon of 49 g C m^{-2} over the entire apex water column, with a range of 50–100 g C m^{-2} in the inner apex to 10 g C m^{-2} in the outer apex (Table 9.2).

Light attenuation in the apex results from absorption and scattering both by detritus and by living phytoplankton, with the phytoplankton accounting for a minor component of total light extinction. Our initial simulation of light penetration in the apex resulted in euphotic zone depths (10% light level) of 7–10 m in the inner apex and 25–30 m beyond. This agreed with observations made by using a secchi disk in August 1974 (Table 9.3), when the 1% light depth ranged from ~7 to 8 m near the Hudson River plume and from ~25 to 40 m in the outer apex (Table 9.3). As a result of increased turbidity of the water column, the tenfold increment of sewage carbon input to the apex results in a substantial reduction of light penetration. Near the apex dumpsites, the 1% light depth is reduced to 2–3 m for the 10× case (Table 9.3). Mixing and dilution of the tenfold increment in sewage carbon loading over the outer apex also results in shallower euphotic zones of 15–20 m depths for the 10× case (Table 9.3). The significance of such

Table 9.2. Observed and Computed Distribution of Particulate Organic Carbon (g C m⁻²) in the Total Water Column[a]

Model Segment	Observed						Model		Location
	1969[b]	1974[c]	1976[d]	1976[e]	1977[f]	1980[g]	Base Run	10×	
60	9.0	9.0	81.8	14.2	14.8	11.6	12.8	101.7	Sewage sludge
61	8.9	8.3	—	6.1	18.9	5.3	18.5	92.5	Dredge spoil
52	—	13.5	75	6.6	16.1	—	16.5	84.1	Hudson plume
42	—	—	49.9	9.5	12.4	10.6	11.4	50.3	Outer apex
41	—	7.8	—	—	—	—	5.0	17.7	Outer apex
32	9.9	—	25–50	—	—	—	5.2	13.9	Hudson shelf
22	10.4	—	13–131	12–21	—	13.1	—	—	New Jersey midshelf

[a]Dash indicates no data.
[b]September (Corwin, 1970).
[c]August (Malone, 1976).
[d]June (Malone et al., 1979).
[e]August–September (Thomas et al., 1979).
[f]July (Malone et al., 1985).
[g]September (Behrens and von Bock, 1983).

Table 9.3. Observed and Computed Distribution of the Depth (m) of the Euphotic Zone (1% Light Depth) within the Apex

Model Segment	Observed Depth[a]	Model Depth		Location
		Base Run	10×	
60	7.5–15.5	10.1	2.1	Sewage sludge
61	7.5–9.0	8.3	2.5	Dredge spoil
52	9.0–15.5	9.4	2.5	Hudson plume
42	15.5–45.0	20.8	7.8	Outer apex
41	23.0	28.4	16.1	Outer apex
32	—[b]	28.1	19.1	Hudson Shelf Valley

[a]Computed from extinction coefficients measured in August 1974 (Malone, 1976).
[b]Dash indicates no data.

reduction in light penetration on primary production by phytoplankton is discussed in the next section.

9.3.3. Phytoplankton

Simulated chlorophyll distributions of the base run (Fig. 9.7) reflected the influence of estuarine discharge of nutrients with maximum concentrations of algal biomass (5.8–11.2 μg liter⁻¹ chlorophyll) found near the estuary and minimum concentrations (1.2–1.4 μg liter⁻¹ chlorophyll) located in the outer apex area. These distributions mimic field observations made in August 1974 (Malone, 1976), July 1977 (Malone et al., 1985), and August 1979 (Han, 1979). Similarly, the sea-

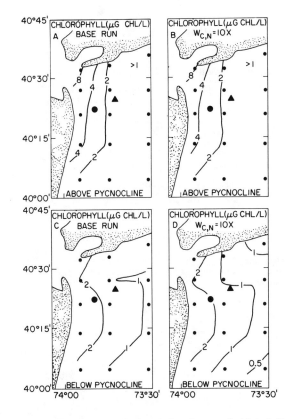

Figure 9.7. Spatial distribution during August of chlorophyll (μg chlorophyll liter⁻¹) above and below the pycnocline in the apex for (a) base run, (b) 10×, (c) base run, and (d) 10× cases. Circles indicate dredged material; triangles indicate sewage sludge.

ward decline of simulated primary production (Table 9.4) reflects the distribution of chlorophyll left behind in the water column, the increasing nitrogen limitation, and the previous measurements of carbon uptake (Malone, 1976; Malone et al., 1985).

The simulated tenfold increase in carbon and nitrogen loading results in negligible changes in the chlorophyll distribution over the New York Bight Apex (Fig. 9.7). Within the Hudson River plume, phytoplankton biomass is reduced by 10–20% as a result of the 60–70% reduction in daily primary production, under light limitation, in these segments (Table 9.4). Beyond the influence of the estuary and the apex dumpsites, chlorophyll increased slightly (5–10%), relative to the base run. Increased turbidity still resulted in declines of primary production over the Hudson Shelf Valley from the inner apex (50–60% reduction) to the outer apex (<5% reduction). At the outer boundary of the apex, primary production increased slightly as a result of higher nitrogen levels and a reduction in turbidity.

9.3.4. Dissolved Oxygen

Above the pycnocline, concentrations of dissolved oxygen for the base run were characterized by maximum values (5.0 ml O_2 liter^{-1}; 99% saturation) over the Hudson Shelf Valley and minimum values (4.6 ml O_2 liter^{-1}; 89% saturation) at the apex dumpsites (Fig. 9.8). Below the pycnocline, minimum oxygen concentrations (3.5 ml O_2 liter^{-1}; 63% saturation) also occurred in the vicinity of the estuary and the apex dumpsites (Fig. 9.9). The model's oxygen fields for the base run match observations from years of relatively high bottom oxygen, such as August 1975 (Thomas et al., 1976) and

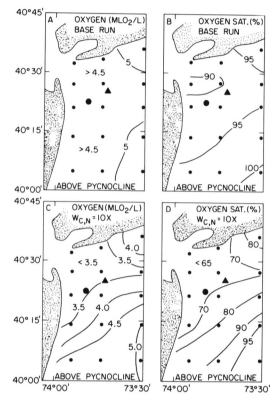

Figure 9.8. Spatial distribution during August of dissolved oxygen above the pycnocline in the apex for (a) base run (ml liter^{-1}), (b) base run (% saturation), (c) 10× (ml liter^{-1}), and (d) 10× (% saturation) cases. Circles indicate dredged material; triangles indicate sewage sludge.

August 1979 (Han, 1979). Minimum concentrations of bottom oxygen of 3 ml O_2 liter^{-1} (37% saturation) were observed in August 1975 near the dumpsites while, beyond the influence of the sewage sludge dumpsite, bottom oxygen was considerably higher (4.5 ml O_2 liter^{-1}; 70% saturation) in the outer apex.

Without an increase of oxygen production from photosynthesis, but with an increase in oxygen demand from oxidation of sewage carbon, the impact of a tenfold increase of urban waste inputs was found to be most significant near the Hudson estuary and the dumpsites. Concentrations of dissolved oxygen are reduced to 3.5 ml O_2 liter^{-1} (60–65% saturation) in the surface layer (Fig. 9.8). Over the inner apex (Fig. 9.9), anoxic conditions in the subpycnocline (<1 ml O_2 liter^{-1}; 17% saturation) result from the marked increase of just the oxygen demands in the water column from 168–487 ml O_2 m^{-2} d^{-1} of the base run to 638–1554 ml O_2 m^{-2} d^{-1} of the

Table 9.4. Observed and Computed Primary Production (g C m^{-2} d^{-1})

Model Segment	Observed[a]	Model		Location
		Base Run	10×	
60	1.3–2.1	0.74	0.17	Sewage sludge
61	2.4–4.4	1.96	0.55	Dredge spoil
52	1.7–1.8	1.92	0.58	Hudson plume
42	0.5	1.44	0.70	Outer apex
41	0.68	1.19	1.03	Outer apex
32	—[b]	1.31	1.30	Hudson Shelf Valley

[a]Calculated from chlorophyll distributions and assimilation numbers in August 1974 (Malone, 1976) and July 1977 (Malone et al., 1985).
[b]Dash indicates no data.

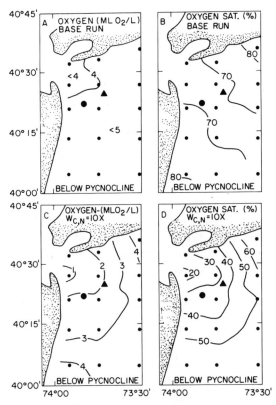

Figure 9.9. Spatial distribution during August of dissolved oxygen below the pycnocline in the apex for (a) base run (ml liter^{-1}), (b) base run (% saturation), (c) 10× (ml liter^{-1}), and (d) 10× (% saturation) cases. Circles indicate dredged material; triangles indicate sewage sludge.

10× case (Table 9.5). This is a minimal estimate since oxygen consumption of the seabed was assumed constant for both the base run and the 10× case. The several simulations thus did not include any potential increase in oxygen demand of the seabed that might result from an increase in detrital carbon loading at the apex dumpsites; total oxygen demand in the subpycnocline (water column + seabed), therefore, only ranged from 1529 to 1980 ml O$_2$ m^{-2} d^{-1}.

9.4. DISCUSSION

Computed distributions of chlorophyll and primary productivity for the base run, within the range of observed biomass and rates of production, reflected the opposing seaward gradients of inorganic nitrogen abundance and light penetration in the water column. Consistent with the early hypotheses of Malone (1976), the model results indicated that light attenua-

tion is the limiting factor in phytoplankton growth in the apex with nitrogen limitation becoming significant beyond the apex, where nitrogen is <1 μg-atom N liter^{-1} during summer (Walsh et al., 1978).

The simulated 10× distribution of primary productivity also reflected the interaction of opposing seaward gradients of increased turbidity of the water column and nitrogen abundance. High turbidity levels from the increased carbon loading resulted in significant reductions in primary productivity over the inner apex. Beyond the influence of the coastal plume and the apex dumpsites, however, low turbidity and the increase in nitrogen abundance resulted in a small increase in biomass and primary productivity that was distributed over a larger area of the midshelf. If the bottom remineralization of ammonia between the two simulation cases had been changed to reflect increased detrital carbon loading to the sea floor, the area of unlimited nitrogen growth would have spread seaward, but the onset of anoxia within the inner apex would not have been averted for the 10× case.

The simulated increase of sewage carbon loading to the apex resulted in an increase of the total carbon content from 5–10 g C m^{-2} for the base run to 50–100 g C m^{-2} for the 10× case *and* the onset of anoxia within the inner apex. The simulated initiation of anoxia within the 10× case is of particular significance in relation to the anoxic episode in 1976, since the magnitudes of the estimated POC content in 1976 (80– 125 g C m^{-2}) (Table 9.2) and the concentration of sewage carbon in the simulated 10× model are similar. The location of anoxic bottom waters in 1976 was farther south off the New Jersey coast (Fig. 9.1) than the 10× case of our model (Fig. 9.9). This reflects the different origin of the carbon loading (i.e., offshore waters for *Ceratium tripos* and the apex for our sewage carbon), but the inferred processes of the oxygen budget are evidently similar. If we had driven the model with southerly forcing to increase the residence time of sewage carbon within the apex, our anoxic regions (Fig. 9.9) would have spread southward along the New Jersey coast as well. For comparison to other anoxic marine ecosystems, our results for the 10× simulation are also consistent with observations of the range of POC content in the water column (25– 50 g C m^{-2}) associated with eutrophication and anoxia in Tokyo Bay (Tsuji et al., 1974).

In contrast to Malone (1984) and Garside et al. (1976), Segar and Berberian (1976) hypothesized that an increase in nitrogen loading to the apex should result in increased phytoplankton production and in more frequent anoxic episodes within the eutrophic apex. The results of this analysis sug-

Table 9.5. Computed Consumption in the Water Column (ml O$_2$ m^{-2} d^{-1})

Model Segment	Above Pycnocline		Below Pycnocline		Seabed[a]	Location
	Base run	10×	Base run	10×		
60	811	5544	262	949	738	Sewage sludge
61	882	4265	404	1197	332	Dredge spoil
52	708	3392	423	1396	365	Hudson plume
42	381	1221	487	1554	426	Outer apex
41	244	483	265	602	146	Outer apex
32	270	441	282	504	823	Hudson Shelf Valley

[a]Calculated for ambient bottom temperature (8.5–14.5°C) by using Q$_{10}$ = 1.88 (Thomas et al., 1976).

gest, however, that a coupled loading of carbon and nitrogen wastes to the apex would result in an increase of light limitation and a corresponding decrease in primary productivity, with only a minor change in the abundance of chlorophyll within the apex itself. Depending upon seasonal changes in the seaward transport of the phytoplankton (Malone et al., 1983), the fate of phytoplankton carbon, produced outside the apex, is either consumption on the shelf or export to depositional areas on the slope (Walsh et al., 1981).

Although the increase in sewage-related nitrogen loading over the past few decades has resulted in higher rates of nanoplankton production, the impact on oxygen depletion of bottom water during summer has been small since >80% of production is metabolized within the plume of the Hudson River because of food chain processes within the surface layer. Particulate organic matter, packaged as detrital sewage carbon, thus exerts a much greater impact on oxygen demands beneath the pycnocline than does particulate organic matter packaged as nanoplankton carbon (Malone, 1984).

In our simulation, the significant increase in oxygen demand of nearshore waters (Table 9.5) resulted from the additional detrital load of sewage carbon, which was unable to escape the apex within our "best case" flow field. The simulated onset of anoxia that resulted from the tenfold increment in urban carbon loading substantiates our conclusion that a major factor in the onset and progression in the anoxia of bottom water in 1976 off the New Jersey coast was the decay of another source of detrital carbon, that derived from the anomalous *Ceratium* bloom (Falkowski et al., 1980; Stoddard, 1983).

Models, like data sets, can always be improved. In future evaluations of the assimilative capacity of these coastal waters for urban waste loading, our present model structure could be refined further to account for the fate of sewage-related nitrogen inputs and phytoplankton production with terms that account for algal mortality and accumulation of nonliving algal biomass in the detrital carbon pool. In addition, oxygen consumption of the seabed and benthic remineralization of ammonia could be explicitly computed as a function of the flux rate of detrital carbon to the sediments and remineralization of the organic material within the sediment–water interface (DiToro and Connolly, 1980). The results of the present model appear sufficiently robust, however, to avoid fine tuning of the assumptions until a larger, unaliased data set becomes available (e.g., from *in situ* or remote biological sensors).

9.5. SUMMARY AND CONCLUSIONS

A two-layered ecosystem model of the New York Bight has been used to evaluate the impact on water quality of a tenfold increase in carbon and nitrogen loading to the New York Bight Apex. Distributions of nitrogen, carbon, chlorophyll, light attenuation, primary production, and dissolved oxygen in the base run model are in agreement with the available summer data within the apex (e.g., 1974, 1975, 1977, 1979), reproducing both the range of observations and the significant spatial gradients observed seaward of the Hudson River plume. In particular, the assumptions of the organic carbon sub-model are verified with the base run POC results of 10 g C m^{-2}, matching the range of observations (8–12 g C m^{-2}) over several years within the apex.

Our analysis of a tenfold increase in carbon and nitrogen inputs represents a significant departure from the above interannual quasi-steady state. Under this 10× condition, the analysis indicates a major reduction in light penetration into the water column, a decrease in primary productivity within the apex, and an increase in the area of nonlimiting nitrogen concentrations. Within the inner apex, the increased oxygen demand from the additional urban carbon loading results both in subpycnocline anoxia and in a reduction of surface layer oxygen to 60–70% saturation from the base run level of ~90% saturation.

Our analysis indicates the possible nature of the nearfield impact of loading from the estuary and the apex dumpsites on water quality within this coastal zone. Significant oxygen depletion (<40% saturation) may be generally limited to a radius of ~30 km within the inner apex. Mixing by "best case" physical transport processes appears to result in relatively minor impacts on the water quality up to 60 km from the estuary in the outer apex; "worst case" flow regimes that increased the residence time of particles within the apex would lead to more extensive zones of bottom anoxia.

The similarity of the response to our simulated detrital carbon content for the 10× case within the inner apex (50–100 g C m^{-2}) and the observed June 1976 POC content of *Ceratium* within the apex and the New Jersey midshelf (25–125 g C m^{-2}) (Table 9.2) suggests that the model results of oxygen depletion in the subpycnocline after the additional urban carbon loading are a reasonable representation of detrital carbon–oxygen dynamics in the apex. Our results are consistent with preliminary estimates of the assimilative capacity (37 g C m^{-2}) of the New York Bight for the input of urban carbon (Goldberg, 1979) and suggest that a detrital carbon loading of the water column of 50–100 g C m^{-2} is sufficient to initiate bottom anoxia in the apex.

The reliability of this estimate, based on our model results, is supported by the estimated carbon content of the *Ceratium* bloom and the associated onset of oxygen depletion in the bottom water which was observed in the summer of 1976, over the New Jersey shelf. Such a determination of the assimilative capacity of the New York Bight for carbon loading has significant application as a criterion in the regulatory decision-making process for dumpsite designation for disposal of wastes into the ocean at either the existing apex 12-mile Dumpsite or the Deepwater Dumpsite-106 (U.S. EPA, 1985).

ACKNOWLEDGMENTS

We thank G. Han for allowing us to use the results from his diagnostic circulation model and D. A. Dieterle for additional transformation of the circulation field. We also thank the editor, Douglas A. Wolfe, two anonymous reviewers, and Thomas C. Malone for their critical reading and helpful comments on this manuscript. Financial support was provided by the Marine Ecosystems Analysis New York Bight Project of the National Oceanic and Atmospheric Administration under Contract No. N0-80RAG-02206. Support was also provided under Contract No. DEAC02-76CH00016 with the Department of Energy. J. J. Walsh was the principal investigator for both contracts. The work reported herein was submitted by A. Stoddard in partial fulfillment of the requirements for the degree of Doctor of Philosophy at the University of Washington in Seattle. We thank Diane Simmons of Science Applications International Corporation for her capable word-processing skills.

REFERENCES

Anon. 1984. ES+T Currents: States. *Environmental Science and Technology*, **18**, 205A.

Behrens, W. E., and K. von Bock (Eds.). 1983. Atlantic Coastal Experiment VI, *R/V Knorr* Cruise, 23 August–11 September 1980. Report No. BNL-33174, Brookhaven National Laboratory, Upton, New York, 556 pp.

Corwin, N. 1970. Reduced Data Reports for *GOSNOLD* Cruise 140 and *ATLANTIS II* Cruise 52. Appendix I. U. S. Atomic Energy Commission Report No. NY0-3862039, Woods Hole Oceanographic Institution Reference No. 70-15, Woods Hole Oceanographic Institution, Massachusetts, Station Numbers 1502–1519.

DiToro, D. M., and J. P. Connolly. 1980. Mathematical Models of Water Quality in Large Lakes, Part 2: Lake Erie. U.S. Environmental Protection Agency Report No. 600/3-80-065, Environmental Research Laboratory, U.S. Environmental Protection Agency, Duluth, Minnesota, 225 pp.

Falkowski, P. G., and S. O. Howe. 1976. Preliminary report to IDOE on the possible effects of the *Ceratium tripos* bloom in the New York Bight, March–July 1976. *In*: Proceedings of the Special Symposium Conference by International Decade of Ocean Exploration (IDOE). Washington, D.C., pp. 57–62.

Falkowski, P. G., T. S. Hopkins, and J. J. Walsh. 1980. An analysis of factors affecting oxygen depletion in the New York Bight. *Journal Marine Research*, **38**, 479–506.

Garside, C., and T. C. Malone. 1978. Monthly oxygen and carbon budgets of the New York Bight Apex. *Estuarine, Coastal and Marine Science*, **6**, 93–104.

Garside, C., T. C. Malone, O. A. Roels, and B. F. Shorfstein. 1976. An evaluation of sewage-derived nutrients and their influence on the Hudson Estuary and the New York Bight. *Estuarine, Coastal and Marine Science*, **4**, 281–289.

Goldberg, E. D. (Ed.). 1979. Assimilative Capacity of U.S. Coastal Waters for Pollutants. U.S. National Oceanic and Atmospheric Administration, Boulder, Colorado, 284 pp.

Han, G. 1979. Cruise Report: XWCC-24, 13–23 August 1979. Marine EcoSystems Analysis (MESA) Program, New York Bight Project, Stony Brook, New York, 17 pp.

Han, G., D. V. Hansen, and A. Cantillo. 1979. Diagnostic model of water and oxygen transport. *In*: Oxygen Depletion and Associated Benthic Mortalities in New York Bight, 1976, R. L. Swanson and C. J. Sindermann (Eds.). U.S. National Oceanic and Atmospheric Administration Professional Paper No. 11, U.S. Department of Commerce, Rockville, Maryland, pp. 165–192.

Han, G., D. V. Hansen, and J. A. Galt. 1980. Steady-state diagnostic model of the New York Bight. *Journal Physical Oceanography*, **10**, 1998–2020.

Ketchum, B. H., A. C. Redfield, and J. C. Ayers. 1951. The oceanography of the New York Bight. *Papers Physical Oceanography and Meteorology*, **12**, 1–46.

Ketchum, B., D. R. Kester, and P. K. Park. 1981. Ocean Dumping of Industrial Wastes. Plenum Press, New York, 525 pp.

Mahoney, J. B. 1979. Plankton dynamics and nutrient cycling, Part 2: Bloom decomposition. *In*: Oxygen Depletion and Associated Benthic Mortalities in New York Bight, 1976, R. L. Swanson and C. J. Sindermann (Eds.). U.S. National Oceanic and Atmospheric Administration Professional Paper no. 11, U.S. Department of Commerce, Rockville, Maryland, pp. 219– 230.

Malone, T. C. 1976. Phytoplankton Productivity in the Apex of the New York Bight: September 1973–August 1974. U.S. National Oceanic and Atmospheric Administration Technical Memorandum ERL-MESA-5, U.S. National Oceanic and Atmospheric Administration, Boulder, Colorado, 46 pp. + appendices.

Malone, T. C. 1977. Plankton Systematics and Distribution. New York Bight Atlas Monograph 13, Marine EcoSystems Analysis (MESA) Program, New York Sea Grant Institute, Albany, New York, 45 pp.

Malone, T. C., 1984. Anthropogenic nitrogen loading and assimilation capacity of the Hudson River estuarine system, U.S.A. *In*: The Estuary as a Filter, V.S. Kennedy (Ed.). Academic Press, New York, pp. 291–311.

Malone, T. C., W. E. Esaias, and P. G. Falkowski. 1979. Plankton dynamics and nutrient cycling, Part 1: Water column processes. *In*: Oxygen Depletion and Associated Benthic Mortalities in New York Bight, 1976, R. L. Swanson and C. J. Sindermann (Eds.). U.S. National Oceanic and Atmospheric Administration Professional Paper No. 11, U.S. Department of Commerce, Rockville, Maryland, pp. 193–218.

Malone, T. C., T. S. Hopkins, P. G. Falkowski, and T. E. Whitledge. 1983. Production and transport of phytoplankton biomass over the continental shelf of the New York Bight. *Continental Shelf Research*, **1**, 305–337.

Malone, T. C., M. D. Chervin, J. P. Stepien, C. Garside, C. D. Litchfield, and J. P. Thomas. 1985. Synoptic Investigations of Nutrient Cycling in the Coastal Plume of the Hudson and Raritan Rivers: Plankton Dynamics. U.S. National Oceanic and Atmospheric Administration Report, U.S. National Oceanic and Atmospheric Administration, Rockville, Maryland, 119 pp.

Mayer, G. F. (Ed.). 1982. Ecological Stress and the New York Bight: Science and Management. Estuarine Research Foundation, Columbia, South Carolina, 715 pp.

Mueller, J. A., J. S. Jeris, A. R. Anderson, and C. F. Hughes. 1976. Contaminant Inputs to the New York Bight. U.S. National Oceanic and Atmospheric Administration Technical Memorandum ERL-MESA-6, U.S. National Oceanic and Atmospheric Administration, Boulder, Colorado, 347 pp.

Officer, C. B., and J. H. Ryther. 1977. Secondary sewage treatment versus ocean outfalls: An assessment. *Science*, **197**, 1056–1060.

Redfield, A. C., and L. A. Walford. 1951. A Study of the Disposal of Chemical Waste at Sea: Report of the Committee on Investigation of Waste Disposal. National Research Council Publication No. 201, U.S. National Academy of Science, Washington, D.C., 49 pp.

Segar, D. A., and G. A. Berberian. 1976. Oxygen depletion in the New York Bight Apex: Causes and consequences. *American Society of Limnology and Oceanography Special Symposium*, **2**, 220–239.

Stoddard, A. 1983. Mathematical Model of Oxygen Depletion in the New York Bight: An Analysis of Biological, Chemical and Physical Factors in 1975 and 1976. Ph.D. Dissertation, University of Washington, Seattle, 364 pp.

Swanson, R. L., and C. J. Sindermann (Eds.). 1979. Oxygen Depletion and Associated Benthic Mortalities in New York Bight, 1976. U.S. National Oceanic and Atmospheric Administration Professional Paper No. 11, U.S. Department of Commerce, Rockville, Maryland, 345 pp.

Swanson, R. L., and M. Devine. 1982. The pendulum swings again: Ocean dumping policy. *Environment*, **24**(5), 14–20.

Thomas, J. P., W. C. Phoel, F. W. Steimle, J. E. O'Reilly, and C. E. Evans. 1976. Seabed oxygen consumption—New York Bight Apex. *American Society of Limnology and Oceanography Special Symposium*, **2**, 354–369.

Thomas, J. P., J. E. O'Reilley, A. Draxler, J. A. Babinchak, C. N. Robertson, W. C. Phoel, R. Waldhauer, C. A. Evans, A. Matte, M. Cohn, M. Nitkowski, and S. Dudley, 1979. Biological processes in the water column and on the seabed during the anoxic episode in the New York Bight. *In*: Oxygen Depletion and Associated Benthic Mortalities in New York Bight, 1976, R. L. Swanson and C. J. Sindermann (Eds.). U.S. National Oceanic and Atmospheric Administration Professional Paper No. 11, U.S. Department of Commerce, Rockville, Maryland, pp. 231– 262.

Tsuji, T., H. Seki, and A. Hattori. 1974. Results of red tide formation in Tokyo Bay. *Journal Water Pollution Control Federation*, **46**, 165–172.

U.S. Court of Appeals. 1979. *National Sea Clammers Association and Lovgren, G.* v. *City of New York et al.*, No. 79-1360, U.S. Court of Appeals for the District of New Jersey, Newark, New Jersey.

U.S. Environmental Protection Agency. 1985. Ocean Dumping: Notice of Final Determination to Deny Petitions to Redesignate the 12-Mile Site. *Federal Register*, **50**(70), 14335–14353.

U.S. National Advisory Committee on Oceans and Atmosphere (NACOA). 1981. The Role of the Ocean in a Waste Management Strategy. Special Report to the President and Congress, National Advisory Committee on Oceans and Atmospheres, Washington, D.C., 103 pp. + appendices.

Walsh, J. J. 1975. A spatial simulation model of the Peru upwelling ecosystem. *Deep-Sea Research*, **22**, 201–236.

Walsh, J. J. 1984. The role of the ocean biota in accelerated ecological cycles: A temporal view. *Bioscience*, **34**, 449–507.

Walsh, J. J., and S. O. Howe. 1976. Protein from the sea: A comparison of the simulated nitrogen and carbon productivity in the Peru upwelling system. *In*: Systems Analysis and Simulation in Ecology, Vol. 4, B. C. Patten (Ed.). Academic Press, New York, pp. 47–61.

Walsh, J. J., T. E. Whitledge, F. W. Barvenik, C. D. Wirick, S. O. Howe, W. E. Esaias, and J. T. Scott. 1978. Wind events and food chain dynamics within the New York Bight. *Limnology and Oceanography*, **23**, 659–683.

Walsh, J. J., G. T. Rowe, R. L. Iverson, and C. P. McRoy. 1981. Biological export of shelf carbon is a neglected sink of the global CO_2 cycle. *Nature*, **291**, 196–201.

Chapter 10

The Acute Toxicity of Sewage Sludge to Marine Fish, Mysids, and Copepods

Don C. Miller, Martha Marcy, Walter Berry,
Christopher Deacutis, Suzanne Lussier, Ann Kuhn,
Margarete Heber, Steven C. Schimmel, and Eugene Jackim

Environmental Research Laboratory
U.S. Environmental Protection Agency
Narragansett, Rhode Island

Abstract	**103**
10.1. Introduction	**103**
10.2. Methods	**104**
10.2.1. Sewage Sludge Collection, Handling, and Storage	104
10.2.2. Collection, Holding, and Culture of Animals	105
10.2.2a. Fish	*105*
10.2.2b. Mysids	*105*
10.2.2c. Copepods	*105*
10.2.3. Experimental Design, Preparation of Treatments, and Data Analysis	105
10.2.4. Test Procedures	107
10.2.5. Comparison of Test Methods	107
10.3. Results	**107**
10.3.1. Evaluation of ERLN Bioassay Methodologies for Sludge	107
10.3.2. Comparison of ERLN and Presently Used Sludge Bioassays	109
10.4. Discussion	**109**
10.5. Summary and Conclusions	**112**
Acknowledgments	**112**
References	**112**

ABSTRACT

Research was undertaken on the reliability of acute toxicity methodologies with mysid shrimp and juvenile fish that are now used in tests to characterize waste in municipal sewage sludge. Three new acute bioassays using mysid shrimp, larval fish, and calanoid copepods were designed expressly to test sewage sludge; and results of these tests were compared with results from tests presently used to regulate dumping of sewage sludge into the ocean. Similar results were obtained by using the different mysid and fish tests in bioassays on the same sludge samples from three wastewater treatment plants. The present, easier-to-conduct methods appear satisfactory to characterize the acute toxicity of sludge. The current use of these acute toxicity data alone to estimate environmentally acceptable concentrations is questionable, however, and a more extensive hazard assessment is recommended. The acute toxicity was low for sludge from the three treatment plants studied with 96-h LC_{50} (the lethal concentration resulting in death to 50% of the test organisms) values of 1–10% whole sludge for fish, 0.5–2.5% for mysid shrimp, and 0.03 to >0.8% for copepods. The copepods usually were more acutely sensitive to sludge than were mysids by a factor of 6–9. The acute toxicity of sludge from a given treatment plant was quite variable over time. One source of variation may be the length of time the sludge is held in storage tanks. Toxicity of sludge supernatant increased by an order of magnitude during storage of one aerobically produced sludge.

10.1. INTRODUCTION

The Marine Protection, Research and Sanctuaries Act of 1972 calls for the regulation of the transport and dumping of materials into ocean waters of the United States. The act established a permit program, administered by the U.S. Environmental Protection Agency (EPA), for ocean disposal of wastes that will not unreasonably degrade or endanger human health or the environment. The procedures and criteria used by the EPA in issuing permits are detailed in regulations published by the U.S. EPA (1977). Bioassays are intended to test the potential for significant undesirable effects of wastes, including the toxicity and bioaccumulation of contaminants.

In practice, a waste proposed for ocean disposal is usually assessed through a two-tier procedure. The first-tier studies are waste characterization, which provide a preliminary description of physical, chemical, biological, and toxicological properties. Second-tier studies are undertaken only if additional information is needed for a permit decision. These might include tests for sublethal and chronic effects, bioaccumulation kinetics, and further assessment of the fate and transport of the waste. Operationally, the information generated on the biological effects of the waste (effects assessment) is interpreted in the context of a predicted or measured concentration of this waste in the environment (exposure assessment).

Ninety-six hour acute bioassays typically are used to describe the toxicity of a material for first-tier waste-characterization studies. Acute tests also may be required periodically over the duration of a permit to test for changes in toxicity of the waste. The particular methods and species used for regulatory purposes are specified by the relevant permitting authority. At present, methods for such tests are developed largely from the guidance manual, "Bioassay Procedures for the Ocean Disposal Permit Program" (U.S. EPA, 1978). The assays cited in this manual were developed primarily for single compounds in the dissolved phase and not for particulate material containing a mixture of contaminants.

The studies described in this chapter were undertaken to evaluate whether special bioassay procedures should be adopted for testing sewage sludge, given its particulate nature, low toxicity, and high chemical oxygen demand (COD), and biochemical oxygen demand (BOD). Three bioassays, developed expressly for sewage sludge at the EPA Environmental Research Laboratory, Narragansett (ERLN), were examined for sensitivity and variability of response by testing a number of sludge samples from one treatment plant. These bioassays were then compared with present U.S. EPA (1978) assay methods carried out by a contract laboratory, New York Testing Laboratory (NYTL). Samples of the same sludge from three treatment plants were used in this study.

The ERLN bioassays incorporated many state-of-the-art procedures cited in American Society for Testing and Mate-

rials (ASTM) (1980) Standard Practice for Acute Assays. Test animals selected were larval fishes (*Cyprinodon variegatus, Menidia menidia,* and *Menidia beryllina*), mysid post-larvae (24 h old) (*Mysidopsis bahia*), and copepods (*Eurytemora herdmani* and *Pseudocalanus minutus*). The static-exposure method was adopted after it was determined that flow-through exposure systems could not reliably control the high concentrations of sludge required to obtain an LC_{50} (the lethal concentration resulting in death to 50% of test organisms). Larval fish were tested because they may be more sensitive than are the juvenile Atlantic silversides (*Menidia menidia*) presently used. The conspecific *Menidia beryllina* and *C. variegatus* were included due to the almost year-around availability of these eggs. Copepods were tested because they are ecologically highly significant in the ocean, and they are more sensitive to some contaminants than presently used mysids (*Mysidopsis bahia*). The oceanic copepod, *Pseudocalanus minutus*, was included to compare its acute sensitivity with that of the coastal copepod, *E. herdmani*.

10.2. METHODS

This section describes the ERLN 96-h static bioassays for sewage sludge, briefly summarizes the procedures used in the NYTL tests, and cites methods of a 15-min Microtox® (Beckman Instruments, Berkeley, California) toxicity test conducted on sludge supernatant. Additional details on study methods may be found in a report by Miller et al. (1984).

10.2.1. Sewage-Sludge Collection, Handling, and Storage

Sewage sludge used for assay development and the first set of definitive bioassays at ERLN was obtained from the Middlesex County Utilities Authority, Sayerville, New Jersey. The manner of sample collection differed during the study period. Samples 1–7 were collected from the bottom of one of four storage tanks (samples 1–5 were used for preliminary studies only), sample 8 was from the pipe carrying sludge to the storage tanks, 11 was a composite from the bottom of two storage tanks, and 9B and 10 were composites made up of samples collected at the start, midway, and end of pumping from two storage tanks to a barge. The latter procedure is used to sample barged sludge at this treatment plant for quarterly monitoring purposes. Sludge was transported to ERLN in polyethylene containers surrounded by ice and held in an insulated box. At the laboratory, sludge was poured through a 0.2-cm sieve to remove coarse material, stored in polyethylene containers, and refrigerated at $4 \pm 2°C$. Precautions were taken to ensure that freezing did not occur.

Sludge samples used for subsequent comparison of methods were collected by treatment-plant personnel. Each sample was a composite of three to five subsamples collected at regular intervals during the pumping of sludge from storage tanks into barges. Each composite sample was split into two subsamples by NYTL, then handled as above by the two laboratories, except that subsamples were not sieved prior to use.

10.2.2. Collection, Holding, and Culture of Animals

10.2.2a. Fish

Adult *Menidia menidia* and *Menidia beryllina* were collected from the Pettaquamscutt River, Rhode Island, by using a bag seine (61-mm mesh). Fish were held in the laboratory in filtered (15-μm pore size) flowing seawater controlled at 15–17°C, 27–31‰ salinity, and illuminated on a 12-h light:12-h dark cycle. The fish were fed daily with Tetra SM 80® (Tetra Werke, Melle, Federal Republic of Germany) and *Artemia salina* nauplii, Columbian strain. *Menidia* spp. were brought into reproductive condition, spawned, and larvae cultured by using procedures described by Middaugh and Takita (1983).

Sheepshead minnow (*C. variegatus*) larvae were obtained by using methods similar to those of Hansen et al. (1978). Adult sheepshead were collected by beach seine at Santa Rosa Island, Escambia County, Florida, and at Succotash Salt-marsh, Jerusalem, Rhode Island, and held in 160-liter aquaria supplied with flowing seawater controlled at $26 \pm 1°C$ and $30 \pm 2‰$ salinity.

10.2.2b. Mysids

Mysidopsis bahia were cultured in flow-through 76-liter glass aquaria by using the methods of Gentile et al. (1983). The aquaria were continuously supplied with filtered (15-μm pore size) natural seawater controlled at $25 \pm 1°C$, $30 \pm 2‰$ salinity, and illuminated on a 14-h light:10-h dark cycle with dawn and dusk simulation. *Artemia salina* (Brazil strain) nauplii were provided freely as food.

10.2.2c. Copepods

A laboratory culture of *E. herdmani* was established at ERLN using ~100 females from a Narragansett Bay plankton tow. Culture conditions were 15°C and 25–30‰ salinity, using filtered (0.45-μm pore size) water from the Pettaquamscutt River. Copepods were reared in groups, which were initially composed of nauplii hatched within a 7-d period. Copepods were held in 11.4-cm Carolina® (Carolina Biological Supply Co., Burlington, North Carolina) culture dishes containing ~300 nauplii, 200–250 copepodids, or 150 adults per dish. The copepod culture medium was changed weekly.

All copepod life stages in the laboratory culture were fed daily with a mixed algal diet of *Rhodomonas baltica, Skeletonema costatum,* and *Pavlova lutheri* combined in approximately equal amounts by volume. Algal densities varied with life stage: nauplii, 0.25 ml algal mix 100 ml^{-1} seawater; copepodids, 0.75 ml algal mix 100 ml^{-1} seawater; and adults, 0.55 ml algal mix 100 ml^{-1} seawater. The phytoplankton was cultured in 100 ml lots of f/2 medium (Guillard and Ryther, 1962), modified in that only the prescribed EDTA (ethylene-dinitrilotetraacetic acid), iron, zinc, and manganese were added to the trace metal mix; no other buffers or chelators were included. Silicates were added at half strength. Phytoplankton cultures fed to copepods were between 7-d and 14-d old.

Female *Pseudocalanus minutus* used in bioassays were collected from lower Narragansett Bay during the winter 72–96 h prior to the test. In the laboratory, animals were held at 10°C in filtered, 30‰ salinity water from the Pettaquamscutt River and fed daily on a mixed diatom diet of *Skeletonema costatum, Thalassiosira pseudonana,* and *Thalassiosira weissflogii.*

10.2.3. Experimental Design, Preparation of Treatments, and Data Analysis

Experimental design for the ERLN bioassays consisted of one control treatment and at least five sludge concentrations. At a minimum, duplicate exposure chambers were used for each concentration, with a total of at least 20 animals per concentration. Organisms were distributed randomly into exposure chambers, which, except for copepod assays, were randomly placed on exposure tables. Specifics of each bioassay design are given in Table 10.1.

Concentrations of sewage sludge for each treatment were selected on the basis of prior experience and modified as

Table 10.1. Summary of Acute Test Methods for Sewage Sludge Employed by Environmental Research Laboratory—Narragansett (ERLN) and New York Testing Laboratory (NYTL)[a]

Parameter	Fish Bioassay		Mysid Bioassay		Copepod Bioassay	
	ERLN	NYTL	ERLN	NYTL	NYTL	ERLN
Species	*Menidia menidia* *Menidia beryllina* *Cyprinodon variegatus*	*Menidia menidia*	*Mysidopsis bahia*	*Mysidopsis bahia*	*Mysidopsis bahia*	*Eurytemora herdmani* *Pseudocalanus minutus*
Life history stage	*Menidia*: 2–4 week larvae *Cyprinodon*: newly hatched	Juvenile	1 day post-hatch	1–2 day post-hatch		Adult, female
Source	Laboratory cultured	Field collected	Laboratory cultured	Laboratory cultured	Laboratory cultured	*E. herdmani*: laboratory cultured *P. minutus*: field collected
Pre-exposure holding	1–24 h	≥14 d	None	24 h		*E. herdmani*: 1–5 day post-maturity *P. minutus*: 3–4 day post-maturity
Exposure mode	Static, no renewal	Static, no renewal	Static, no renewal	Static, no renewal		Static, 24-h renewal
Exposure chamber	Crystallizing dish, 1.2 liter	Aquarium, 38 liter	Crystallizing dish, 2.6 liter, containing 3 sub-chambers	Crystallizing dish, 2.6 liter		Erlenmeyer flask, 250 ml
Experimental design:						
Number treatments including control	6–7	4–6	6	4–6		7
Number organisms per chamber	12	10	15 (5 per sub-chamber)	15		5
Number treatment replicates	2	1	2	2		4
Test Solution Volume (liter)	1	15	1	1		0.1
Treatment Aeration:						
Pretest	≥1 h	None	30 min	None		60 min
Test	Vigorously by pipette, Dissolved oxygen >85% saturation	None and 100 bubbles min⁻¹ by pipette	Air lift	100 bubbles min⁻¹ by pipette		Orbital shaker
Seawater	Natural, 15-μm sand filtered	Natural, 5-μm diatomaceous earth filtered	Natural, 15 μm sand filtered	Natural, 5-μm diatomaceous earth filtered		Natural, 15-μm sand filtered
Temperature (°C)	22 ± 2	Ambient (~18–20)	25 ± 1	Ambient (~18–20)		12 ± 1
Salinity (‰)	31 ± 4	27 ± 2	30 ± 2	27 ± 2		28 ± 2
Illumination	100 LX Cool White, 12L:12D	Ambient	100 LX Cool White, 14L:10D	Cool White, 14L:10D		Cool White Sho, 12L:12D
Test Food	*Artemia* nauplii daily	None	*Artemia* nauplii daily	*Artemia* nauplii daily		None

[a]Exceptions noted in text.

necessary when initial bioassays on a given sludge sample were completed. Range-finding assays were usually not conducted. A wide range of concentrations was used due to the relatively low, but variable, toxicity of sewage sludge. The following ranges usually spanned the LC_{50} for whole sludge: fish, 0.5–10%; mysids, 0.1–4%; and copepods, 0.01–0.4%. The particular test concentrations used were determined by logarithmic series (Rand et al., 1975). Sludge treatments were prepared on a volume-to-volume basis with a specified volume of well-mixed sewage sludge diluted in a known volume of sand-filtered (15-μm pore size) water from Narragansett Bay (25–30‰ salinity). All treatments were aerated for 30 min (for mysids) or at least 60 min (for copepods and fish) before the animals were added. New treatment solutions were prepared daily for tests having 24-h waste renewal. Exposure concentrations in the copepod assays were measured gravimetrically at least once during each test.

Results are presented as LC_{50} values. These values were estimated by using a program (C. E. Stephen, personal communication) that computes the LC_{50} by the probit (Finney, 1971) and the moving average method (Thompson, 1947) if the condition of two partial kills is met, and also by the binomial method. The program also includes Abbott's formula (Booth, 1975) to correct for control mortality. Missing animals were counted as dead when results of the larval fish and mysid tests were analyzed; for copepods, missing animals were subtracted from the initial sample size before data analysis. Each LC_{50} value reported is the best estimate obtained by one of the above methods for the data available, based on the smallest confidence interval. No LC_{50} values are reported for larval fish or mysid tests with control mortality exceeding 10%. Control mortality below 10% was not achieved for copepod tests with some sludge samples, as noted in the results.

10.2.4. Test Procedures

Test conditions and certain procedures for the ERLN and NYTL 96-h tests are cited in Table 10.1. The ERLN tests were conducted largely according to ASTM Standard Methods (ASTM, 1980); Miller et al. (1984) provide further details of test equipment, procedures for animal and waste handling, test monitoring, and animal enumeration. Two exceptions to procedures cited in Table 10.1 occurred in copepod tests on sludge samples 6–11. In these tests, whole sludge was aerated vigorously for at least 30 min before instead of after dilutions were mixed, and copepods were added within 30 min of preparing treatment solutions.

Sludge supernatant was prepared for the Microtox® test by centrifuging sludge at 2000 × G for 5 min at 5°C. The supernatant was tested for toxicity by the standard Microtox® technique (Beckman Instruments, Inc., 1982). The toxicant incubation time was 15 min. Salinity was adjusted with Microtox® osmotic adjusting solution. Absorbance correction was generally not required.

10.2.5. Comparison of Test Methods

Bioassays using the ERLN methods were conducted at the Narragansett Laboratory during the same period (±2 weeks) that NYTL carried out quarterly sludge bioassays on sludge from three treatment plants. Subsamples of test sludges were obtained from NYTL for the Narragansett bioassays. Test procedures used by NYTL and ERLN in this study are summarized in Table 10.1. NYTL methods were developed from the U.S. EPA (1978) bioassay guidance manual and are detailed in the NYTL Manual of Practice (undated).

10.3. RESULTS

10.3.1. Evaluation of ERLN Bioassay Methodologies for Sludge

A limited series of static, acute 96-h bioassays were conducted between April 1983 and February 1984 to evaluate the need for improvements in the ERLN methods used to measure sewage-sludge toxicity. These assays were used to examine test replicability, the need for 24-h renewal versus nonrenewal of sludge in 96-h assays, relative sensitivity of test species to sludge, and variability in toxicity of different sludge samples from the same plant.

Results of 96-h bioassays (Table 10.2) showed good within-sample replication for mysid and larval fish tests. For example, the ratio of the highest to lowest LC_{50} value for replicate tests on a given sludge was 1.5 for *C. variegatus*, 1.7 for *Menidia menidia*, and 1.1 and 1.6 for *Mysidopsis bahia*.

Results from 96-h static toxicity tests using *Menidia bahia* both with and without 24-h renewal of sludge solutions (Table 10.2) suggested that renewal is not required to ensure maintenance of contaminant concentrations for this sludge. Triplicated 96-h tests receiving renewal of sludge solutions had LC_{50} values ranging from 2.3 to 2.6 versus 2.6 for a test without waste renewal.

There was variation in LC_{50} values for tests on different sludge samples from the same treatment plant (Table 10.2), in contrast to good agreement among replicate tests on the same sample. Two samples tested with mysids had LC_{50} values differing by a factor of 5 (LC_{50} range: 0.51–2.6), while results for four different sludge samples tested on copepods had a range exceeding one order of magnitude (<0.02–0.36%).

The possibility that storage time and sampling location for sludge may contribute to the variability between samples in sludge toxicity was explored at the Middlesex County treatment plant by using Microtox®, a rapid test for toxicity. Microtox® measures the inhibition of bacterial luminescence by the test material after 15-min incubation. Since this test requires a translucent sample, it was possible to test only sludge supernatant, not whole sludge. Sludge entering a storage tank from the gravity thickener had a supernatant EC_{50} (the effective concentration that produced 50% luminescence inhibition in the test organisms) value of ~30%, while supernatant toxicity was as much as an order of magnitude greater for the samples from the storage tank, with EC_{50} values ranging from 2.1 to 9.7% (Table 10.3). Toxicity of sludge supernatant also appeared to increase with storage time, since three of four sludge samples collected from the same section of the sludge blanket in the storage tank showed even lower EC_{50} values when sampled 24 h later. The 95%

Table 10.3. Toxicity of Middlesex County Sewage Sludge Supernatant Collected at Different Locations on Two Successive Days

Sampling Location[a]	Tank Section Sampled	Tank Sludge Depth (m)	EC_{50}[b]
	18 July 1983		
2	Bottom	6.5	2.4
2	Middle	3.7	3.0
2	Top	2.0	2.1
4	Bottom	6.6	5.6
4	Middle	3.4	7.2
4	Top	1.1	8.9
1	Bottom	1.2	3.8
3	Bottom	5.8	9.7
	19 July 1983		
2	Bottom[c]	6.6	3.3
4	Bottom[c]	1.1	2.5
1	Bottom	1.2	2.9
3	Bottom	6.8	3.7
Sludge line to storage tanks			~30.0

[a]Numbers refer to tank identification. Each tank was sampled at its base.
[b]Microtox EC_{50} = percent of sludge supernatant sample causing 50% inhibition of bacterial luminescence.
[c]First two 19 July "bottom" samples from storage tanks represent "top" sludge of 18 July remaining in tank following the 18 July drawdown for barging.

Table 10.2. Results of Initial Static Acute Bioassays Using ERLN Methods for Sewage Sludge[a]

| Sample Number | Sample Type | Larval Fish | | Mysid | Copepods | |
		Cyprinodon variegatus	*Menidia menidia*	*Mysidopsis bahia*	*Eurytemora herdmani*	*Pseudocalanus minutus*
6	Storage tank	—	—	—	—	0.19(0.12,1.0)B
7	Storage tank	—	—	2.5(1.0, 8.6)P[b] 2.6(1.9, 3.3)M[b] 2.3(0.02, 6.8)P[b] 2.6(1.9, 3.5)P	0.19(0.13,0.29)P	—
8	Line to storage tanks	5.0(4.1, 6.1)P 7.5(5.6, 10.0)P	3.9(1.8, 5.6)B 6.5(5.6, 10.0)B	—	—	—
9B	Barge composite	—	—	—	<0.08 <0.02 <0.02	—
10	Barge composite	—	—	—	0.03(0.01,0.45)P 0.09(0.05,0.15)P[c]	—
11	Storage tank composite	>10.0	—	0.84(0.49,1.1)P 0.51(0.35,0.67)P	0.36(0.02,0.50)P 0.10(0.08,0.14)P[c]	0.11(0.08,0.15)P 0.13(0.1, 0.18)P[c]

[a]Sludge samples collected from Middlesex County Utilities Authority. LC_{50} as percent whole sludge (95% confidence interval) calculated by Probit (P), Binomial (B), or Moving average (M) method after Abbott's correction for control mortality. Dash indicates no tests performed.
[b]Sludge treatments renewed each 24 h.
[c]Control mortality >10%.

confidence intervals for this Microtox® test were calculated to be about 10% of the reported values.

The species sensitivity indicated by toxicity tests on a single whole sludge sample (sample 11) (Table 10.2) suggests the following relationship: copepods > mysids > fish larvae. Tests on samples 8 and 11 indicate no appreciable differences in sensitivity between the two species of fish or between the two copepod species tested.

10.3.2. Comparison of ERLN and Presently Used Sludge Bioassays

The 96-h LC_{50} values obtained by the ERLN bioassays were slightly higher for each sludge sample tested with mysids and for two of three samples tested with fish when compared with results of the test methodologies conducted by the contract laboratory (Table 10.4). Except for the fish test with Middlesex sludge, however, the LC_{50} values of the mysid and fish tests are considered to be similar, since all test results are within a factor of 2.4 or less. Differences of this magnitude are commonly encountered among laboratories testing the same species with the same methodology. In an EPA interlaboratory study, six different laboratories that used similar static 96-h acute test protocols and test species reported LC_{50} values that varied by a factor of 2.2 for mysids and 2.5 for the fish *C. variegatus* for an inorganic compound and by at least a factor of 2.9 for an organic chemical (Schimmel, 1981). In contrast, the different LC_{50} values obtained here by the two different fish assays on the Middlesex County sample may be toxicologically significant. It cannot be determined from this study whether this difference is due to intrinsic differences in bioassay protocols; or to the test species and life stage; or to other variables, such as source of dilution water, source of test organisms, or condition of test organisms.

According to the ERLN results (Table 10.4), copepods were more sensitive than mysids by a factor of 5.7 for sample 13 and by a factor of 9.3 for sample 14. This is consistent with the greater sensitivity observed with copepods (by a factor of 5–14) during initial definitive bioassays on Middlesex County sludge (Table 10.2). Relative sensitivity of copepods and mysids to Westchester County sludge cannot be determined. The mysid LC_{50} value was 1.8%, while only 35% of the copepods in 0.8% sludge died. Control mortalities in copepod assays were 13% for sample 13, 20% for sample 14; and 15% for sample 15. These control mortalities are not considered excessive for sensitive test organisms such as copepods.

10.4. DISCUSSION

The initial series of bioassays on Middlesex County sewage sludge conducted during development of the ERLN methods provides some insight into the performance of these assays. Where data are available, there was good within-sample replication in ERLN mysid and larval fish assays. Copepod assays were more variable, since two out of three varied by a factor of three. Acute toxicity of Middlesex County sludge was low for fish and mysids, with 3.9% whole sludge the lowest LC_{50} value for fish and 0.51% the lowest for mysids; however, copepods were more sensitive since LC_{50} values ranged from <0.02 to 0.36%.

The comparison of ERLN and presently used regulatory assays for sewage sludge indicates that these two methods

Table 10.4. Results of Split-Sample Study Comparing ERLN Sewage Sludge Acute Bioassay Methods with NYTL Methods[a]

Sludge Sample Number	Treatment Plant	Fish		Mysids		Copepods
		Juvenile *Menidia menidia* NYTL	Larval *Menidia beryllina* ERLN	(*Mysidopsis bahia*)		(*Eurytemora herdmani*)
				NYTL	ERLN	ERLN
13	Bergen Co.	2.1(1.6,2.7)P	5.0(3.3,6.7)P	0.91(0.70,1.4)P	1.9(1.5,3.1)P	0.34(0.28,0.47)M[b]
14	Middlesex Co.	1.0(0.78,1.3)P	8.1(7.5,8.8)P	0.66(0.49,1.3)P	1.1(0.76,1.7)P	0.12(0.10,0.15)P[b]
15	Westchester Co.	2.6(1.5,5.0)B	2.3(1.7,3.1)B	0.85(0.51,1.2)P	1.5(0.28,3.6)P	>0.8[b]

[a]LC_{50} expressed as percent whole sludge, calculated by Probit (P), Moving average (M), or Binomial (B) method after Abbott's correction for control mortality; 95% confidence interval in parentheses.
[b]Control mortality 13–20%.

Table 10.5. Acute Toxicity of Sewage Sludge Reported by NYTL for Seven Metropolitan New York and New Jersey Wastewater Treatment Plants[a]

Treatment Plant	Mean LC$_{50}$ ± Standard Deviation(n)[b] Coefficient of Variation		Ratio LC$_{50}$ Silversides:Mysids for Same Sample $\bar{x}$ (range)	Sample Mysid LC$_{50}$ < Silverside LC$_{50}$ (%)
	Mysids	Atlantic Silversides		
Middlesex County 3/82–4/84	0.42 ± 0.23(8) 55	1.3 ± 0.38(7) 29	3.2(1.5–6.2)	100
Newtown Creek[c] 6/80–10/82	0.70 ± 0.53(15) 76	1.3 ± 0.33(14) 25	3.5(0.5–14.4)	86
Bergen County 3/81–3/84	0.72 ± 0.22(12) 31	2.2 ± 1.3(11) 56	3.5(1.7–7.8)	100
Westchester County 1/81–4/84	1.0 ± 0.5(12) 50	2.2 ± 0.83(10) 38	2.1(0.6–3.5)	89
Hunts Point[c] 6/80–10/82	1.1 ± 0.48(14) 42	1.6 ± 0.71(14) 44	1.4(0.6–3.0)	79
Wards Island[c] 1/81–10/82	1.2 ± 0.27(13) 22	2.0 ± 0.96(12) 48	1.8(0.7–2.8)	72
Rockaway[c] 1/81–10/82	1.6 ± 0.84(13) 54	2.0 ± 0.58(12) 29	1.4(0.5–2.6)	70

[a]LC$_{50}$ values calculated by binomial method.
[b]N = number of samples tested.
[c]Source: City of New York (1983).

produce comparable results, with one exception. The number of sludges included in this study were small, with only three treatment plants sampled; however, in the absence of major differences in the comparison study of test methods, we conclude that the fish and mysid assays presently used for regulation are satisfactory for waste characterization.

Additional data on acute toxicity determined by NYTL for sewage sludge from seven metropolitan New York and New Jersey treatment plants are summarized in Table 10.5 in order to compare the present results with a more extensive database. Data for this table were compiled from quarterly toxicity results using present regulatory tests on composite samples of barged sludge. Close agreement is evident between NYTL LC$_{50}$ values for samples 13, 14, and 15 of the present study (Table 10.4) and mean values in Table 10.5 for the same treatment plants. This suggests that the acute toxicity of sludge used in the present study is typical for these three plants.

The summary of toxicity data for quarterly sludge samples (Table 10.5) also shows high within-plant variability in acute toxicity for the seven treatment plants considered. The present study suggests that one source of this variation at the Middlesex County plant may be length of time sludge is held in storage tanks prior to sampling. The toxicity survey for sludge from storage tanks (Table 10.3) must be considered preliminary, since sludge supernatant rather than whole sludge was tested. For the present, however, storage time should be considered as a potentially important variable when collecting sludge samples for toxicity tests, pending more conclusive studies. For some sludges, the supernatant may give a reasonable indication of relative toxicity of whole sludge, depending on the sensitivity of the test. Ecological Analysts, Inc. (City of New York, 1983), detected no significant differences in acute toxicity between paired samples of supernatant and anaerobically digested whole sludge with the *Palaemonetes pugio* test for 10 of 12 sludges or with the *Menidia menidia* test for 9 sludges. The acute test using mysids was more sensitive, showing whole sludge to be more toxic for 10 of 12 samples, although only by a factor of 2–3 in 5 of these samples. It is unknown whether a similar relationship exists with aerobically digested Middlesex County sludge.

One application of acute toxicity data from tests of sewage sludge is to regulate the rate of discharge of sewage sludge from barges during ocean disposal. The regulations governing the disposal of wastes into the ocean (U.S. EPA, 1977) establish a Limiting Permissible Concentration (LPC) of a waste that cannot be exceeded either outside of the dumpsite during dumping or within the dumpsite after an initial 4-h mixing period. The LPC is intended to protect organisms at the dumpsite from unreasonable acute or chronic toxicity or other sublethal adverse effects. The LPC for sewage sludge is set by EPA Region 2 (New York, New Jersey, Puerto Rico, and Virgin Islands) based on acute bioassays with the whole waste. The LPC is calculated as 0.01 of the second lowest LC_{50} reported by each discharging treatment plant during the previous 2 y. These regulations call for use of bioassay species that are among the most sensitive as documented in the scientific literature or species accepted by the EPA as reliable indicators of the anticipated impact on the ecosystem at the disposal site.

Although available information is quite limited at present, it appears reasonable to consider the mysid (*Mysidopsis bahia*) and Atlantic silverside (*Menidia menidia*) as appropriate sensitive marine organisms for acute regulatory tests on sewage sludge. They are used in marine testing because they are available through culture or capture, their survival is acceptable in culture and testing, and they are reasonably sensitive (Anderson et al., 1974; Hansen, 1984). These species are neither as sensitive as copepods nor, possibly, the developmental stages of certain crustaceans; however, certain complexities of copepod culture and testing presently limit the routine application of this test. In acute tests of sludges from 12 New York City treatment plants, mysids were found to be most sensitive in 91.5% of 35 tests on whole sludge, Atlantic silversides most sensitive in 8.5%, and adult grass shrimp always least sensitive (City of New York, 1983). This is consistent with the NYTL results summarized in Table 10.5, and indicates that the mysid LC_{50} values are used most frequently to calculate the LPC for various metropolitan New York and New Jersey sludges.

Regarding the relevance of the mysid and Atlantic silverside to dumpsites in the Atlantic Ocean, the Atlantic silverside inhabits the northeast U.S. continental shelf out to 50 m during winter, but in other seasons it inhabits intertidal creeks, marshes, and the shore zone of estuaries (Conover and Murawski, 1982). The mysid *Mysidopsis bahia* occurs only in shallow tropical and semi-tropical bays (Stuck et al., 1979), but may be a reasonable surrogate for continental shelf mysid species for toxicological purposes. Acute and chronic bioassays with cadmium, for example, produced comparable results with *Mysidopsis bahia* and *Mysidopsis bigelowi* (Gentile et al., 1982). The latter species ranges along the entire eastern U.S. coast and on Georges Bank.

The extent that the LPC may be protective of adverse acute and chronic effects on tested or untested species at an ocean disposal site is largely untested. The 0.01 factor used to calculate the LPC from acute toxicity tests was not developed experimentally, but was adopted from Federal Water Pollution Control Administration (1968) Water Quality Criteria. This generalized factor was recommended to estimate chronically acceptable concentrations of an individual persistent chemical or waste, based on acute toxicity data alone. The utility of this factor to estimate chronically acceptable concentrations of sewage sludge has not been determined in chronic or partial-chronic studies with marine organisms. However, unless probabilities for chronic exposure to sewage sludge at dumpsites can be defined, it is debatable whether these complex tests should be conducted. At present, there is no accepted approach for the use of acute toxicity data in environmental situations for wastes such as sewage sludge, where waste concentrations and bioavailability of contaminants are expected to be quite variable over time. Hansen (1984) has pointed out that acute toxicity tests are most appropriately used to measure relative toxicity of substances or relative sensitivity of species to a particular substance and not to predict environmentally acceptable concentrations.

Presently used acute bioassays using mysids and Atlantic silversides, if conducted according to U.S. EPA (1978) or ASTM (1980) guidelines, should provide a reliable and reproducible measure of the toxicity of sewage sludge in order to characterize the toxicity of this waste; however, use of this acute toxicity data alone to calculate the LPC and to estimate environmentally acceptable concentrations is questionable. Rather, environmental acceptability must be evaluated by more extensive investigations that estimate waste-exposure concentrations in the field over time and contrast these against the potentials for adverse effects and bioaccumulation of contaminants as determined in appropriate tests with marine organisms. Such a hazard assessment strategy has been discussed by Gentile et al. (1987) and should form the basis for a scientifically credible procedure to evaluate the environmental safety of disposal of sewage sludge into the ocean.

10.5. SUMMARY AND CONCLUSIONS

Test methods developed at ERLN to test the acute toxicity of sewage sludge corroborated that three metropolitan New York and New Jersey sludges tested had generally low acute toxicities. The 96-h LC_{50} values observed ranged from 1 to 10% whole sludge for fish, 0.5 to 2.5% for mysids, and 0.03 to >0.8% for copepods.

The newly developed methods produced results for fish and mysids similar to those from methods presently used for regulatory decision making. This indicates that the present, easier-to-conduct methods may be satisfactory to measure acute toxicity of sludge relative to other wastes or to document changes over time in acute toxicity of sludges from a given treatment plant. One exception to this conclusion may be the fish bioassay for an aerobically produced sludge. The newly developed larval fish test suggested lower acute toxicity than did the presently used method for this sludge sample.

The acute toxicity of sewage sludge from a given treatment plant may be quite variable over time, as shown by high coefficients of variation for seven within-plant comparisons of quarterly LC_{50} values. Toxicity of supernatant of one aerobically produced sewage sludge was found to increase up to an order of magnitude during storage. The potential for variability within and between tanks should be considered when sampling sewage sludge tanks.

Mysids (*Mysidopsis bahia*) are usually 1.4–3.5 times more acutely sensitive to sewage sludge than are juvenile Atlantic silversides (*Menidia menidia*), based on 76 regulatory toxicity tests on sludge from seven metropolitan treatment plants. Our tests showed that copepods may be more acutely sensitive than this mysid by as much as a factor of 9.

Acute toxicity tests are considered suitable to judge relative toxicity of sludges; however, they should not be used alone to estimate environmental hazards of sewage sludges. Acute toxicity tests provide only the first evidence on the potential effect of sludges, and this information must be considered with potential exposure information as part of a complete assessment of environmental hazard.

ACKNOWLEDGMENTS

We acknowledge with thanks the excellent cooperation and assistance provided during this project by personnel of the Middlesex County Utilities Authority, Bergen County Utilities Authority, and the Yonkers Joint Waste Water Treatment Plant, Westchester County, New York. We also greatly appreciate the cooperation of New York Testing Laboratory, Westbury, New York, particularly R. Gigante, President, and J. Barbieri, Manager, Bioassay Laboratory, for their participation in the comparison of test methods. We thank D. Hansen and R. Voyer for their review of the manuscripts. This project was supported by the EPA Office of Water Regulations and Standards, Criteria and Standards Division. This is Contribution No. 666 of the Environmental Research Laboratory, Narrangansett. Although the research described in this article was funded by the U.S. Environmental Protection Agency, it has not been subjected to Agency review and therefore does not necessarily reflect the views of the Agency and no official endorsement should be inferred. Mention of trade names or commercial products does not constitute endorsement or recommendation for use.

REFERENCES

American Society for Testing and Materials (ASTM). 1980. Conducting acute toxicity tests with fishes, macroinvertebrates, and amphibians. *In*: Annual Book of ASTM Standards. American Society for Testing and Materials, Philadelphia, pp. 1–23.

Anderson, J. W., J. M. Neff, B. A. Cox, H. E. Tatem, and G. M. Hightower. 1974. Characteristics of dispersions and water-soluble extracts of crude and refined oils and their toxicity to estuarine crustaceans and fish. *Marine Biology*, **27**, 75–88.

Beckman Instruments, Inc. 1982. Beckman Microtox® System Operating Manual. Beckman Instructions Publication No. 015-555879, Beckman Instruments, Carlsbad, California, 12 sections, paginated separately.

Booth, G. D. 1975. On the use of Abbott's formula: a correction for natural response. *Biometrics*, **31**, 590.

City of New York. 1983. A Special Permit Application for the Disposal of Sewage Sludge from Twelve New York City Water Pollution Control Plants at the 12-Mile Site, Vol. 1 and 2. City of New York, Department of Environmental Protection, New York, 18 sections + appendix, paginated separately.

Conover, D. O., and S. A. Murawski. 1982. Offshore winter migration of the Atlantic silverside. *Menidia menidia. Fishery Bulletin*, **80**, 145–150.

Federal Water Pollution Control Administration. 1968. Water Quality Criteria. U.S. Department of Interior, Washington, D.C., 234 pp.

Finney, D. J. 1971. Probit Analysis. Cambridge University Press, London, 333 pp.

Gentile, S. M., J. H. Gentile, J. Walker, and J. F. Heltshe. 1982. Chronic effects of cadmium on two species of mysid shrimp: *Mysidopsis bahia* and *Mysidopsis bigelowi. Hydrobiologia*, **93**, 195–204.

Gentile, J. H., S. M. Gentile, G. Hoffman, J. F. Heltshe, and N. Hairston, Jr. 1983. The effects of a chronic mercury exposure on survival, reproduction and population dynamics of *Mysidopsis bahia. Environmental Toxicology and Chemistry*, **2**, 61–68.

Gentile, J. H., V. J. Bierman, Jr., J. F. Paul, H. A. Walker, and D. C. Miller. 1987. A hazard assessment research strategy for ocean disposal. *In*:

Oceanic Processes in Marine Pollution, Vol. 3: Waste Management in the Ocean. M. A. Champ and P. K. Park (Eds.). R. E. Krieger Publishing Company, Melbourne, Florida, 199–212.

Guillard, R. R. L., and J. H. Ryther. 1962. Studies on marine planktonic diatoms. *I. Cyclotella nana* Hustedt and *Detonula confervacea* (Cleve) Gran. *Canadian Journal of Microbiology*, **8**, 229–239.

Hansen, D. J. 1984. Utility of toxicity tests to measure effects of substances on marine organisms. *In*: Concepts in Marine Pollution Measurements, H. White (Ed.). Maryland Sea Grant College, College Park, Maryland, pp. 33–56.

Hansen, D. J., P. R. Parrish, S. C. Schimmel, and L. R. Goodman. 1978. Life-cycle toxicity test using sheepshead minnows (*Cyprinodon variegatus*). *In*: Bioassay Procedures for the Ocean Disposal Permit Program, U.S. Environmental Protection Agency Publication No. 600/9-78/010, Environmental Research Laboratory, Gulf Breeze, Florida, pp. 109–117.

Middaugh, D. P., and T. Takita. 1983. Tidal and diurnal spawning cues in the Atlantic silverside, *Menidia menidia*. *Environmental Biology of Fishes*, **8**, 97–104.

Miller, D. C., M. Marcy, W. Berry, C. Deacutis, S. Lussier, A. Kuhn, M. Heber, S. C. Schimmel, and E. Jackim. 1984. Final Report: Evaluation of Methods to Measure the Acute Toxicity of Sewage Sludge. U.S. Environmental Protection Agency, Environmental Research Laboratory, Narragansett, Rhode Island, 39 pp. + appendix.

New York Testing Laboratories. Undated. Manual of Practice: Bioassays. New York Testing Laboratories, Westbury, New York, 12 pp.

Rand, M. C., A. E. Greenberg, and M. J. Taras (Eds.). 1975. Standard Methods for the Examination of Water and Wastewater, 14th edition. American Public Health Association, Washington, D.C., 1193 pp.

Schimmel, S. C. 1981. Results: Interlaboratory Comparison—Acute Toxicity Tests Using Estuarine Animals. U.S. Environmental Protection Agency Publication No. 600/4-81-003, Environmental Research Laboratory, Gulf Breeze, Florida, 14 pp.

Stuck, K. C., H. M. Perry, and R. W. Heard. 1979. Records and range extensions of Mysidacea from coastal and shelf waters of the eastern Gulf of Mexico. *Gulf Research Reports*, **6**, 239–248.

Thompson, W. R. 1947. Use of moving averages and interpolation to estimate median–effective dose. I. Fundamental formulas, estimation of error, and relation to other methods. *Bacteriological Reviews*, **11**, 115–145.

U.S. Environmental Protection Agency. 1977. Ocean Dumping Regulations and Criteria. *Federal Register*, **42**, 2468–2493.

U.S. Environmental Protection Agency. 1978. Bioassay Procedures for the Ocean Disposal Permit Program. U.S. Environmental Protection Agency Publication No. 600/9-78-010, Environmental Research Laboratory, Gulf Breeze, Florida, 121 pp.

Chapter 11

The Application of a Hazard Assessment Research Strategy to the Ocean Disposal of a Dredged Material: Overview

John H. Gentile and Gerald G. Pesch

Environmental Research Laboratory
U.S. Environmental Protection Agency
Narragansett, Rhode Island

Thomas M. Dillon

Environmental Research Laboratory
U.S. Army Corps of Engineers
Vicksburg, Mississippi

Abstract	**115**
11.1. Introduction	**116**
11.2. Strategy for Assessing Consequences of Ocean Disposal	**117**
11.3. Hazard Assessment Application to Dredged Material—A Case Study	**118**
11.3.1. Site Characterization	118
11.3.2. Sediment Characterization	119
11.3.3. Exposure Assessment	119
11.3.4. Effects Assessment	119
11.3.5. Hazard Assessment	120
11.3.6. Monitoring	121
11.4. Confined Upland Disposal and Wetland Creation	**121**
11.5. Summary	**122**
Acknowledgments	**122**
References	**122**

ABSTRACT

Under the Marine Protection, Research and Sanctuaries Act the U.S. Environmental Protection Agency (EPA) has responsibility for establishing and applying criteria for reviewing and evaluating permits for dumping wastes into the ocean, and the U.S. Army Corps of Engineers (COE) has responsibility for issuing permits for the disposal of dredged material into the ocean. After several years of operational experience, the EPA and the COE have reexamined the strengths and weaknesses of this permit program and the general state of the art in sediment testing for the evaluation of the disposal of dredged material into the marine environment. This chapter describes a predictive hazard assessment strategy and decision rationale for disposal that can be used as the basis for revisions both in the ocean dumping regulations and in the permitting program. The strategy requires the physical, chemical, and biological characterization of the dredged material and the dumpsite sediment. This characterization provides a basis for developing a comprehensive, tiered testing and analysis program for determining the potential environmental exposures and biological effects. The synthesis of the exposure and effects data supports an overall hazard assessment of the potential environmental effects, which, in turn, forms the basis for an initial permitting decision. The disposal activity is monitored specifically to verify the prediction of hazard and to support future revisions of the permit requirements.

11.1. INTRODUCTION

The Marine Protection, Research and Sanctuaries Act (MPRSA) (U.S. Congress, 1972) states that it is the policy of the United States to regulate the dumping of all types of materials into ocean waters and to prevent or strictly limit the dumping of any material that would adversely affect human health or welfare, the marine environment, or ecological systems. The implementation of this law through the issuance of permits is jointly shared by the U.S. Environmental Protection Agency (EPA) and the U.S. Army Corps of Engineers (COE).

The EPA has responsibility for establishing and applying criteria for reviewing and evaluating permits for dumping wastes into the ocean. The issuance of permits for the ocean disposal of dredged material is the responsibility of the COE and is described in the MPRSA. Briefly, in establishing such criteria, consideration is given but not limited to the following: demonstration of a need for ocean dumping; effects on human health and welfare; effects on fisheries resources; ecosystem effects with respect to transport and fate of materials, changes in marine ecosystem diversity, productivity, and population dynamics; the amounts, concentrations, and persistence of contaminants; and appropriate alternative methods of disposal and the environmental and economic impacts of such alternatives.

In 1977, the EPA published final regulations and criteria for ocean dumping (U.S. EPA, 1977). These regulations reflected the experience of the EPA in the implementation of the MPRSA and specified in more detail the considerations that go into determining whether a permit will be issued. The EPA also improved the site-designation process and incorporated recent scientific advances into the establishment of criteria. These changes in no way alter the original intent of the MPRSA, which is to eliminate the ocean dumping of unacceptable materials. The regulations address the environmental impact of the ocean disposal of dredged materials and define the types of environmental information that will be required by the EPA to determine the suitability of the material for disposal into the ocean.

In order to implement the regulations, the EPA and the COE jointly prepared technical guidance in the form of an implementation manual (U.S. EPA–U.S. COE, 1977). The manual specified which test procedures were to be followed in collecting the information to be used in making a disposal decision. Among the procedures were those for chemically characterizing the proposed dredged material; for determining the acute toxicity of liquid, suspended-particulate, and solid phases; for estimating the potential for contaminant bioaccumulation; and for describing the initial mixing during disposal.

These procedures represented the technical state of the art and were never intended to be inflexible standards. The recommended test methods were chosen to provide technical information that was consistent with the criteria specified in the regulations. Because the technical state of the art is a dynamic process, it was recognized from the outset that the implementation manual would require both augmentation and revision on a periodic basis.

Several years of operational experience with the sediment test methods and the interpretive guidance provided in the manual have led to the identification of the following technical issues:

1. The toxicity test methods are limited to measuring mortality over a short (4–10 d) exposure period from which long-term assessments of impact are to be inferred.

2. Generally, insensitive species have been selected for all the testing, including sediment toxicity and bioaccumulation; if mortality is to be a useful endpoint for regulating sediment disposal, then only the most sensitive species should be used.

3. The testing of a liquid phase is relevant to assessing only the short-term water-column effects that might occur during the disposal operation; the utility of this liquid phase is questionable. In addition, the preparation of the liquid phase (elutriate test) does not have credible scientific support for use as a measure of the bioavailability of contaminants.

4. The currently utilized experimental design is not appropriate for assessing effects outside the dumpsite.

5. There is no strategy or rationale for synthesizing or interpreting the information on toxicology and bioaccumulation.

Test methods have two functions: detection and assessment. In the case of detection, the purpose is to quantify a biological response as a function of exposure to a particular material or compound. Current mortality-oriented tests do address the problem of the significance of that measure beyond the level of biological organization at which it was conducted. Similarly, bioaccumulation tests allow only for the quantification of a contaminant in an organism but provide no information about the biological significance of the resulting contaminant residue in the tissue. Assessment methods attempt to address the "so what" question and are generally integrative in nature. Responses such as changes in growth, survival, or reproduction can be assessed relative to the long-term integrity of populations, and therefore may be viewed in a more meaningful and predictive fashion.

The above-mentioned issues and limitations have lead the COE and the EPA to reexamine the state of the art in sediment testing for the evaluation of dredged-material disposal in the marine environment. The intent of this evaluation has been to increase and improve the test methods and endpoints being used and to determine the limits of applicability of laboratory tests to the environment through field verification. The evaluation process has led to the development and application of a hazard assessment strategy in which data from laboratory measures of biological effects are synthesized with estimates of the concentrations of environmental contaminants to predict risk to populations and communities.

This chapter describes a decision rationale for ocean disposal based upon this predictive hazard assessment strategy and presents a site-specific case study designed to evaluate the applicability of the strategy for the disposal of dredged materials. This case study is a joint effort between the EPA and the COE with the primary objective of evaluating the methodologies used to conduct a hazard assessment of open-water disposal of dredged material. This is the first use of these test methods in the evaluation of dredged material, and their application as such should be viewed as experimental. The experience obtained from this program will provide an effective suite of test methods as well as an evaluation of all aspects of the hazard assessment research strategy.

11.2. STRATEGY FOR ASSESSING CONSEQUENCES OF OCEAN DISPOSAL

If the ocean disposal of contaminated sediments is to continue as a waste-management option, then decision makers

must be provided with a rationale that is both expeditious and scientifically sound. In addition to providing guidance for the acquisition and interpretation of information, the rationale must include a predictive assessment procedure so that environmental consequences of disposal alternatives can be evaluated *a priori*. The predicted consequences must include appropriate levels of confidence to facilitate comparison of alternative disposal options.

The assessment must include explicit coupling of pollutant source inputs with ecosystem impacts. Ecosystem impacts are typically inferred from tests on individual species from which forecasts are made to the population and community levels of biological organization. These forecasts can be accomplished by relating the source inputs (e.g., pollutant type and loading rate) to the biological effects through measurements of environmental exposure. Pollutant input rates are the source terms for fate and transport models that are used to predict pollutant concentration isopleths on defined spatial and temporal scales. Such isopleths are directly compatible with laboratory measurements of biological effects that are typically described as functions of pollutant concentration and exposure duration (Fig. 11.1). Hazard assessment is a process that estimates the probability of environmental impact through a comparison of the predicted exposure to an environmental contaminant with contaminant concentrations known to produce biological effects.

Bierman et al. (1986) proposed a research strategy for ocean disposal that supports a decision rationale based upon a

Figure 11.1. Hazard assessment strategy: exposure and effects definitions.

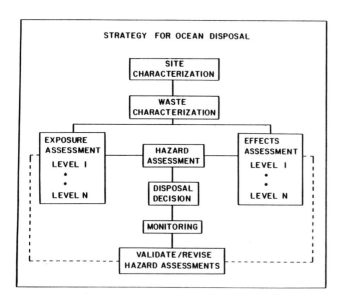

Figure 11.2. Decision rationale for ocean disposal.

predictive hazard assessment approach. This rationale contains several components, each involving the acquisition and synthesis of information that leads to a regulatory decision. One of its principal features is that the effects and exposure components are tiered (Fig. 11.2). The ordering of the tiers implies increasing degrees of complexity, resolution, and predictive confidence (Cairns et al., 1978). An additional assumption is that there are clearly defined criteria for decisions at each level of the hierarchy, which then trigger the need for increased data acquisition at higher, more complex tiers. A prediction of hazard is made by comparing the predicted concentration of the material through environmental exposure (exposure assessment) and the concentration producing biological effects in the laboratory studies (effects assessment) at each tier. The greater the difference between the exposure concentration and that causing biological effects the less will be the probability of hazard. Hazard is quantified through the use of a probability function, which represents the degree of overlap resulting from the intersection of the variances about the exposure and effects concentrations. If the confidence of the prediction is unacceptable, then additional levels of testing can be conducted. Thus, the level of predictive confidence desired for the management decision will influence the level of complexity and resolution of the technical data. This approach permits the development of a series of testable hypotheses that are amenable to both labora-

tory and field verification. It also permits selective, limited testing as needed, rather than the application of a prescribed suite of tests in all cases, as is presently done.

11.3. HAZARD ASSESSMENT APPLICATION TO DREDGED MATERIAL—A CASE STUDY

The EPA and the COE are jointly conducting a comprehensive Field Verification Program (FVP) to evaluate the risks associated with the disposal of dredged material into the ocean. This program has three primary objectives: (1) to demonstrate the adaptability of existing predictive techniques to dredged material, and to determine the reproducibility of those techniques in the laboratory; (2) to utilize field studies to verify the accuracy of the laboratory predictions; and (3) to compare and evaluate the overall impact of disposal in upland, wetland, and open-water environments.

A hazard assessment evaluation has been applied to the aquatic disposal alternative as a site- and waste-specific application of the ocean-disposal rationale (Fig. 11.2). This case study allows the evaluation of the hazard assessment strategy as a framework for predicting the impact of a material disposed of into the ocean and the development and testing of hypotheses relevant to the overall assessment and regulatory approach. Although this chapter emphasizes the ocean-disposal alternative of the FVP, a short summary of activities occurring in the upland and intertidal environments has been included for completeness in section 11.4.

11.3.1. Site Characterization

The aquatic dumpsite for the FVP is a historical site known as the Central Long Island Sound (CLIS) Disposal Site, which is located ~15 km off the coast of Connecticut (Fig. 11.3). This area was previously known as the New Haven Dump Site and was the first site designated in Long Island Sound after the passage of the MPRSA in 1972 (U.S. Congress, 1972). The dumpsite is rectangular in shape, measures 3.7 km in the east–west and 1.8 km in the north–south direction and is 20 m deep. Tidal currents (20–40 cm s^{-1}) typically dominate the east–west water motion, resulting in a near-bottom net northerly drift of 5 cm s^{-1}. Sedimentology of the dumpsite and adjacent reference site is primarily silt–clay with a mean grain size of 0.013 mm. Salinities range from 24 to 30 g kg^{-1}.

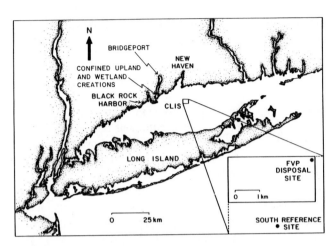

Figure 11.3. Location of the study site for dredged-material disposal in Central Long Island Sound. Reference site is 3 km southeast of the disposal site.

Temperatures span the annual seasonal range, and thermal stratification occurs from April to September. The suspended-solids concentration measured 1 m above the bottom typically averages 5 mg liter^{-1}, with moderate storm-associated values of 25 mg liter^{-1} and intense storm activity producing values in excess of 100 mg liter^{-1}.

11.3.2. Sediment Characterization

The dredging site for the field verification study is Black Rock Harbor (BRH), Connecticut, where maintenance dredging provided a channel 46 m wide and 5.2 m deep at mean low water. Approximately 57,000 m^3 of material dredged from this site was disposed of in the northeastern corner of the CLIS dumpsite. Homogenized BRH dredged material contains substantial concentrations of both organic and inorganic contaminants. The polychlorinated biphenyls (PCB) concentration is 6,800 ng g^{-1} (dry wt), and the polynuclear aromatic hydrocarbon (PAH) concentrations range from 3,400 ng g^{-1} for the napthalenes to 13,400 ng g^{-1} for the benzopyrenes and to 22,800 ng g^{-1} for the benzanthracenes. The total organic carbon content is 5.6%. The principal inorganic contaminants present in BRH dredged material are Cu (2300 μg g^{-1}), Cr (1430 μg g^{-1}), Zn (1200 μg g^{-1}), Pb (380 μg g^{-1}), Ni (140 μg g^{-1}), Cd (23 μg g^{-1}), and Hg (1.7 μg g^{-1}) (Paul et al., Chapter 12).

11.3.3. Exposure Assessment

The exposure assessment component of hazard assessment relates the source input of the dredged material and its contaminants to the distributions of the contaminants in space and time in the vicinity of the disposal mound. The specific objectives of exposure assessment in this case study are to relate the source of contaminants in the dredged-material disposal mound to the near-field measurements through modeling of the vertical transport of specific contaminants and particulate materials, and to quantify the environmental processes controlling BRH contaminant-phase partitioning (Paul et al., Chapter 12). This information is then used to describe contaminant characteristics at designated stations for the determination of biological effects in the water column (pelagic zone), near the sediment–water interface (epibenthic zone), and in the sediments (benthic zone).

The conceptual model used for the exposure assessment component of the FVP assumes that the dredged material on the mound can be resuspended by various processes, such as tidal currents and wind-generated waves (Paul et al., Chapter 12). Repartitioning of the contaminants between the dissolved and the particulate phases will result as the dredged material is mixed with background material, transported both vertically and horizontally, and redeposited. These processes create an exposure field, which can vary continuously in space and time in the vicinity of the dumpsite. The physical and chemical components of the exposure environment are described in the quantitative terms needed to conduct effects assessment measurements.

11.3.4. Effects Assessment

The purpose of the effects assessment component of hazard assessment is to develop and to verify in the field methodologies for determining the biological effects of contaminants in dredged material. The effects component of the FVP is constructed in a hierarchical manner proceeding from the individual organism level of biological organization to the population level and, ultimately, to effects on communities (Fig. 11.4). At the level of the individual organism, a variety of endpoints are being examined, ranging from short-term biochemical responses to integrative whole-organism responses, such as survival, growth, and reproduction. From these latter responses, population inferences can be made through the use of demographic techniques (Phelps et al., Chapter 13).

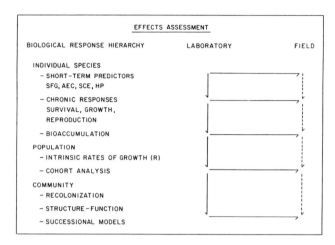

Figure 11.4. Schematic diagram for conceptual model for the effects assessment component of the FVP, showing the hierarchy of biological responses, scope for growth (SFG), adenylate energy charge (AEC), sister-chromatid exchange (SCE) and histopathology (HP), and the laboratory–field interrelations.

The hierarchy of test methods is being conducted on selected indigenous and introduced species under both laboratory and field exposure conditions. In addition, certain species are being used only in laboratory studies to test the utility of surrogate species. The utility of laboratory tests will be verified by comparing the exposure–response relationships from the laboratory studies with analogous data collected from the same species along an exposure gradient at the dumpsite.

Assessment of the biological consequences of residues of contaminants in tissue (resulting from the bioaccumulation of contaminants) focuses on comparing the residues in tissue for selected organic and inorganic contaminants with the hierarchy of effects measurements from organisms exposed both in the laboratory and in the field. This is necessarily a correlative analytical approach because it would be impossible to determine an unequivocal cause–effect relationship on a contaminant-specific basis with such a complex waste material.

11.3.5. Hazard Assessment

Hazard assessment compares the predicted duration and magnitude of concentrations of the contaminant in the environment to concentrations of the contaminant that cause

toxicity responses in laboratory studies. When properly quantified, this comparison provides an estimate of the probability of hazard to the aquatic environment.

To illustrate how this approach can be utilized to make an initial prediction of hazard, we have synthesized data for predicted exposure and for laboratory effects for two species (Fig. 11.5). Environmental concentrations of suspended BRH dredged material were predicted at 1 m above the bottom under three sets of conditions: (1) normal background level of suspended solids (2) average storm conditions, and (3) a storm of hurricane intensity and duration. The effects component consists solely of laboratory studies of contaminant concentrations in bedded and suspended solids that elicited short-term, acute responses and long-term, chronic re-

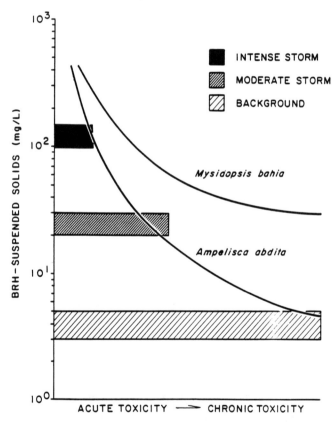

Figure 11.5. Response isopleths for *Mysidopsis bahia* and *Ampelisca abdita* exposed to Black Rock Harbor dredged material in the suspended phase. Measured responses ranged from 96-hr LC_{50} (lethal dose at which 50% of the test organisms die within 96 h) values to chronic mortality, reduced reproduction, and reduced intrinsic rates of growth for populations. Predicted field exposures are represented by the concentration of total suspended solids on the ordinate and exposure duration on the abscissa.

sponses. These laboratory studies did not simulate environmental exposure conditions, so they do not represent a field verification.

The effects data are for the mysid shrimp, *Mysidopsis bahia* (a surrogate species), and for the infaunal amphipod, *Ampelisca abdita* (an indigenous species), exposed to suspended solids from BRH. The response curve of effects on *M. bahia* (Fig. 11.5) includes mortality under short-term, intermediate, and chronic exposure conditions and decreased growth, reproduction, and intrinsic rates of population growth as a function of differing magnitudes (ordinate) and duration (abscissa) of exposure. For example, the exposures to suspended solids required to produce short-term effects would be approached only under worst-case conditions resulting from a storm of hurricane intensity and duration. Normal background concentrations of suspended solids of 5 mg liter^{-1} are well below the concentrations causing both acute effects [LC$_{50}$ (lethal concentration at which 50% of the test organisms die within 96 h) = 260 mg liter^{-1}] and those adversely affecting reproduction (50 mg liter^{-1}) in this species. In contrast, *A. abdita* could experience acute mortalities in the environment under worst-case exposure conditions, sub-lethal effects under typical storm conditions, and direct effects on population growth at normal background concentrations of suspended solids—if they consisted totally of BRH sediments. There was no attempt to estimate the probability of hazard for these examples because the data on environmental exposures were of a semi-qualitative nature and did not have variance estimates. Estimating the probability of hazard to the environment at large would require an adequate definition of the toxicological relationships between the subset of test species used in this study and the populations and communities existing at the dumpsite, a task that is at this time incomplete.

11.3.6. Monitoring

The monitoring component of the FVP is a research effort with the primary goal of providing "real world" data to evaluate the laboratory methods used in the hazard assessment strategy. Laboratory predictions of exposure and effects must be confirmed by measurements in the field. The tiered testing used in the laboratory is repeated to the extent possible in the field in order to verify all levels of biological response. Field measurements are also conducted to determine the degree of concurrence between predicted exposure concentrations in the environment and those measured in the field.

The impact of responses at the population and community level in the field provides an ecologically meaningful measure of the adequacy of the methodologies that comprise the hazard assessment strategy (Phelps et al., Chapter 13).

11.4. CONFINED UPLAND DISPOSAL AND WETLAND CREATION

Research on the upland and wetland disposal alternatives has focused on three specific areas of investigation. The first is to provide documentation for and field verification of techniques for the prediction of effects on the water quality from disposal of dredged material into a confined upland environment. The confined dumpsite, located near the entrance to Bridgeport Harbor (Fig. 11.3), was designed, constructed, and managed in order to ensure adequate sedimentation and optimum fill configuration. Monitoring wells were installed at the site to determine potential contaminant movement into groundwater, and water samples were analyzed to determine background conditions prior to filling. Laboratory tests were conducted to determine rates of settling, consolidation, and drying, and to predict the water quality of the effluent discharged during the filling operation. In addition, sediment was placed in a soil bed, and the drying process was carefully monitored in the laboratory. The quality of the surface runoff (i.e., suspended sediments and contaminant loading) was determined over time after a simulated rainfall event was applied to the soil beds that had different moisture contents.

Construction of the confinement area began in 1982. Water-quality parameters were monitored extensively in the influent, in the effluent, and at selected stations within the disposal area. Laboratory predictions of effluent quality were compared to field measurements at the confined site during the filling operation. Following disposal, the quality of surface-water runoff was determined by controlled simulation of rainfall events and collection of surface-water samples. Surface-water quality will continue to be monitored as the sediment is naturally dewatered in the confined site. In addition, potential groundwater contamination will be monitored through the use of wells adjacent to and within the disposal area.

The second area of investigation documents and verifies bioassay procedures that predict contaminant movement into upland and wetland plants. These laboratory tests used *Cyperus esculentus* in simulated upland conditions and *Spartina alterniflora* in simulated wetland conditions. These same plants are being harvested from the field each year and analyzed for contaminants. The field and laboratory results are being compared to verify the predicted uptake by plants.

The third area of investigation documents and verifies that existing bioassay procedures on a terrestrial animal (the earthworm, *Eisenia foetida*) can be used to predict sediment toxicity and contaminant bioaccumulation in upland animals. A parallel investigation is being conducted on the wetland animals *Nereis* sp. (sandworm), *Arenicola* sp. (lugworm), and *Littorina* sp. (snail). In both the upland and the wetland studies, the results of laboratory and field studies of toxicity and bioaccumulation are being compared to determine the degree of field verification.

11.5. SUMMARY

Hazard assessment provides a holistic strategy that identifies and synthesizes the information needed for reasonable environmental management. The approach is tiered so that data may be gathered on a least-cost basis to meet specific needs on a case-by-case basis. The FVP is a case study and a research effort in which a multiple-tiered hazard assessment strategy is being implemented. The techniques used to gather data in the components of hazard assessment are useful to the extent that these data support predictions of actual environmental consequences; therefore, the hazard assessment protocol provides a framework for evaluating testing approaches and techniques. The technical success of this program can be measured by the degree of agreement between the predicted and the measured environmental consequences of the open-water disposal of BRH dredged material. Once evaluated, the hazard assessment research strategy can be used to provide the conceptual framework and criteria for the technical assessments that are an integral component of environmental management decisions.

ACKNOWLEDGMENTS

This chapter describes work performed by the U.S. Environmental Protection Agency, Environmental Research Laboratory, Narragansett, Rhode Island, as part of the Interagency Field Verification of Testing and Predictive Methodologies for Dredged Material Disposal Alternatives Program (Field Verification Program). This program is sponsored by the Office, Chief of Engineers, and assigned to the U.S. Army Engineer Waterways Experiment Station, Vicksburg, Mississippi.

REFERENCES

Bierman, V. J., J. H. Gentile, J. F. Paul, D. C. Miller, and W. A. Brungs. 1986. Research strategy for ocean disposal: Conceptual framework and case study. *In*: Environmental Hazard Assessment of Effluents, H. L. Bergman, R. H. Kimerle, and A. W. Maki (Eds.). Pergamon Press, Elmsford, New York, pp. 313–329.

Cairns, J., Jr., K. L. Dickson, and A. W. Maki (Eds.). 1978. Estimating the Hazard of Chemical Substances to Aquatic Life. American Society for Testing Materials, Philadelphia, Pennsylvania, 283 pp.

U.S. Environmental Protection Agency. 1977. Ocean Dumping: Final Revision of Regulations and Criteria. *Federal Register*, **42**, 2462–2490.

U.S. Environmental Protection Agency–U.S. Army Corps of Engineers. 1977. Ecological Evaluation of Proposed Discharge of Dredged Material into Ocean Waters. Technical Committee for Criteria for Dredged and Fill Material. Implementation Manual for Section 103 of Public Law 92-532. U.S. Army Engineer Waterways Experiment Station, Vicksburg, Mississippi, multiple pagination.

Chapter 12

The Application of a Hazard Assessment Research Strategy to the Ocean Disposal of a Dredged Material: Exposure Assessment Component

John F. Paul, Victor J. Bierman, Jr., Wayne R. Davis, and Gerald L. Hoffman

Environmental Research Laboratory
U.S. Environmental Protection Agency
Narragansett, Rhode Island

Wayne R. Munns, Jr.

Science Applications International Corporation
Narragansett, Rhode Island

Carol E. Pesch, Peter F. Rogerson, and Steven C. Schimmel

Environmental Research Laboratory
U.S. Environmental Protection Agency
Narragansett, Rhode Island

Abstract	**123**
12.1. Introduction	**124**
12.2. Exposure Assessment Plan	**124**
12.2.1. Objectives	124
12.2.2. Predisposal Sediment Characterization	125
12.2.3. Field Data Acquisition	126
12.3. Results of Field Work	**127**
12.3.1. Physical Information	127
12.3.2. Information on Trace Metal Chemistry	129
12.3.3. Organic Chemistry Information	132
12.4. Summary	**134**
Acknowledgments	**134**
References	**135**

ABSTRACT

The exposure assessment component of the aquatic portion of the Field Verification Program (FVP), jointly run by the U.S. Environmental Protection Agency and the U.S. Army Corps of Engineers, relates the source input of the contaminants in dredged material to the corresponding concentration distributions in space and time in the vicinity of the disposal mound. The specific objectives for this component are (1) to determine the environmental exposure field in the water column (pelagic zone), in the sediments (benthic zone), and near the bottom at the sediment–water interface (epibenthic zone); (2) to relate the source (dredged-material disposal mound) to the near-field exposure measurements by using process models for the vertical transport of contaminants and particulate materials; and (3) to determine the environmental processes controlling contaminant phase partitioning. Approximately 55,000 m^3 of material was disposed of during May 1983, creating a mound ~200 m in radius in water 20 m deep. Concentrations of contaminants in the water column from dredged material were three to eight times that of the background level in the vicinity of the disposal mound for about a month after the disposal operation, then approached background levels. Residues of contaminants in the tissues of caged mussels, deployed 1 m above the bottom, also showed elevated levels for the first month after disposal, then returned to background levels. The contaminant signal in the sediments was more persistent and was measurable (two to three times that of the background level) at 1 km from the disposal mound three months after disposal. Residues of contaminants were also elevated (two to three times that of the background level) in polychaete tissue 1 km from the disposal mound three months after disposal. This exposure assessment information will be used to link the laboratory and field data in the hazard assessment phase of the FVP.

12.1. INTRODUCTION

The U.S. Army Corps of Engineers and the U.S. Environmental Protection Agency (EPA) are jointly conducting a comprehensive study, referred to as the Field Verification Program (FVP), to evaluate the risks associated with various disposal options for dredged materials (Gentile et al., Chapter 11). The approach is to evaluate and to validate in the field assessment methodologies for predicting the environmental impacts of the disposal of dredged material in aquatic, upland, and wetland environments. The EPA Environmental Research Laboratory—Narragansett (ERLN) is conducting the aquatic portion of this program (Gentile et al., Chapter 11).

This chapter describes the exposure assessment component of the aquatic portion of the FVP, including the data acquisition and synthesis necessary to meet the overall objectives of the FVP (Gentile et al., Chapter 11). The characterization of the material that was disposed and the conditions at the dumpsite are described for the predisposal period and for the first full season after the disposal operation.

12.2. EXPOSURE ASSESSMENT PLAN

The exposure assessment component of the FVP provides the information necessary to simulate field exposure conditions in the laboratory and to estimate the spatial and temporal variability of important environmental parameters in the vicinity of the dumpsite. This information also will be used to develop and to validate process models for vertical transport and for phase partitioning of contaminants at the dumpsite. These models will provide a basis for extending the exposure assessment results from this study to other disposal operations at this and at other sites.

12.2.1. Objectives

The general objective of the exposure assessment component of the aquatic portion of the FVP was to develop and validate in the field quantitative assessment methods for relating dredged-material inputs to the transport, transformation, and fate of the associated contaminants. There were three specific objectives: 1. to determine the environmental exposure field in the water column (pelagic zone), in the sediments (benthic zone), and near the sediment–water interface (epibenthic zone) by using a combination of field sampling and *in situ* instrumentation; 2. to relate the source (disposal mound) to the near-field exposure measurements by using process models for the vertical transport of contaminants and particulate materials; and 3. to determine the environmental processes controlling contaminant phase partitioning pertinent to bioavailability and contaminant transport and fate.

Our conceptual model for the exposure assessment component has three vertical compartments that correspond to the zones used in the effects assessment (Fig. 12.1). The dredged material on the disposal mound, along with the associated contaminants in particulate and dissolved phases, is considered to be the source input. Resuspension of the bottom sediments occurs through a combination of various processes, such as tidal currents and wind-generated waves. This resuspension promotes mixing of the dredged material with background material and repartitioning of contaminants between the dissolved and the particulate phases. The mate-

air-sea interface

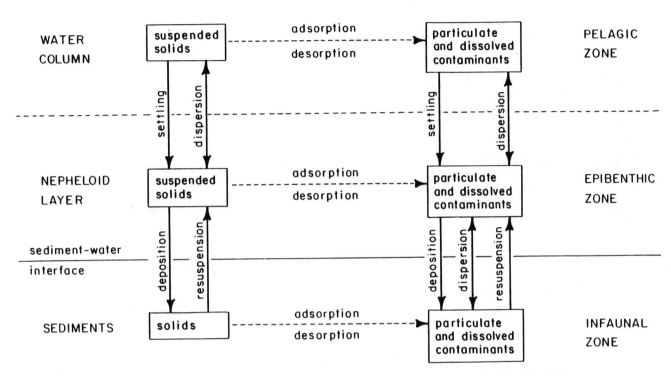

Figure 12.1. Schematic diagram of conceptual model for the exposure assessment component of the FVP.

rial may thus undergo continuous deposition, resuspension, and horizontal transport. Contaminants are repartitioned continuously in this process between dissolved and particulate phases. The resultant exposure field in the vicinity of the dumpsite will vary nearly continuously in space and time. This exposure field must be quantified in a way that is compatible with the effects assessment measurements (Phelps et al., Chapter 13).

12.2.2. Predisposal Sediment Characterization

Black Rock Harbor (BRH) is located at Bridgeport, Connecticut, on Long Island Sound (LIS) (Fig. 12.2). Bottom sediments were collected for predisposal characterization with a 0.1-m² gravity box corer to a depth of 1.21 m at 25 locations within the study area. Sediments were placed in 210-liter drums and transported at 4°C to the Waterways Experiment

Station in Vicksburg, Mississippi. The contents of these barrels were emptied into a nitrogen-purged cement mixer, homogenized, and replaced in the 25 barrels. The contents of each barrel were wet-sieved through a 1-mm mesh sieve to remove larger particles prior to use in dosing experiments in the laboratory (Phelps et al., Chapter 13). Samples were routinely collected from the barrels during the dosing experiments and analyzed for chemical content.

Reference sediment for the studies was collected from the Central Long Island Sound (CLIS) Disposal Site South Reference Station (Fig. 12.2), ~700 m south of the dumpsite. The reference material was collected with a Smith-McIntyre grab sampler (0.1 m²) to a depth of ~25 cm.

Qualitative waste characterization was also conducted by exposing mussels (*Mytilus edulis*) to suspended BRH sediment and then analyzing the mussels for accumulated contaminants (Rogerson et al., 1985). This process identified the biologically available contaminants in the sediment.

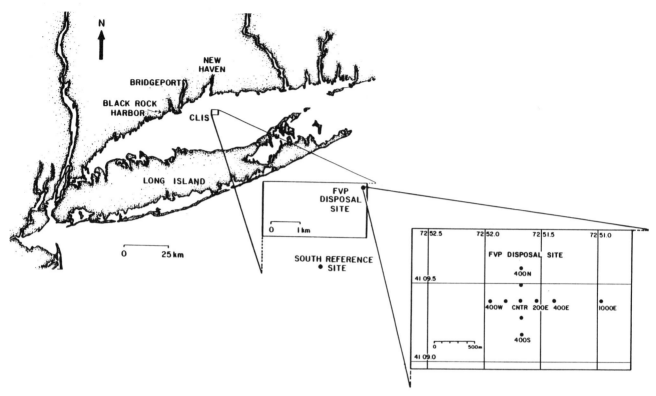

Figure 12.2. Sampling stations for the exposure assessment component of the FVP.

Analysis for trace metals was performed by using flame and flameless atomic absorption. Organic material was analyzed by using electron capture gas chromatography (GC) and gas chromatography–mass spectroscopy (GC/MS) with fused silica capillary columns. Total polychlorinated biphenyls (PCB) were quantified as Arochlor 1254 by electron capture GC, while quantification by GC/MS was based on molecular ion intensities. Results of analyses for trace metals are listed in Table 12.1. Organic contaminant levels detected included PCB at 6800 ng g^{-1} and total aromatic hydrocarbons at 177,000 ng g^{-1}. Details of the chemical analysis procedures are presented by Rogerson et al. (1985).

12.2.3. Field Data Acquisition

The field sampling plan was designed to measure the exposure concentrations of environmental contaminants at the locations where biological-effects assessment measurements were conducted. Sediment exposures were determined by analyses of sediment cores collected at various locations and at time intervals of 1–3 months (corresponding with the cruise sampling periods). Exposures to contaminants in the water column were determined by (1) field sampling at various stations, at different depths in the water column, and at time intervals of 1–3 months for concentrations of contaminants and suspended solids; and (2) continuous deployment of *in situ* instrumentation by the University of Connecticut (Bohlen, 1982) for determination of concentrations of suspended solids 1 m above the bottom at a single station, with burst sampling intervals of 15-min separation. One meter above the bottom corresponds with the deployment depth of caged mussels used as a biological measure in the field work on effects assessments (Phelps et al., Chapter 13). The exposures near the sediment–water interface were determined by another *in situ* instrument, the acoustic profilometer system developed by Ohio State University (Bedford et al., 1982). The acoustic profilometer measures concentration profiles of suspended solids from a point 1 m above the bottom to the sediment–water interface, at approximately 1-cm intervals. This provides estimates of exposure for organisms that live near the sediment–water interface.

In the field program we determined the variability that occurs on the important temporal scales: subtidal, tidal, monthly, and seasonal. Vertical variability was investigated by sampling for selected parameters at 1-m intervals. Horizontal variability was investigated by placing a grid of sampling stations over the dumpsite (Phelps et al., Chapter 13) as shown in Fig. 12.2. The measurement stations for biological effects are the center of the mound (CTR), 200 m east of CTR (200E), 400 m east of CTR (400E), 1000 m east of CTR (1000E), and the South Reference Station (SREF). The 200E station is located on the flank of the mound, 400E is on the fringe of the mound, 1000E is a kilometer away in the predominant tidal direction, and SREF is a reference station used as a control in this study. Additional sampling stations were located around the mound so that parameters could be measured both upstream and downstream of the mound, irrespective of the tidal flow direction.

12.3. RESULTS OF FIELD WORK

Approximately 55,000 m³ of dredged material from BRH was disposed of at the northeastern corner of the CLIS Disposal Site (Fig. 12.2) in May 1983. This created a mound 150–200 m in radius, in water 20 m deep. The height of the disposal mound was ~1–2 m at the center. The central part of the disposal mound was composed of sand-sized particles mixed with silty material, while the flanks and fringes of the mound were composed entirely of extremely fine-grained material.

The composition of the central part of the disposal mound was different from the material collected from BRH for pre-disposal characterization. It is hypothesized either that the extremely fine portion of the BRH material was not fully collected by the clamshell dredges used, or that it remained in suspension upon disposal and was transported away from the site by tidal currents. In either case, the heavier, sand-sized particles were deposited at the disposal buoy, while a portion of the finer material was deposited on the flanks and fringes of the mound.

The following sections present the physical and chemical information obtained for the water column, sediment, and biota at the study site, before and after disposal. The post-disposal conditions through September 1983 are presented, providing information for a full season after the disposal operation.

12.3.1. Physical Information

Weather data for 1983 were obtained from the National Weather Service station at Bridgeport, Connecticut. Major storms were present through April and after October, but the immediate FVP postdisposal period was relatively quiet in terms of storm activity.

Approximately 98% of the variation in temperature of the surface and near-bottom water can be accounted for by a yearly harmonic (Fig. 12.3a). Thermal stratification at the site started in late March, coincident with the increase in air temperature. Thermal overturn occurred in September, coinciding with the seasonal decrease in air temperature.

Salinity is generally lower in surface water than in bottom water over the entire year (Fig. 12.3b), consistent with the basic estuarine circulation that exists in LIS (Riley, 1956). Denser, more saline oceanic water flows through the eastern end of LIS along the bottom, mixes with freshwater runoff that enters along the coastline, and flows out of the sound through the eastern end at the surface. The sharp decrease in salinity in March coincides with large surface runoff into the sound from the major tributaries in Connecticut (U.S. Geological Survey, 1984). This yearly picture of temperature and salinity variation in the sound is in agreement with that observed by Riley (1956).

The small-scale variation in water temperature in Fig. 12.3a was due to (1) daily heating of surface water (as much as 4°C) that occurred over a cruise day and (2) tidally induced motion of the horizontally non-homogenous water masses in the sound. Diurnal surface heating was evident, along with the effect of tidal motion, in a series of vertical temperature profiles obtained on 22 April 1983 (Fig. 12.4a).

Vertical profiles of light transmissivity also varied throughout the day (Fig. 12.4b). The increase that consistently occurred between 5 and 10 m corresponds with lower concentrations of suspended solids, and was coincident with the depth of the pycnocline (Fig. 12.4a and 12.4b). Decreased light transmissivity below 10 m was due to tidal resuspension of bottom material and mixing of this material below the pycnocline. The pycnocline acts as a barrier to upward movement of this resuspended bottom material. Temporal variation was due to variation in the magnitude of the tidal currents. Decreased light transmissivity in surface waters was due to the surface primary productivity occurring at this time in the sound.

In situ instrumentation from the University of Connecticut was deployed 1 m above the bottom at station 1000E during

18–26 April 1983 (Bohlen and Winnick, 1984). Small-scale temperature and salinity variations over this period were on the order of 1°C and 0.5‰, respectively (Fig. 12.5a, b). Oscillations due to tidal, inertial, and internal wave motions can be seen. The background concentration of suspended solids at the site during this time was ~5 mg liter^{-1} (Fig. 12.5c). Excursions up to ~9 mg liter^{-1} are predominantly due to tidal motions, with storm activity responsible for some of the increased levels. The first four tidal harmonics (M2, S2, K1, and O1) account for > 88% of the variation in the observed currents, which is consistent with the work of Swanson (1971).

The *in situ* instrumentation was also deployed during the disposal operation (26 April–23 May 1983). Sharp spikes that exceeded 20 mg liter^{-1} were observed in the record of suspended solids present during the disposal period. These spikes represent the passage of disposal plumes that were transported past the instrumentation array (Bohlen and Winnick, 1984). These were plumes from material disposed at the FVP site as well as from other concurrent disposal operations in the southwestern corner of the CLIS Disposal Site. The origin of these spikes was confirmed by comparing the records of the disposal operations with data on the currents. These spikes were of relatively short duration (<1 h).

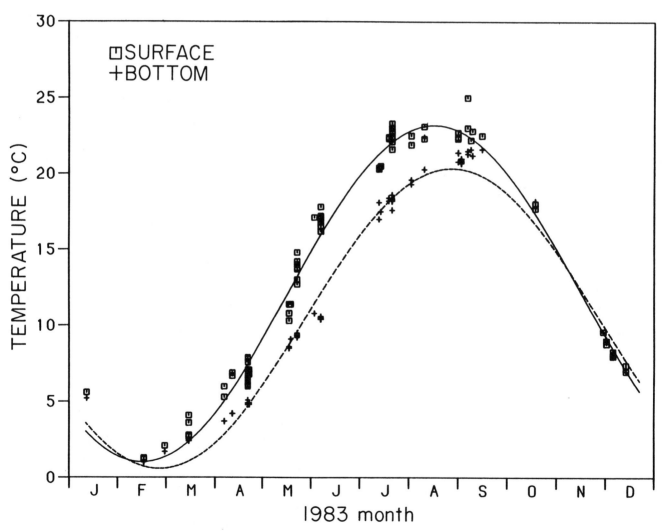

Figure 12.3. (a) Surface and bottom temperature at the FVP site in 1983.

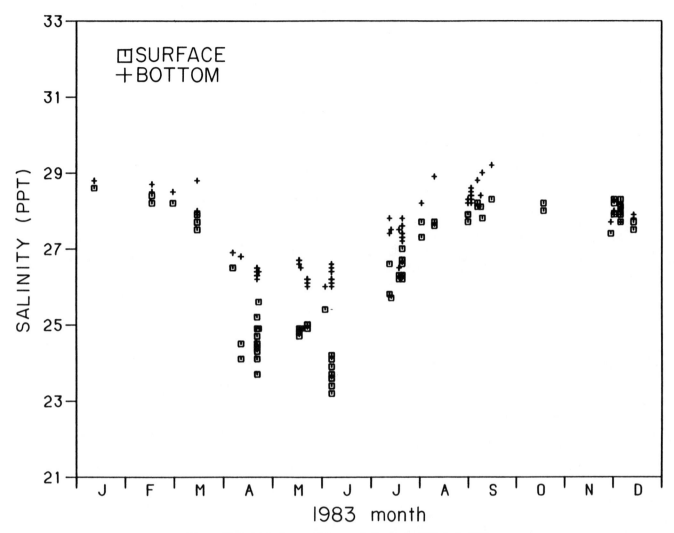

Figure 12.3. (b) Surface and bottom salinities at the FVP site in 1983.

12.3.2. Information on Trace Metal Chemistry

Water samples were collected for chemical analysis of trace metals when the vertical profiles were taken for temperature, salinity, and light attenuation. Duplicate samples were collected for analyses of total, as well as particulate and dissolved, contaminant concentrations and for determination of concentrations of suspended solids. The samples that were collected for analysis of particulate and dissolved contaminants were filtered with 0.45-μm Nucleopore (Nucleopore Corp., Pleasanton, California) filters on board the vessel

within 1 h of sampling. Details on sample preparation and analysis are provided by Lake et al. (1985).

Sediment samples were collected by using a Smith-MacIntyre grab sampler. Initially, subsamples were scraped from the surface of the grab sample and stored in collection bottles. Starting in July 1983, cores were taken from the grab sample by using 7.6-cm (inside diameter) acrylic plastic tubes. All sediment samples were frozen until analyses were conducted. The initial samples were homogenized and subsampled for analysis. The cores were sectioned, homogenized, and then subsampled for analysis. The sectioning performed so far has been 0–2 cm (surface sample) and 5–10 cm (subsurface

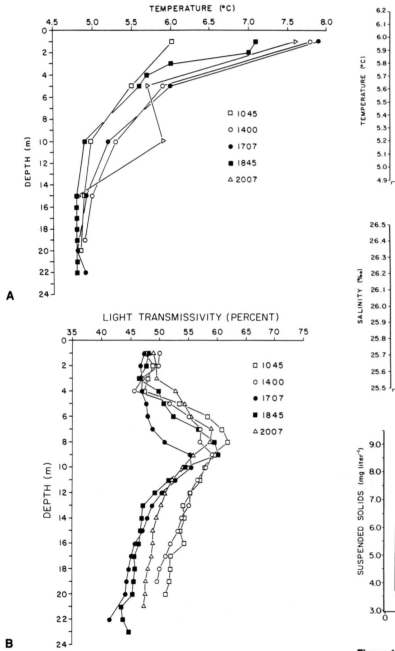

Figure 12.4. Vertical profiles at the FVP site on 22 April 1983: (a) temperature and (b) light transmissivity.

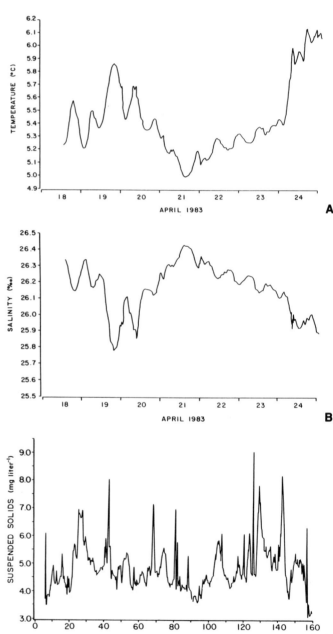

Figure 12.5. Results from *in situ* instrumentation for 18–26 April 1983 1 m above the bottom at station 1000E (after Bohlen and Winnick, 1984): (a) temperature, (b) salinity, and (c) suspended solids.

sample). The samples were split and used both for trace metal and for organic chemistry analyses. For details of sample preparation and analysis, see Lake et al. (1985).

The infaunal organism used for chemistry analysis, the polychaete *Nephtys incisa*, was collected by sieving Smith-MacIntyre grab samples through 2.0- and 0.5-mm sieves. In most instances, sufficient biomass was obtained so that both trace metal and organic analyses could be performed. Mussels that had been caged 1 m above the bottom (Phelps et al., Chapter 13) were also analyzed. These polychaete and mussel populations that were subsampled for chemical analyses were important in the field portion of the effects assessments tests for the FVP (Phelps et al., Chapter 13). For the details of sample preparation and analysis, see Lake et al. (1985).

Table 12.1 shows a comparison of the levels of trace metals between BRH material and sediment collected from the FVP and south reference sites prior to disposal. The metals that were significantly elevated were Cd, Cu, and Cr, and those that were slightly elevated were Zn, Pb, and Ni. Iron occurred at equally high levels both in the BRH material and in the LIS sediments, while Mn was lower in the BRH material than in the LIS sediments. The ratios of other metals to Fe can be used as a check on internal consistency. For illustrative purposes, the presentation of results for trace metals will be limited in this chapter to Cu.

Predisposal sampling of the water column on 22 April 1983 indicated that the differences in metal concentrations among stations were not significant once account was made for the variation in concentrations of suspended solids. Since sampling was conducted over a tidal cycle on this cruise day,

concentrations of suspended solids varied according to the stage of the tide. A regression analysis of the concentrations of total metals against concentrations of suspended solids gave correlation coefficients >0.9.

Samples from the water column collected immediately after disposal on 23 May 1983 indicated a definite BRH contaminant signal in the immediate vicinity of the disposal mound at 1 m above the bottom. Figure 12.6 shows that the values (mean of two samples) for Cu at stations CTR and 400E were outside of the 95% confidence interval determined from samples collected at the other stations. The water samples from other postdisposal sampling cruises have not been analyzed for trace metals at this time.

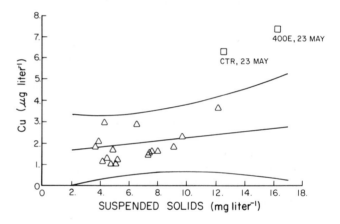

Figure 12.6. Total Cu concentration in the water column as a function of the concentration of suspended solids, collected on 22 April and 23 May 1983.

Table 12.1. Concentrations of Trace Metals (mg kg⁻¹, dry wt) in Dredged Material from Black Rock Harbor, in Sediments from the Disposal and Reference Sites, and in Mussels (*Mytilus edulis*) Used for Testing[a]

Trace Metal	Black Rock Harbor[b]		FVP Site[c]		Reference Station[d]		Exposed Mussels[e]		Control Mussels[f]	
Fe	29,600	(809)	20,205	(1,980)	24,400	(567)	500	(191)	213	(7)
Mn	359	(37)	765	(374)	505	(6)	11	(4.9)	13	(7)
Zn	1,200	(59)	145	(10)	161	(3)	333	(84)	221	(63)
Cu	2,385	(112)	63	(5)	67	(2)	55	(18)	17	(5)
Pb	378	(16)	52	(6)	50	(1)	14	(4.7)	6.5	(2.6)
Cd	23.4	(0.9)	0.35	(0.15)	0.39	(0.02)	7.0	(1.9)	2.8	(0.5)
Cr	1,431	(77)	51	(7)	18	(0.07)	25	(11)	2.0	(0.5)

[a]Numbers represent mean (standard deviation) in mg kg⁻¹, dry wt.
[b]Material collected prior to dredging operations in the harbor for predisposal characterization (Rogerson et al., 1985).
[c]Composite of stations CTR, 200E, 400E, and 1000E collected on 2 March 1983.
[d]Station SREF samples collected on 2 March 1983.
[e]Mussels exposed to suspended BRH for 28 d (Rogerson et al., 1985).
[f]Mussels used as a control (28 d) for BRH exposure study (Rogerson et al., 1985).

Results of sediment samples collected before disposal also indicated no significant differences among stations. The BRH contaminant signal was clearly evident, however, in the samples collected immediately after disposal, on 3 June 1983 (Fig. 12.7). Levels of trace metals at the disposal mound were lower than would have been expected from the analyses on material collected from the harbor for predisposal characterization (Table 12.1). This is probably because most of the metals were adsorbed onto the fine fraction of the BRH material, which was not deposited at the center of the disposal mound. Sediment samples collected on 1 September 1983 are shown in Fig. 12.8. Since there were no major storms during the summer of 1983, only small changes occurred between June and September. Figure 12.8 suggests that stations 200E and 400E, and possibly 1000E, might have a thin layer of BRH contaminated sediments over the background material.

Residues of contaminants in the tissues of *Nephtys incisa* collected on 13 July 1983, after disposal, showed no differences between any two station values. However, no organisms were collected on the disposal mound (station CTR) since *Nephtys incisa* had not recolonized this station at that time. Mussels deployed during the disposal operations (May) and immediately after disposal (June) indicated approximately a 60% increase of Cu in tissue at stations 400E and 1000E relative to station SREF (Fig. 12.9). Values for Cu in mussel tissues should not be compared directly across time periods due to the seasonal physiological changes that the mussels exhibit (Phelps et al., Chapter 13).

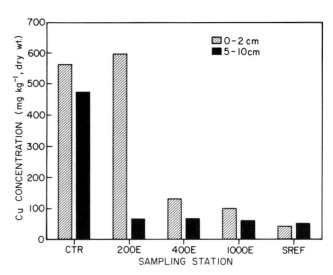

Figure 12.8. Concentrations of Cu in the sediment of sections of core samples collected on 1 September 1983.

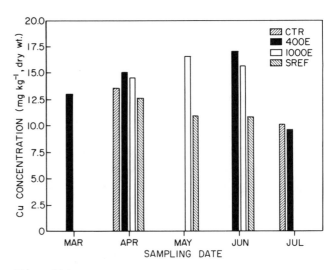

Figure 12.9. Cu residues in tissue from caged mussels deployed for 1-month periods 1 m above the bottom.

12.3.3. Organic Chemistry Information

Water samples were collected for analysis of the concentrations of total, particulate, and dissolved organic contaminants. Twenty-liter water samples were collected in duplicate for analysis of total contaminant concentration. These samples were collected within a 5-min span, and concurrent water samples were taken for the determinations of total suspended

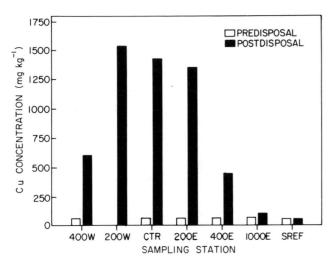

Figure 12.7. Concentrations of Cu in the surficial sediment collected before disposal (4 March 1983 and 23 April 1983) and immediately after disposal (3 June 1983).

solids. For analysis of particulate and dissolved organic material, 100-liter samples were pumped through a 0.1-μm glass fiber filter to collect the particulate fraction, and then through a polyurethane foam plug to collect the dissolved fraction. Filtering the 100 liters necessary for analysis normally required ~2 h. Additional water samples were collected both before and after pumping for determination of suspended solids. Sediment and biota samples were collected as discussed in the previous section. The organic extraction and analytic procedures are detailed by Lake et al. (1985).

For presentation in this chapter, discussion will be limited to polychlorinated biphenyls (PCB) that have been quantified as Arochlor 1254. The results for the polynuclear aromatic hydrocarbons (PAH) are similar to those for the PCB. Predisposal water samples from 7 April 1983 had PCB levels of 0.5 ng liter^{-1} at 1 m above the bottom, and 0.4 ng liter^{-1} at 5 m below the water surface. There were no significant differences between the stations SREF and CTR. Figure 12.10 shows a time plot of the PCB levels at 1 m above the bottom at the stations CTR and SREF. There was an elevated PCB signal after disposal (up to eight times the background level), which approached the background level by September. There was no detectable increase in PCB levels in the near-surface waters (5 m below the surface) over the disposal mound.

The partition coefficient for the water column PCB was determined from the particulate and dissolved fractions. A regression analysis of the partition coefficient against the concentration of suspended solids indicated no significant variation with the concentration of suspended solids over the range of 1–15 mg liter^{-1}. The 95% confidence limits for the partition coefficient in this regression were at approximately 10^5 and 10^6.

The PCB levels in the sediments indicated the same trends as were shown by the results of the trace metal analyses. There was a distinct BRH contaminant signal in the vicinity of the mound, with little change between June and September. Also, the levels in the disposal mound were lower than one may have expected based upon the levels (6800 ng g^{-1}, dry wt) in material collected from the harbor prior to dredging (Rogerson et al., 1985).

The predisposal values for residues of PCB in tissues of *Nephtys incisa* are uniform across stations (Fig. 12.11). There were increased PCB levels in the organisms collected in September at 400E (4 times background) and at 1000E (2.5 times background). The polychaetes collected in September had been exposed to the contaminants from the BRH material for up to 90 d.

The contaminant residues in the tissues of caged mussels deployed for 1-month periods before and after disposal are shown in Fig. 12.12. As discussed in the previous section, comparisons of the predisposal and postdisposal results must

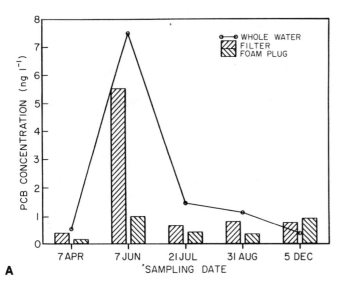

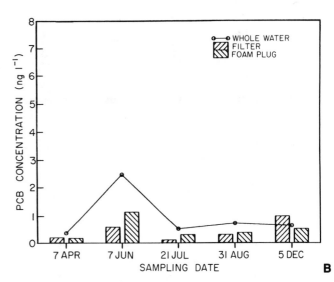

Figure 12.10. Levels of PCB in the water column at 1 m above the bottom. PCB were analyzed as individual isomers and quantified as Arochlor® 1254 on whole water samples, and in dissolved (foam plug) and particulate (filter) fractions: (a) station CTR and (b) station SREF.

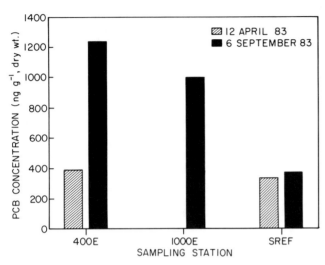

Figure 12.11. PCB residues in the tissues of *Nephtys incisa* collected before disposal (12 April 1983) and after disposal (6 September 1983). No predisposal organisms were collected at station 1000E. PCB were analyzed as individual isomers and quantified as Arochlor® 1254.

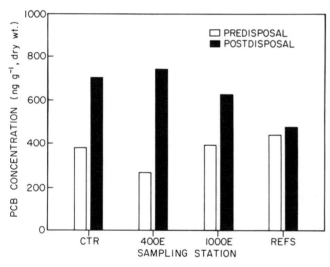

Figure 12.12. Residues of PCB in the tissues of caged mussels deployed for 1-month periods 1 m above the bottom. PCB were analyzed as individual isomers and quantified as Arochlor® 1254.

be done with care because of possible physiological differences in the mussels. Nonetheless, the results indicate that after disposal there were increased residues in the vicinity of the mound, a situation that is consistent with the data for trace metals.

12.4. SUMMARY

The exposure assessment component of the FVP provided the information required to simulate field exposure conditions in the laboratory and provided estimates of the spatial and temporal variability on the controlling environmental parameters. Also, this information is being used to develop and validate process models for sediment–water interactions and for phase partitioning of contaminants. These models will provide the basis for extending the exposure assessment results from this study to other dumpsites.

The results for the first full season after the disposal operation indicate that the BRH signal in the water column was limited to about a month. After this period, both the water column values and the residues of contaminants in the tissues of caged mussels at 1 m above the bottom approached background levels. The BRH signal was more persistent in the sediments. BRH material was detectable 1 km from the dumpsite after 3 months, and infaunal organisms 1 km from the dumpsite indicated elevated tissue residues.

These exposure results, along with information of effects in the field (Phelps et al., Chapter 13), are now being compared to preliminary results from tests of effects in the laboratory (Johns et al., 1985; Nelson et al., 1985; Pesch et al., 1985; and Zaroogian et al., 1985). Revised laboratory tests, simulating exposures in the field, will then be conducted to provide the hazard assessment phase of the FVP.

ACKNOWLEDGMENTS

We thank G. G. Pesch, K. J. Scott, and J. A. Nocito for their critical comments on this manuscript. W. F. Bohlen, University of Connecticut, EPA CR810776-01, provided the *in situ* instrumentation data for temperature, salinity, suspended solids, and currents. C. D. Hunt, University of Rhode Island, EPA CR809268-03 and Contract No. N-0362-NCSA and No. N-0543-NCSA, performed some of the water sampling and sample preparation for trace metal analysis. R. Lapan, K. Schweitzer, W. Boothman, and F. Osterman assisted in the sampling and analysis for trace metals. J. Lake, B. Reynolds, S. Pavignano, R. Bowen, L. LeBlanc, A. Elskus, and C. Norwood assisted in the organic chemistry sampling and analysis. M. Balboni, G. Pesch, A. Beck, and H. Walker assisted in the field sampling. Special thanks to the crews of the *R/V UConn* and *R/V Shang Wheeler* for field sampling support. The exposure assessment component of the Field

Verification Program was made possible by supplemental funding from the Environmental Protection Agency Office of Environmental Processes and Effects Research. This chapter is contribution No. 656 of the Environmental Research Laboratory–Narragansett.

REFERENCES

Bedford, K. W., R. E. Van Evra, and H. Valizahed-Alavi. 1982. Ultrasonic measurements of sediment resuspension. *In*: Proceedings of the American Society of Civil Engineers Hydraulics Specialty Conference, P. Smith (Ed.). ASCE Publications, New York, pp. 575–583.

Bohlen, W. F. 1982. In-situ monitoring of sediment resuspension in the vicinity of active dredge spoil disposal area. *In*: Proceedings of the Marine Technology/Institute for Electrical Investigations Oceans '82, Washington, D.C., pp. 1028–1033.

Bohlen, W. F., and K. B. Winnick. 1984. Observations on Near-Bottom Suspended Material Concentrations at the FVP Site, Central Long Island Sound Dredged Materials Disposal Area: Immediate Pre-Disposal, Disposal, and Immediate Post-Disposal Period, April 18, 1983–June 29, 1983. Prepared for Science Applications Inc., Newport, Rhode Island, by the Marine Science Institute, University of Connecticut, Groton, Connecticut, 40 pp.

Johns, D. M., R. Gutjahr-Gobell, and P. Schauer. 1985. Use of Energetics to Investigate the Impact of Dredged Material on Benthic Species: A Laboratory Study with Polychaetes and Black Rock Harbor Material. Technical Report No. D-85-7, prepared by U.S. Environmental Protection Agency, Narragansett, Rhode Island, for the U.S. Army Engineer Waterways Experiment Station, Vicksburg, Mississippi, 76 pp.

Lake, J., G. L. Hoffman, and S. C. Schimmel. 1985. The Bioaccumulation of Contaminants from Black Rock Harbor Material by Mussels and Polychaetes. Technical Report No. D-85-2, prepared by U.S. Environmental Protection Agency, Narragansett, Rhode Island, for the U.S. Army Engineer Waterways Experiment Station, Vicksburg, Mississippi, 150 pp.

Nelson, W. G., D. Black, and D. K. Phelps. 1985. Utility of the Scope for Growth Index to Assess the Physiological Impact of Black Rock Harbor Suspended Sediment on the Blue Mussel, *Mytilus Edulis*: A Laboratory Evaluation. Technical Report No. D-85-6, prepared by U.S. Environmental Protection Agency, Narragansett, Rhode Island, for the U.S. Army Engineer Waterways Experiment Station, Vicksburg, Mississippi, 56 pp.

Pesch, G. G., C. Mueller, C. E. Pesch, J. Heltshe, and P. S. Schauer. 1985. Application of Sister Chromatid Exchange in Marine Polychaetes to Black Rock Harbor Sediments. Technical Report No. D-85-1, prepared by U.S. Environmental Protection Agency, Narragansett, Rhode Island, for the U.S. Army Engineer Waterways Experiment Station, Vicksburg, Mississippi, 50 pp.

Riley, G. A. 1956. Oceanography of Long Island Sound, 1952–1954. II. Physical oceanography. *Bulletin of the Bingham Oceanographic Collection*, **15**, 15–46.

Rogerson, P. F., S. C. Schimmel, and G. Hoffman. 1985. Chemical and Biological Characterization of Black Rock Harbor Dredged Material. Technical Report No. D-85-9, prepared by U.S. Environmental Protection Agency, Narragansett, Rhode Island, for the U.S. Army Engineer Waterways Experiment Station, Vicksburg, Mississippi, 122 pp.

Swanson, R. L. 1971. Some Aspects of Currents in Long Island Sound. Ph.D. Dissertation, Department of Oceanography, Oregon State University, Corvallis, 150 pp.

U.S. Geological Survey (U.S.G.S.). 1984. Water Resources Data, Connecticut, Water Year 1983. U.S. Geological Survey Water-Data Report CT-83-1, 327 pp.

Zaroogian, G. E., C. Pesch, P. Schauer, and D. Black. 1985. Laboratory Evaluation of Adenylate Energy Charge as a Test for Stress in *Mytilus edulis* and *Nephtys incisa* Treated with Dredged Material. Technical Report No. D-85-3, prepared by U.S. Environmental Protection Agency, Narragansett, Rhode Island, for the U.S. Army Engineer Waterways Experiment Station, Vicksburg, Mississippi, 56 pp.

Chapter 13

The Application of a Hazard Assessment Research Strategy to the Ocean Disposal of a Dredged Material: Effects Assessment and Monitoring Component

Donald K. Phelps, D. Michael Johns, K. John Scott,
Walter B. Galloway, Bruce H. Reynolds, William G. Nelson,
Jeffrey S. Rosen, Dianne Black, James L. Lake,
Ruth Gutjahr-Gobell, Suzanne Lussier, Cornelia Mueller,
Michele Redmond, Paul S. Schauer, Carolyn A. Yevich,
Paul P. Yevich, Gerald E. Zaroogian, and James Heltshe

Environmental Research Laboratory
U.S. Environmental Protection Agency
Narragansett, Rhode Island

Abstract	**137**
13.1. Introduction	**138**
13.2. Methods	**138**
13.2.1. Disposal Site	138
13.2.2. Exposure Systems in the Laboratory	138
13.2.3. Species Selection	139
13.2.4. Biological Methods	139
13.3. Descriptions of Methods and Results	**140**
13.3.1. Adenylate Energy Charge	140
13.3.2. Sister Chromatid Exchange	140
13.3.3. Histopathology	140
13.3.4. Energetics	140
13.3.5. Scope for Growth	140
13.3.6. Bioaccumulation	141
13.3.7. Population Demography	141
13.3.8. Community Structure	141
13.3.8a. Traditional approach	141
13.3.8b. REMOTS® sediment-interface-camera benthic survey	141
13.4. Results by Species	**142**
13.4.1. Nephtys incisa	142
13.4.2. Neanthes arenaceodentata	142
13.4.3. Nereis virens	142
13.4.4. Mytilus edulis	142
13.4.5. Yoldia limatula	143
13.4.6. Ampelisca abdita and Mysidopsis bahia	143
13.5. Summary	**143**
Acknowledgments	**144**
References	**144**

ABSTRACT

The conceptual framework of the effects assessment and monitoring components of the hazard assessment strategy is examined in a combined laboratory and field research project involving the disposal of highly contaminated dredged material. This approach involves the testing and evaluation of a variety of exposure systems, representative species, and a hierarchy of biological responses in order to examine (1) the relationships between short-term toxicity tests and long-term effects, and (2) the degree to which laboratory and field effects may be linked. The correlation of laboratory and field results should strengthen management of dredge-disposal activities by linking predisposal laboratory screening (i.e., effects assessment) of candidate dredged materials directly to postdisposal monitoring. Preliminary results demonstrate potentially useful correlations between laboratory and field results for (1) scope for growth (the method), (2) *Mytilus edulis* (the species) and (3) the laboratory dose–response system and the field station at the center of the disposal mound (exposure). It remains to be seen how, however, well such laboratory-to-field relationships can serve as precise predictive tools.

13.1. INTRODUCTION

The purpose of this chapter is to present the conceptual framework within which the biological effects and monitoring components of a hazard assessment strategy (Gentile et al., Chapter 11) are being studied in the Field Verification Program (FVP). The primary objective of these studies is to identify the most effective combination of laboratory and field measurements for environmental assessment and management as related to the disposal of dredged materials into the marine environment. Our approach has been to compare the results of laboratory and field studies by utilizing a variety of exposure routes, representative marine species, and a hierarchy of biological responses. This approach is based on the premise that the parallel use and subsequent evaluation of exposure levels, species, and methods between the laboratory and field will achieve the primary objective.

The program had two phases: In Phase I, termed laboratory documentation, we investigated the applicability, precision, and reproducibility of a variety of test exposures, species, and methods. In Phase II, called field verification, we examined relationships between field observations and results from field simulation in the laboratory. The important difference between Phase I and Phase II is in the nature of the laboratory exposure designs. In Phase I, a dose-response study was used. The intent was to elicit a biological response to the candidate dredged material independent from what the actual exposure levels might be in the field. Phase II actually simulated, in exposure systems in the laboratory, the expected exposure levels as determined from exposure assessment activities in the field (Paul et al., Chapter 12). This chapter focuses primarily on the results of Phase I laboratory dose-response studies. Some preliminary field results are presented to compare results in the sensitivities of biological methods between laboratory dose-response experiments, and field-monitoring activities.

13.2. METHODS

13.2.1. Disposal Site

The field-study site for the FVP was created by the disposal of polluted dredged material from Black Rock Harbor (BRH) in Bridgeport, Connecticut, and is located in Central Long Island Sound, ~15 km south of the Connecticut shore (Gentile et al., Chapter 11). Surveys were conducted prior to, during, and after the disposal activity to determine the physical, chemical, and biological characteristics of the site. Precision bathymetry, side-scan sonar, suspended solids, current measurements, REMOTS® (Science Applications International, Newport, Rhode Island) camera-image analyses, and benthic grabs (0.1 m²) were employed during the surveys. Survey results indicated that the study area was relatively uniform (i.e., low degree of large-scale variability) and that five replicate 0.1-m² grab samples at each station would be adequate for describing the benthic community.

Stations were positioned at the study site along a transect that originated at the center of the disposal mound. The mound was regarded as the point source. Additional stations were located 200, 400, and 1000 m to the east of the mound. These stations were located along the axis of tidal currents as determined during the predisposal surveys. A reference site was located 3 km to the south–southwest in an area where there was little likelihood that contaminated sediment would occur. The conceptual design of this sampling strategy was to create an analogue of the laboratory dose-response exposure system in the field. The center mound station represents the highest dose, and increasing dilution in the laboratory is analogous to increasing distance from the mound. The reference site is conceptualized as being analogous to a laboratory control.

13.2.2. Exposure Systems in the Laboratory

Sediments were collected from the BRH dredge site and the Long Island Sound reference (REF) station. Laboratory systems were designed to expose selected species both to the BRH dredged material and to the REF sediments in three combinations including: either bedded sediments (Johns et al., 1985; Pesch et al., 1985; Yevich et al., 1985), or suspended particulate material (Lake et al., 1985; Nelson et al.,

1985; Rogerson et al., 1985; Yevich et al., 1985), or a combination of bedded sediments and suspended particulate material (Johns et al., 1985; Pesch et al., 1985; Yevich et al., 1985). Combinations of BRH and REF sediments were used to generate exposure conditions ranging from a presumed no-effect level of suspended and solid phases (100% REF) to the presupposed "worst case" of 100% BRH dredged material in both systems (Gentile et al., 1985; Nelson et al., 1985; Pesch et al., 1985). In this manner, exposures in the laboratory would be expected to bracket the full range of possible exposure levels in the field, but in no way were the exposures in the laboratory expected to simulate actual exposure levels along the transect at the FVP dumpsite. Simulation of exposure levels at the FVP study site will be derived from data gathered by Paul et al. (Chapter 12) and will be the core of Phase II studies.

An extensive discussion of the Exposure Assessment component of the Hazard Assessment strategy appears in Paul et al. (Chapter 12). Discussions of exposure systems are limited in this chapter to laboratory dose-response studies and field-simulation experiments, as well as preliminary field collection made along the transect through the center of the disposal mound.

13.2.3. Species Selection

Test species were chosen to include representatives of several phyla, as well as feeding types appropriate to the problem at hand (i.e., deposit feeders *Nephtys incisa* and *Yoldia lima-tula*) and suspended-particulate feeders (*Mytilus edulis, Ampelisca abdita,* and *Mysidopsis bahia*). With the exception of *Mytilus edulis*, all of the species come into direct contact with the sediment through activities such as resting, burrowing, or tube building. Abundance and role in the Long Island Sound benthic community were also considered in the process of selection.

Species were obtained from a variety of sources. *Mytilus* used in the field studies were collected from a "clean" reference site in Narragansett Bay, Rhode Island; placed in plastic cages; then transplanted to the station at the FVP study site. Mussels used in laboratory studies were brought directly from the collection site into the laboratory. Organisms were collected either at the FVP study site (prior to the disposal activity), or after that time, at the reference station in Long Island Sound. Collections of indigenous organisms were also made along the study transect after disposal had occurred. *Neanthes arenaceodentata* and *Mysidopsis bahia* were cultured at Environmental Research Laboratory Narragansett (ERLN) for these studies. *Nereis virens* were purchased from commercial bait dealers. Table 13.1 shows the various combinations of species and methods selected both for the laboratory and for the field components of the study. The field component also included community-structure surveys.

13.2.4. Biological Methods

Three criteria were used in the selection of methods (biological "endpoints") for this study. Methods (Table 13.1) were

Table 13.1. Species and Methods Used for FVP Laboratory and Field Studies

Study Method	Species[a]						
	Nephtys	**Neanthes**	**Nereis**	**Mytilus**	**Yoldia**	**Ampelisca**	**Mysidopsis**
AEC	L,F			L,F			
SCE	L,F	L					
Histopathology	L,F	L	L	L,F	L	L	
Growth	L	L		L		L	L
Reproduction						L	L
Energetics	L,F	L					
SFG		L		L,F			
Bioaccumulation	L,F		L	L,F			
Demography						L	L
Community	(field study only, all indigenous species)						
REMOTS®	(field study only, species independent)						

[a]L = laboratory studies; F = field studies.

chosen, first, to represent different levels of biological organization, from the subcellular to the community, and, second, to achieve a mix of traditional and innovative techniques. Finally, each method had been successfully applied previously, either in the laboratory or the field. A brief description of each method and an evaluation of its usefulness are presented in the following section. The evaluation is limited to experience gained from Phase I of the exposure studies in the laboratory and preliminary results from the field (monitoring) studies.

13.3. DESCRIPTIONS OF METHODS AND RESULTS

13.3.1. Adenylate Energy Charge

Adenylate Energy Charge (AEC) is an indicator of the amount of energy available to an organism from the adenylate pool (Atkinson, 1971). The AEC value is an indicator of an organism's ability to maintain homeostatic integrity through the partitioning of its internal energy supply in the adenylate pool. Values for AEC are expected to permit interpretation of the extent to which an organism is stressed as a result of exposure to dredged materials. In the laboratory, the measure of AEC in *Nephtys incisa* and *Mytilus edulis* proved sensitive (Zaroogian et al., 1985) but not according to the expected dose response. Highest values were found in organisms exposed to a 50% mixture of BRH:REF sediments rather than at the 100% BRH dose. No differences among stations were established in the FVP field studies using indigenous *Nephtys incisa* and transplanted *Mytilus edulis*.

13.3.2. Sister Chromatid Exchange

Sister chromatid exchange (SCE) is used to determine the occurrence of genetic damage. It is a visual measurement of the breakage and reciprocal exchange of identical DNA (deoxyribonucleic acid) material between two sister chromatids of a chromosome (Latt et al., 1981). Sister chromatid exchange is an empirical measure of mutagenic activity and correlates well with point mutation responses (Carrano et al., 1978). The long-term consequences of genetic damage could be a loss in viability of the individual organism and a reduction in the ecological fitness to successive generations. As tested in the FVP on *Nephtys incisa* and *Nucula annulata* SCE produced results comparable to AEC. For *Nephtys incisa* it

proved a sensitive measure of effects caused by the presence of BRH sediments under laboratory conditions; however, it did not show the expected dose response (Pesch et al., 1985). The highest apparent impact was at the 50% mixture of BRH:REF sediments rather than at the 100% BRH exposure. No differences among stations were observed in the FVP field studies. *Neanthes arenaceodentata* was unresponsive when exposed to BRH sediments under laboratory conditions.

13.3.3. Histopathology

Histopathological examination, under the light microscope, can elucidate the effects of pollutants on aquatic animals as it has traditionally done for diseases in humans and other mammals (Epstein, 1972). Animal tissues examined for the FVP (Yevich et al., 1985) included gonad, digestive tract, epidermis, kidney, gill, and digestive diverticulum (*Mytilus edulis*). Tissues were examined in order to detect changes in structure that may be related to exposure to disposed dredged materials. While changes in tissue structure were noted for animals held in exposure systems in the laboratory (Yevich et al., 1985), no correlations were observed between level of exposure and noted structural changes. No differences that could be attributed to the presence of BRH disposal materials were noted among stations for indigenous or transplanted animals collected from the FVP field sites.

13.3.4. Energetics

Energetics measures examined the energy balance of the organisms as a whole and were employed as a measure of integration among the various physiological functions. Physiological measurements were made repetitively on the same organism over time to evaluate changes in actual growth (Johns et al., 1985). Net growth efficiencies followed a dose-response pattern for juvenile *Nephtys incisa* both in suspended and in bedded sediments in laboratory experiments. No energetics measurements were made directly on animals collected from the FVP field-study site.

13.3.5. Scope for Growth

Scope for Growth (SFG) is a physiological index that measures the amount of energy an organism has available for growth and reproduction, after accounting for routine metabolic costs (Warren and Davis, 1967). Lowered SFG measurements have been shown to be ecologically significant through a reduction in fecundity and growth efficiency (Bayne et al., 1981). *Mytilus edulis* showed a reduction in SFG in a typical dose-response pattern as a result of exposure to suspended BRH sediments under laboratory conditions (Nelson et al., 1985). Field studies showed a reduction in *Mytilus edulis* SFG values at the center of the disposal mound at a time when concentrations of both polychlorinated biphenyls (PCB) and inorganic materials were elevated.

13.3.6. Bioaccumulation

Bioaccumulation and analyses for the residue of contaminants in tissues were sensitive indicators of the availability of chemical compounds found in dredged materials for a variety of species under laboratory and field conditions (Lake et al., 1985). Results from these studies hold promise for establishing meaningful links between chemical characterization of disposal materials (Rogerson et al., 1985) and subsequent biological uptake of some of those chemicals.

Both *Mytilus edulis* and *Nereis virens* bioaccumulate organic and inorganic contaminants from BRH sediments under laboratory experimental conditions (Lake et al., 1985). A steady-state condition between the organism and its environment was achieved between the first and second weeks of exposure.

Mytilus edulis transplanted to the field site demonstrated elevated levels of organic and inorganic chemicals from the stations around the dumpsite as compared to the reference site (Paul et al., Chapter 12). As discussed below, elevated levels of Cr and Cu were found in mussels transplanted to the dumpsite as compared to those placed at the reference site, while no significant differences in Cd concentrations in mussels from the two areas were found.

13.3.7. Population Demography

Demographic analysis involved the use of age-specific survival and fecundity data for individuals to calculate such population parameters as intrinsic rate of population growth and multiplication rate per generation. These measurements proved to be sensitive indicators of impacts on population stability resulting from the presence of BRH sediments under laboratory conditions (Gentile et al., 1985). Two cultured

crustacean species, *Ampelisca abdita* and *Mysidopsis bahia*, were used to demonstrate such impacts. Field studies of the possible effects of BRH disposal materials on the demography of *Nephtys incisa* are underway at the FVP study site, but no results are available as yet.

13.3.8. Community Structure

13.3.8a. Traditional approach

Predisposal sampling of the benthic community was done to establish the following: (1) overall community structure, (2) small- and large-scale variability, (3) dominant species, (4) seasonal changes in the community structure, and (5) optimal postdisposal sampling strategies. The community found at the study area was the classical Nephtys–Nucula community previously described for Long Island Sound (Sanders, 1956; Rhoads and Young, 1970).

The preliminary survey indicated that the benthic community structure was patchy on a small scale and that the patchiness was fairly consistent over the entire study area. Due to the patchiness, it will be difficult to detect statistical differences among stations on any sampling date unless the difference in change of percent composition by each species is very large (e.g., (*Nucula annulata*, 110%; *Yoldia limatula*, 59%; and *Nephtys incisa*, 48%). Other traditional community measures such as diversity indexes, extremes, transitional species, and rare species will also be evaluated for their sensitivity in the detection of changes.

13.3.8b. REMOTS® sediment-interface-camera benthic survey

A full discussion of the REMOTS® sediment-interface camera and its application in benthic surveys is given by Rhoads and Germano (1982), and the specific application to FVP is found in a paper by Scott et al. (1985). In Long Island Sound, REMOTS® was used to conduct a predisposal survey and to map the areal extent of dredged material immediately following disposal; to assess conditions of the benthic habitat [boundary roughness, modal grainsize, oxidation–reduction (redox) and successional stage]; and to estimate habitat indexes (Rhoads and Germano, 1982). When used in conjunction with precision bathymetry, REMOTS® provided a very good estimate of the dispersion of dredged material. REMOTS® demonstrated change in the condition of the benthic habitat from predisposal surveys (redox depth >4 cm at all stations) and postdisposal surveys (redox depth ≤2 cm) inside the area encompassed by the deposited dredged materials. Redox depth was demonstrated to increase gradually but steadily in a series of postdisposal observations. The habitat indexes (Rhoads and Germano, 1982) decreased from a healthy 9.0 determined in predisposal surveys to <5 in the area affected by disposal activities.

13.4. RESULTS BY SPECIES

13.4.1. *Nephtys incisa*

In both exposure systems in the laboratory (suspended matter and mixture of bedded and suspended sediments), *Nephtys incisa* proved most sensitive to the 50% BRH:REF mixtures for AEC (Zaroogian et al., 1985) and SCE (Pesch et al., 1985), and less sensitive to either 100% BRH or REF sediment. These results are not consistent with those expected from a dose-response experiment. *Nephtys incisa* showed histological sensitivity at 100% BRH sediment (i.e., extensive epidermal metaplasia, muscle degeneration of the parapodia, and destruction of mucus-secreting cells) (Yevich et al., 1985).

Net growth efficiencies of juvenile *Nephtys incisa* followed a dose-response pattern in the solid phase (bedded) exposures with lower efficiencies related to increasing percentages of BRH sediment (Johns et al., 1985). A similar pattern in net growth efficiencies was observed in the particulate-phase assays.

Preliminary field results indicate that *Nephtys incisa* failed to show differences between stations for either AEC or SCE. At 8 and 16 weeks after disposal, PCB concentrations were higher in *Nephtys incisa* at stations near the mound (400E and 1000E) relative to predisposal and REF samples. At 44 weeks, polychaetes had recolonized the dumpsite, and PCB concentrations in these organisms and in those from 400E were significantly higher than those from the REF station. Metal analyses done on *Nephtys incisa* collected 2 weeks after cessation of disposal activities failed to show any differences among stations for any of the trace metals determined.

13.4.2. *Neanthes arenaceodentata*

In the laboratory SFG experiments, *Neanthes arenaceodentata* proved sensitive to exposures both of suspended and of

solid (bedded sediment) phases of BRH material (Johns et al., 1985). In SCE experiments, however, this species was uniformly nonresponsive to BRH sediment in either the particulate or the solid phase. No field observations were made on *Neanthes arenaceodentata*.

13.4.3. *Nereis virens*

Nereis virens was found to bioaccumulate organic and inorganic contaminants from BRH sediment (Lake et al., 1985) in exposures in the laboratory. Polycyclic aromatic hydrocarbons and PCB were concentrated significantly above reference levels by organisms exposed both to BRH and to REF. Some histological damage (i.e., extensive epidermal metaplasia, muscle degeneration of the parapodia, and destruction of mucus-secreting cells) was observed in polychaetes exposed to BRH sediments. No field observations were made on *Nereis virens*.

13.4.4. *Mytilus edulis*

In Phase I laboratory studies, *Mytilus edulis* showed a dose response to suspended sediments (bedded-sediment studies were not conducted on this species) for SFG (Nelson et al., 1985). For AEC (Zaroogian et al., 1985) the highest apparent impact was observed at the 50% BRH:REF mixture as opposed to either extreme mix (100% BRH or 100% REF). Histological changes (Yevich et al., 1985) were observed in the female reproductive system, metaplasia and hyperplasia were noted in the kidney, and lesions of the heart were observed in some of the mussels exposed to BRH. Mussels exposed to BRH sediment accumulated organic compounds (Lake et al., 1985) and some inorganic elements, reaching steady-state values between the first and second weeks of a 28-d exposure period for most of the compounds analyzed. Depuration of organic compounds was rapid during the first week after exposure, with the depuration rate being inversely related to the compound's *n*-octanol:water partition coefficient.

Immediately after cessation of disposal activities, SFG was reduced in caged mussels placed over the center of the disposal mound when compared to mussels from other stations; however, there were no observed differences in SFG among stations after that collection. There were no observed differences in mussel AEC values or histology among stations during any sampling periods. Two weeks after cessation of the disposal activity, the tissue levels of PCB in caged mussels collected at 400E and 1000E were elevated relative to those held at the reference station. High concentrations of PCB persisted in mussels held at the center of the mound and at stations 400E and 1000E for six months when compared to levels observed in mussels held at REF. Two weeks after cessation of disposal activities, Cr and Cu were also significantly elevated in mussels held at 400E and 1000E when compared to those at REF. The chemical characterization phase of this study (Rogerson et al., 1985) indicted that Cr, Cu, and Cd were, respectively, 27, 51, and 61 times higher in BRH sediments than in sediments from the reference site. Mussels held at stations over the center of the mound and at stations 400E and 1000E reflected the higher levels of Cr and Cu found in the BRH sediments, but did not seem to reflect the higher levels of Cd found in those sediments.

13.4.5. *Yoldia limatula*

Yoldia limatula showed no sensitivity to the presence of BRH sediments in laboratory histological studies. No other data were available, and no field observations were made on this species.

13.4.6. *Ampelisca abdita* and *Mysidopsis bahia*

Laboratory studies were conducted simultaneously for both of these species in suspended and bedded sedimentary exposure systems (Gentile et al., 1985). Growth was a sensitive indicator of stress for *Ampelisca abdita*, and reduced growth was reflected in delays in reproduction. After exposure to BRH material, results from the species indicated that reproduction was the most sensitive chronic response measured. Survival was significantly decreased, and intrinsic rate of population growth and multiplication rate per generation were depressed as well. No field observations were made for these species at the FVP site.

13.5. SUMMARY

All methods and all species except *Yoldia limatula* and *Neanthes arenaceodentata* used in exposure systems in the laboratory exhibited sensitivity with reasonable precision and re-

producibility to the presence of BRH sediments and to the mixture of BRH and REF sediments. Not all species and methods exhibited typical dose-response curves, however. Similarly, the field-transect studies (Gentile et al., Chapter 11) indicated that some methods and species exhibited sensitivity to the dose-response design of field stations; however, for all biological endpoints, sensitivity of the species was markedly reduced in the field compared to the laboratory study. It appears that while some methods and species may be appropriate for use in the laboratory, they may not be sensitive enough for field monitoring activities and may not be useful in the development of laboratory-to-field links.

Table 13.2 summarizes the results of the various combinations of biomonitoring methods and species as conducted in the laboratory and in the field at the FVP dumpsite. The following species were used only in laboratory studies; therefore, no laboratory-to-field linkage was possible: *Nucula annulata*, *Nereis virens*, *Yoldia limatula*, *Ampelisca abdita*, and *Mysidopsis bahia*. Two species, *Mytilus edulis* and *Nephtys incisa*, were used both in laboratory and in field studies. Of these, only *Mytilus edulis* appears to hold promise for achieving the primary objective of the study on the basis of these preliminary results. The effectiveness of *Mytilus edulis* as a biological and chemical monitor has been established in several other field studies as reported in Phelps et al. (1987).

Differences between the effectiveness of *Mytilus edulis* and *Nephtys incisa* for field studies may be due to the nature of the respective organisms. *Mytilus edulis* was caged and therefore held captive at the site of transplant. *Nephtys incisa* is an errant polychaete that is capable of coming out of the substrate and actively relocating its burrow. Laboratory observations by Johns et al. (1985) indicate that in the laboratory study of 100% BRH sediment, juvenile *Nephtys incisa* would not burrow into the bedded sediments of the experimental exposure system. They actively burrowed into the 50% BRH:REF mix, however, and therefore were exposed to the BRH sediments. This difference may account for the absence of the expected dose response noted above. Under field conditions, animals that leave their burrows for whatever reason (including perhaps the presence of BRH sediments) are free to swim about and to test new areas before creating a new burrow. Such behavior in the area of the field study could lead to variability that might prevent the detection of differences among stations, as found in these preliminary studies.

The primary objective of this chapter is to evaluate the sensitivity of a variety of biological responses to BRH sediments in the laboratory and, to a limited extent, at the FVP field site. Phase I laboratory studies, based on a dose-re-

Table 13.2. Sensitivity of the Various Methods and Species

Study Method	Species[a]						
	Nephtys	*Neanthes*	*Nereis*	*Mytilis*	*Yoldia*	*Ampelisca*	*Mysidopsis*
AEC	−L,−F			+L,−F			
SCE	?L,−F	−L					
Histopathology	+L,−F	+L	+L	?L,−F	−L	+L	
Growth	+L	+L		+L		+L	+L
Reproduction						+L	+L
Energetics	+L	+L					
SFG		+L		+L,+F			
Bioaccumulation	+L,?F		+L	+L,+F			
Demography						+L	+L
Community	(?F)	(all indigenous species)					
REMOTS®	(+F)	(species independent)					

[a]L = laboratory studies; F = field study; + = a positive correlation between dose and response; ? = mixed results, not sensitive enough to produce a response; − = no correlation between dose and response.

sponse experimental design, indicated that most species and all methods tested proved sensitive to the presence of BRH sediment. Preliminary examination of field data indicated that SFG and bioaccumulation in *Mytilus edulis* held the greatest promise for links between laboratory and field monitoring measures. More detailed elucidation of laboratory-to-field linkage, and the degree to which the field transect mimics a laboratory simulation, remains to be done under Phase II of the FVP.

ACKNOWLEDGMENTS

This project was supported by the U.S. Army Corps of Engineers, Waterways Experiment Station Environmental Laboratory, with Richard Peddicord and Tom Dillon as Project Managers. The Environmental Protection Agency Technical Director was Jack Gentile. We thank G. Pesch for his critical comments on the manuscript. We also thank the following researchers at the Environmental Research Laboratory Narragansett who assisted in various phases of the monitoring project. G. Hoffman, R. Lapan, K. Schweitzer, W. Boothman, and F. Osterman assisted in the trace metal analyses. P. Rogerson, S. Pavignano, R. Bowen, L. LeBlanc, A. Elskus, and C. Norwood assisted in the organic chemistry analyses and M. Johnson assisted in the adenylate energy charge analyses. E. Peters and M. Casey assisted in the histopathology analyses. G. Tracey, N. Rubinstein, and D. Moffatt (University of Connecticut) assisted in the diving. Other assistance was provided by J. Heltshe, P. Sherman, W. Giles, and C. Katz. Special thanks are due also to the crews of the *R/V UConn, R/V Shang Wheeler*, and the *Hazel W. III.*

REFERENCES

Atkinson, D. E. 1971. Regulation of enzyme function. *Annual Review of Microbiology*, **23**, 47–68.

Bayne, B. L., K. R. Clark, and M. N. Morse. 1981. Some practical considerations in the measurement of pollution effects on bivalve molluscs, and some possible ecological consequences. *Aquatic Toxicology*, **1**, 159–174.

Carrano, A. V., L. H. Thompson, P. A. Lindl, and H. L. Minkler. 1978. Sister chromatid exchange as an indicator of mutagenesis. *Nature* (London), **271**, 551–553.

Epstein, S. S. 1972. Environmental pathology—a review. *American Journal of Pathology*, **66**, 352–373.

Gentile, J. H., K. J. Scott, S. Lussier, and M. Redmond. 1985. Application of Laboratory Population Responses for Evaluating the Effects of Dredged Material. Technical Report No. D-85-8, prepared by U.S. Environmental Protection Agency, Narragansett, Rhode Island, for the U.S. Army Engineer Waterways Experiment Station, Vicksburg, Mississippi, 89 pp.

Johns, D. M., R. Gutjahr-Gobell, and P. S. Schauer. 1985. Use of Bioenergetics to Investigate the Impact of Dredged Material on Benthic Species: A Laboratory Study with Polychaetes and Black Rock Harbor Material. Technical Report No. D-85-7, prepared by U.S. Environmental Protection Agency, Narragansett, Rhode Island, for the U.S. Army Engineer Waterways Experiment Station, Vicksburg, Mississippi, 85 pp.

Lake, J., G. Hoffman, and S. C. Schimmel. 1985. Bioaccumulation of Contaminants from Black Rock Harbor Dredged Material by Mussels and Polychaetes. Technical Report No. D-85-2, prepared by U.S. Environmental Protection Agency, Narragansett, Rhode Island, for the U.S. Army Engineer Waterways Experiment Station, Vicksburg, Mississippi, 150 pp.

Latt, S. A., J. Allen, S. E. Bloom, A. Carrano, E. Falke, D. Kram, E. Schneider, R. Schreck, R. Tice, B. Whitfield, and S. Wolff. 1981. Sister chromatid exchange: a report of the Gene-Tox Program. *Mutation Research*, **87**, 17–62.

Nelson, W. G., D. Black, and D. K. Phelps. 1985. Utility of the Scope for Growth Index to Assess the Physiological Impact of Black Rock Harbor Suspended Sediment on the Blue Mussel, *Mytilus edulis*: A Laboratory Evaluation. Technical report No. D-85-6, prepared by U.S. Environmental Protection Agency, Narragansett, Rhode Island, for the U.S. Army Engineer Waterways Experiment Station, Vicksburg, Mississippi, 56 pp.

Pesch, G. G., C. Mueller, C. E. Pesch, J. Heltshe, and P. S. Schauer. 1985. Application of Sister Chromatid Exchange in Marine Polychaetes to Black Rock Harbor Sediment; Laboratory Documentation Phase. Technical Report No. D-85-1, prepared by U.S. Environmental Protection Agency, Narragansett, Rhode Island, for the U.S. Army Engineer Waterways Experiment Station, Vicksburg, Mississippi, 50 pp.

Phelps, D. K., C. H. Katz, K. J. Scott, and B. H. Reynolds. 1987. Coastal monitoring: Evaluation of monitoring methods in Narragansett Bay, Long Island Sound, and New York Bight, and a general monitoring strategy. *In*: New Approaches to Monitoring Aquatic Ecosystems, T. P. Boyle (Ed.). Special Technical Publication No. 940, American Society for Testing and Materials, Philadelphia, Pennsylvania, pp. 107–124.

Rhoads, D. C., and J. D. Germano. 1982. Characterization of organism–sediment relations using sediment profile imaging: an efficient method of remote ecological monitoring of the seafloor. (REMOTS (TM) Systems) *Marine Ecology Progress Series* **8**, 115–128.

Rhoads, D. C., and D. K. Young. 1970. The influence of deposit feeding organisms on the sediment stability and community structure. *Journal of Marine Research*, **28**(2), 150–178.

Rogerson, P. F., S. C. Schimmel, and G. Hoffman. 1985. Chemical and Biological Characterization of Black Rock Harbor Dredged Material. Technical Report No. D-85-9, prepared by U.S. Environmental Protection Agency, Narragansett, Rhode Island, for the U.S. Army Engineers Waterways Experiment Station, Vicksburg, Mississippi, 123 pp.

Sanders, H. L. 1956. Oceanography of Long Island Sound, 1952–1954, Vol. X: Biology of marine bottom communities. *Bulletin of the Bingham Oceanographic Collection*, **15**, 345–414.

Scott, K. J., R. W. Morton, W. F. Bohlen, J. D. Germano, G. D. Paquette, D. C. Rhoads, and L. L. Steward. 1985. Field verification program (FVP). *In*: Disposal Area Monitoring System (DAMOS) Summary of Program Results, 1981–1984, R. W. Morton, J. H. Parker, and W. B. Richmond (Eds.). DAMOS Contribution No. 46, Vol. II, part C-III, Narragansett, Rhode Island, 231 pp.

Warren, C. E., and G. E. Davis. 1967. Laboratory studies on the feeding, bioenergetics and growth of fish. *In*: The Biological Basis of Freshwater Fish Production, S. D. Gerking (Ed.). Blackwell Scientific Publications, Oxford, England, pp. 174–219.

Yevich, P. P., C. A. Yevich, K. J. Scott, M. Redmond, D. Black, P. S. Schauer, and C. E. Pesch. 1985. Histopathological Effects of Black Rock Harbor Dredged Material on Marine Organisms: A Laboratory Investigation. Technical Report No. D-86-1, prepared by U.S. Environmental Protection Agency, Narragansett, Rhode Island, for the U.S. Army Engineer Waterways Experiment Station, Vicksburg, Mississippi, 72 pp.

Zaroogian, G. E., C. E. Pesch, P. S. Schauer, and D. Black. 1985. Laboratory Evaluation of Adenylate Energy Charge as a Test for Stress in *Mytilus edulis* and *Nephtys incisa* Treated with Dredged Material. Technical Report No. D-85-3, prepared by U.S. Environmental Protection Agency, Narragansett, Rhode Island, for the U.S. Army Engineers Waterways Experiment Station, Vicksburg, Mississippi, 56 pp.

PART IV: CONTAMINANT EFFECTS AND STATUS IN PUGET SOUND

Chapter 14

Temporal Trends of Contamination in Puget Sound

Eric A. Crecelius and Nickolas Bloom

Pacific Northwest Laboratory
Battelle Marine Research Laboratory
Sequim, Washington

Abstract	149
14.1. Introduction	149
14.2. Methods	150
14.3. Results and Discussion	150
14.3.1. Heavy Metals	150
14.3.2. Organic Chemicals	152
14.4. Summary	153
Acknowledgments	154
References	154

ABSTRACT

Trends in contaminant loading to the central basin of Puget Sound (Washington State, U.S.A.) have been inferred from the chemical composition of age-dated sediment cores. The sedimentary histories of several chemicals, including Pb, Hg, Ag, Cu, and hydrocarbons, show increased concentrations paralleling the urbanization of the Seattle–Tacoma area. Contaminant concentrations began to increase above background in the late 1800s and reached maximum concentrations usually in sediments deposited in 1945–1965. Synthetic organic compounds such as polychlorinated biphenyls, DDT, and chlorinated butadienes first appeared in sediments deposited in the 1930s or later and reached a maximum in the 1960s. The presence of the subsurface maximum concentrations in the fine-grained, deepwater sediments suggests that pollution-control strategies have improved the sediment quality of central Puget Sound.

14.1. INTRODUCTION

Puget Sound (Washington State, U.S.A.) has been used as a waste dumpsite for more than 100 y. Since the establishment of communities and industry on the shores of the sound during the second half of the 19th century, the sound has been receiving a variety of wastes including municipal sewage, industrial wastewater, coal combustion waste, storm water runoff, and particles from metal smelters. The residence time, or flushing rate, for seawater in Puget Sound is ~6 months (Ebbesmeyer et al., 1984), while the residence time of particles in the water column is generally less than a month (Baker, 1984). Most of the contaminants discharged into the sound either are attached already to particulate matter or are dissolved forms that are sequestered by suspended sediments and accumulate in the fine-grained sediments (Romberg et al., 1984). Those contaminants that tend to remain dissolved in seawater, such as As and Zn, are transported out of Puget Sound into the Pacific Ocean (Crecelius et al., 1975; Romberg et al., 1984).

The purpose of this chapter is to discuss the temporal trends of contamination that can be inferred from the chemical composition of age-dated sediment cores from central Puget Sound. Relatively undisturbed, fine-grained sediment (<10% sand) is accumulating in the deep region (>150 m) of central Puget Sound at a rate of ~1 cm y^{-1}, providing a sedimentary record of the history of contamination.

The area of consideration is the deep basin of central Puget Sound, which is bounded on the north by Admiralty Inlet and on the south by the Narrows. The central basin is ~66 km long, 6 km wide, and 225 m deep. The fine-grained sediments, composed primarily of silt and clay, cover most of the deep region of the basin (Roberts, 1979). These sediments are accumulating at rates of between 0.1 and 1.2 g cm^{-2}y^{-1} (Crecelius et al., 1983; Carpenter et al., 1984). The circulation of Puget Sound was reviewed by Cannon (1983), and the patterns of suspended particle distribution and transport were discussed by Baker (1984).

14.2. METHODS

This chapter draws upon data from several publications on the distribution of contaminants in age-dated sediment cores collected from central Puget Sound. The intent of this chapter is to summarize temporal trends for a variety of contaminants but not to review or discuss all available data. Additional data are available from several studies that have evaluated the sources and fates of contaminants in central Puget Sound (Table 14.1).

14.3. RESULTS AND DISCUSSION

14.3.1. Heavy Metals

Temporal trends in the mean concentrations of Pb, Cu, Hg, Cd, and Ag for nine age-dated sediment cores from central Puget Sound are shown in Fig. 14.1 and 14.2. Details on

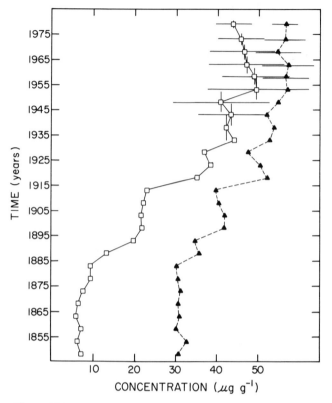

Figure 14.1. Profiles of mean concentrations of Pb (square) and Cu (triangle) in nine fine-grained (less than 10% sand) sediment cores as a function of sediment age. Concentrations are in μg g^{-1} dry wt. Horizontal error bars are the 95% confidence intervals for the standard error of the mean. The vertical error bars are ± one standard deviation.

Table 14.1. References on the Sources and Fate of Contaminants in Puget Sound

Reference	Contaminant Type	Sources	Fate	Field Data	Modeling
Barrick et al., 1980	acyclic hydrocarbons	X[a]	X	X	no[b]
Barrick, 1982	aliphatic and PAH hydrocarbons	X	X	X	X
Bates, et al, 1984	aliphatic and PAH hydrocarbons	X	X	X	X
Bothner, 1973	Hg	X	X	X	X
Carpenter et al., 1978	As	X	X	X	X
Crecelius et al., 1975	As, Sb, and Hg	X	X	X	X
Crecelius et al., 1985	PAH, PCB, chlorinated butadienes, and heavy metals	X	X	X	no
Curl, 1982	heavy metals and hydrocarbons	X	X	X	X
Dexter et al., 1981	PCB, PAH, chlorinated butadienes, and heavy metals	X	X	X	X
Furlong and Carpenter, 1982	azaarenes	X	X	X	no
Pavlou and Dexter, 1979	PCB	X	X	X	X
Romberg et al., 1984	EPA priority pollutants	X	X	X	X
Schell and Nevissi, 1977	heavy metals	X	X	X	X
U.S. EPA, 1983	EPA priority pollutants	X	no	no	no

[a]X = information present in references.
[b]no = information not in references.

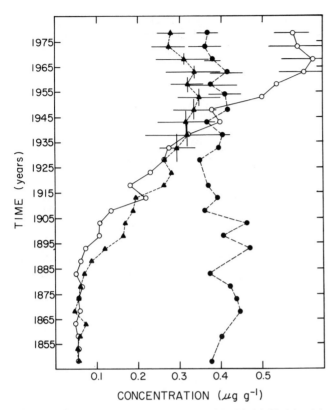

Figure 14.2. Profiles of mean concentrations of Ag (circle), Hg (triangle), and Cd (solid circle) in nine fine-grained (less than 10% sand) sediment cores as a function of sediment age. Concentrations are in μg g⁻¹ dry wt. Error bars are 95% confidence intervals.

sampling locations, methods, and chemical analyses are described by Romberg et al. (1984).

The surface sediment of each core was analyzed for grain size. Greater than 90% of the particles were <0.0625 mm in diameter with approximately equal masses of silt (0.062–0.004 mm) and clay (<0.004 mm). The variation in sediment grain size versus depth in cores was evaluated by analyzing 20 sections of each core for both wet sediment density and percent dry weight. Both the wet sediment density and the percent dry weight increase slightly with depth in the cores, averaging 1.29 ± 0.03 g ml⁻¹ [standard deviation (s.d.)] for wet density and $36 \pm 4\%$ dry wt for sediments deposited in the 1960s and 1970s. Sediments deposited in the 1800s averaged 1.32 ± 0.04 g ml⁻¹ density and $41 \pm 3\%$ dry wt.

The major feature of all these heavy metal profiles, except Cd, is the concentration increases that began during the years 1880–1890, reached a maximum during the years 1950–

1960, and, in the case of Pb, Ag, and Hg, decreased in the last 10–20 y. The apparent trend of decreasing metal concentrations in Puget Sound sediment deposited after 1955 was tested for statistical significance by calculating the linear correlation coefficient (r). The r for the linear regression of Hg concentration in 59 sediment samples deposited between 1955 and 1981 was -0.72, significant at the 0.1% level. The r for Pb was -0.52, significant at the 0.1% level. The correlation coefficients for Ag, Cu, and Cd were not significant at the 1% level, indicating that the concentrations of these metals have not decreased significantly. The mean concentration of Pb decreased 12% between 1955 and 1981. The mean concentration of Hg decreased 20% between the 1950s and the 1970s. In the late 1960s, Ag decreased only 8% between the subsurface maximum and the surface. Copper showed no significant change during the last three decades. Cadmium exhibited no significant change over the entire length of these cores. Sediment cores from urban embayments in Puget Sound do indicate, however, that in relatively shallow areas near contaminant sources there has been a history of Cd contamination along with other heavy metals (Crecelius et al., 1984; Crecelius et al., 1985).

The major feature in the metal profiles (Figs. 14.1–2) is the almost linear increase in the concentrations of Pb, Cu, Ag, and Hg that began at background concentrations in the late 1800s and reached a maximum in the middle of the 1900s. This increase roughly parallels the population growth in the Seattle–Tacoma area. Industrial development began about the turn of the century along the shores of Puget Sound. The American Smelting and Refining Company lead–copper smelter began operating in 1889 near Tacoma. Coal particles in sediments deposited during the early 1900s probably resulted from coal shipping when Tacoma was a major coal shipping port (Furlong and Carpenter, 1982). Increases in the concentrations of metals from anthropogenic sources in sediments have been reported for numerous other water bodies (Förstner and Wittmann, 1983). What is of more interest than these past increases is the decrease in contaminants that is now occurring in Puget Sound.

The presence of the subsurface maxima for Pb, Ag, and Hg should be of great significance to regulatory agencies if the decreases are indeed the result of reductions in the pollutant loading to Puget Sound. The subsurface maxima suggest that Puget Sound was more contaminated 10–30 y ago and that, as the loading decreased during the last decade, the sediment quality has improved. In order for the sediment quality to improve, cleaner sediment must be deposited on the older sediment. Also, the rate of sediment mixing must be slow relative to the sedimentation rate or else a small change in input rate could not be detected for many years. Evaluation of the sources of contaminants to Puget Sound indicates that rivers and shoreline erosion supply relatively clean sediments to the basin (Dexter et al., 1981; Curl, 1982; Crecelius et al., 1983). The residence time for particles in the sediment mixed layer is on the order of 10 y in the fine-grained sediments (Carpenter et al., 1984); therefore, when changes occur in the rate of discharge of contaminants to Puget Sound, corresponding changes should occur in surface sediments within 10 y. This must be qualified with the statement that only those contaminants that attach to particles will be deposited in the sediment. Contaminants that remain in solution, such as As, Cd, and Zn, will be advected out of the sound within a year. Carpenter et al. (1984) calculated that coarser-grained sediments generally have slower sedimentation rates that result in particle residence times in the mixed layer of several decades.

Thus, some sediments may respond to a change in contaminant loading at a much slower rate than do the fine-grained sediments.

14.3.2. Organic Chemicals

The sedimentary history of hydrocarbons recorded in fine-grained sediments of the central basin shows increased concentrations paralleling the urbanization of the Seattle–Tacoma area. The maximum concentrations of polynuclear aromatic hydrocarbons (PAH), combustion PAH (CPAH), unresolved complex mixture (UCM), and *n*-alkanes were found in sediments deposited in 1940–1950 (Figs. 14.3–4). Gschwend and Hites (1981) report similar PAH maxima in sediment cores from Europe and the United States. Bates et al. (1984)

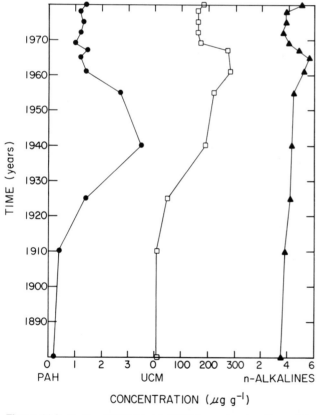

Figure 14.3. Profile of PAH (circle), UCM (square), and *n*-alkanes (triangle) in fine-grained sediments from the Central Basin of Puget Sound as a function of sediment age. Concentrations are in μg g⁻¹ dry wt. Data are from Bates et al. (1984).

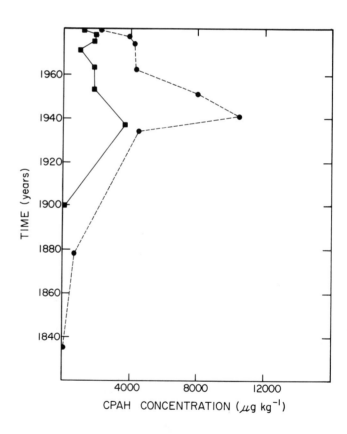

Figure 14.4. Profiles of CPAH as a function of sediment age in Meadow Point (solid square) and Elliott Bay (solid circle), Washington. Concentrations are in μg kg⁻¹ dry wt. Data are from Romberg et al. (1984).

suggest these maxima correspond to the period when the maximum number of Seattle area dwellings used coal or wood for heating. More recently, dwellings have been heated with gas, electricity, or oil, which produce relatively small amounts of combustion particles.

Barrick (1982) estimated that sewage and atmospheric dust fall are the major inputs of PAH to central Puget Sound. Although total anthropogenic emissions are probably still increasing, air-pollution control devices used to reduce particle emissions may be keeping concentrations of particulate PAH in the atmosphere at a steady state.

The sedimentary histories of *n*-alkanes and UCM, composed of branched and cyclic alkanes, show a similar increase with the increased industrialization of the Seattle–Tacoma area (Fig. 14.3), (Barrick et al., 1980; Bates et al., 1984). However, the maximum concentrations are found at approx-

imately 1965, which is more recent than the maximum concentrations for PAH (Fig. 14.4). This time period is when Seattle's largest sewage treatment plant (METRO) came on line. Prior to that time much of Seattle's sewage was discharged untreated into Puget Sound. The decline in UCM and *n*-alkane concentrations in recent sediments may be attributable to METRO.

Barrick (1982) estimated that sewage is the major terrestrial source of aliphatic hydrocarbons to central Puget Sound. The UCM profile, composed primarily of anthropogenic hydrocarbons, implicates developing urban areas rather than recently established oil refineries as the primary anthropogenic source.

The temporal trends in the contamination of central Puget Sound with synthetic organic chemicals, such as polychlorinated biphenyls (PCB), chlorinated butadienes (CBD), and

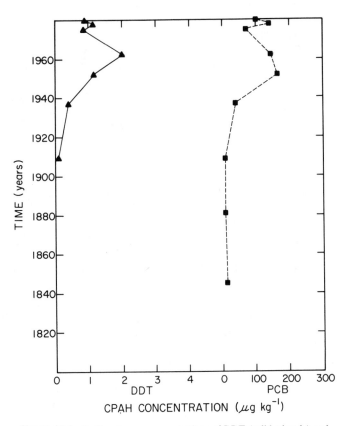

Figure 14.5. Profile of mean concentrations of DDT (solid triangle) and PCB (solid square) in three sediment cores from central Puget Sound as a function of sediment age. Concentrations are in μg kg⁻¹ dry wt. Data are from Romberg et al. (1984).

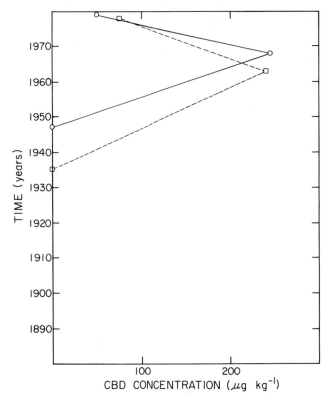

Figure 14.6. Profiles of CBD in sediment cores from central Puget Sound as a function of sediment age. Concentrations are in μg kg⁻¹ dry wt. Data are from Crecelius et al. (1985).

the pesticide DDT are similar to those of the metals and hydrocarbons except these chemicals did not appear until about the 1930s (Figs. 14.5–6). These compounds all show subsurface maxima in the 1950s or 1960s. The profiles of these chemicals generally follow the history of industrial production and release to the environment. The surface sediments of Puget Sound have been gradually recovering since the discharge of these chemicals to Puget Sound was stopped or greatly reduced.

14.4. SUMMARY

The temporal trends of contamination in central Puget Sound were inferred from the chemical composition of age-dated sediment cores. Heavy-metal contamination began in the late 1800s, reached a maximum in the mid-1900s, and began to decrease in the last decade. Hydrocarbon contamination parallels that of the heavy metals. Synthetic organic materials appear in sediments deposited in 1930 and reach a maximum in the 1960s. Due to the relatively rapid flushing and sedimentation rates, changes in contaminant loadings to the sound will result in relatively rapid changes in surficial sediment quality.

ACKNOWLEDGMENTS

This study was supported by contracts from the U.S. Department of Energy, Contract No. DE-ACO6-76RLO 1830; U.S. National Oceanic and Atmospheric Administration, Contract No. TD1979; and the Municipality of Metropolitan Seattle (METRO), Contract No. 3543.

REFERENCES

Baker, E. T. 1984. Patterns of suspended particle distribution and transport in a large fjordlike estuary. *Journal of Geophysical Research*, **89**, 6553–6566.

Barrick, R. C. 1982. Flux of aliphatic and polycyclic aromatic hydrocarbons to central Puget Sound from Seattle (Westpoint) primary sewage effluent. *Environmental Science and Technology*, **16**, 682–692.

Barrick, R. C., J. I. Hedges, and M. L. Peterson. 1980. Hydrocarbon geochemistry of the Puget Sound region—I. Sedimentary acyclic hydrocarbons. *Geochimica et Cosmochimica Acta*, **44**, 1349–1362.

Bates, T. S., S. E. Hamilton, and J. D. Cline. 1984. Vertical transport and sedimentation of hydrocarbons in the central main basin of Puget Sound, Washington. *Environmental Science and Technology*, **18**, 299–305.

Bothner, M. H. 1973. Mercury: Some Aspects of Its Marine Geochemistry in Puget Sound, Washington. Ph.D. Dissertation, University of Washington, Seattle, 126 pp.

Cannon, G. A. 1983. An Overview of Circulation in the Puget Sound Estuarine System. Technical memorandum ERL PMEL-48, U.S. National Oceanic and Atmospheric Administration, Seattle, Washington, 30 pp.

Carpenter, R., M. L. Peterson, and R. A. Jahnke. 1978. Sources, sinks and cycling of arsenic in the Puget Sound region. *In*: Estuarine Interactions, M. L. Wiley (Ed.). Academic Press, New York, pp. 459–480.

Carpenter, R., M. L. Peterson, J. T. Bennett, and B. L. K. Somayajulu. 1984. Mixing and cycling of uranium, thorium and ^{210}Pb in Puget Sound sediments. *Geochimica et Cosmochimica Acta*, **48**, 1949–1963.

Crecelius, E. A., M. H. Bothner, and R. Carpenter. 1975. Geochemistry of arsenic, antimony, mercury, and related elements in sediments of Puget Sound. *Environmental Science and Technology*, **9**, 325–333.

Crecelius, E. A., N. S. Bloom, and G. Massoth. 1983. Sediment mass balance for the main basin of Puget Sound. *American Geophysical Union Transactions* EOS, **64**, 1104.

Crecelius, E. A., N. S. Bloom, and J. M. Gurtisen. 1984. Chemical Analysis of Sediment Cores from the East Waterway (Everett, Washington). Final report PNL-5045, Battelle, Pacific Northwest Laboratory, Richland, Washington, 26 pp.

Crecelius, E. A., R. G. Riley, N. S. Bloom, and B. L. Thomas. 1985. History of Contamination of Sediments in Commencement Bay, Tacoma, Washington. Technical memorandum NOS OMA 14, U.S. National Oceanic and Atmospheric Administration, Rockville, Maryland, 44 pp.

Curl, H. C., Jr. 1982. Estuarine and Coastal Pollutant Transport and Transformations: The Role of Particulate Matter. Fiscal Year 1980–1982 Office of Marine Pollution Assessment Annual Report, Section 202, Research Programs, Pacific Marine Environmental Laboratory, Seattle, 227 pp.

Dexter, R. N., D. E. Anderson, E. A. Quinlan, L. S. Goldstein, R. M. Strickland, S. P. Pavlou, J. R. Clayton, Jr., R. M. Kocan, and M. Landolt. 1981. A Summary of Knowledge of Puget Sound Related to Chemical Contaminants. Technical memorandum OMPA 13, U.S. National Oceanic and Atmospheric Administration, Boulder, Colorado, 435 pp.

Ebbesmeyer, C. C., C. A. Coomes, J. M. Cox, J. M. Helseth, L. R. Hinchey, G. A. Cannon, and C. A. Barnes. 1984. Technical memorandum NOS OMS 5, U.S. National Oceanic and Atmospheric Administration, Rockville, Maryland, 73 pp.

Förstner, U., and G. T. W. Wittmann. 1983. Metal Pollution in the Aquatic Environment. Springer-Verlag, New York, pp. 486.

Furlong, E. T., and R. Carpenter. 1982. Azaarenes in Puget Sound sediments. *Geochimica et Cosmochimica Acta*, **46**, 1385–1396.

Gschwend, P. M., and R. A. Hites. 1981. Fluxes of polycyclic aromatic hydrocarbons to marine and lacustrine sediments in the northeastern United States. *Geochimica et Cosmochimica Acta*, **45**, 2359–2367.

Pavlou, S. P., and R. N. Dexter. 1979. Distribution of polychlorinated biphenyls (PCB) in estuarine ecosystems. Testing the concept of equilibrium partitioning in the marine environment. *Environmental Science and Technology*, **13**, 65–71.

Roberts, R. W. 1979. Sediment Distribution Maps for the Puget Sound Region. Unpublished, School of Oceanography, University of Washington, Seattle, 6 maps.

Romberg, G. P., S. P. Pavlou, R. F. Shokes, W. Hom, E. A. Crecelius, P. Hamilton, J. T. Gunn, R. D. Muench, and J. Vinelli. 1984. Toxicant Pretreatment Planning Study Technical Report Cl: Presence, Distribution and Fate of Toxicants in Puget Sound and Lake Washington. Technical report, Municipality of Metropolitan Seattle (METRO), Seattle, Washington, 231 pp.

Schell, W. R., and A. Nevissi. 1977. Heavy metals from waste disposal in central Puget Sound. *Environmental Science and Technology*, **11**, 887–893.

U.S. Environmental Protection Agency. 1983. Water Quality Management Program for Puget Sound: Part I, Management Activities, Data Requirements and Data Base. Report No. EPA-910/9-83-106A, U.S. Environmental Protection Agency, Region 10, Seattle, Washington, 302 pp.

Chapter 15

Bioaccumulation of Toxic Substances in Puget Sound Organisms

Thomas C. Ginn and Robert C. Barrick

PTI Environmental Services
Bellevue, Washington

Abstract	157
15.1. Introduction	157
15.2. Bioaccumulation of Metals	158
15.3. Organic Contaminants	161
15.4. Public Health Considerations	166
15.5. Conclusions and Recommendations	166
References	167

ABSTRACT

This chapter presents an overview and synthesis of available information on bioaccumulation in Puget Sound (Washington, U.S.A.) organisms and relates existing concentrations of contaminants in the environment (i.e., water or sediment) to concentrations in organisms. Concentrations of toxic substances in the tissues of organisms from industrialized embayments were compared both with those in organisms from Puget Sound reference areas and with available health hazard criteria. Although there is considerable sediment contamination by metals in industrialized embayments, Puget Sound fish do not generally accumulate metals in muscle tissue above the reference level. Metal concentrations are elevated, however, in bivalve mollusks, crustacea, fish livers, and birds in industrialized areas of Puget Sound. The most commonly detected organic compounds are polychlorinated biphenyls (PCB), which have been detected in all biotic groups studied. Residues of DDT are also detected commonly, at relatively low concentrations (<20 μg kg^{-1} wet wt). Of the organic compounds present in Puget Sound fish, PCB may represent the greatest potential hazard to human health. Concentrations of PCB in the edible muscle tissue of bottom fish from industrialized areas generally range from 100 to 1000 μg kg^{-1} wet wt.

15.1. INTRODUCTION

Past studies have demonstrated that water and sediments from several industrialized embayments of Puget Sound in Washington (U.S.A.) are substantially contaminated by various inorganic and organic substances. Although nonindustrialized embayments and the main basins of the sound appear to have much lower levels of toxic contaminants, there is concern regarding the ultimate fate and potential effects in localized areas of greatest contamination. Evaluation of management alternatives for controlling contamination involves assessments of whether these substances are available for uptake by marine organisms and of the potential hazards, either to the organisms or to human health, associated with a given level of bioaccumulation.

Studies conducted by the U.S. National Oceanic and Atmospheric Administration (NOAA) (Malins et al., 1980, 1982) have been instrumental in documenting sediment contamination of areas such as Elliott Bay (Port of Seattle), Commencement Bay (Port of Tacoma), and Sinclair Inlet (Bremerton) (Fig. 15.1). Sediments from these areas contain high levels of several contaminant groups that have a high potential for bioaccumulation in Puget Sound organisms. Of special importance is the occurrence of high levels of polychlorinated biphenyls (PCB) in the Duwamish Waterway of Elliott Bay, and of organic compounds, such as hexachlorobenzene (HCB) and chlorinated butadienes (CBD), in Hylebos Waterway of Commencement Bay. Moreover, high levels

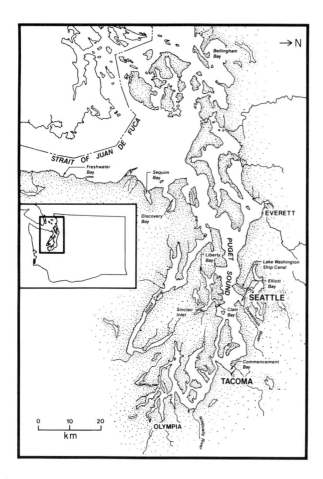

Figure 15.1. Location map for the Puget Sound (Washington) region.

gesting contaminated seafood. Effects on Puget Sound biota are evaluated by Chapman (Chapter 16).

15.2. BIOACCUMULATION OF METALS

Studies of bioaccumulation of metals in Puget Sound organisms have involved invertebrates (mainly bivalve mollusks) and vertebrates (mainly fish). Such studies have generally focused on areas potentially influenced by port activities and municipal or industrial discharges. For example, bivalves (mussels) showed elevated Hg concentrations near a chloralkali plant located on Bellingham Bay, and elevated Cu and Zn concentrations near the American Smelting and Refining Company (ASARCO) copper refinery on Commencement Bay (Bothner and Piper, 1973; Rasmussen and Williams, 1975; Washington Department of Ecology, 1979). Concentrations of Cr, Pb, and Zn were also higher in mussels collected at sites near major Seattle sewage outfalls than in those from reference areas (Schell et al., 1977). Dungeness crab contained Cr, Cu, and Pb concentrations that were two to five times higher in industrialized areas (e.g., Hylebos and City waterways in Commencement Bay) than in reference areas (e.g., Discovery Bay with average Cr, Cu, and Pb concentrations of 0.065, 4.3, and 0.37 mg kg^{-1} wet wt, respectively). Other metals (e.g., As and Ni) have not been reported in elevated concentrations in invertebrates from contaminated areas of the sound.

Metals have been analyzed in the muscle tissues of demersal fish (e.g., starry flounder, Dover sole, English sole, and rock sole) from numerous locations in Puget Sound (Cummins et al., 1976; Sherwood and McCain, 1976; Olsen and Schell, 1977; Schell et al., 1977; Malins et al., 1980, 1982; Gahler et al., 1982; McCain et al., 1982). Relative to the concentrations in fish from reference areas (e.g., Hood Canal), lead and Cu concentrations were elevated in liver tissues of sole collected near Seattle. Despite variations in metals concentrations of up to two orders of magnitude in sediments from these areas, levels of metals in the muscle tissue of fish generally were similar among areas. There were no consistent differences associated with proximity to known sources of contamination by metals or to concentrations of metals in muscle tissue from fish.

Sampling for metals in marine birds from Puget Sound has been limited to analyses of liver and kidney tissues in birds from two industrialized areas of Puget Sound (Commencement Bay and Elliott Bay) and the nonindustrialized Strait of Juan de Fuca (Riley et al., 1983). Concentrations of Cd, Hg,

of metals such as As, Cu, Hg, and Pb have been recorded in the major port areas and near industrial discharges.

Much of the concern about chemical contamination in Puget Sound results from possible impacts on biological resources. Puget Sound contains important stocks of salmon, cod, rockfish, and other species that support major commercial and recreational fisheries. In addition, there is extensive commercial and recreational harvest of shellfish, much of it occurring near industrialized areas of the sound. Assessment of bioaccumulation effects requires that three kinds of questions be addressed: (1) Are the contaminants accumulated by indigenous organisms? (2) Does the bioaccumulation result in effects in the organisms? (3) Does the bioaccumulation represent a threat to public health? This chapter evaluates the degree to which contaminants are accumulated by Puget Sound organisms and the potential health hazards from in-

Pb, and Zn were significantly elevated in glaucous-winged gull tissues from one or both industrialized areas compared with those from the Strait of Juan de Fuca. Although bioaccumulation was indicated on a regional basis, all metal concentrations except Zn were within the reported range for wild birds. Elevated concentrations of Hg and Pb were also found in tissues from great blue herons and pigeon guillemots collected from Commencement and Elliott bays.

Liver and kidney tissues of harbor seals from southern Puget Sound have also been analyzed for metals (Calambokidis et al., 1984). In general, the concentrations of metals in tissue were within the range of values reported for other coastal areas.

The available data for levels of metals in tissue from Puget Sound biota do not demonstrate a clear relationship between bioaccumulation and the degree of sediment or water contamination. This situation may result in part from a lack of synoptic sampling of biotic and abiotic metal levels and from various study-design deficiencies, including lack of reference samples, low sample size, and variations in species sampled over time or space. Studies conducted in Commencement Bay probably provide the best data to evaluate the bioaccumulation of metals in fish. The studies by Gahler et al. (1982) provide a relatively comprehensive assessment of concentrations of metals in the muscle tissue of English sole from Hylebos Waterway, City Waterway, the Ruston–Pt. Defiance Shoreline, and a relatively unpolluted reference area, Discovery Bay (Fig. 15.1). Data from several sources [summarized by Johnson et al. (1983a,b)] provide a good spatial characterization of concentrations of metals in sediment throughout the area sampled by Gahler et al. (1982). Moreover, many of the fish species sampled by Gahler et al. are relatively sedentary, demersal forms (e.g., English sole) that could be expected to display elevated concentrations of metals in tissue if significant bioaccumulation is occurring in the area.

Relative contamination levels of sediments and tissues were compared by expressing each mean value as a ratio of the concentrations in Commencement Bay to the concentration in Puget Sound reference areas, which are removed from known pollutant sources. Expressing the data in this manner enables an assessment of whether metal enrichment in the sediment is associated with elevated metal levels in the tissues of indigenous fish.

Comparisons of elevations (above reference concentrations) in sediments from the Commencement Bay waterways with those in muscle tissues from English sole are presented

in Figs. 15.2 and 15.3. Concentrations of four metals (Cu, Hg, Pb, and Zn) were elevated in sediments of Hylebos and City waterways, but not in muscle tissue from English sole. Although As was enriched in the sediments of both waterways by greater than an order of magnitude, As concentrations in muscle tissue of fish from the waterways were only slightly higher than those from the Discovery Bay reference area.

The only metals in Hylebos and City waterways displaying concentrations in muscle tissue more than two times background levels were Cr and Ni (Figs. 15.2 and 15.3). Although maximum Cr and Ni concentrations in tissue were less than

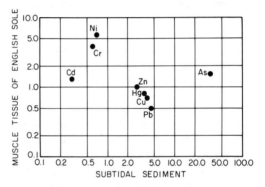

Figure 15.2. Comparison of relative sediment and tissue concentrations of metals in Hylebos Waterway. Axes represent ratios of concentrations in Hylebos samples to those in samples from uncontaminated reference locations. *Sources*: Malins et al. (1980, 1982), Gahler et al. (1982), Johnson et al. (1983b).

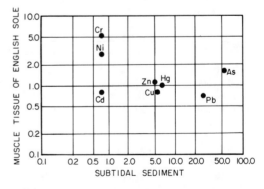

Figure 15.3. Comparison of relative sediment and tissue concentrations of metals in City Waterway. Axes represent ratios of concentrations in City samples to those in samples from uncontaminated reference locations. *Sources*: Malins et al. (1980, 1982), Gahler et al. (1982), Johnson et al. (1983a).

six times background levels, it is interesting to note that neither of these metals displayed elevated concentrations in surficial sediments. These data suggest that the uptake routes for Cr and Ni may be through the water column rather than through the sediments.

A direct comparison of metal concentrations in sediments and of those in muscle tissue cannot be conducted for the Ruston–Pt. Defiance Shoreline (Commencement Bay, Fig. 15.1) because of an absence of data for metal concentrations in subtidal sediments in the study area (i.e., at depths <20 m). It is important to note that average concentrations of As and Pb in muscle tissue from English sole were higher in samples from the Point Defiance Dock area than in samples from the other areas sampled by Gahler et al. (1982). Moreover, the highest individual As and Pb concentrations in English sole (14.6 and 10.4 mg kg^{-1} wet wt, respectively) were measured at the Point Defiance Dock. Chromium concentrations in sediments collected at the Point Defiance Dock were also elevated relative to reference conditions and were comparable to those measured in Hylebos and City waterway sediments.

A comparison of average concentrations of metals in samples of fish muscle from two Puget Sound areas with documented elevations in metal concentrations in the sediment is presented in Table 15.1. Elliot Bay sediments, especially in the areas of the dredged-material dumpsite and the Port of Seattle, have considerably higher concentrations of Hg and Pb. The Ruston–Pt. Defiance Shoreline of Commencement Bay is contaminated by As, Cu, and other metals. Both data

sets presented in Table 15.1 represent several fish species, including cod, salmon, sole, walleye pollock, and sculpin. A comparison of analyses of muscle tissue from fish from these two industrialized areas with analyses of samples from nonindustrialized Discovery Bay indicates a negligibly increased bioaccumulation of most metals in the contaminated areas. Although As concentrations in fish from the Ruston–Pt. Defiance Shoreline were approximately three times higher than background levels, this increase is relatively small compared to the degree of As contamination in sediments from the area. Recent studies have documented sediment concentrations near the Ruston–Pt. Defiance Shoreline of over 1000 times Puget Sound background levels (Tetra Tech, 1985). The data in Table 15.1 on Pb are difficult to interpret. The lowest values recorded for fish were from Elliott Bay, where sediments were highly contaminated by Pb. The apparently high concentration of Pb in fish from the Ruston–Pt. Defiance Shoreline was due in part to one extremely high value (10.4 µg g^{-1}).

The absence of substantial bioaccumulation of metals by Puget Sound fish, relative to the levels of sediment contamination, is consistent with available information that indicates the considerable ability of marine fish to regulate levels of most metals in their muscle tissue (Halcrow et al., 1973; Eustace, 1974; Greig et al., 1976). Some metals, however, can be elevated in fish inhabiting areas of high contamination, especially if the metals exist in alkylated or methylated forms.

Data from Puget Sound and from many other areas (Alexander and Young, 1976; Martin and Castle, 1984) indicate that analyses of metals in tissues of filter-feeding bivalve mollusks may provide a sensitive assessment of water and sediment contamination. Such organisms are susceptible to bioaccumulation of metals because they filter contaminated particulate matter from the water and have considerable water–tissue contact for uptake of dissolved forms. Moreover, they have less ability to regulate metals than do vertebrates.

Data for several metals in the tissue of blue mussels (*Mytilus edulis*) from Puget Sound are compiled in Table 15.2. These data indicate that mussels that are not near major pollutant sources in the central basin of Puget Sound do not display elevated tissue concentrations of Cu and Hg when compared with those from nearby unpolluted waters. Available studies indicate substantial bioaccumulation of Cu and Hg in mussels collected near the ASARCO refinery. The data also suggest the possibility of elevated Pb concentrations in mussels from the central basin.

Table 15.1. Comparison of Metal Concentrations (mg kg^{-1} wet wt) in the Muscle Tissue of Fish from the Puget Sound Region[a]

Metal	Elliott Bay[b]	Pt. Defiance[c] (Commencement Bay)	Discovery Bay[c]
As	3.12 (6.10)[d]	7.80 (34.1)	2.40 (5.3)
Cd	0.006 (0.006)	0.005 (0.012)	0.005 (0.013)
Cr	0.16 (0.16)	0.18 (0.41)	0.10 (0.48)
Cu	0.75 (0.89)	0.62 (1.2)	0.45 (0.93)
Hg	1.130 (0.180)		
	(0.08)	0.050 (0.11)	
Pb	0.024 (0.032)	1.18 (10.4)	0.40 (0.61)
Zn	4.4 (5.0)	7.4 (10.7)	5.5 (7.3)

[a]Species sampled include sole (three species), walleye pollock, cod, salmon, and sculpin.
[b]Galvin et al. (1984).
[c]Gahler et al. (1982).
[d]Average concentration (maximum concentration).

Table 15.2. Average Concentrations (mg kg^{-1} wet wt) of Selected Metals in Tissue from Mussels (*Mytilus edulis*) from Puget Sound[a]

	Hg	Pb	Cd	Cu
Puget Sound[b] (Central Basin)	0.109	6.6	3.7	7.4
Commencement Bay[c] (Near refinery)	0.836	—[d]	3.6	75.0
Puget Sound[e] (U.S. mussel watch)	—	1.2	2.0	4.3
Willapa Bay, WA[e] (U.S. mussel watch)	—	2.2	3.0	5.9
Sequim Bay[c]	0.102	—	5.2	5.8

[a]Only mean concentrations were available for several data reports.
[b]Schell et al. (1977).
[c]Roesijadi et al. (1984).
[d]Dash indicates no data.
[e]Goldberg et al. (1983).

Assessment of biomagnification as a function of trophic level is complicated by the lack of studies involving collection of several trophic classes of organisms from a single locality (i.e., with similar metal exposure levels). Moreover, data interpretation is confounded by the effects of life span and lipid content on the accumulation of some metals, such as Hg.

The occurrence of biomagnification can be partially addressed by examining concentrations of selected metals in tissues of fish at different trophic levels. The data reported by Gahler et al. (1982) were used to evaluate levels of As, Cd, and Hg in English sole, walleye pollock, and hake. English sole feed primarily on polychaetes, and walleye pollock and Pacific hake feed primarily on other fish. For the City Waterway collections, there was no apparent increase in Cd and Hg

concentrations in higher-trophic-level fish (Fig. 15.4). Moreover, As was much more concentrated in the benthic-feeding English sole than in the other two species. The available evidence indicates that Hg (probably in the methylated form) accumulates to high levels in long-lived species with high lipid contents (e.g., marine mammals). In addition, most metals are accumulated by invertebrates and mussels located near pollutant sources; however, there is no evidence for a generalized accumulation of metals in Puget Sound fish, or for biomagnification of metals in higher-trophic-level fish.

15.3. ORGANIC CONTAMINANTS

Concentrations of organic compounds in Puget Sound vary widely among sites, among species, and within a given species at a single site. For example, the overall seasonal and random variability of hydrocarbon concentrations in a rocky intertidal community (i.e., Strait of Juan de Fuca) remote from obvious petroleum sources was at least twofold on a dry-weight basis (Clark, 1983). The total weight of extractable organic matter (EOM) in tissues has not been reported in the bulk of Puget Sound studies. The EOM is a preferable alternative means of normalizing tissue concentrations of lipophilic organic contaminants, and is useful when comparing different types of tissue, tissues of the same species whose physiological condition varies, or tissues of different species. For example, edible salmon flesh may contain 4–12% fat, while sole may contain only 0.8–1.4% fat (Sidwell et al., 1974). Exposure to similar contaminant levels could result in higher wet-weight concentrations in salmon tissue compared with levels in sole tissue if organic contaminants are bioaccumulated in proportion to body fat. A comparison of tissue concentrations normalized to the lipid content of organisms at different trophic levels also provides evidence for or against biomagnification of organic contaminants via the food chain in a particular area.

Bioaccumulation studies of organic compounds in Puget Sound have typically focused on biota collected in urban embayments contaminated by multiple discharges with overlapping chemical compositions. Several hundred organic compounds have been detected in these analyses (Gahler et al., 1982), but the lack of authentic reference standards has limited confirmed identification to only a few substances. Dominant contaminants observed include selected aromatic hydrocarbons, chlorinated hydrocarbons [e.g., polychlorinated biphenyls (PCB), DDT, and chlorinated benzenes and butadienes], and phthalate esters. The most frequently de-

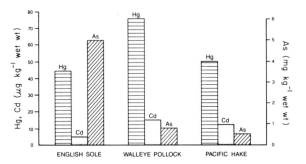

Figure 15.4. Average metal concentrations in muscle tissue for three fish species from City Waterway (Commencement Bay).

tected compounds in higher organisms (e.g., fish, birds, and marine mammals) are PCB and DDT and its metabolites (primarily p,p'-DDE). There have been no quantitative measurements of metabolites of organic compounds in field studies done in Puget Sound, although limited evidence of their existence in Puget Sound biota has been recently provided (Clark, 1983; Malins et al., 1983).

All studies of invertebrates (Table 15.3) and of demersal and semi-demersal fish collected from industrialized urban areas of Puget Sound showed elevated concentrations of PCB relative to those from nonurban reference areas (Sherwood and McCain, 1976; Mowrer et al., 1977; Stout and Beezhold, 1981; Gahler et al., 1982; Malins et al., 1982; Galvin et al., 1984). Data summarized by Harper-Owes (1983) show that whole-body PCB concentrations declined from >3 mg kg^{-1} wet wt to <1 mg kg^{-1} wet wt during the 1970s in fish collected from the Duwamish River estuary (the most contaminated area). A decline in PCB concentrations in fish samples from the Hudson River has also been documented by Sloan et al. (1983). Other chlorinated organic compounds have been found in elevated concentrations in the tissue of invertebrates and fish, but generally only near specific sources. For example, CBD concentrations were elevated in livers from English sole (maximum 2.2 mg kg^{-1} wet wt) and in invertebrates (maximum 0.076 mg kg^{-1} wet wt in a polychaete sample) collected from the contaminated Hylebos Waterway in Commencement Bay relative to reference areas, but not in other industrialized areas of the sound (Malins et al., 1982).

Liver, kidney, and adipose (fat) tissues of five great blue herons collected in Puget Sound contained few organic con-taminants other than PCB (Riley et al., 1983). Concentrations of PCB in adipose tissue of great blue herons from Elliott and Commencement bays ranged from 14 to 80 mg kg^{-1} wet wt, compared with a concentration of 5.5 mg kg^{-1} in a single bird from Sequim Bay (a Strait of Juan de Fuca reference area). Concentrations of PCB in liver tissue ranged from 0.19 to 3.2 mg kg^{-1} wet wt for three bird species from urban areas, compared with a range of 0.03–0.75 mg kg^{-1} for birds from reference areas. Contaminant levels in actual prey items for these birds were not reported, but elevated PCB levels in the birds' adipose tissue likely result from the interactions among food intake, lipid storage, and excretion.

Concentrations of PCB in blubber from harbor seals collected in southern Puget Sound ranged up to 750 mg kg^{-1} wet wt (Calambokidis et al., 1984). Although this maximum value was not replicated in an intercalibration comparison, the PCB concentrations reported are among the highest found worldwide. The average PCB concentration for all samples of seal blubber (110 mg kg^{-1} wet wt) collected in southern Puget Sound was 6 times the average for those from Hood Canal and 10 times the average for those from northern Puget Sound. The PCB source has not been clearly identified. Aromatic hydrocarbons were not detected in seal blubber, with the exception of a few μg kg^{-1} of phenanthrene in a single sample. Concentrations of DDE found in the blubber samples were also highest in samples from southern Puget Sound (ranging up to 42 mg kg^{-1} wet wt) but were similar to or lower than reported values for other coastal regions.

Studies of Commencement Bay by Gahler et al. (1982) provide the most extensive data to evaluate bioaccumulation of organic contaminants in fish relative to sediment contam-

Table 15.3. Range of PCB Concentrations (μg kg^{-1} wet wt) in Invertebrate Tissue from Puget Sound[a]

Organism	Duwamish River (Elliott Bay)	Hylebos Waterway (Commencement Bay)	Reference Areas
Polychaete[b]	250	66–260	45
Mussel[c]	92–210	72	10–30
Clam[b]	50–180	54–120	<2–30
Shrimp[b]	480	800	26–54
Crab			
Hepatopancreas[b]	9600	3600	130
Muscle[d]	76	47–58	U[e](10)

[a]Single values are given when only a single analysis was reported.
[b]Malins et al. (1980).
[c]Mowrer et al. (1977).
[d]Galvin et al. (1984); Gahler et al. (1982).
[e]U indicates undetected at detection limit shown.

ination. For this review, data on organic contaminants in tissues and sediments were treated like corresponding data on metals, with the mean value expressed as a ratio of the concentrations observed in Commencement Bay to the concentrations in Puget Sound reference areas distant from known pollutant sources. Weights of the total EOM in tissues and organic carbon content in the sediment are not available for this data set; therefore, the data were not normalized for variations in the lipid content of organisms or for the ratios of organic to inorganic material in regional sediments.

Elevations in the concentrations of organic compounds in the sediment from two Commencement Bay waterways were compared with those in muscle tissues from English sole (Fig. 15.5). These limited data show that, unlike selected metals, none of the organic contaminants examined were elevated in muscle tissue of fish to an extent greater than the average elevation in sediments.

Compounds such as PCB appeared to be elevated to roughly the same extent in sediments and in muscle tissue of fish (Fig. 15.5). Conversely, hexachlorobutadiene (HCBD) and selected polynuclear aromatic hydrocarbons (PAH) concentrations were highly elevated in Hylebos and City waterway sediments, but were not detected or were at low concen-

trations in muscle tissues of fish. Pesticides such as DDT fall in between, with somewhat higher elevations above reference for subtidal sediments than for muscle tissues of fish. High HCB elevations were found both for sediments and for fish tissue in Hylebos Waterway, but only for sediments in City Waterway. This anomaly may reflect sampling and analytical limitations; more recent sediment samples from City Waterway did not contain detectable quantities of HCB (Tetra Tech, 1985).

Similar comparisons of elevations above reference concentrations in Discovery Bay are presented in Fig. 15.6 for selected organic compounds in liver tissue from English sole and in sediments from Hylebos Waterway. Unlike muscle tissues of fish, liver tissues of fish had HCBD elevations above reference similar to those for sediments. Elevations of other chlorinated compounds (e.g., HCB, DDT, and PCB) were similar in muscle and liver tissues of fish (Fig. 15.5 and 15.6). Neither muscle nor liver tissue of fish exhibited elevated PAH concentrations, although sediment PAH concentrations in Hylebos Waterway were more than an order of magnitude above reference levels. These results reflect both the potentially low bioavailability of sediment-absorbed PAH from significant sources, including combustion processes (Prahl and Carpenter, 1983) and oils (Neff and Breteler,

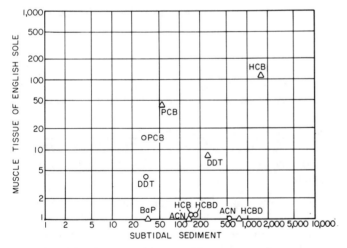

Figure 15.5. Comparison of concentrations of organic substances above reference level for subtidal sediment and muscle tissue of English sole in Hylebos (triangles) and City (circles) waterways. Axes represent ratios of concentrations in waterway samples to those in samples from uncontaminated reference locations. Key: Pyr: pyrene, Flu: fluoranthene, ACN: acenaphthyelene, HCB: hexachlorobenzene, HCBD: hexachlorobutadiene, BaP: benzo(*a*)pyrene. *Sources:* Gahler et al. (1982), Malins et al. (1980, 1982), Johnson et al. (1983a,b), Riley et al. (1981).

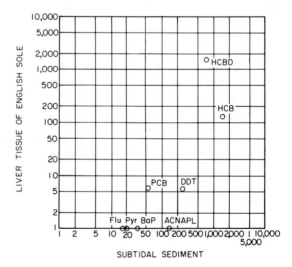

Figure 15.6. Comparison of concentrations of organic substances above reference level for subtidal sediment and liver tissue of English sole in Hylebos (triangles) and City (circles) waterways. Axes represent ratios of concentrations in waterway samples to those in samples from uncontaminated reference locations. Key: Pyr: pyrene, Flu: fluoranthene, ACN: acenaphthyelene, HCB: hexachlorobenzene, HCBD: hexachlorobutadiene. *Sources:* Gahler et al. (1982), Malins et al. (1980, 1982), Johnson et al. (1983a,b), Riley et al. (1981).

1983), as well as the rapid metabolism of any PAH accumulated.

Average concentrations of organic compounds in muscle samples from English sole were compared for two Puget Sound areas with documented elevations in concentrations of organic contaminants in the sediment (Table 15.4). Concentrations of organic compounds in several other fish species (e.g., cod, salmon, walleye pollock, and sculpin) follow the general trends shown by the English sole, but fewer data are available for review. Organic compounds detected in the industrialized areas were elevated above Discovery Bay reference concentrations by factors of 3–70, with the exception of DDT in samples from Elliott Bay. In some cases, these elevations were probably conservative estimates because of high detection limits for undetected substances in samples from the reference area.

Concentrations of PCB were elevated in muscle tissues of fish from both Commencement and Elliott bays, as they were in sediments from both regions. This correspondence provides the most consistent evidence for bioaccumulation of contaminants in edible tissues of organisms captured in contaminated urban embayments.

Concentrations of PCB in muscle tissues of several bottom-dwelling fish species on the eastern and western coasts of the United States are presented in Table 15.5. Maximum PCB

Table 15.5. Concentrations of PCB (μg g^{-1} wet wt) in Muscle Tissue from East and West Coast Bottomfish

Area	Species	Mean Concentration (μg g^{-1})	Range
New Bedford Harbor, MA[a]	Winter flounder	6.4	N.D.–22[b]
Hudson River, NJ[c]	Summer flounder	1.5	NR[d]
Palos Verdes Shelf, CA[e]	Dover sole	1.3	0.06–2.5
Elliott Bay, WA[f]	English sole	1.0	0.36–2.1
Hylebos Waterway, WA[f,g]	English sole	0.57	0.13–1.0
Raritan Bay, NJ[e]	Summer flounder	0.56	NR
Los Angeles Harbor, CA[h]	White croaker	0.42	NR
New York Bight, NY[i]	Winter flounder	0.06	0.01–0.1

[a]Weaver (1984).
[b]N.D. indicates concentration not detected; detection limit not stated.
[c]Belton et al. (1982).
[d]NR indicates concentration not reported.
[e]McDermott-Ehrlich et al. (1978).
[f]Malins et al. (1982).
[g]Gahler et al. (1982).
[h]Gossett et al. (1983).
[i]MacLeod et al. (1981).

concentrations in Puget Sound are lower than the average concentrations recently reported for New Bedford Harbor (Weaver, 1984) by a factor of three, but minimum concentrations reported for Puget Sound urban areas are twice the average reported for the New York Bight (MacLeod et al., 1981).

Gahler et al. (1982) reported volatile chlorinated ethylenes at concentrations of ~30–40 μg kg^{-1} (wet wt) in muscle tissues of fish from Hylebos Waterway, where volatile substances have also been detected in local point-source inputs (Johnson et al., 1983a). These results have been confirmed in recent studies (Tetra Tech, 1985) suggesting that levels of some volatile organic substances in fish tissues may be related to concentrations in water and sediments near the point of capture.

The analyses of DDT residues in fish tissues collected from several areas of Puget Sound must be evaluated with caution. Recent confirmations of results of the determination of chlorinated pesticide levels by gas chromatography/mass spectrometry (GC/MS) for sediments from Commencement Bay have shown that a number of "false positive" readings for pesticides occur with electron capture (EC) detection, even with double-column GC/EC confirmation. These "false positive" readings appear to be reduced when analyses are conducted with high-resolution capillary GC columns rather

Table 15.4. Comparison of Average Concentrations (μg kg^{-1} wet wt) of Organic Compounds in Muscle Tissue from English Sole from Elliott Bay, Commencement Bay, and Discovery Bay

	Elliott Bay[a]	Commencement Bay[b] Hylebos Waterway	Commencement Bay[b] City Waterway	Discovery Bay[b]
PCB	900	570	190	<13
DDT	7	20	17	<5
Hexachlorobenzene	U (20)[c]	110	U (1)	U (1)
Napthalene	U (1.6)	U (2)	510[d]	U (2)
Phenanthrene	U (5)[e]	U (5)	U (5)	U (5)
Benzo(a)pyrene	U (13)	U (40)	U (40)	U (40)
Phthalate esters	360[f]	420	<560	<300

[a]Galvin et al. (1984); Romberg et al. (1984); Malins et al. (1982).
[b]Gahler et al. (1982); Malins et al. (1982).
[c]U indicates undetected at detection limit shown.
[d]Value reported for a single English sole sample.
[e]Phenanthrene was detected in salmon tissue only (470 μg kg^{-1}; one sample).
[f]Higher concentrations of phthalates were found in single cod (7,200 μg kg^{-1}) and salmon (51,000 μg kg^{-1}) samples from Elliott Bay.

than with packed columns. Historically, high levels of various pesticides have been reported in sediments from Commencement Bay, but recent analyses using GC/MS have not confirmed any of these levels (Tetra Tech, 1985).

Data for organic contaminants in fish livers suggest that bioaccumulation may be significant for several compounds. Still undetermined is the significance of the potential accumulation of metabolites of organic contaminants. For example, PAH concentrations were, with some exceptions, near or below detection limits in samples of liver tissues of fish, although substantial PAH accumulations have been found in lower organisms that lack an enzymatic detoxification system (e.g., mussels). Examples of hazardous metabolites include oxygenated compounds, such as polycyclic aromatic ketones (Ramdahl, 1983), and organic free radicals (molecules with unpaired electrons) that can derive from contaminants such as aromatic hydrocarbons and their substituted derivatives. Malins et al. (1983) measured the intensity of electron paramagnetic resonance (EPR) signals as an indicator of the levels of organic free radicals in liver microsomes from healthy and diseased English sole. The intensity of the EPR signal was significantly higher ($\alpha = 0.05$) in livers with lesions than in livers without lesions. Homogenates from lesion-free livers were also incubated with four separate organic fractions (alkane, aromatic, PCB, and polar) of an extract of sediment from the Duwamish River and with similar fractions of an extract from a less contaminated central Puget Sound sediment (Meadow Point north of Seattle). A detectable EPR signal was found only in tests with the aromatic fraction from the Duwamish River sediment. A potential link among liver lesions, organic free radicals, and sediment accumulations of aromatic contaminants was suggested but not confirmed.

Data on organic contaminants in the tissue of mussels analogous to those previously presented for metals in *Mytilus edulis* in Puget Sound are limited; however, mussels have been used recently in a study of biomagnification as a function of trophic level. Clark (1983) used ³H-naphthalene as a tracer compound to demonstrate the transfer of petroleum hydrocarbons in a seawater–phytoplankton–herbivore–carnivore food chain, which is representative of a stable rocky-intertidal community in Puget Sound. Mussels feeding on ³H-naphthalene-labeled diatoms showed a low degree of biomagnification, with 93% of the radioactivity measured as unmetabolized ³H-naphthalene. Oregon triton snails (*Fusitriton oregonensis*) that were fed mussels with known exposure histories to ³H-naphthalene-labeled algae accumulated <0.2% of the available labeled compound. Detection of approximately half of the radioactivity in the polar fraction of snail

extracts indicated that metabolism and subsequent discharge of water-soluble products was likely the major fate of the labeled naphthalene in these carnivores. The direct uptake of dissolved ³H-naphthalene from seawater was two orders of magnitude greater than that observed via the food pathway for the mussels and the three snail species. In confirming earlier theoretical work, Clark (1983) concluded that equilibrium of dissolved hydrocarbons across membranes that are exposed to seawater may be the most important route for petroleum contamination for most aquatic animals. Clayton et al. (1977) also concluded that biomagnification in the food chain was not a controlling factor in attaining observed PCB concentrations in the tissue of Puget Sound zooplankton.

There is little evidence of biomagnification of unmetabolized aromatic hydrocarbons in the food chain of fish or marine mammals (Gahler et al., 1982; Calambokidis et al., 1984). Residues of PCB and pesticides showed no apparent increase in wet-weight concentration in fishes at different trophic levels represented by the bottom-feeding English sole and the primarily piscivorous walleye pollock and Pacific hake (Fig. 15.7). However, PCB appeared to be accumulated by all Puget Sound biota examined, especially marine mammals at the top of the food chain. Like metals, most organic compounds present in the sediments appeared to accumulate to varying degrees in invertebrates and mussels. There may be a generalized accumulation in fish livers of many organic contaminants present in contaminated sediments, but only the chlorinated compounds appear to accumulate with regularity in muscle tissues of fish. The presence of potentially hazardous metabolites in edible tissues has not been established.

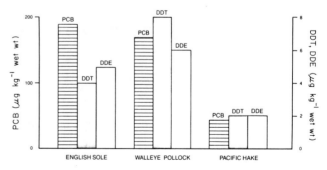

Figure 15.7. Average concentrations of PCB and DDT in muscle tissue for three fish species from City Waterway (Commencement Bay).

15.4. PUBLIC HEALTH CONSIDERATIONS

From a management perspective, it is important to assess the potential risks to human health associated with the contamination of Puget Sound biota. It is also important to evaluate possible economic impacts on local fisheries. For this review, risks to human health were evaluated according to the methodology developed by the U.S. Environmental Protection Agency's Carcinogen Assessment Group (CAG) (U.S. EPA, 1984) and economic impacts were assessed by comparing tissue concentrations with Food and Drug Administration (FDA) action levels (U.S. FDA, 1984) (Table 15.6). Average concentrations of contaminants in the muscle tissue of fish from industrialized areas of Puget Sound are compared with contaminant levels (C_i) in tissue corresponding either to an individual lifetime risk of 10^{-6} for carcinogens or to the acceptable daily intake level for noncarcinogens. The calculations are based on a 70-kg person with an average daily fish consumption of 6.5 g.

Levels of Hg (the only noncarcinogen included in Table 15.6) in fish tissue are well below the FDA action level of 1.0 mg kg^{-1} wet wt and the acceptable daily intake level of 3.1 mg kg^{-1} wet wt. Average As concentrations of 7.8 mg kg^{-1} wet wt in fish from the Pt. Defiance area of Commencement Bay far exceed the 10^{-6} risk level defined by the CAG methodology. According to this approach, ingestion of Puget Sound fish at the specified rate would result in an estimated individual lifetime risk of about 10^{-2}. This apparently high risk associated with As ingestion results from the very high carcinogenic potency factor for As in the CAG methodology. It should be noted that the As potency factor is based on limited data for ingestion of inorganic As and that most of the

As in fish tissue is probably in the form of much less toxic organoarsenic compounds. Moreover, there is no evidence for a generalized increase in As bioaccumulation in Puget Sound fish relative to those from less contaminated coastal areas. Most As levels in Puget Sound biota range from 0.5 to 10 mg kg^{-1} wet wt. Similar concentrations in fish tissue have been reported for the eastern Pacific (LeBlanc and Jackson, 1973) and the Atlantic coast (Greig et al., 1977); therefore, the CAG methodology estimates a relatively high risk associated with As ingestion for most seafood consumed in the United States. There is considerable uncertainty, however, concerning the accuracy of the risk estimate for As. The CAG carcinogenic-risk score for As is based on limited epidemiological data, and As has not been confirmed as a carcinogen in animal studies.

All of the average concentrations for organic compounds in fish tissue are well below the corresponding FDA action levels. Of the organic compounds detected in Puget Sound fish, the highest estimated risk to human health is associated with PCB. Application of the CAG risk assessment methodology indicates a substantial estimated risk ($>10^{-4}$) associated with ingestion of PCB-contaminated fish from Elliott Bay. Calculated risks for ingestion of fish contaminated by DDT and HCB are considerably lower, in the range of about 10^{-5}.

15.5. CONCLUSIONS AND RECOMMENDATIONS

Available data indicate that Puget Sound fish do not generally accumulate metals above reference levels in edible muscle tissue. There is evidence, however, of elevated levels of

Table 15.6. A Comparison of Contaminants in the Tissue of Fish from Puget Sound with Available Human Health Criteria[a]

	Mean Concentration in Muscle Tissue (mg kg^{-1} wet wt)	Area	C_i[c]	FDA Action Level
As	7.8 ± 150%[d]	Point Defiance	0.0007	—[e]
Hg	0.13 ±40%	Elliott Bay	3.1	1.0
DDTs	0.023 ± 55%	Hylebos Waterway	0.0013	5.0
Hexachlorobenzene	0.11 ± 40%	Hylebos Waterway	0.0064	0.5
PCB	0.60 ± 110%	Elliott Bay	0.0025	2.0

[a]Species sampled included sole (three species), walleye pollock, Pacific cod, and salmon.
[b]Data from Gahler et al. (1982) and Romberg et al. (1984).
[c]C_i = tissue concentration corresponding to individual lifetime risk of 10^{-6} (for carcinogens) or to acceptable daily intake level (noncarcinogens). The calculation assumes a consumption rate of 6.5 g d^{-1} and a 100% assimilation efficiency.
[d]Coefficient of variation (i.e., percent relative standard deviation).
[e]Dash indicates no data.

metals in the tissue of bivalve mollusks, crustacea, fish (livers), and birds found in industrialized areas of Puget Sound. Elevated levels of PCB have been detected in all biotic groups studied in Puget Sound. Other organic compounds that have been detected above reference levels in selected biotic groups and at specific locations include DDE and hexachlorobenzene. Evaluation of human health considerations indicates that PCB probably represent the greatest potential risk to human health.

Evaluation of available information on bioaccumulation of toxic substances in Puget Sound biota indicates that although there are considerable data, there are also significant data gaps. Because of the documented contamination in industrialized areas and the important biological resources of Puget Sound, it is recommended that studies of bioaccumulation be included in future monitoring programs, as follows:

1. Tissue analyses of indigenous mussels may provide useful indicators of the temporal and spatial patterns of contamination by both metals and organic compounds.
2. Because of limited available data, contamination of commercial and recreational shellfish resources should be evaluated.
3. Data on contamination of muscle tissues of fish are limited in areas other than Commencement Bay. Selected species should be evaluated in other industrialized and nonindustrialized areas.
4. Future monitoring programs should concentrate efforts on selected species, such as English sole and salmon, to provide temporal and spatial consistency.
5. Studies of the spatial extent of PCB contamination should be conducted, especially relative to commerical or recreational species (e.g., salmon, clams, and crabs).

REFERENCES

Alexander, G. V., and D. R. Young. 1976. Trace metals in southern California mussels. *Marine Pollution Bulletin*, **7**, 7–9.

Belton, T. J., B. E. Ruppel, and K. Lockwood. 1982. PCBs (Aroclor 1254) in Fish Tissues Throughout the State of New Jersey: A Comprehensive Survey. New Jersey Department of Environmental Protection, Trenton, New Jersey, 36 pp.

Bothner, M. H., and D. Z. Piper. 1973. The distribution of mercury in sediment cores from Bellingham Bay, Washington. *In*: Symposium on Mercury in the Western Environment, D. R. Buhler (Ed.). Oregon State University Press, Corvallis, pp. 36–44.

Calambokidis, J., T. Peard, G. H. Steiger, and J. C. Cubbage. 1984. Chemical Contaminants in Marine Mammals from Washington State. Technical Memorandum NOS OMS 6, U.S. National Oceanic and Atmospheric Administration, Seattle, Washington, 167 pp.

Clark, R. C., Jr. 1983. The Biogeochemistry of Aromatic and Saturated Hydrocarbons in a Rocky Intertidal Marine Community in the Strait of

Juan de Fuca. Ph.D. Dissertation, University of Washington, Seattle, 268 pp.

Clayton, J. R., Jr., S. P. Pavlou, and N. F. Breitner. 1977. Polychlorinated biphenyls in coastal marine zooplankton: bioaccumulation by equilibrium partitioning. *Environmental Science and Technology*, **11**, 676–682.

Cummins, J. M., R. R. Bauer, R. H. Rieck, W. B. Schmidt, and J. R. Yearsley. 1976. Chemical and Biological Survey of Liberty Bay, Washington. Report No. EPA 910/9-76-029, U.S. Environmental Protection Agency, Seattle, Washington, 132 pp.

Eustace, I. J. 1974. Zinc, cadmium, copper, and manganese in species of finfish and shell fish caught in the Derwent Estuary, Tasmania. *Australian Journal of Marine Freshwater Research*, **25**, 209–220.

Gahler, A. R., J. M. Cummins, J. N. Blazevich, R. H. Rieck, R. L. Arp, C. E. Gangmark, S. V. W. Pope, and S. Filip. 1982. Chemical Contaminants in Edible Nonsalmonid Fish and Crabs from Commencement Bay, Washington. Report No. EPA 910/9-82-093, U.S. Environmental Protection Agency, Seattle, Washington, 117 pp.

Galvin, D. H., G. P. Romberg, D. R. Houck, and J. H. Lesniak. 1984. Toxicant Pretreatment Planning Study Summary Report. Municipality of Metropolitan Seattle, Seattle, Washington, 202 pp.

Goldberg, E. D., M. Koide, V. Hodge, A. R. Flegal, and J. Martin. 1983. U.S. mussel watch: 1977–1978 results on trace metals and radionuclides. *Estuarine Coastal and Shelf Science*, **16**, 69–93.

Gossett, R. W., H. W. Puffer, R. H. Arthur, Jr., and D. R. Young. 1983. DDT, PCB and benzo(*a*)pyrene levels in white croaker (*Genyonemus lineatus*) from southern California. *Marine Pollution Bulletin*, **14**, 60–65.

Greig, R. A., D. R. Wenzloff, and J. B. Pearce. 1976. Distribution and abundance of heavy metals in finfish, invertebrates, and sediments collected at a deepwater disposal site. *Marine Pollution Bulletin*, **7**, 185–187.

Greig, R. A., D. R. Wenzloff, A. Adams, B. Nelson, and C. Shelpuk. 1977. Trace metals in organisms from ocean disposal sites of the middle eastern United States. *Archives of Environmental Contamination and Toxicology*, **6**, 395–409.

Halcrow, W., D. W. Mackay, and I. Thornton. 1973. The distribution of trace metals and fauna in the Firth of Clyde in relation to the disposal of sewage sludge. *Journal of the Marine Biological Association, United Kingdom*, **53**, 721–739.

Harper-Owes. 1983. Water Quality Assessment of the Duwamish Estuary, Report No. EPA P-000233-01 (May 1983) prepared for Municipality of Metropolitan Seattle, Washington, 193 pp.

Johnson, A., W. Yake, and D. Norton. 1983a. Summary of Priority Pollutant Data for Point Sources and Sediment in Inner Commencement Bay: Part 1. Hylebos Waterway. Washington State Department of Ecology, Olympia, 29 pp.

Johnson, A., W. Yake, and D. Norton. 1983b. Summary of Priority Pollutant Data for Point Sources and Sediment in Inner Commencement Bay: Part 2: City Waterway. Washington State Department of Ecology, Olympia, 15 pp.

LeBlanc, P. J., and A. L. Jackson. 1973. Arsenic in marine fish and invertebrates. *Marine Pollution Bulletin*, **4**, 88–90.

MacLeod, W. D., Jr., L. S. Ramos, A. J. Friedman, D. T. Burrows, P. G. Prohaska, D.L. Fisher, and D. W. Brown. 1981. Analyses of Residual Chlorinated Hydrocarbons, Aromatic Hydrocarbons and Related Compounds in Selected Sources, Sinks, and Biota of New York Bight. Technical Memorandum OMPA-6, U.S. National Oceanic and Atmospheric Administration, Boulder, Colorado, 128 pp.

Malins, D. C., B. B. McCain, D. W. Brown, A. K. Sparks, and H. O. Hodgins. 1980. Chemical Contaminants and Biological Abnormalities in

Central and Southern Puget Sound. Technical Memorandum OMPA-2, U.S. National Oceanic and Atmospheric Administration, Boulder, Colorado, 295 pp.

Malins, D. C., B. B. McCain, D. W. Brown, A. K. Sparks, H. O. Hodgins, and S. L. Chain. 1982. Chemical Contaminants and Abnormalities in Fish and Invertebrates from Puget Sound. Technical Memorandum OMPA-19, U.S. National Oceanic and Atmospheric Administration, Boulder, Colorado, 168 pp.

Malins, D. C., M. S. Myers, and W. T. Roubal. 1983. Organic free radicals associated with idiopathic liver lesions of English sole (*Parophys vetulus* from polluted marine environments. *Environmental Science and Technology,* **17**, 679–685.

Martin, M., and W. Castle. 1984. Petrowatch: Petroleum hydrocarbons, synthetic organic compounds, and heavy metals in mussels from the Monterey Bay area of central California. *Marine Pollution Bulletin,* **15**, 259–266.

McCain, B. B., M. S. Meyers, U. Varanasi, D. W. Brown, L. D. Rhodes, W. D. Gronlund, D. G. Elliott, W. A. Palsson, H. O. Hodgins and D. C. Malins. 1982. Pathology of Two Species of Flatfish from Urban Estuaries in Puget Sound. Report No. EPA 600/7-82-001, U.S. Environmental Protection Agency, Washington, D. C., 100 pp.

McDermott-Ehrlich, D., D. R. Young, and T. C. Heesen. 1978. DDT and PCB in flatfish around southern California municipal outfalls. *Chemosphere,* **6**, 453–461.

Mowrer, J., J. Calambokidis, N. Musgrove, B. Drager, M. Beug, and S. Herman. 1977. Polychlorinated biphenyls in cottids, mussels and sediment in southern Puget Sound, Washington. *Bulletin of Environmental Contamination and Toxicology,* **18**, 588–594.

Neff, J. M., and R. T. Breteler. 1983. Waste disposal in the marine environment. Biological availability of organic contaminants to marine invertebrates. *In:* Proceedings Oceans '83. Institute of Electrical Electronics Engineers, New York, pp. 970–972.

Olsen, S. J., and W. R. Schell. 1977. Baseline Study of Trace Heavy Metals in Biota of Puget Sound. Prepared for the Municipality of Metropolitan Seattle by the College of Fisheries, University of Washington, Seattle, 66 pp.

Prahl, F. G., and R. Carpenter. 1983. Polycyclic aromatic hydrocarbon (PAH)-phase associations in Washington coastal sediment. *Geochimica et Cosmochimica Acta,* **47**, 1013–1023.

Ramdahl, T. 1983. Polycyclic aromatic ketones in environmental samples. *Environmental Science and Technology,* **17**, 666–670.

Rasmussen, L. F., and D. C. Williams, 1975. The occurrence and distribution of mercury in marine organisms in Bellingham Bay. *Northwest Science,* **49**, 87–94.

Riley, R. G., E. A. Crecelius, M. L. O'Malley, K. H. Abel, and D. C. Mann. 1981. Organic Pollutants in Waterways Adjacent to Commencement Bay (Puget Sound). Technical Memorandum OMPA-12, U.S. National Oceanic and Atmospheric Administration, Boulder, Colorado, 90 pp.

Riley, R. G., E. A. Crecelius, R. E. Fitzner, B. L. Thomas, J. M. Gurtisen, and N. S. Bloom. 1983. Organic and Inorganic Toxicants in Sediment and Marine Birds from Puget Sound. Technical Memorandum NOS OMS 1, U.S. National Oceanic and Atmospheric Administration, Rockville, Maryland, 125 pp.

Roesijadi, G., J. S. Young, A. S. Drum, and J. M. Gurtisen. 1984. Behavior of trace metals in *Mytilus edulis* during a reciprocal transplant field experiment. *Marine Ecology Progress Series,* **18**, 155–170.

Romberg, G. P., S. Pavlou, R. Shoakes, W. Hom, E. Crecelius, P. Hamilton, T. Gunn, B. Muench, and J. Vinelli. 1984. Draft Toxicant Pretreatment Planning Study Technical Report C1: Evaluation of Toxicant Transport and Fate. Municipality of Metropolitan Seattle, Seattle, 231 pp. + appendices.

Schell, W. R., A. Nevissi, D. Piper, G. Christian, J. Murray, D. Spyradakis, S. Olsen, D. Huntamer, E. Knudsen, and D. Zafiropoulos. 1977. Heavy Metals near the West Point Outfall and in the Central Basin of Puget Sound. Final Report prepared for the Municipality of Metropolitan Seattle by the College of Fisheries and the Departments of Oceanography, Chemistry, and Civil Engineering, University of Washington, Seattle, 174 pp.

Sherwood, M. J., and B. B. McCain. 1976. Comparison of fin erosion disease: Los Angeles and Seattle. *In:* Coastal Water Research Project Annual Report, W. Bascom (Ed.). Southern California Coastal Water Research Project, El Segundo, California, pp. 143–147.

Sidwell, V. D., P. R. Foncannon, N. S. Moore, and J. C. Bonnet. 1974. Composition of the edible portion of raw (fresh or frozen) crustaceans, finfish, and molluscs. I: Protein, fat, moisture, ash, carbohydrate, energy value, and cholesterol. *Marine Fisheries Review,* **36**, 21–35.

Sloan, R. T., K. W. Simpson, R. A. Schroeder, and C. R. Barnes. Temporal trends toward stability of Hudson River PCB contamination. *Bulletin Environmental Contamination Toxicology,* **31**, 377–385.

Stout, V. F., and F. L. Beezhold. 1981. Chlorinated hydrocarbon levels in fishes and shellfish of the northeastern Pacific Ocean, including the Hawaiian Islands. *Marine Fisheries Review,* **43**, 1–12.

Tetra Tech. 1985. Commencement Bay Nearshore/Tideflats Remedial Investigation, Vol. I–IV. Report No. EPA-910/9-85-134b. Prepared by Tetra Tech, Bellevue, Washington, prepared for Washington Department of Ecology and U.S. Environmental Protection Agency, separate pagination.

U.S. Environmental Protection Agency. 1984. Proposed guidelines for carcinogen risk assessment: request for comments. *Federal Register,* **49**, 46294–46301.

U.S. Food and Drug Administration (FDA). 1984. Levels for Poisonous or Deleterious Substances in Human Food and Animal Feed. U.S. FDA, Washington, D.C., 13 pp.

Weaver, G. 1984. PCB contamination in and around New Bedford, MA. *Environmental Science Technology,* **18**, 22A–27A.

Chapter 16

Summary of Biological Effects in Puget Sound—Past and Present

Peter M. Chapman

E.V.S. Consultants
North Vancouver, British Columbia
Canada

Abstract	**169**
16.1. Introduction	**169**
16.2. Historical Perspective	**170**
16.3. Present Biological Conditions	**171**
16.3.1. Benthos	171
16.3.2. Fish	173
16.3.3. Marine Mammals	174
16.3.4. Marine Birds	175
16.3.5. Histopathological Abnormalities	175
16.3.6. Other Indicators	176
16.3.6a. Sediment bioassays	*176*
16.3.6b. Bacterial contamination of shellfish beds	*177*
16.3.6c. Dinoflagellate blooms	*177*
16.4. Significance of Biological Effects in Puget Sound	**177**
16.4.1. Comparison with Other Areas	177
16.4.2. Natural versus Pollution Effects	179
16.4.3. Adaptation	179
16.5. Management Implications	**180**
Acknowledgments	**180**
References	**180**

ABSTRACT

This chapter is concerned with the historical and current biological effects in Puget Sound (Washington, U.S.A.) that are related to ocean disposal of waste materials. Although chemical analysis of dated sediment cores indicates that chemical contaminants have been discharged into Puget Sound throughout this century, initial environmental concerns focused on massive faunal kills (fish and invertebrates) recorded from 1930 to 1970 in areas subject to pulp-mill discharge. These biological effects were the result of reduced oxygen and increased sulfide levels and were largely resolved by the implementation of secondary treatment at coastal mills. As a result, marine fauna now reside in areas from which they were previously excluded, and present concerns relate to the effects of chemical contaminants accumulated in these and other areas. Evidence exists that both acute lethal and sublethal effects presently occurring in Puget Sound are related to contaminant inputs. Acute lethal effects include mortality of oyster larvae due to dinoflagellate blooms (which may be pollution-related), mortality of sensitive benthic infauna due to toxic sediments, and reproductive failures in harbor seals related to bioaccumulation of such compounds as polychlorinated biphenyls. Sublethal effects include histopathological abnormalities in fish and invertebrates, changes in phytoplankton species composition due to dinoflagellate blooms, changes in benthic infaunal communities in areas with contaminated sediments due to sublethal effects including avoidance, and bacteriological contamination resulting in closure of shellfish beds. Evidence for these effects is reviewed in this chapter. The effects are most evident in coastal areas that are highly developed or that have significant riverine inputs.

16.1. INTRODUCTION

A number of approaches have been used to study the biological effects of contaminants on Puget Sound (Washington,

U.S.A.) biota and ecosystems. The purpose of this chapter is to provide a perspective on the biological health of Puget Sound and to delineate major documented, adverse biological effects that appear to require remedial action.

A variety of chemical contaminants exist in Puget Sound, with the highest concentrations in the sediments of particular urban embayments (Malins et al., 1980, 1982a). Intuitively, one would hypothesize that these chemical contaminants might affect the resident fauna, particularly the benthos, which is in intimate contact with these contaminants. This hypothesis is reinforced by the fact that Puget Sound food webs are detritus-based (Simenstad et al., 1979; Dames and Moore, 1981); thus, chemical contamination might affect lower trophic levels and become incorporated into food chains from the sediments. It is difficult, however, to establish clear-cut relationships between chemical contamination and biological effects.

Acute lethal effects of chemical contaminants are rarely observed in the marine environment mainly because contaminant buildups are slow, progressive, and generally accompanied by slow ecological succession instead of catastrophic collapses (Bascom, 1982). However, even if significant kills of fish or other fauna occur in certain parts of Puget Sound, the effect of these on the Puget Sound ecosystem as a whole may be insignificant over the long term. Despite massive faunal kills in Everett, Bellingham, Anacortes, Commencement bays, and other areas associated with pulp mills in the period from 1930 to 1970, these impacted areas were not permanently damaged. Far more serious effects on the marine resources of Puget Sound have occurred as a result of overfishing (Simenstad et al., 1982). Both fishing effort and natural variability can have a profound effect on populations, masking or even rendering insignificant any contaminant-related effects (Waldichuk, 1983).

Subtle effects, such as slight reductions in growth or changes in other physiological and biochemical processes, are extremely difficult to detect and interpret. Changes in the species structure of ecosystems have been recorded, but these are often due to natural causes and can only rarely be attributed unequivocally to pollution [United Nations Environment Programme (UNEP), 1982].

This chapter reviews presently available data on pollution-related biological effects in Puget Sound. Historical and present biological conditions are evaluated to provide an overall assessment of the ecological health of Puget Sound. Major embayments and other areas mentioned in the text are shown in Fig. 16.1.

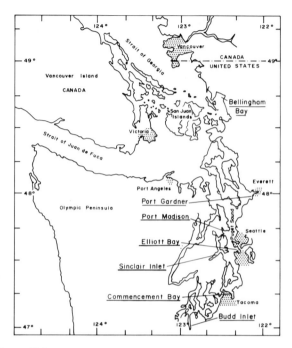

Figure 16.1. Map of Puget Sound, Washington, showing major embayments and other features. Shading indicates urban areas.

16.2. HISTORICAL PERSPECTIVE

Prior to the late 1970s, pulp and paper mills were the major recognized source of pollution [primarily biochemical oxygen demand (BOD) and acutely toxic effluents] to Puget Sound (Quinlan et al., 1985). Pollution abatement has reduced this organic pollution that historically resulted in large kills of fish, including salmonids, and other fauna. The pulp- and paper-mill problem received considerable attention and study from the 1930s to the 1970s and is summarized in Section 16.2.1. Another major documented effect on Puget Sound fisheries occurred in 1913 when a major rockslide on the Fraser River (British Columbia) impaired salmon runs and greatly reduced salmonid populations, particularly sockeye salmon, in Puget Sound (Chasan, 1981).

New product development presents an increasing complexity of chemical pollution. In addition, many present-day chemical toxic effects may be due to historical accumulations of particular chemicals in marine sediments that are slowly leaching into the water column. Crecelius et al. (1985) recently attempted to derive a history of sediment contamination in Commencement Bay by chemical analysis of dated cores. Their investigation indicates that inputs of metals, aromatic hydrocarbons, and chlorinated butadienes have occurred throughout this century. Peak levels of metals and chlorinated butadienes were noted in the 1960s; aromatic hydrocarbon increases were noted as early as 1900, peaking in 1950. High arsenic levels were attributed to the American Smelting and Refining Company (ASARCO) smelter near Tacoma, which began operations in 1889; lead inputs were attributed to the smelter and to increasing gasoline and sewage inputs. Early increases in aromatic hydrocarbons were attributed to the transport and combustion of coal. Peak levels of chlorinated butadienes in the 1960s were attributed to the dumping of chemical waste (mainly from industries along the Hylebos Waterway) into Commencement Bay (Orlob et al., 1950a).

The Port Gardner (Everett) case study illustrates well the nature and extent of historical pulp-mill impacts. Many of the events and patterns recorded for this embayment also occurred in other Puget Sound embayments subject to pulp-mill discharges, including Port Angeles, Bellingham, Anacortes, Elliott, and Commencement bays. Further historical pollution-related data on these latter embayments are provided by Quinlan et al. (1985).

The Port Gardner area (Fig. 16.1) was the subject of the most consistently documented pollution-related studies of fish kills from the 1930s to the 1960s. These acute effects were ascribed to reduced ambient oxygen levels caused by pulp-mill effluents.

In the 1940s, the main pollution source in Port Gardner was waste sulfite liquor (WSL) from two sulfite mills that together accounted for 97% of the total oxygen demand of all discharged wastes (Townsend et al., 1941; Cheyne and Foster, 1942). The main effect of pollution in the 1940s was a depletion of oxygen in the surface waters, which resulted in documented fish kills involving a wide variety of species. Fish kills were reported by residents almost every day of the year and varied in intensity from 1–2 fish to "barrels full" (Cheyne and Foster, 1942). Throughout the year significant areas of Port Gardner had dissolved oxygen (DO) levels that remained below 5 mg liter^{-1}. The area of lethality extended up to 0.8 km away from the mills.

In the early 1950s, serious oxygen deficiencies extended up to 5.6 km from Everett to Mukilteo (Orlob et al., 1950b; Eldridge and Orlob, 1951). Herring and salmon kills were common at this time. These species apparently suffocated in areas with DO levels not greater than 3.6 mg liter^{-1} and often <1 mg liter^{-1}. The area near the channel mouth at Port Gardner was continually unsuitable for the sustenance of fish

life and provided a barrier to the natural migration of salmonids.

A large portion of the bottom of Port Gardner was covered by a deposit of decomposing organic matter from domestic sewage, fish cannery waste, and pulp-mill discharge (Orlob et al., 1950b). Bottom conditions in the area were judged unfit to support bottom species, such as shrimp, sole, and flounder. Grab samples of the bottom revealed either a complete absence of macrofauna or only "sludge worms."

Reductions in pulp-mill waste discharged into Port Gardner and into other affected embayments began in the early 1970s. Reduction of discharge was accomplished through treatment and discharge through deeper outfalls. As a result, DO levels in Port Gardner increased, and toxicity decreased (as determined by the oyster larvae bioassay) [Washington State Department of Ecology (WDOE), 1976]. Fish kills due to pollution no longer occur in Port Gardner or in any of the other embayments receiving pulp-mill effluents. With the regulation of pulp-mill effluents and a consequent decrease in visible, acute toxicity effects, public and regulatory concern has more recently focused on sublethal biological effects, including histopathological abnormalities.

16.3. PRESENT BIOLOGICAL CONDITIONS

A large number and variety of species presently exist in Puget Sound. One method of examining possible contaminant-related biological effects at the population or community level would be to compare species composition before industrialization with species composition for successive periods in relation to the chemical changes that have occurred. Unfortunately, no data exist prior to the middle of this century when industrialization was already extensive. The available data relating pollution to benthos, fish, marine mammals, and marine birds for the period 1950 (when reliable data were first gathered) to 1984 are detailed in Quinlan et al. (1985) and are summarized in the following pages.

16.3.1. Benthos

Some of the earliest data on the composition of benthic species are those collected by Orlob et al. (1950a) for Commencement Bay benthos. Ten taxa were identified by Orlob et al. (1950a) for inner Commencement Bay and Waterways in sufficient detail to allow comparison with present data (e.g., Dames & Moore, 1981). Five of these taxa were also present 30 y later, and the apparent absences of the other five taxa from 1980 collections cannot be attributed solely to pollution (Quinlan et al., 1985).

The structure of the benthic community in Commencement Bay appears to have been relatively constant since 1950, composed mainly of polychaetes and bivalves. However, industrialization was nearly complete by 1950; hence, these data provide no indication of changes related to industrialization. The final development of Commencement Bay involved extensive dredging, channeling, and landfill activities, which would lead to considerable faunal changes. For example, waterfowl were displaced from the extensive pre-1900 estuarine and marsh areas of Commencement Bay. A close examination of benthic infaunal data also indicates some biological effects.

Dames and Moore (1981) determined that in certain locations in Commencement Bay, and in particular the Waterways, the invertebrate communities contained few taxa but many individuals. This low diversity is characteristic of stressed communities. Commencement Bay fauna are very similar to the fauna described by Leon (1980) for Kellogg Island in the Duwamish River, another area affected by pollution. In the Hylebos Waterway, Dames and Moore (1981) found a low species abundance and diversity for bottom-dwelling organisms and suggested that more sensitive organisms and/or life-history stages may be excluded from areas greatly affected by contamination. The Hylebos is used as a particular example because polychlorinated biphenyls (PCB) and chlorinated butadiene (CBD) levels are extremely high

there relative to other parts of Puget Sound, and Malins et al. (1980) classified the mouth of the Hylebos as among the most contaminated waters in Puget Sound.

A factor confounding interpretation of data for benthic species in many areas is the high natural variability in population composition (Webber, 1979; Zeh and Houghton, 1981). The variability in composition of benthic species is best illustrated by two examples from areas of significant contaminant inputs: the Duwamish River and the Denny Way combined sewage overflow (CSO) (Seattle waterfront). Table 16.1 lists the six most common polychaete and mollusk taxa determined in the Duwamish River by three studies conducted between 1975 and 1980. Major differences among studies are noted for three (50%) of these taxa. The Cirratulidae, which were collected infrequently in 1976, were abundant in 1980; the Spionidae, which were not collected in 1976, were present and abundant in 1980. These differences cannot be ascribed entirely to different sieve sizes, methods and taxonomic expertise, small-scale patchiness, or season, nor have profound changes in pollutant loadings occurred over these 5 y.

The second example of species variability is provided by the much-studied Denny Way CSO. The area affected is very localized (Armstrong et al., 1978, 1981; Tomlinson et al., 1980) and intuitively one would expect the fauna to be reasonably similar over the short time interval from 1978 to 1983. However, as is apparent from Table 16.2, such is not the case. The only common species determined in each of four studies conducted over these 5 y, was the polychaete *Capitella capitata*, which has shown great seasonal variation near the outfall (Comiskey et al., 1984; Thom and Chew, in press).

Table 16.1. Common Infaunal Polychaetes and Mollusks in the Duwamish River as Determined by Three Separate Studies

Taxa	Weitkamp and Katz, 1976[a]	Leon, 1980[b]	Port of Seattle, 1980[a]
Polychaete Families			
Cirratulidae[c]	present	abundant	abundant (esp. *Tharyx* sp.)
Spionidae[c]	absent	present	abundant (esp. *Boccardia proboscidea*)
Lumbrinereidae	abundant	abundant	abundant (esp. *Lumbrinereis* sp.)
Maldanidae[c]	abundant	rare	rare
Mollusk Species			
Macoma spp.	abundant	abundant	abundant
Axinopsida serricata	abundant	abundant	abundant

[a]0.5-mm sieve.
[b]1.0-mm sieve.
[c]Taxa with different abundances with different studies.

Table 16.2. Dominant Infaunal Invertebrate Species at the Denny Way CSO as Determined by Four Separate Studies

Taxa	Armstrong et al., 1978	Thom and Chew, in press (from 1978 studies)	Tomlinson et al., 1980	Comiskey et al., 1984
Common to All Studies				
Capitella capitata (polychaete)	yes[a]	yes	yes	yes
Common to Two Studies				
Nebalia pugettensis (arthropod)	no[b]	yes	yes	no
Axinopsida serricata (bivalve)	no	yes	no	yes
Common to One Study				
Nereis vexillosa (polychaete)	yes	no	no	no
Lumbrinereis luti (polychaete)	no	no	no	yes
Tharyx sp. (polychaete)	no	no	no	yes
Spiochaetopterus costarum (polychaete)	no	no	no	yes
Anisogammarus pugettensis (amphipod)	yes	no	no	no
Gnorimosphaeroma oregonensis (isopod)	yes	no	no	no

[a]Indicates species found "commonly" or "abundantly" in that study.
[b]Indicates species not found "commonly" or "abundantly" in that study.

Long-term changes in benthic infaunal communities have also occurred in Puget Sound. Nichols (1985) compared 20 y of data for benthic fauna collected since 1964 at a single station located at a depth of 200 m, northwest of West Point (Seattle). These data indicate substantial variability in the benthic fauna of the Main Basin that is confirmed for other stations in Puget Sound. The dominant organism between 1969 and 1970 was the polychaete *Pectinaria californiensis*. From 1964 to 1968 and 1971 to 1981 the dominant organism was the clam *Macoma carlottensis*, while after 1981 the clam *Axinopsida serricata* and the polychaete *Ampharete acutifrons* began to dominate. Unfortunately, with the exception of measurements of water quality conducted routinely by Metro Seattle, historical chemical information does not exist for this area. At present these changes in the benthic fauna cannot be ascribed to pollution (for instance, data on sediment texture are not available). The recent increase in the numbers of *Ampharete acutifrons*, which is a recognized indicator of organically polluted conditions, may be significant (Nichols, 1985).

Chapman et al. (1985a) characterized pollution-receiving muddy embayments as containing benthic infauna dominated by polychaetes and mollusks. In less affected, muddy areas, the infauna included a large proportion of echinoderms and arthropods. In particular, the sensitive amphipod family Phoxocephalidae was found only in relatively unaffected areas (Long and Chapman, 1985).

16.3.2. Fish

The present status of pollution-related effects on Puget Sound fisheries is difficult to determine. A total of 53 species of ground fishes presently contribute to the Puget Sound commercial and recreational fishery (Pedersen and DiDonato, 1982). Although benthic infaunal richness is lowest in such chemically contaminated areas as Commencement Bay Waterways, richness and diversity of demersal fish species are highest in these areas, in particular in Elliott and Commencement bays (Long, 1982; Malins et al., 1982a).

Populations of certain species have diminished in recent times, however. For instance, lingcod catches in Puget Sound show an erratic but downward trend since the early 1960s (Bargmann, 1982). The reason for this decline is unknown, but a combination of erratic recruitment and overfishing is believed to be mainly responsible. Other species showing significant recent declines include the sand lance (Mathematical Sciences Northwest, 1977) and Pacific hake (Kimura and Millikan, 1977). In contrast, 1984 proved to be one of the best years on record for returns of Lake Washington sockeye salmon (A. Mearns, personal communication).

With the possible exception of histopathological effects on bottom fish (Section 16.3.5), fish populations in Puget Sound show little evidence of pollution-related effects. Chemically contaminated estuaries, including the Duwamish estuary, the Puyallup River, and the various waterways in Commencement Bay, support a diverse aquatic community, including significant salmonid populations. Chum runs have declined substantially in recent years, but the cause is unknown (Harper-Owes, 1982). Commercial fishing by Indians under treaty, with occasional openings to all commercial fishermen, occurs in Commencement Bay, and sportfishing is extensive (Dames and Moore, 1981). These estuaries serve as rearing and feeding areas for many species, including salmonids. Juvenile salmonids feed mainly on harpacticoid copepods and gammarid amphipods in sediments and on calanoid copepods and drift insects in the water column (Dames and Moore, 1981). Both harpacticoid copepods and gammarid amphipods are extremely abundant at the mouth of the Hylebos Waterway, reaching densities in excess of 30,000 m^{-2}. This area, which includes eelgrass beds, is considered critical to salmon (Meyer and Vogel, 1978). This "critical" area for salmon feeding and rearing has also been described as "among the most contaminated in Puget Sound" (Malins et al., 1980). Other fish species, including flatfish, also use this area, feeding on the benthic bivalves and polychaetes common in Commencement Bay and on sediment organic material (Dames and Moore, 1981). Although long-term chronic effects of chemical contaminants in the sediment on these species and on juvenile salmonids cannot be ruled out, the present data suggest that these contaminants are not affecting these key organisms.

A general review of the state of Puget Sound salmonid populations was recently completed by Simenstad et al. (1982), who noted that wild runs of chinook, coho, and chum salmon declined in Puget Sound from 1900 to 1935. They attributed this decline mainly to alterations in habitat due to development, specifically (1) destruction of habitat by dredging and filling activities, (2) watershed activities (e.g. logging), and (3) changes in the sources and amount of organic carbon entering detritus-based food webs. Simenstad et al. (1982) speculated that toxicants may also have been a factor in the reductions of food organisms but had no data to substantiate the possibility of direct effects of toxicants on salmonids. Adverse toxicant-related impacts are possible at all life-history stages of salmonids, but the juvenile stages would be expected to be the most vulnerable because of their more intimate association with the benthos through feeding, relatively long residence time in industrialized estuarine areas, and relatively high sensitivity when compared to adults. Presently, no evidence suggests, however, that toxicants are affecting salmonid populations in the Puget Sound area.

In Puget Sound, although declines in various fisheries have occurred, neither the extent of declines compared to fisheries levels prior to industrialization nor the exact causes for these declines is known. Accurate statistics for fisheries were first compiled in 1935. Since this time fishing techniques and regulations have changed substantially and hatchery-reared fish have made an increasing contribution (Simenstad et al., 1982). As a result, possible pollution-related effects on fisheries cannot be determined.

16.3.3. Marine Mammals

A major concern regarding toxicant effects on food webs is the significance to top predators. In Puget Sound there is evidence that toxicants may be causing significant adverse effects on harbor seals (*Phoca vitulina*). Arndt (1973) found significantly higher concentrations of PCB in the liver and blubber of harbor seals from south Puget Sound than in those from north Puget Sound and Grays Harbor and speculated that these might have caused the high pup mortalities that he observed in south Puget Sound. Calambokidis et al. (1978), in subsequent studies, noted that seal populations with the highest pup mortalities bioaccumulated PCB and the DDT metabolite DDE, apparently from the diet.

Calambokidis et al. (1984) summarized results of PCB and DDT tissue levels in ~100 marine mammals from Puget Sound. Species tested included harbor seals; minke, killer, and pygmy sperm whales; harbor and Dall's porpoise; and sea lions. The authors concluded that harbor seals were bioconcentrating PCB and DDT from the fish they ate; concentrations were among the highest found anywhere in the world and are in the same range as those implicated in reproductive disorders in Europe (Baltic and Wadden seas) and California (Channel Islands) (Calambokidis et al., 1984). Concentrations of PCB were also high in harbor porpoise and killer whales. No other chemical contaminants measured in tissues [including metals, polynuclear aromatic hydrocarbons (PAH), and other chlorinated organic compounds] were present at high enough levels to suggest a serious health concern. As a result, and because DDT levels in Puget Sound have decreased to the point that they are no longer of major concern, Calambokidis et al. (1984) concluded that PCB are the primary pollutants of concern for marine mammals in Puget Sound.

Calambokidis et al. (1979) conducted a census of the harbor seal population for 1977–1978 and estimated that there were 2645 harbor seals in Puget Sound and 7000 total in the state of Washington. Present data indicate that harbor seal populations are increasing in Puget Sound, probably due to marine mammal protection; however, populations within Puget Sound are increasing more slowly than are outer-coast populations (Calambokidis et al., 1984). This difference suggests either that mortality is higher in Puget Sound or that Puget Sound populations are less able to reproduce successfully compared to outer-coast populations.

16.3.4. Marine Birds

Census data on bird populations in the area of Puget Sound are available only since the 1950s, when the Washington Department of Game began regular aerial censuses. Human activities have led to increased numbers of some species such as gulls and decreased numbers of others (Wahl et al., 1981); however, none of these changes appears to threaten seriously the present viability of resident populations (Brewer and Myers, 1982).

Changes in populations of marine birds reflect a number of factors, including habitat changes. In the 1900s, the Duwamish River provided over 2000 acres of intertidal habitat; this has been reduced by over an order of magnitude (Canning et al., 1979). Some species, such as gulls and terns, have taken advantage of new artificial habitats (i.e., pilings, jetties, marinas, and even dredge spoils) for nesting (Angell and Balcomb, 1982). Other species, such as puffins, have declined in numbers due both to loss of habitat and to increasing human disturbances (Angell and Balcomb, 1982).

A large number of bird species are found in such industrialized, contaminated areas as Commencement Bay [76 species of waterfowl (Dames and Moore, 1981)] and the Duwamish River [76 species (U.S. Army Corps of Engineers, 1982)] including resident and migratory species. In Commencement Bay, many species feed on intertidal invertebrates in such areas as the Hylebos Waterway and the mouth of the Puyallup River; breeding waterfowl in the area include glaucous-winged gulls, Barrow's goldeneye ducks, mallards, and Canada geese (Dames and Moore, 1981).

Limited evidence suggests that chemical contamination in such areas as the Duwamish Waterway is affecting some species of marine birds. Riley et al. (1984) conducted bird surveys in industrialized embayments and collected tissue samples for contaminant analyses. They found only two nests of pigeon guillemot in the Duwamish West Waterway, with two live young and four addled eggs, indicating a hatching

success rate of only 33%. One of these eggs was found to have high levels of PCB, which may be significant in reduced reproductive success. They found that the only organic contaminant accumulated to elevated levels in tissues of waterfowl was PCB, although metals such as mercury were also accumulated. They ascribed contaminant accumulation to feeding on fish with high levels of contaminants in their tissues and hypothesized that neither aromatic hydrocarbons nor chlorinated butadienes were detected because these compounds are generally metabolized. Although concentrations of PCB were higher in tissues of birds from Puget Sound than in those from many other areas of the world, the sample size was small, consisting of only 5 blue herons, 4 juvenile pigeon guillemots and 8 eggs, and 15 juvenile gulls.

Preliminary data on marine birds (Riley et al., 1984) together with high mortalities in harbor seal pups due to high levels of PCB in their tissues, suggest a classic bioaccumulation pattern up the food chain with maximum adverse effects manifested at the highest trophic levels. The available data suggest that certain marine birds and mammals may presently be adversely affected by chemical pollution in Puget Sound.

16.3.5. Histopathological Abnormalities

Histopathological abnormalities of organisms in Puget Sound, and particularly in flatfish, received a great deal of recent attention. Because natural factors (i.e., parasites) may be a major causative agent in external abnormalities (i.e., epidermal papillomas) and fin rot in bottom-dwelling fish (Angell et al., 1975; Campana, 1983), the following discussion concentrates on internal abnormalities, in particular, flatfish liver disorders, which are more closely related to chemical pollution.

Malins et al. (1980, 1981, 1982a) conducted histopathological surveys in a few areas of Puget Sound. Their findings are summarized by Long (1982) in terms of the following demonstrated biological effects: (1) neoplasms (tumors), necroses, lesions, and other cellular disorders in fish livers; (2) lesions and hyperplasia in fish gills; (3) lesions in fish kidneys, skin, fin, heart, gastrointestinal tract, spleen, gonad, and gall bladder; (4) necroses and melanized nodules and granulomas in shrimp gills; (5) necrotic and abnormal conditions in shrimp and crab hepatopancreas, antennal gland, bladder, and midgut; and (6) parasitic infestations.

Fish species affected include English sole, rock sole, Pacific tomcod, and staghorn sculpins. Clams and marine worms were not found to have histopathological disorders, but shrimp and crabs were. Non-specific necroses were most numerous in fish from Elliott and Commencement bays, as were lesions in shrimp, particularly those from the Hylebos Waterway and Duwamish River.

Malins et al. (1980) noted that 32% of adult English sole collected from the Duwamish River had liver lesions and suggested that PCB might be the causative agent. At the same time, they stated that it was not possible to conclude "that a major contaminant identified through limited chemical analysis is causing a certain type of biological damage. Actually, the cause may be a minor contaminant of exceptionally high toxicity that escapes detection." In fact, the cause of histopathological disorders in Puget Sound biota has not yet been demonstrated.

McCain et al. (1982) could not induce any histopathological changes in the laboratory, although they exposed English sole to contaminated sediments from the Duwamish River for 3 months, injected them with sediment extracts, and exposed them for 24 h to high concentrations of labeled benzo(*a*)pyrene (BaP). They did demonstrate that sediments from the Duwamish River contain factors that can be toxic to English sole but could not demonstrate any real effect on survival.

Long (1983) noted that the highest incidences of all types of histopathological fish disorders in Puget Sound occur in the Duwamish River, Commencement Bay Waterways, and Seattle waterfront. These locations generally contain the highest concentrations of aromatic hydrocarbons or of mixtures of metals and aromatic hydrocarbons.

In a recent review, Harper-Owes (1982) computed declines in the incidence of liver neoplasia, especially among older English sole from the Duwamish River: 1975–1976, 32%; 1978–1980, 20%. The significance of these observed declines remains to be assessed. The data were not normalized to age classes, and the trend could be due either to an increased density of young fish or to improvements in water quality in affected areas. Malins et al. (1982b) noted both increased and decreased incidences of specific internal lesions in areas of Puget Sound first surveyed in 1978 and subsequently in 1979 and 1980. It is impossible at this point to determine with any surety whether the above trends reflect changes in pollution patterns or merely represent a high noise-to-signal ratio.

Data on liver lesions and tissue chemistry (Malins et al., 1980; 1982b) were compared statistically by Zeh (1982). Although the statistical tests had little power because of small sample size ($n = 24$), the results suggest a relationship

between PCB and chlorinated hydrocarbon pesticides in tissue and histopathological disorders in the livers of bottom-dwelling fish from Puget Sound. The causal factors, however, remain far from clear.

As noted above, some data suggest that internal histopathological disorders (i.e., liver lesions) in bottom-dwelling fish from Puget Sound are related to high levels of chemical contamination in bottom sediments (Malins et al., 1980, 1982a; Gronlund et al., 1983; Quinlan et al., 1985; Chapman et al., 1985a; Tetra Tech, 1985). At this point, however, the biological significance of documented internal histopathological abnormalities is uncertain. It is not known if these abnormalities affect survival either directly or indirectly. More specific evidence of significant adverse biological effects is provided by bioassay tests with sediment from Puget Sound.

16.3.6. Other Indicators

16.3.6a. Sediment bioassays

Bioassays have been used extensively in Puget Sound to test the relationship of water-column toxicity to specific discharges. Sensitive test species include oyster larvae (Cardwell et al., 1979) and salmonids (Ziebell et al., 1970). In contrast, sediment bioassays that involve laboratory exposures of test species to field-collected sediments have only recently been applied to Puget Sound. Because sediment is a major repository for persistent aquatic contaminants sediment bioassays provide data on the toxicity of contaminants that may be released to the water column through dredging or natural scouring processes and that may be affecting marine fauna living in, on, or near the bottom sediment.

Some of the more sensitive species are killed rapidly and directly by exposure to contaminated sediments from certain areas of Puget Sound. These species include the grass shrimp *Palaemonetes pugio* (Shuba et al., 1978), the clam *Macoma inquinata* (Swartz et al., 1979), and the phoxocephalid amphipods *Grandifoxus grandis* (Pierson et al., 1983) and *Rhepoxynius abronius* (Chapman et al., 1982a,b, 1984; Chapman and Fink, 1983; Fink, 1983; Swartz et al., 1979, 1981, 1982, 1985).

Sublethal sediment bioassays including partial or complete life-cycle tests have also been conducted in Puget Sound. Such testing has shown effects on (1) the respiratory response of oligochaetes (*Monopylephorus cuticulatus*) exposed to sediment elutriates (Chapman and Fink, 1983; Chapman et al., 1982a,b, 1984); (2) reproductive impairment effects on oyster larvae (*Crassostrea gigas*), surf smelt (*Hypomesus pretiosus pretiosus*), and the polychaete *Capitella capitata* (Chapman et al., 1983, 1985b); and (3) cytotoxic and genotoxic responses in cultured fish cells (Chapman et al., 1982a, 1984; Landolt and Kocan, 1984; Landolt et al., 1984).

Sediment bioassays have been conducted at up to 119 stations in Puget Sound, including eight separate geographic areas. Good, but not exactly corresponding, results have been noted for different bioassay tests at a given station, which would be expected since different biological tests might not respond to the same toxicant(s) (Samolloff et al., 1983). The combined results of all sediment bioassays to date suggest that the three most toxic areas are the Elliott Bay waterfront, the Duwamish River, and the Commencement Bay Waterways (Chapman et al., 1984, 1985a). These findings are consistent with data on present biological conditions in these and other areas of Puget Sound.

16.3.6b. Bacterial contamination of shellfish beds

A clearly documented, adverse biological effect of anthropogenic inputs to Puget Sound is that of bacteriological contamination resulting in closure of shellfish beds. Contributory sources include sewage outfalls, septic tank seepage, urban and agricultural run-off, discharges from recreational vessels, and river discharge. Areas recently affected by growing urbanization include Burley Lagoon and Minter Bay, which were once prime growing areas for the Pacific oyster *Crassostrea gigas* (Cunningham, 1983), and Samish Bay (Verber, 1983).

16.3.6c. Dinoflagellate blooms

Dinoflagellate blooms appear to be responsible for significant adverse biological effects including mortality of bivalve larvae in many regions of Puget Sound (Cardwell et al., 1979). Dinoflagellate blooms during the late summer in some enclosed bays and inlets are toxic to larvae of such species of bivalve mollusks as Pacific oysters (*Crassostrea gigas*), Manila littleneck clams (*Venerupis japonica*), and Olympia oysters (*Ostrea lurida*). The dinoflagellate blooms may be due to allochthonous inputs of organics from such sources as run-off, sewage, and upwelling; and the areal extent of toxicity may encompass many square kilometers.

Saunders et al. (1982) suggest that the incidence of red tide and other dinoflagellate groups is increasing spatially; cysts of *Gonyaulax catenella* are now found widely distributed in bottom sediment from Puget Sound. Dinoflagellate blooms have been linked with fish kills due either to direct effects (respiratory paralysis due to toxin release) or to bioaccumulation of toxins through food; toxin bioaccumulation has also been implicated in the deaths of marine birds (Saunders et al., 1982).

Paralytic shellfish poisoning (PSP) produced by red tide blooms is responsible for the closure of shellfish beds to both recreational and commercial harvesting. Recent evidence suggests that the incidence of dinoflagellate blooms, and of red tides in particular, is also increasing temporally (Strickland, 1983). Whether these apparent spatial and temporal increases are due to anthropogenic influences is uncertain.

16.4. SIGNIFICANCE OF BIOLOGICAL EFFECTS IN PUGET SOUND

Types of biological effects looked for and documented in Puget Sound (excluding the results of laboratory bioassay tests) and bacteriological contamination causing closure of shellfish beds are listed in Table 16.3. Biological effects fall into two general categories: those that involve death of a particular species (acutely lethal) and those that involve more subtle responses (sublethal).

16.4.1. Comparison with Other Areas

The death and disappearance of particular species in Puget Sound is not occurring, although severe lethal effects on resident populations were observed up to the 1970s in areas receiving pulp-mill effluents. Examination of presently determined biological effects in the New York Bight and the Southern California Bight also suggests that the death and disappearance of particular species are not presently occurring. The main effects of pollution in the New York Bight appear to be a reduction in the capacity of organisms and populations to adapt to normal environmental changes and a greater susceptibility to predation and disease (Mayer, 1982). Pollution-related effects observed in the New York Bight where sewage-sludge deposits occur include shell disease and black gill disease in rock crabs (*Cancer irroratus*) (Sawyer, 1982). Shell disease is a characteristic change in carapace marking and coloration; black gill disease affects the crabs'

Table 16.3. Types of Biological Impacts That May Be Pollution Related in Puget Sound[a]

Effects	Species	Reference(s)	Comments
Acute lethality	Fish and invertebrates	Quinlan et al., 1985	mass mortalities were common priot to effluent controls on pulp mills and other discharges
		Strickland, 1983	mortalities occur in areas where oxygen deficiencies occur (i.e., Budd Inlet)
	Phoxocephalid amphipods, esp. *Rhepoxynius abronius*	Quinlan et al., 1985	absent from contaminated areas (i.e., Commencement Bay, Denny Way CSO) possible due to sediment lethality
	Oyster larvae, *Crassostrea gigas*	Cardwell et al., 1977, 1979	mortalities occur due to dinoflagellate blooms, which may be pollution-related
Histopathological abnormalities			
Lesions	clams, *Macoma carlottensis*	Malins et al., 1980	limited sampling
	shrimp, *Pandalus danae*	Malins et al., 1980	limited sampling
	crab, *Cancer magister*	Malins et al., 1980	limited sampling
	crab, *Cancer productus*	Malins et al., 1980	limited sampling
	crab, *Cancer gracilis*	Malins et al., 1980	limited sampling
	sculpin, *Leptocottus armatus*	Malins et al., 1980, 1982a	broad-scale sampling
	sole, *Parophrys vetulus*	Malins et al., 1980, 1982a	broad-scale sampling
	sole, *Microstomus pacificus*	Malins et al., 1980, 1982a	broad-scale sampling
	tomcod, *Microgadus proximus*	Malins et al., 1980	limited sampling
Fin rot	sole, *Parophrys vetulus*	Harper-Owes, 1982; Malins et al., 1982b	broad-scale sampling
	flounder, *Platichthys stellatus*	Harper-Owes, 1982; Malins et al., 1982b	broad-scale sampling
Community changes	Phytoplankton	Quinlan et al., 1985	an increased prevalence of red tides and dinoflagellate blooms may be occurring in Puget Sound
	Benthic fauna	Quinlan et al., 1985	differences in benthic community species composition have been noted in chemically contaminated areas compared to reference areas
Avoidance response	polychaetes: *Mediomastus californiensis* *Laonice cirrata* *Nephthys ferruginea* *Tauperia oculata* *Acontorhina cyclia* *Euphilomedes producta*	Comiskey et al., 1984	"avoid" the area of the Denny Way CSO
Possible reproductive effects			
	marine mammals:	Calambokidis et al., 1984	high tissue PCB levels, possible reproductive failures in 1960–1970s
	seal, *Phoca vitulina richardsii* porpoise, *Phocena phocena* waterfowl:	Riley et al., 1984	high tissue PCB levels, addled eggs
	Guillemot, *Cephus columba*		

[a]Does not include laboratory sediment bioassay data; refers to *in situ* effects observed over large spatial areas.

gills, turning them black. In addition, Atlantic mackerel (*Scomber scomber*) eggs in surface waters of the New York Bight show lower viability in areas impacted by chemical contaminants (Longwell, 1976; Longwell and Hughes, 1982).

Although pollution has affected communities and ecosystems in the New York Bight, adaptation to present conditions has also occurred for some groups of organisms. In contaminated sediments, both bacteria and phytoplankton have developed resistant strains with exposure to marine pollutants (Mayer, 1982).

Bascom (1982) recently reviewed 10 y of study by the Southern California Coastal Water Resources Project (SCC-WRP) and concluded that the single largest cause of environmental damage in this area was due to high DDT discharges. These discharges have now been eliminated and, except in marine mammals, recovery appears to have occurred, indicating a high degree of resiliency.

16.4.2. Natural versus Pollution Effects

The overall significance of pollution-related effects on Puget Sound is difficult to assess even in severe cases in which large-scale mortalities have occurred, because large-scale mortalities continue to occur, apparently due to natural causes. For example, in Budd Inlet depressions of DO levels were and are a common feature in late summer, resulting in substantial kills of fish and other fauna. Kruger (1979) conducted water-quality surveys in Budd Inlet from 1976 to 1978 and showed that organic enrichment from incoming water from Puget Sound caused extensive algal blooms in summer. When these died and decayed, DO levels dropped. Enrichment from three major sewage treatment plants (STPs) discharging into Budd Inlet was not considered to be a significant contributory factor (Kruger, 1979).

Whether low DO levels in Budd Inlet would have occurred in the absence of human inputs is difficult to determine. Pollution is usually thought of in terms of industrialization; however, simply clearing land with consequent increased runoff can have adverse effects on the environment. Schelske et al. (1983) provided evidence that eutrophication in the lower Great Lakes may have begun in the mid-1800s due to early settlement and forest clearance.

16.4.3. Adaptation

It is entirely possible that fauna from Puget Sound that presently inhabit areas subject to high contaminant levels have adapted to this regime. Spies et al. (1982) documented adaptation of flatfish to contaminated environments (oil and PCB). Hauschildt-Lillge (1982) detailed the adaptation of an intertidal oligochaete, *Lumbricillus lineatus*, to chronic petroleum pollution. This species, like the polychaete *Capitella capitata*, is opportunistic and in typical fashion compensates for detrimental effects in one phase of its life cycle by overproducing in another (Grassle and Grassle, 1974). *Lumbricillus lineatus* exhibited reduced hatching fertility but

compensated for this by increasing cocoon production. As a result, at low levels of contamination, population increases actually resulted. Only the F1 generation appeared to be affected. Subsequent populations, which had presumably adapted, showed no positive or negative life-cycle effects.

The fact that *Lumbricillus lineatus* populations were enhanced at low toxicant levels is an example of hormensis. Hormensis is described as the apparent enhancement of a physiological process by low toxicant doses and is a well-known phenomenon in pharmacology and toxicology. For instance, Laughlin et al. (1981) showed an enhanced growth rate for crab zoea exposed to low concentrations of oil. Similar enhancement has been observed by Chapman et al. (1983) for the polychaete *Capitella capitata* raised in contaminated sediment from Puget Sound and for surf smelt egg hatching associated with contaminated sediment. Hormensis has been attributed, mechanistically, to "transient overcorrections by control mechanisms to inhibitory changes well within [an organism's] capacity to counteract" (Stebbing, 1979). The fact of hormensis is evidence both of faunal resilience and of compensatory physiological strategies.

Contaminant-induced effects may be positive or negative depending upon dose level, life-history stage, and interactions with other pollutants. Interactions of two mutually inhibitory compounds may produce positive effects. Vangilder and Peterle (1983) found that mallard ducks (*Anas platyrhynchos*) that were fed petroleum and chlorinated hydrocarbons separately showed a decline in egg quality; however, ducks fed these two compounds together at low, environmentally realistic levels showed enhanced egg quality. In other words, hormensis was manifest only for toxicant combinations.

Even when a large proportion of a particular species is killed by a toxicant, effects on the whole population may not be of a long-term nature; a decreased mortality rate among survivors and their off-spring, due to reduced population density, may result in rapid population recovery (Monk, 1983). Bascom (1982) suggested that acute effects of metals are rare in the real marine environment because metals are either unavailable or can be detoxified by the protein metallothionein, while a tripeptide called glutathione acts the same way for organic material. Spies et al. (1982) found that the bothid flatfishes *Citharichthys sordidus* and *Citharichthys stigmaeus* adapted to chronic intake of petroleum hydrocarbons in the Santa Barbara area by increased hepatic mixed function oxydase (MFO) activity. This functional adaptation was positive in that it prevented accumulation of PAH in tissue; however, Spies et al. (1982) suggested that it may also compromise the health of these fishes in contaminated environments. An example of functional adaptation in Puget Sound is provided by the worm *Capitella capitata*, which often dominates the benthic fauna in chemically contaminated areas such as the Denny Way CSO (Comiskey et al., 1984), and is apparently able to adapt to sublethal stress induced by contaminated sediments (Chapman et al., 1983).

16.5. MANAGEMENT IMPLICATIONS

Despite present levels of chemical contamination and demonstrated toxicity in sediment bioassays, including effects on resident species, significant biological activity and productivity continue in chemically contaminated areas of Puget Sound. Fish and shellfish use contaminated areas, such as Commencement Bay, for a portion of their life history and are harvested in local recreational, commercial, and subsistence fisheries (concentrations of contaminants in tissue presently meet the U.S. Food and Drug Administration criteria for human consumption). Fish now reside in Commencement Bay and other areas of Puget Sound where they were excluded by earlier levels of organic pollution that resulted in lethally low oxygen levels in the water.

Initial management of earlier Puget Sound pollution problems was singularly successful. Once the cause (pulp-mill effluents) was recognized and treated (secondary treatment of the effluent), the effects (massive faunal kills) ceased, and marine life re-established itself in areas from which it had been previously excluded.

Because of present pollution control and effluent treatment technologies, it is highly unlikely that any part of Puget Sound will again experience such extensive faunal kills related to pollution. In addition, it is expected that the incidence of mortalities in harbor seal pups and possible reproductive effects in marine birds will decrease over time, since these appear to be residual effects of DDT and PCB, which are no longer manufactured or disposed of in large quantities. Four major adverse biological effects still need to be addressed as part of a Puget Sound management plan: (1) sediment toxicity and associated absences of sensitive benthic infauna from contaminated areas, (2) histopathological abnormalities in bottom fish and other species living in or near contaminated areas, (3) increased incidence of dinoflagellate blooms (if indeed these are pollution-related), and (4) bacteriological contamination resulting in closure of shellfish beds.

The ultimate environmental consequences of the above documented biological effects and their continuance in the Puget Sound ecosystem are unknown. It is reasonable, however, to assume that mitigation of these effects will invariably assist in maintaining the overall health of Puget Sound, provided the management alternatives and their consequences are carefully weighed. For instance, reduction of sediment toxicity will allow recolonization by sensitive infaunal species and will affect upper-trophic-level prey species that feed on the benthos. Consequently, management studies and actions in Puget Sound should concentrate primarily on the alleviation of these four major adverse biological effects.

ACKNOWLEDGMENTS

A large proportion of the data review reflected in this chapter was undertaken under subcontract to URS Engineers (Seattle), with funding from the Ocean Assessments Division of the U.S. National Oceanic and Atmospheric Administration (NOAA). I am particularly grateful to Ed Long of NOAA for his continued assistance, encouragement, and suggestions, to Al Mearns of NOAA for his review of an early draft of this chapter, and to Bob Dexter of E.V.S. Consultants for his input. Valuable comments and suggestions on the manuscript were provided by Douglas Wolfe of NOAA and two anonymous reviewers. The paper was word processed by Sarah Irwin and Marla Mees.

REFERENCES

Angell, T., and K. C. Balcomb III. 1982. Marine Birds and Mammals of Puget Sound. University of Washington Press, Seattle, 145 pp.

Angell, C. L., B. S. Miller, and J. R. Wellings. 1975. Epizootiology of tumors in a population of juvenile English sole (*Parophrys vetulus*) from Puget Sound, Washington. *Journal of the Fisheries Research Board of Canada*, **32**, 1723–1732.

Armstrong, J. W., R. M. Thom, K. K. Chew, B. Arpke, R. Bohn, J. Glock, R. Hieronymus, E. Hurlburt, K. Johnson, B. Mayer, B. Stevens, S. Tettleback, and P. Waterstrat. 1978. The Impact of the Denny Way Combined Sewer Overflow on the Adjacent Flora and Fauna in Elliott Bay, Puget Sound, Washington. Unpublished report, University of Washington College of Fisheries, Seattle, 102 pp.

Armstrong, J. W., R. M. Thom, and K. K. Chew. 1981. Impact of a combined sewer overflow on the abundance, distribution and community structure of subtidal benthos. *Marine Environmental Research*, **4**, 3–23.

Arndt, D. P. 1973. DDT and PCB Levels in Three Washington State Harbor Seal (*Phoca vitulina richardsii*) Populations. M. S. Thesis, University of Washington, Seattle, 65 pp.

Bargmann, G. G. 1982. The Biology and Fisheries for Ling Cod (*Ophiodon elongatus*) in Puget Sound. Technical Report No. 66, Washington State Department of Fisheries, Seattle, 69 pp.

Bascom, W. 1982. Director's statement. *In*: Coastal Water Research Project Biennial Report 1981–1982, W. Bascom (Ed.). Southern California Coastal Water Research Project, Long Beach, California, pp. 1–3.

Brewer, C., and W. Myers. 1982. Aerial Counts in the Skagit-Fraser River Area. Unpublished aerial waterfowl survey data for Port Susan, Skagit, Padilla and Samish Bays October–November, Washington State Department of Game, Tacoma, 12 pp.

Calambokidis, J., K. Bowman, S. Carter, J. Cubbage, P. Dawson, T. Fleischner, J. Schuett-Hames, J. Skidmore, and B. Taylor. 1978. Chlorinated Hydrocarbon Concentrations and the Ecology and Behavior of Harbor Seals in Washington State Waters. Unpublished report, Evergreen State College, Olympia, Washington, 121 pp.

Calambokidis, J. A., R. D. Everitt, J. C. Cubbage, and S. D. Carter. 1979. Harbor seal census for the inland waters of Washington, 1977–1978. *Murrelet*, **60**, 110–112.

Calambokidis, J., J. Peard, G. H. Steiger, J. C. Cubbage, and R. L. DeLong. 1984. Chemical contaminants in marine mammals from Washington State. Technical Memorandum NOS OMS 6, U.S. National Oceanic and Atmospheric Administration, Rockville, Maryland, 167 pp.

Campana, S. E. 1983. Mortality of starry flounders (*Platichthys stellatus*) with skin tumors. *Canadian Journal of Fisheries and Aquatic Sciences*, **40**, 200–207.

Canning, D. J., S. G. Herman, and G. B. Shea. 1979. Terminal 107 Environmental Studies, Wildlife Study. Technical Report prepared by the Oceanographic Institute of Washington, submitted to the Port of Seattle, Seattle, 142 pp.

Cardwell, R. D., C. E. Woelke, M. I. Carr, and E. W. Sanborn. 1977. Evaluation of Water Quality of Puget Sound and Hood Canal in 1976. Technical Memorandum ERL MESA-21, U.S. National Oceanic and Atmospheric Administration, Rockville, Maryland, 36 pp.

Cardwell, R. D., S. Olsen, M. I. Carr, and E. W. Sanborn. 1979. Causes of Oyster Larvae Mortality in South Puget Sound. Technical Memorandum ERL MESA-39, U.S. National Oceanic and Atmospheric Administration, Rockville, Maryland, 73 pp.

Chapman, P. M., and R. Fink. 1983. Additional Marine Sediment Toxicity Tests in Connection with Toxicant Pretreatment Planning Studies, Metro Seattle. Technical Report prepared by E. V.S. Consultants, submitted to the Municipality of Metropolitan Seattle, Seattle, 29 pp.

Chapman, P. M., G. A. Vigers, M. A. Farrell, R. N. Dexter, E. A. Quinlan, R. M. Kocan, and M. L. Landolt. 1982a. Survey of Biological Effects of Toxicants upon Puget Sound Biota. 1: Broad-Scale Toxicity Survey. Technical Memorandum OMPA-25, U.S. National Oceanic and Atmospheric Administration, Rockville, Maryland, 98 pp.

Chapman, P. M., M. A. Farrell, R. M. Kocan, and M. L. Landolt. 1982b. Marine Sediment Toxicity Tests in Connection with Toxicant Pre-Treatment Planning Studies, Metro Seattle. Technical Report prepared by E.V.S. Consultants, submitted to the Municipality of Metropolitan Seattle, Seattle, 15 pp.

Chapman, P. M., D. R. Munday, J. Morgan, R. Fink, R. M. Kocan, M. L. Landolt, and R. N. Dexter. 1983. Survey of Biological Effects of Toxicants upon Puget Sound Biota. II: Tests of Reproductive Impairment. Technical Report NOS 102 OMS-1, U.S. National Oceanic and Atmospheric Administration, Rockville, Maryland, 58 pp.

Chapman, P. M., R. N. Dexter, J. Morgan, R. Fink, D. Mitchell, R. M. Kocan, and M. L. Landolt. 1984. Survey of Biological Effects of Toxicants upon Puget Sound Biota. III: Tests in Everett Harbor, Samish and Bellingham Bays. Technical Memorandum NOS OMS-2, U.S. National Oceanic and Atmospheric Administration, Rockville, Maryland, 48 pp.

Chapman, P. M., R. N. Dexter, R. D. Kathman, and G. A. Erickson. 1985a. Survey of Biological Effects of Toxicants upon Puget Sound Biota. IV: Inter-relationships of Infauna, Sediment Bioassay and Sediment Chemistry Data. Technical Memorandum NOS OMA-9, U.S. National Oceanic and Atmospheric Administration, Rockville, Maryland, 57 pp.

Chapman, P. M., R. N. Dexter, R. M. Kocan, and E. R. Long. 1985b. An overview of biological effects testing in Puget Sound, Washington: methods, results and implications. *In*: Aquatic Toxicology and Hazard Assessment: Seventh Symposium, R. D. Cardwell, R. Purdy, and R. C. Bahner (Eds.). Special Technical Publication 854, American Society for Testing and Materials, Philadelphia, pp. 344–363.

Chasan, D. J. 1981. The Water Link—A History of Puget Sound as a Resource. University of Washington Press, Seattle, 179 pp.

Cheyne, H., and R. Foster. 1942. Supplementary Report on Pollution of Everett Harbor. Pollution Series Bulletin 23, Washington State Pollution Control Commission, Seattle, 15 pp.

Comiskey, C. A., T. A. Farmer, and C. C. Brandt. 1984. Dynamics and Biological Impacts of Toxicants in the Main Basin of Puget Sound and Lake Washington, Vol. IIA. Technical Report prepared by Science Applications, submitted to the Municipality of Metropolitan Seattle, Seattle, 183 pp.

Crecelius, E. A., R. G. Riley, N. S. Bloom, and B. L. Thomas. 1985. History of Contamination of Sediments in Commencement Bay, Tacoma, Washington. Technical Memorandum NOS OMA-14, U.S. National Oceanic and Atmospheric Administration, Rockville, Maryland, 34 pp.

Cunningham, R. 1983. Minter Bay/Burley Lagoon Study Outline. Technical Memorandum 8 February, Washington Department of Ecology, Olympia, 8 pp.

Dames & Moore. 1981. Baseline Studies and Evaluations for Commencement Bay Study/Environmental Impact Assessment, Vols. I–VII. Series of reports submitted to the Seattle District, U.S. Army Corps of Engineers, Seattle, paginated separately.

Eldridge, E. F., and G. T. Orlob. 1951. Investigation of pollution of Port Gardner Bay and Snohomish River estuary. *Sewage and Industrial Wastes*, **23**, 782–795.

Grassle, J. F., and J. P. Grassle. 1974. Opportunistic life histories and genetic systems in marine benthic polychaetes. *Journal of Marine Research*, **32**, 253–284.

Gronlund, W., B. McCain, and M. Myers. 1983. Port Gardner bottomfish survey completed. *In*: Northwest and Alaska Fisheries Center, Quarterly Report, April–May, U.S. Department of Commerce, National Marine Fisheries Service, Seattle, pp. 18–19.

Harper-Owes. 1982. Water Quality Assessment of the Duwamish Estuary. Technical Report, submitted to the Municipality of Metropolitan Seattle, Seattle, 169 pp.

Hauschildt-Lillge, D. 1982. Long-term effects of petroleum hydrocarbons on the life cycle and productivity of the littoral oligochaete *Lumbricillus lineatus*. *Netherlands Journal of Sea Research*, **16**, 502–510.

Kimura, D. K., and A. R. Millikan. 1977. Assessment of the Population of Pacific Hake (*Merluccius productus*) in Puget Sound, Washington. Technical Report 35, Washington State Department of Fisheries, Seattle, 46 pp.

Kruger, D. M. 1979. Effects of Point-Source Discharges and Other Inputs on Water Quality in Budd Inlet, Washington. DOE 79-11, Washington Department of Ecology, Seattle, 112 pp.

Landolt, M. L., and R. M. Kocan. 1984. Lethal and sublethal effects of marine sediment extracts on fish cells and chromosomes. *Helgoländer Wissenschaftiche Meeresuntersuchungen*, **37**, 479–491.

Landolt, M. L., R. M. Kocan, and R. N. Dexter. 1984. Anaphase aberrations in cultured fish cells as a bioassay for marine sediments. *Marine Environmental Research*, **12**, 101.

Laughlin, R. B., Jr., J. Ng, and H. E. Guard. 1981. Hormensis: a response to low environmental concentrations of petroleum hydrocarbons. *Science*, **211**, 705–707.

Leon, H. 1980. Terminal 107. Environmental Studies. Benthic Community Impact Study for Terminal 107 (Kellogg Island) and Vicinity. Technical Report prepared by Pacific Rim Planners, submitted to the Port of Seattle, Seattle, 98 pp.

Long, E. R. 1982. An assessment of marine pollution in Puget Sound. *Marine Pollution Bulletin*, **13**, 380–383.

Long, E. R. 1983. A multi-disciplinary approach to assessing pollution in coastal waters. *In*: Proceedings of the Third Symposium on Coastal and Ocean Management, San Diego, Marine Technological Society, Washington, D.C., pp. 163–178.

Long, E. R., and P. M. Chapman. 1985. A sediment quality Triad: measures of sediment contamination, toxicity and infaunal community composition in Puget Sound. *Marine Pollution Bulletin*, **16**, 405–415.

Longwell, A. C. 1976. Chromosome Mutagenesis in Developing Mackerel Eggs Sampled from the New York Bight. Technical Memorandum ERL MESA-7, National Oceanic and Atmospheric Administration, Rockville, Maryland, 61 pp.

Longwell, A. C., and J. B. Hughes. 1982. Cytologic, cytogenetic, and embryologic state of Atlantic mackerel eggs from surface waters of the New York Bight in relation to pollution. *In*: Ecological Stress and the New York Bight: Science and Management, G. F. Meyer (Ed.). Estuarine Research Foundation, Columbia, South Carolina, pp. 381–388.

Malins, D. C., B. B. McCain, D. W. Brown, A. K. Sparks, and H. O. Hodgins. 1980. Chemical Contaminants and Biological Abnormalities in Central and Southern Puget Sound. Technical Memorandum OMPA-2, National Oceanic and Atmospheric Administration, Rockville, Maryland, 295 pp.

Malins, D. C., S-L Chan, B. B. McCain, D. W. Brown, A. K. Sparks, and H. O. Hodgins. 1981. Puget Sound Pollution and Its Effects on Marine Biota. Unpublished report, National Marine Fisheries Service, Seattle, 74 pp.

Malins, D. C., B. B. McCain, D. W. Brown, A. K. Sparks, H. O. Hodgins, and S-L Chan. 1982a. Chemical Contaminants and Abnormalities in Fish and Invertebrates from Puget Sound. Technical Memorandum OMPA-19, National Oceanic and Atmospheric Administration, Rockville, Maryland, 168 pp.

Malins, D. C., B. B. McCain, H. O. Hodgins, and S-L Chan. 1982b. Frequency of Occurrence of Biological Abnormalities. Final report for Mesa Puget Sound Work Unit 82-7, prepared by Northwest and Alaska Fisheries Center, Seattle, Washington, 10 pp.

Mathematical Sciences Northwest. 1977. Washington Coastal Areas of Major Biological Significance November 1977. Washington Department of Ecology Baseline Studies Program Report, Seattle, 651 pp.

Mayer, G. F. (Ed.). 1982. Ecological Stress and the New York Bight: Science and Management. Estuarine Research Federation, Columbia, South Carolina, 715 pp.

McCain, B. B., M. S. Myers, U. Varanasi, D. W. Brown, L. D. Rhodes, W. D. Gronlund, D. G. Elliott, W. A. Palsson, H. O. Hodgins, and D. C. Malins. 1982. Pathology of Two Species of Flatfish from Urban Estuaries in Puget Sound. Technical Report 600/7-82-001, U.S. Environmental Protection Agency, Seattle, Washington, 100 pp.

Meyer, J. H., and D. A. Vogel. 1978. An Examination of the Smaller Benthic Invertebrates in Hylebos Waterway, Tacoma, Washington. Unpublished report, U.S. Department of the Interior, Fish and Wildlife Service, Seattle, 11 pp.

Monk, D. C. 1983. The uses and abuses of ecotoxicology. *Marine Pollution Bulletin*, **14**, 284–288.

Nichols, F. H. 1985. Abundance fluctuations among benthic invertebrates in two Pacific estuaries. *Estuaries*, **8**, 136–144.

Orlob, G. T., D. R. Peterson, and K. R. Jones. 1950a. An Investigation of Pollution in Commencement Bay and the Puyallup River System. Tech-

nical Bulletin 8, Washington State Pollution Control Commission, Seattle, 26 pp.

Orlob, G. T., M. D. Anderson, and D. L. Hansen. 1950b. An Investigation of Pollution in Port Gardner Bay and the Lower Snohomish River. Unpublished report, Washington State Pollution Control Commission, Seattle, 25 pp.

Pedersen, M. G., and G. DiDonato. 1982. Groundfish Management Plan for Washington's Inside Waters. Progress Report 170, Washington Department of Fisheries, Olympia, 123 pp.

Pierson, K. B., B. D. Ross, C. L. Melby, S. D. Brewer, and R. E. Nakatani. 1983. Biological Testing of Solid Phase and Suspended Phase Dredge Material from Commencement Bay, Tacoma, Washington. Technical Report DACW67-82-C-0038, U.S. Army Corps of Engineers, 59 pp.

Port of Seattle. 1980. Environmental Impact Statement on Alternative Uses for Terminal 91 (Piers 90/91): Appendices. Port of Seattle, Research and Planning Department, Seattle, 79 pp.

Quinlan, E. A., P. M. Chapman, R. N. Dexter, D. E. Konasewich, G. A. Erickson, B. R. Kowalski, T. A. Silver, and C. C. Ebbesmeyer. 1985. Application of Information on Puget Sound Ecosystems to Pollution Related Issues. Technical Memorandum NOS OMA-10, U.S. National Oceanic and Atmospheric Administration, Rockville, Maryland, 334 pp.

Riley, R. G., E. A. Crecelius, R. E. Fitzner, B. L. Thomas, J. M. Gurtisen, and N. S. Bloom. 1984. Organic and Inorganic Toxicants in Sediments and Birds from Puget Sound. Technical Memorandum NOS OMS-1, U.S. National Oceanic and Atmospheric Administration, Rockville, Maryland, 107 pp.

Samolloff, M. R., J. Bell, D. A. Birkholz, G. R. B. Webster, E. G. Arnott, R. Pulak, and A. Madrid. 1983. Combined bioassay-chemical fractionation scheme for the determination and ranking of toxic chemicals in sediments. *Environmental Science and Technology*, **17**, 329–334.

Saunders, S., T. Sample, and R. Matsuda. 1982. Paralytic Shellfish Poisoning: Its History, Processes and Impacts As Applicable to Puget Sound. Unpublished report, Water Pollution Control Department, Municipality of Metropolitan Seattle, Seattle, 42 pp.

Sawyer, T. K. 1982. Distribution and seasonal incidence of "Black Gill" in the rock crab, *Cancer irroratus*. *In*: Ecological Stress and the New York Bight: Science and Management, G. F. Mayer (Ed.). Estuarine Research Federation, Columbia, South Carolina, pp. 199–212.

Schelske, C. L., E. F. Stoermer, D. J. Conley, J. A. Robbins, and R. M. Glover. 1983. Early eutrophication in the Lower Great Lakes: new evidence from biogenic silica in sediments. *Science*, **222**, 320–322.

Shuba, P. J., H. E. Tatum, and J. H. Carroll. 1978. Biological Assessment Methods to Predict the Impact of Open-Water Disposal of Dredged Material. Technical Report D-78-50, Dredged Material Research Program, Department of the Army, Vicksburg, Virginia, 77 pp.

Simenstad, C. A., B. S. Miller, C. F. Nyblade, K. Thornburgh, and L. J. Bledsoe. 1979. Food Web Relationships of Northern Puget Sound and the Strait of Juan de Fuca. A Synthesis of the Available Knowledge. Technical Report 600/7-79-529, U.S. Environmental Protection Agency, 335 pp.

Simenstad, C. A., K. L. Fresh, and E. O. Salo. 1982. The role of Puget Sound and Washington coastal estuaries in the life history of Pacific salmon: an unappreciated function. *In*: Estuarine Comparisons, V. S. Kennedy (Ed.). Academic Press, New York, pp. 343–364.

Spies, R. B., J. S. Felton, and L. Dillard. 1982. Hepatic mixed-function oxidases in California flatfishes are increased in contaminated environments and by oil and PCB ingestion. *Marine Biology*, **70**, 117–127.

Stebbing, A. R. D. 1979. An experimental approach to the determinants of biological water quality. *Philosophic Transactions of the Royal Society of London*, **286**(B), 465–481.

Strickland, R. M. 1983. The Fertile Fjord: Plankton in Puget Sound. University of Washington Press, Seattle, 146 pp.

Swartz, R. C., W. A. DeBen, and F. A. Cole. 1979. A bioassay for the toxicity of sediment to marine macrobenthos. *Journal of the Water Pollution Control Federation*, **51**, 944–950.

Swartz, R. C., D. W. Schultz, G. R. Ditsworth, W. A. DeBen, and F. A. Cole. 1981. Sediment toxicity, contamination and benthic community structure near ocean disposal sites. *Estuaries*, **4**, 258.

Swartz, R. C., W. A. DeBen, K. A. Sercu, and J. O. Lamberson. 1982. Sediment toxicity and the distribution of amphipods in Commencement Bay, Washington, U.S.A. *Marine Pollution Bulletin*, **13**, 359–364.

Swartz, R. C., W. A. DeBen, J. K. Phillips, J. O. Lamberson, and F. A. Cole. 1985. Phoxocephalid amphipod bioassay for marine sediment toxicity. *In*: Aquatic Toxicology and Hazard Assessment: Seventh Symposium, R. D. Cardwell, R. Purdy, and R. C. Bahner (Eds.). Special technical publication 854, American Society for Testing and Materials, Philadelphia, pp. 284–307.

Tetra Tech. 1985. Commencement Bay Nearshore/Tideflats Remedial Investigation Report. Report No. EPA-910/9-85-134a prepared for the U.S. Environmental Protection Agency by Tetra Tech, Inc., Bellevue, Washington, U.S. EPA, Washington, D. C.

Thom, R. M., and K. K. Chew. In Press. The response of subtidal infaunal communities to a change in wastewater discharge. *In*: Conference Proceedings, Urban Stormwater and Combined Sewer Overflow Impact on Receiving Water Bodies. Orlando, Florida, 26–28 November 1979.

Tomlinson, R. D., B. N. Bebee, A. A. Heyward, S. G. Munger, R. G. Swartz, S. Lazoff, D. E. Spyridakis, M. F. Shepard, R. M. Thom, K. K. Chew, and R. R. Whitney. 1980. Fate and Effects of Particulates Discharged by Contained Sewers and Storm Drains. Technical Report 600/2-80-111, U.S. Environmental Protection Agency, 165 pp.

Townsend, L. D., A. Eriksen, and H. Cheyne. 1941. Pollution of Everett Harbor. Pollution Series-Bulletin No. 3, Washington State Pollution Control Commission, Seattle, 56 pp.

United Nations Environment Programme (UNEP). 1982. The Health of the Oceans. Reports and Studies No. 16, UNEP Regional Seas, Geneva, Switzerland, 108 pp.

U.S. Army Corps of Engineers (U.S. COE). 1982. East, West and Duwamish Waterways Navigation Improvement Study. Draft feasibility report and draft environmental impact statement, U.S. COE Seattle District, Seattle, 212 pp.

Vangilder, L. D., and T. J. Peterle. 1983. Mallard egg quality: enhancement by low levels of petroleum and chlorinated hydrocarbons. *Bulletin of Environmental Contamination and Toxicology*, **30**, 17–23.

Verber, J. L. 1983. Interim Report of Samish Bay, Washington, December 1982 Sanitary Survey. Technical Memorandum, Department of Health and Human Services, Seattle, 18 pp.

Wahl, T. R., S. M. Speich, D. A. Manuwal, K. V. Hirsch, and C. Miller. 1981. Marine Bird Populations of the Strait of Juan de Fuca, Strait of Georgia, and Adjacent Waters in 1978 and 1979. Technical Report 600/7-81-156, U.S. Environmental Protection Agency, 789 pp.

Waldichuk, M. 1983. Pollution in the Strait of Georgia: a review. *Canadian Journal of Fisheries and Aquatic Sciences*, **40**, 1142–1167.

Washington State Department of Ecology (WDOE). 1976. Ecological Baseline and Monitoring Study for Port Gardner and Adjacent Waters. A summary report for the years 1972 through 1975, WDOE, Seattle, 189 pp.

Webber, H. H. 1979. The Intertidal and Shallow Subtidal Benthos of the West Coast of Whidbey Island Spring 1977 to Winter 1978: First Year Report. Technical Memorandum ERC MESA-37, U.S. National Oceanic and Atmospheric Administration, Rockville, Maryland, 108 pp.

Weitkamp, D. E., and M. Katz. 1976. Southeast Harbor Environmental Studies. Biological Survey and Assessment of Impacts of Alternative Redevelopments. Report prepared by Parametrix, submitted to the Port of Seattle, Seattle, 77 pp.

Zeh, J. E. 1982. Letter report to E. R. Long (NOAA/OMPA, Seattle) 29 June. Prepared by Mathematical Sciences Northwest, Seattle, 15 pp.

Zeh, J. E., and J. P. Houghton. 1981. Evaluation of Existing Marine Intertidal and Shallow Subtidal Biologic Data. Technical Report 600/7-81/036, U.S. Environmental Protection Agency, 362 pp.

Ziebell, C. D., R. E. Pine, A. D. Mills, and R. K. Cunningham. 1970. Field toxicity studies and juvenile salmon distribution in Port Angeles harbor, Washington. *Journal of the Water Pollution Control Federation*, **42**, 229–236.

Chapter 17

Implications of Opportunistic Predation for Predicting the Impacts of Ocean Dumping on Demersal Fish

D. Scott Becker

PTI Environmental Services
Bellevue, Washington

Abstract	185
17.1. Introduction	186
17.2. Experimental Methods	186
17.2.1. Field	186
17.2.2. Laboratory	187
17.2.3. Statistical Analysis	187
17.3. Results	188
17.3.1. Sediment Characteristics	188
17.3.2. Prey Selection	188
17.3.3. Prey Size Selection	188
17.3.4. Diel Patterns of Predation	189
17.4. Discussion	189
17.4.1. Observed Patterns	189
17.4.2. Implications	190
17.4.3. A Better Approach	190
Acknowledgment	191
References	191

ABSTRACT

Trophic models, which are used to predict impacts of ocean dumping on demersal fish, sometimes rely upon data collected in undisturbed areas in order to identify potential prey spectra of the fish. However, because these models do not account for predation on the opportunistic species that generally dominate benthic invertebrate assemblages in disturbed areas, they may give false estimates of the impacts of ocean dumping. This chapter describes the foraging patterns of three flatfishes (Pleuronectidae) in Puget Sound, Washington, (U.S.A.) on *Capitella* spp., a well-known group of opportunistic polychaetes, and illustrates how the foraging behavior of demersal fish may respond to habitat disturbance. The target species were English sole (*Parophrys vetulus*), Dover sole (*Microstomus pacificus*), and rex sole (*Glyptocephalus zachirus*). *Capitella* spp. proved to be important prey to all three target fishes because all three exhibited nonrandom selection with respect to number and size of these polychaetes. Furthermore, although English sole is primarily a diurnal forager, predation on *Capitella* spp. allowed this species to forage successfully at night. None of these patterns could have been predicted based on direct extrapolations from studies conducted in unimpacted areas. Results of this study indicate that the presence of opportunistic prey in disturbed areas may enhance the food value of such habitats to certain demersal fish. If these food-rich areas attract and retain fish, trophic transfer of sediment contaminants may be accelerated. In addition, if fish experience dietary imbalances from selectively preying upon opportunistic prey, then susceptibility to disease and the toxic effects of contaminants may be enhanced. In the absence of specific fish-feeding information from disturbed areas, predictions of the impact of ocean dumping could be based on information about the generalized foraging patterns of demersal fish. Although this approach cannot conclusively determine how fish will respond to altered benthic invertebrate assemblages, it may identify those species most likely to be attracted to disturbed areas.

17.1. INTRODUCTION

To develop trophic models capable of predicting impacts of ocean dumping on demersal fish (e.g., community changes, bioaccumulation, disease), it is necessary to understand how alterations of benthic invertebrate assemblages influence predator–prey relationships between the invertebrates and their piscine predators. Unfortunately, this type of information is rare for marine ecosystems in general (Mills, 1975).

One method of compensating for data gaps of trophic coupling in disturbed habitats is to extrapolate from information collected in unimpacted areas (Boesch, 1982). However, such a procedure can potentially lead to erroneous conclusions. Ocean dumping of a variety of wastes (e.g., dredged material, mine tailings, sewage sludge) frequently produces atypical benthic invertebrate assemblages in impacted areas (Oliver et al., 1977; Pearson and Rosenberg, 1978; Rhoads et al., 1978; Boesch, 1982). These assemblages are generally dominated by one or more opportunistic species that are adapted to rapidly colonize disturbed environments. Because these opportunists often reside at or near the sediment–water interface, they represent a potential food bonanza to demersal fish. It seems likely that when fish encounter such an abundant and accessible food source, species that are capable of modifying their foraging behavior will do so to fully exploit this windfall. Such opportunistic consumption of temporally or spatially variable superabundant prey has been found for a variety of fish (Nilsson, 1960; Ivlev, 1961; Zaret and Rand, 1971; Murdoch et al., 1975) and is one prediction of optimal foraging theory (review in Pyke et al., 1977). Basing a trophic model solely upon information collected in unimpacted areas may therefore fail to account for the ability of many fish to exploit opportunistic invertebrates, and thereby underestimate the value of altered benthic invertebrate assemblages as forage bases for demersal fish.

This chapter describes the foraging patterns of three flatfishes (Pleuronectidae) in Puget Sound, Washington, on *Capitella* spp., a well-known group of opportunistic polychaetes (Grassle and Grassle, 1974; Pearson and Rosenberg, 1978). The chapter illustrates how a group of demersal fishes may adapt its feeding patterns to a disturbed habitat dominated by opportunistic benthic invertebrates. The target species are English sole (*Parophrys vetulus*), Dover sole (*Microstomus pacificus*), and rex sole (*Glyptocephalus zachirus*). These fishes belong to the small-mouthed subgroup of pleuronectids identified by Moiseev (1953) and, as such, prey primarily upon small infaunal and epifaunal benthic invertebrates. These species also form a numerically important component

of demersal fish assemblages in Puget Sound (Miller et al., 1977; Wingert and Miller, 1979; Becker, 1984) and in most nearshore areas along the west coasts of the United States and Canada (Alverson et al., 1964; Day and Pearcy, 1968; Hart, 1973; Allen, 1982).

17.2. EXPERIMENTAL METHODS

17.2.1. Field

The study was conducted on the delta of the Puyallup River (Fig. 17.1). This dynamic area is influenced by a variety of anthropogenic and natural discharges. For example, the river discharges ~5.5 metric tons (t) of sediments in a seasonally variable manner (Dexter et al., 1981). In addition, the city of Tacoma releases primary-treated sewage into the river at an annual average flow rate of 0.9 m^3 s^{-1} ~2.4 km upstream from the river mouth (Tetra Tech, 1981). A preliminary survey conducted by the author showed that benthic invertebrate assemblages throughout much of the delta were dominated by *Capitella* spp.

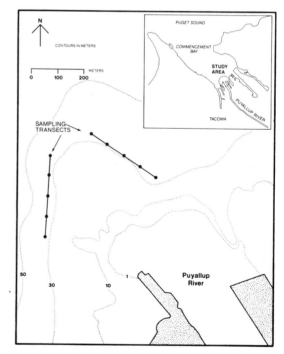

Figure 17.1. Locations of sampling transects and benthic sampling points (i.e., dots) along each transect. Depth contours are shown in meters.

Demersal fishes, benthic invertebrates, and bottom sediments were collected from 26 May to 3 June 1981 along two transects located at a depth of 32 m (Fig. 17.1). Data from the two transects were pooled prior to analysis.

Demersal fishes were sampled using a 7.6-m (headrope) otter trawl with a body mesh size of 3.2 cm (stretched) and a cod-end liner mesh size of 0.8 cm. Trawling was conducted along the 32-m isobath at a constant vessel speed of ~4.6 km h^{-1}. LORAN-C radionavigation was used to determine position. To assess feeding chronologies of the target species, duplicate trawls were made along each transect during four periods of the diel cycle: dawn, 2–3 h after sunrise; day, 6.5–7.5 h after sunrise; dusk, 0.5–1.5 h after sunset; and night, 5.5–7 h after sunset. The overall sampling effort thus yielded 8 hauls per transect for a total of 16 hauls.

At sea, the stomach contents of the target species were fixed by injecting 10% buffered formalin into the body cavity of each individual. The total length (TL) of each fish was then measured to the nearest 1 mm.

Benthic invertebrates along each transect were sampled within 2 d of trawling. Organisms were collected with a 0.1-m^2 van Veen bottom grab, sieved through a 1.0-mm mesh screen, fixed in 10% buffered formalin, and stored in 70% ethanol. A single grab sample was collected during the day at each of five sampling points positioned at approximately equal distances along each transect (Fig. 17.1).

An additional grab sample was collected at each benthic sampling point for analysis of surficial sediments. Two 28-cm^2 core samples were collected to a depth of 2 cm below the sediment surface of each grab sample. One core was frozen immediately for later determination of organic content, and the other core was refrigerated for subsequent particle-size analysis.

17.2.2. Laboratory

Within 5 d of capture, the body cavity of each fish was opened and stomachs that contained prey were removed and stored in 70% ethanol. Empty stomachs were recorded and discarded. For food habits analyses, stomachs were subsampled from those stomachs that contained prey. To minimize potential within-species variation as a result of size-dependent foraging patterns (Gabriel and Pearcy, 1981), only individuals within an 80-mm size range were selected for analysis. The size intervals used for English sole, Dover sole, and rex sole were 240–320, 200–280, and 210–290 mm TL, respec-

tively. The interval used for each species was chosen primarily to maximize the number of stomach samples across both study transects throughout the diel cycle. A maximum subsample of 20 prey-containing stomachs was selected randomly for each time period at each transect, yielding a maximum sample size of 160 prey-containing stomachs for each species. Empty stomachs were added in proportion to their occurrence to each subsample of prey-containing stomachs.

Identifications of invertebrates in stomachs and benthic samples were made using a dissecting microscope. Sizes of *Capitella* spp. were estimated by using the width of the fifth setiger. This measurement was used instead of body length because many of these polychaetes were fragmented during grab sampling or ingestion by the fishes. Setiger widths were measured to the nearest 0.1 mm by using an ocular micrometer.

The organic content of sediment samples was estimated by percent weight loss of ignition at 600°C (Gerlach, 1972). Particle-size distribution was determined by using standard sieve and pipette techniques (Folk, 1968).

17.2.3. Statistical Analysis

Nonrandomness of predation on *Capitella* spp. by the target species was evaluated using a 2 × 2 contingency formulation. Selection was tested by comparing the proportion (based on abundance) of *Capitella* spp. in the diet of each predator with the proportion found in the benthos. For this analysis, data were pooled across the diel cycle. Contingency table analysis is superior to other measures of selectivity because it provides a criterion (i.e., the chi-square statistic) on which nonrandomness can be judged objectively (Pearre, 1982).

Nonrandomness of size selection of prey by each fish was tested by using the Mann–Whitney *U*-test. In making these evaluations, the size distribution of *Capitella* spp. in the stomachs of each predator was compared with the size distribution found in benthic assemblages.

The foraging patterns of English sole differed between habitats where benthic assemblages were dominated by *Capitella* spp. and habitats where assemblages did not include these polychaetes. To study these differences, stomach-fullness values (i.e., the number of prey per stomach) found in the present study were compared with those obtained at six other sites in Puget Sound by Becker (1984). These six sites were located at depths from 12 to 32 m, and fish were sampled and processed by using methods identical to those described for the present study. Stomach-fullness values were compared during each period of the diel cycle by using the Mann–Whitney U-test. Similar analyses could not be conducted for Dover sole and rex sole because these fishes were not sufficiently abundant at the six additional sites.

17.3. RESULTS

17.3.1. Sediment Characteristics

Sediment along the study transects was generally muddy sand. The mean value of percent sand (by wt) at the 10 sampling points was 54.4 ± 13.3 (standard deviation). Organic content of the sediment was relatively low; the mean value for weight loss on ignition was $2.3 \pm 0.5\%$ (standard deviation).

17.3.2. Prey Selection

The prey spectrum of each target species differed considerably from the composition of benthic assemblages (Table 17.1). In general, *Capitella* spp. were relatively more abundant in the diets than in the benthos, whereas most other taxa were relatively less abundant in the diets. A major exception to the latter pattern was predation by Dover sole on crustaceans, where the dietary proportion (22.5%) was much

greater than was the relative abundance of this taxon in the benthos (6.3%).

Nonrandomness of selection of *Capitella* spp. was significant ($p<0.001$) for all three target species; however, the fishes exhibited considerable differences in their degree of selection. Rex sole showed the greatest preference for *Capitella* spp.; these polychaetes composed 81.7% of their diet. By contrast, Dover sole exhibited the least preference for *Capitella* spp., which accounted for only 36.6% of their diet. Finally, English sole showed moderate preference for *Capitella* spp., which constituted 58.5% of their diet.

17.3.3. Prey Size Selection

As with relative abundance (Section 17.3.2.), the size distributions of *Capitella* spp. in the diets of the three target species differed from those in benthic assemblages (Fig. 17.2). Median sizes of the prey of all three fishes were significantly greater ($p<0.001$) than that of benthic assemblages.

Table 17.1. Relative Abundances of Invertebrate Taxa in the Benthos and in the Diets of the Target Species[a]

Taxon	Benthos	English Sole	Dover Sole	Rex Sole
Capitella spp.	25.7	58.5	36.6	81.7
Polychaeta[b]	42.9	25.9	26.5	15.2
Gastropoda	2.4	0	3.5	0
Pelecypoda	22.5	14.0	10.9	1.2
Crustacea	6.3	1.6	22.5	1.9
Ophiuroidea	0.2	0	0	0
Total Number of Prey		6681	2350	1884
Total Number of Stomachs[c]		178	128	68
Fish Size Range (mm TL)		240–320	200–280	210–290

[a]Relative abundances expressed as a percentage.
[b]Excluding *Capitella* spp.
[c]Includes proportionate numbers of empty stomachs.

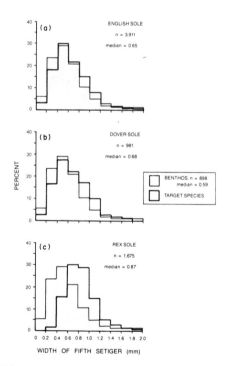

Figure 17.2. Comparisons of size frequencies of *Capitella* spp. between the benthos (shaded area) and the diet of each target species using the Mann-Whitney U-test. In all cases $p<0.001$.

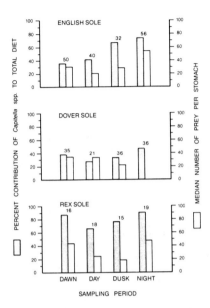

Figure 17.3. Diel predation patterns of the target species. Sample sizes are given above each pair of bars.

Rex sole exhibited the largest degree of size selection, with a median prey size of 0.87 mm, compared to the median size of 0.59 mm found for benthic assemblages. Dover sole and English sole showed similarly moderate degrees of size selection, with median prey sizes of 0.68 mm and 0.65 mm, respectively.

17.3.4. Diel Patterns of Predation

Diel variation of percent contribution of *Capitella* spp. to the total diet was similar among the three fishes (Fig. 17.3). Minimum contributions occurred either during the dawn or day periods, whereas maximum contributions were generally found at night.

For English sole and rex sole, diel variation of median number of prey per stomach closely paralleled the diel pattern of percent *Capitella* spp. in the diet. For Dover sole, however, these two variables showed substantially different diel trends. Median number of prey per stomach was generally stable throughout the dawn and day periods, began to decline at dusk, and dropped to zero at night. By contrast, percent *Capitella* spp. in the diet of Dover sole declined slightly from the dawn to day periods, rose slightly at dusk, and finally peaked during the night.

Diel variation of the median number of prey per stomach for English sole differed substantially between the habitats where *Capitella* spp. were present and other habitats (Becker, 1984) where these polychaetes were absent (Fig. 17.4). Although median prey number did not differ significantly ($p>0.05$) between habitat types during the dawn, day, and dusk periods, values at night were significantly greater ($p<0.001$) at stations where *Capitella* spp. were present than at stations where these prey were absent.

17.4. DISCUSSION

17.4.1. Observed Patterns

Results of this study suggest that *Capitella* spp. can be important prey to English sole, Dover sole, and rex sole when these polychaetes are relatively abundant in benthic assemblages because all three fishes exhibited nonrandom selection in the number and size of these prey. Rex sole exhibited the highest degree of selection among the three fishes, by including *Capitella* spp. in the largest percentage of total diet and by selecting the largest median size of these prey.

Literature accounts of the food habits of English sole, Dover sole, and rex sole (Hagerman, 1952; Kravitz et al.,

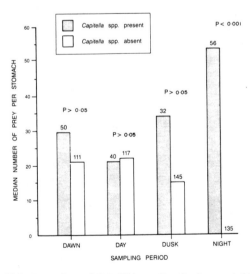

Figure 17.4. Comparisons (Mann-Whitney *U*-test) of stomach-fullness values for English sole collected from the transects in Fig. 17.1 (*Capitella* spp. present, shaded bars), and from other stations in Puget Sound (Becker, 1984) where *Capitella* spp. were absent (open bars). Sample sizes are given above each bar and probability levels appear above each pair of bars.

1977; Hullberg and Oliver, 1978; Pearcy and Hancock, 1978; Kleppel et al., 1980; Gabriel and Pearcy, 1981; Allen, 1982) do not suggest the observed importance of *Capitella* spp. as prey. None of the studies that examined the food habits of these fishes in unimpacted areas identified *Capitella* spp. as prey. Although Kleppel et al. (1980) found that English sole and Dover sole consumed *Capitella capitata* near sewage outfalls off Los Angeles, the dietary contribution of this prey was less than one individual per fish stomach.

Diel variations of stomach fullness at the study sites were consistent with the presumed feeding chronologies of rex sole, a nocturnal forager, and Dover sole, a diurnal predator (Kravitz et al., 1977; Allen, 1982; Becker, 1984). By contrast, English sole exhibited a feeding chronology opposite to the diurnal predatory behavior described for this species (Allen, 1982; Hogue and Carey, 1982; Becker, 1984). This nocturnal foraging, primarily on *Capitella* spp., allowed English sole at the study sites to continue feeding long after most conspecifics in other areas of Puget Sound had reduced or ceased feeding. Thus, the presence of *Capitella* spp. in the benthos allowed at least one of the target species to alter its presumed feeding chronology.

17.4.2. Implications

The results of this study have several implications in the prediction of the impacts of ocean dumping on demersal fish. Above all, these results demonstrate that substantial errors can be made by basing trophic models solely on prey spectra that are determined in unimpacted areas. For example, neither nonrandom selection of *Capitella* spp. by all three target fishes nor nocturnal predation upon these polychaetes by English sole could have been predicted directly from literature sources.

Failure to consider predation on opportunistic prey would underestimate the food value, and presumably the attractive force, of impacted areas to demersal fish. If these food-rich habitats are contaminated, attraction and retention of fish may accelerate trophic transfer of contaminants. For the dumping of wastes into the ocean, such food-web transfer may peak shortly after disposal, when relative abundances of opportunistic invertebrates are highest, and before the disposed material and its associated contaminants have reached equilibrium with ambient conditions.

Failure to consider predation on opportunists could also underestimate the disease-causing potential of waste material

to demersal fish. For instance, Porter et al. (1984) found that susceptibility to viral infection and potential toxicity of Aroclor 1254 [a mixture of polychlorinated biphenyls (PCB)] increased in mice (*Mus musculus* and *Peromyscus maniculatus*) as individuals became malnourished. In the present study, all three target fishes (especially rex sole) restricted their dietary ranges by preying selectively upon *Capitella* spp. Depending upon the duration and degree of dietary restriction, individuals conceivably could suffer eventual nutritional imbalance that could enhance their susceptibility to disease or to the toxic effects of contaminants.

17.4.3. A Better Approach

Faced with a lack of information on fish feeding in impacted areas, perhaps the best approach to predicting impacts on demersal fish would be similar to that used by Allen (1982). Allen classified the major fish of the southern California shelf into a variety of foraging guilds. This guild classification was based on prey spectra determined in unimpacted areas, known habitats and behaviors of prey, and functional morphologies of predators. Depending upon which guild a species belongs to, the potential impacts of benthic alterations can be predicted. For example, changing the dominant prey from highly motile, surface-active crustaceans (e.g., certain amphipods, crabs, and shrimps) to relatively stationary, partly buried polychaetes would be likely to favor a bottom-living benthivore (i.e., a species that feeds only on benthic prey) more than a midwater pelagobenthivore (i.e., a species that feeds primarily on pelagic prey, but also on benthic prey). Such a change would likely have little or no effect on a schooling pelagivore (i.e., a species that feeds only on pelagic or nektonic prey). Allen considers English sole, Dover sole, and rex sole to be bottom-living benthivores, which coincides with the observed ability of these fishes to prey selectively upon *Capitella* spp. in Puget Sound.

An analysis of foraging guilds cannot conclusively determine how a particular species will respond to altered benthic invertebrate assemblages. For example, fish that are otherwise capable of exploiting certain benthic prey may be repelled from an impacted area by such factors as elevated turbidity, low dissolved oxygen, and chemical constituents of disposed material. Despite this shortcoming, however, the foraging-guild analysis may be a useful approach for identifying which, if any, fish would most likely be attracted to disposal sites in the ocean.

ACKNOWLEDGMENT

This research was taken from a Ph.D. Dissertation submitted to the University of Washington, Seattle. Financial support was provided by the Office of Marine Pollution Assessment of the U.S. National Oceanic and Atmospheric Administration (Contract NA80RAD00050).

REFERENCES

Allen, M. J. 1982. Functional Structure of Soft-Bottom Fish Communities of the Southern California Shelf. Ph.D. Thesis, University of California, San Diego, 577 pp.

Alverson, D. L., A. T. Pruter, and L. L. Ronholt. 1964. A Study of Demersal Fishes and Fisheries of the Northwestern Pacific Ocean. H. R. MacMillan Lectures in Fisheries, Institute of Fisheries, University of British Columbia, Vancouver, 190 pp.

Becker, D. S. 1984. Resource Partitioning by Small-Mouthed Flatfishes in Puget Sound, Washington. Ph.D. Thesis, University of Washington, Seattle, 139 pp.

Boesch, D. 1982. Ecosystem consequences of alterations of benthic community structure and function in the New York Bight region. *In*: Ecological Stress and the New York Bight: Science and Management, G. F. Mayer (Ed.). Estuarine Research Federation, Columbia, South Carolina, pp. 543–568.

Day, D. S., and W. G. Pearcy. 1968. Species associations of benthic fishes on the continental shelf and slope off Oregon. *Journal of the Fisheries Research Board of Canada*, **25**, 2665–2675.

Dexter, R. N., D. E. Anderson, E. A. Quinlan, L. S. Goldstein, R. M. Strickland, S. P. Pavlou, J. R. Clayton, R. M. Kocan, and M. Landolt. 1981. A Summary of Knowledge of Puget Sound Related to Chemical Contaminants. Technical Memorandum OMPA-13, U.S. National Oceanic and Atmospheric Administration, Boulder, Colorado, 435 pp.

Folk, R. L. 1968. Petrology of Sedimentary Rocks. University of Texas, Austin, 170 pp.

Gabriel, W. L., and W. G. Pearcy. 1981. Feeding selectivity of Dover sole, *Microstomus pacificus*, off Oregon. *Fishery Bulletin* (U.S.), **79**, 749–763.

Gerlach, S. A. 1972. Substratum: general introduction. *In*: Marine Ecology, Vol. 1, O. Kinne (Ed.). Wiley-Interscience, New York, pp. 1245–1250.

Grassle, J. F., and J. P. Grassle. 1974. Opportunistic life histories and genetic systems in marine benthic polychaetes. *Journal of Marine Research*, **32**, 253–284.

Hagerman, F. B. 1952. The biology of Dover sole, *Microstomus pacificus* (Lockington). California Department of Fish and Game, *Fishery Bulletin* (U.S.), Special Publication No. 85, 48 pp.

Hart, J. L. 1973. Pacific Fishes of Canada. Fisheries Research Board of Canada, Ottawa, 740 pp.

Hogue, E. W., and A. G. Carey. 1982. Feeding ecology of 0-age flatfishes at a nursery ground on the open Oregon coast. *Fishery Bulletin* (U.S.), **80**, 555–565.

Hulberg, L. W., and J. S. Oliver. 1978. Prey availability and the diets of two co-occurring flatfish. *In*: Fish Food Habits Studies, S. J. Lipovski and C. A. Simenstad (Eds.). Washington Sea Grant, University of Washington, Seattle, pp. 29–36.

Ivlev, V. S. 1961. Experimental Ecology of the Feeding of the Fishes. Yale University Press, New Haven, Connecticut, 302 pp.

Kleppel, G. S., J. Q. Word, and J. Roney. 1980. Demersal fish feeding in Santa Monica Bay and off Palos Verdes. *In*: Coastal Water Research Project Biennial Report 1979–1980, W. Bascom (Ed.). Southern California Coastal Water Research Project, Long Beach, California, pp. 309–318.

Kravitz, M. J., W. G. Pearcy, and M. P. Guin. 1977. Food of five species of co-occurring flatfishes on Oregon's continental shelf. *Fishery Bulletin* (U.S.), **74**, 984–990.

Miller, B. S., B. B. McCain, R. C. Wingert, S. F. Borton, K. V. Pierce, and D. T. Griggs. 1977. Ecological and Disease Studies of Demersal Fishes in Puget Sound near Metro-Operated Sewage Treatment Plants and in the Duwamish River. Technical Report No. FRI-UW-7721, Fisheries Research Institute, University of Washington, Seattle, 164 pp.

Mills, E. L. 1975. Benthic organisms and the structure of marine ecosystems. *Journal of the Fisheries Research Board of Canada*, **32**, 1657–1663.

Moiseev, P. A. 1953. Cod and flounder of the Far Eastern Seas. *Fisheries Research Board of Canada, Translation Series* 119, 576 pp.

Murdoch, W. M., S. Avery, and M. E. B. Smyth. 1975. Switching in predatory fish. *Ecology*, **56**, 1094–1105.

Nilsson, N. A. 1960. Seasonal fluctuations in the food segregation of trout, char, and whitefish in 14 north-Swedish lakes. *Institute of Freshwater Research Drottningholm*, **41**, 185–205.

Oliver, J. S., P. N. Slattery, L. W. Hulberg, and J. W. Nybakken. 1977. Patterns of Succession in Benthic Infaunal Communities Following Dredging and Dredged Material Disposal in Monterey Bay. Technical Report D-77-27, U.S. Army Corps of Engineers, Washington, D.C., 186 pp.

Pearcy, W. G., and D. Hancock. 1978. Feeding habits of Dover sole, *Microstomus pacificus*; rex sole, *Glyptocephalus zachirus*; slender sole, *Lyopsetta exilis*; and Pacific sanddab, *Citharichthys sordidus*, in a region of diverse sediments and bathymetry off Oregon. *Fishery Bulletin* (U.S.), **76**, 641–651.

Pearre, S. 1982. Estimating prey preference by predators: use of various indices, and a proposal of another based on chi square. *Canadian Journal of Fisheries and Aquatic Sciences*, **39**, 914–923.

Pearson, T. H., and R. Rosenberg. 1978. Macrobenthic succession in relation to organic enrichment and pollution of the marine environment. *Oceanography and Marine Biology Annual Review*, **16**, 229–311.

Porter, W. P., R. Hinsdill, A. Fairbrother, L. J. Olson, J. Jaeger, T. Yuill, S. Bisgaard, W. G. Hunter, and K. Nolen. 1984. Toxicant–disease–environment interactions associated with suppression of immune system, growth, and reproduction. *Science*, **224**, 1014–1016.

Pyke, G. H., H. R. Pulliam, and E. L. Charnov. 1977. Optimal foraging: a selective review of theory and tests. *The Quarterly Review of Biology*, **52**, 137–154.

Rhoads, D. C., P. L. McCall, and J. Y. Yingst. 1978. Disturbance and production on the estuarine seafloor. *American Scientist*, **66**, 577–586.

Tetra Tech. 1981. Technical Evaluation of City of Tacoma Central Treatment Plant, Section 301(h): Application for Modification of the Requirements of Secondary Treatment. Prepared for U.S. Environmental Protection Agency, Washington, D.C., 299 pp.

Wingert, R. C., and B. S. Miller. 1979. Distributional Analysis of Nearshore and Demersal Fish Species Groups and Nearshore Fish Habitat Associations in Puget Sound. Technical Report No. FRI-UW-7901, Fisheries Research Institute, University of Washington, Seattle, 110 pp.

Zaret, T. M., and A. S. Rand. 1971. Competition in tropical stream fishes: support for the competitive exclusion principle. *Ecology*, **52**, 336–342.

Chapter 18

Effects of Solid Wood Wastes on Marine Benthic Organisms and Habitats

Michael Waldichuk

Department of Fisheries and Oceans
West Vancouver, British Columbia, Canada

Abstract	193
18.1. Introduction	194
18.2. Physical and Chemical Characteristics of Wood Solids and Their Marine Ecological Effects	194
18.2.1. The Physical and Chemical Nature of Wood	194
18.2.2. Sources and Significance of Wood Solids in Effluents from Pulp and Paper Mills	195
18.2.3. Marine Ecological Effects of Wood Solids	195
18.3. Case Studies of Effects of the Discharge of Wood Solids into Coastal Waters of British Columbia	196
18.3.1. Cousins Inlet	197
18.3.2. Northumberland Channel	199
18.4. Colonization Experiment on Sediments Containing Wood Solids	203
18.4.1. Source of Material	203
18.4.2. Experimental Plots	203
18.4.3. Methods of Analysis	204
18.4.3a. Taxonomic analysis	204
18.4.3b. Physical and chemical analyses	204
18.4.4. Results	204
18.5. Discussion	206
18.6. Conclusions	207
Acknowledgments	207
References	207

ABSTRACT

Dredged materials from the vicinity of operations that process coastal forest products contain high proportions of solid wood wastes. Dredging and dumping into the ocean of wood-rich sediments are known to cause fish kills owing to the release of toxic hydrogen sulfide. Log-holding ponds and other areas covered by solid wood materials, such as bark, chips, and fibers, may be depauperated of benthic organisms. Some of the adverse effects may be caused directly by leaching of toxic substances from the wood. Most of the harm, however, appears to be due to the bacterial decomposition of the wood with the associated decrease in dissolved oxygen and the ultimate release of hydrogen sulfide. The benthic habitat is also modified by the solid wood waste, but the impact depends on the quantity and particle size. Two case studies of fiber deposits from pulp mills in British Columbia (Canada) are presented: (1) a sulfite–kraft–groundwood mill of about 300 metric tons (t) d^{-1} at Ocean Falls that discharged its effluent into the surfacewater of Cousins Inlet from 1912 to 1980; and (2) a full-bleach kraft pulp mill at Harmac, commencing operation in 1950, that discharges its effluent with about 15 t d^{-1} of suspended solids through a submarine outfall and diffuser 1.1 km offshore at a depth of 105 m. During 1983 the Canadian Department of Fisheries and Oceans studied the effect of dredged wood wastes on colonization by benthic invertebrates at a 25-m depth in outer Burrard Inlet, a comparatively clean coastal area in British Columbia. Replicate sediment containers with different wood concentrations (0, 20, 50 and 100%) were deployed from 1 August to 20 October. The largest number of taxa colonized the container with 20% wood waste, and the smallest number was in the 100% treatment. The largest number of individual organisms was present in the container with 100% wood waste, but this was not significantly different from that in the 20% treatment. It was concluded that marine benthic recruitment may be enhanced in sediments containing seasoned wood solids up to concentrations of at least 20%. The effects of other variables (e.g., biodegradation), however, were not examined during the short-term exposure.

18.1. INTRODUCTION

Wood solids have always been regarded as producing undesirable effects in aquatic ecosystems, but there has been little quantitative information on how these effects arise. The effects of effluents, including the wood solids, from the pulp and paper industry have been reviewed by Poole et al. (1978). Divers (McDaniel, 1973) and observers in submersibles (Petrie and Holman, 1983) have noted the frequent absence of bottom species where wood has been deposited from log-sorting activities in log ponds or from sawmill and pulp mill effluents. Concerns have been raised by fisheries management agencies when fish kills result from dredging in areas with wood solids in the sediments, for example, Alberni Harbour (Canada) during the late summer of 1956 (Hourston and Herlinveaux, 1957) and Chemainus Harbour in 1965 (Fisheries and Oceans Canada, personal communication). Problems arising from log storage and rafting in coastal waters have been identified by numerous task forces working on issues connected with multiple use of estuaries. For example, the Pacific Northwest Pollution Control Council (1971) noted that bark debris and soluble organic materials (leachates) from log-handling operations are the two major substances affecting water quality. More details on the effects of log rafting and dumping in the marine environment were given by Pease (1973).

When the Ocean Dumping Control Act was promulgated in Canada in 1975, just prior to the implementation of the Convention on the Prevention of Marine Pollution by Dumping of Wastes and Other Matter (London Dumping Convention), to which Canada is a Contracting Party, it was necessary to examine in more detail the effects of substances being dumped into the sea. Because a high proportion of the materials dumped into the sea in Canada is dredged material, and much of the dredging takes place in the vicinity of sawmills

and pulp mills, it was quite obvious that some dredged materials destined for ocean dumping would be rich in wood waste. Studies were initiated, therefore, to examine the effects of these materials on the marine environment. The ecological effects of the dumping of wood-rich dredged material in Alberni Inlet, British Columbia, have been reported by Levings et al. (1985). The effects of this dumping on the organic matter in seawater and surficial sediment of the inlet were also investigated by Iseki et al. (1984).

The purposes of this chapter are to review the general ecological effects of wood solids in the marine environment, to examine problems of wood solids discharged into the sea from pulp and paper mills by using two case studies on the coast of British Columbia, and to describe the results of a short-term experiment on colonization of marine sediment with different concentrations of seasoned wood fibers.

18.2. PHYSICAL AND CHEMICAL CHARACTERISTICS OF WOOD SOLIDS AND THEIR MARINE ECOLOGICAL EFFECTS

18.2.1. The Physical and Chemical Nature of Wood

A tree trunk used for lumber and pulp and paper manufacture consists of an outer covering, or bark, and the interior wood, which is made up of cellulose fibers held together by assorted binding substances of which the major constituent is lignin. The bark is perhaps the most refractory part of a tree, especially in conifers. The bark protects the tree against severe weather conditions, sunlight, desiccation, bacteria, fungi, insects, grazing animals, and, in some cases (e.g., Douglas fir, *Pseudotsuga menziesii*), against fire. The bark may contain leachable natural substances that protect the tree against bacteria, fungi, insects, and grazing animals. Clearly, the bark from most conifers does not decompose rapidly either in the atmosphere or in the aquatic environment and is extremely persistent when deposited into the sea.

The cellulose fibers of a tree are also quite refractory, but not to the same degree as is the bark. Wood fibers from Engleman spruce (*Picea englemanni*) and Douglas fir (*Pseudotsuga menziesii*) range from 3 to 4 mm in length and from

25 to 45 μm in diameter. When the wood is broken down to individual fibers by chemical pulping, the surface area-to-volume ratio increases. Such a large surface area allows a great deal of exposure for attack by bacteria. Moreover, the process of pulping can fracture the outer sheath, of 3–3.5 μm in thickness, which facilitates attack by bacteria on the fiber. Wood fibers are comparatively degradable over a period of time and contribute to the unfavorable long-term effects in coastal waters receiving pulp and paper mill effluents.

A number of studies have been done to investigate the rate of degradation of cellulose in water (Hofsten and Edberg, 1972; Poole et al., 1977; Stanley et al., 1978; Vance, 1978; Vance et al., 1979). For samples of bleached sulfite fiber held in nylon bags at 0.5 m below the surface of a sewage-polluted river, where the temperature varied from 16 to 1°C and the pH was 7.4, there was 20% degradation after 50 d and 70% after 100 d (Hofsten and Edberg, 1972). The same investigators held this fiber in nylon bags at a 1-m depth in the final settling tank after activated sludge treatment in a sewage treatment plant, where the temperature was maintained at 17–10°C and the pH at 7.8, and obtained 88% degradation in 50 d and 98% in 78 d. There was no degradation after 50 d and only 5% after 100 d for the same type of fiber held 3.0 m below the surface of an unpolluted Baltic inlet, with a temperature range of 14–1°C and a pH range of 7.4–8.6 (Hofsten and Edberg, 1972). When unbleached sulfite fiber in nylon bags was placed in the top 5 cm of unpolluted sediment and held at a temperature of 16°C and a pH of 7.1 in a laboratory model ecosystem, 27.7% of the fiber was degraded in 31 d (Poole et al., 1977). But when the same type of fiber was placed in the top 5 cm of anoxic sediment with high fiber content and held at a temperature of 16°C and a pH of 6.7, only 8.5% of the fiber was degraded after 31 d (Poole et al., 1977). The maximum degradation rates for pulp fibers occur in the surface layers of sediment and depend on various environmental factors (Poole et al., 1978). Among the environmental factors that influence the rate of degradation of fibers both in water and in sediment, the availability of nutrients is one of the most important.

The fiber-binding materials in the wood are the least refractory, especially when subjected to heat, pressure, and chemicals. The chemical pulping process removes the lignin, hemicelluloses, and other binding constituents from the fibers. These solubilized materials, along with the digestion chemicals, have been of greatest concern with respect to the short-term biological effects of pulpmill effluents.

18.2.2. Sources and Significance of Wood Solids in Effluents from Pulp and Paper Mills

The volume of raw effluent varies considerably with the type of product generated from pulp and paper processes (Edde, 1984). Most processes result in an effluent of ~50,000–250,000 liter per ton of finished product. These effluents generally contain 10–40 kg of suspended solids per ton of finished product. The suspended solids are always over 50%, and usually over 90%, combustible (Edde, 1984).

In nearly all pulp and paper mills nowadays, an effort is made to settle out the suspended solids in primary holding ponds. The reduction in suspended solids from a 5-d sedimentation for effluents from different types of pulp and paper mills varies according to the type of operation and product produced. It ranges from 68% for deinking mills to 81% for kraft mills and 93% for newsprint mills (Edde, 1984). These data represent settling of solids in a freshwater basin; it can be expected that in seawater the settling efficiency would be even greater because of the ionic effect of dissolved salts. Part of the objective of holding pulp and paper mill effluents in lagoons is to reduce the biochemical oxygen demand (BOD). While the short-term (5-d) BOD is largely due to the dissolved organic constituents in effluents, the long-term (20 d or more) BOD can be attributed also to the more slowly decomposing constituents, such as fibers. Removal of solids that do settle from a kraft pulp mill effluent reduces the BOD only slightly over 20%, but the reduction for a fine paper mill is 60%, and for a tissue mill, where fiber loss can be particularly high, it is over 90% (Edde, 1984).

18.2.3. Marine Ecological Effects of Wood Solids

The marine ecological effects of solid wood wastes are shown schematically in a block diagram in Fig. 18.1. The early effects from the disposal of wood solids appear in the water column, where there may be an impact on plankton and fish. The long-term effects occur largely in the sediment, where the substrate is modified and bacterial action may lead to anoxic conditions, possible production of hydrogen sulfide, and lowered pH and Eh (redox potential). The habitat becomes definitely unsuitable for both infauna and epifauna if a large amount of particulate wood waste (e.g., fibers) has been deposited and bacterially decomposed.

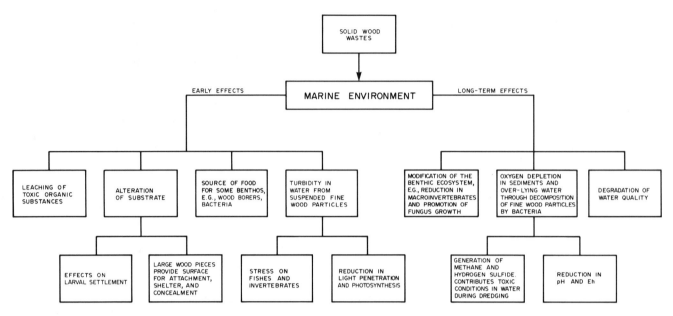

Figure 18.1. Schematic block diagram showing the ecological effects of solid wood waste in the marine environment.

The ecological impact of solid wood waste in the marine environment is related to the wood particle size, as schematically shown in Fig. 18.2. The so-called "white water" from paper machines in pulp and paper mills is essentially a colloidal suspension of tiny (≤ 1μm in diameter) fiber particles. Once this type of effluent reaches seawater, a certain amount of agglomeration takes place; however, some of the finer colloidal particles remain suspended in the water and give it an opalescent turbidity. Larger aggregates of fiber fragments settle from the seawater and can create thick fiber mats, depending on the rate of fiber deposition. They alter the substrate and render it unsuitable for certain sensitive organisms, although fiber-rich substrate may be attractive at least initially for some opportunistic species (Pearson and Rosenberg, 1978). These fiber mats undergo bacteriological decomposition, deplete the oxygen in both the sediments and overlying water, and may generate gases, including methane and hydrogen sulfide (Werner, 1968). At this stage, all macro- and microfauna are eliminated, and only anaerobic bacteria can survive. The gases generated sometimes lift the fiber mats to the sea surface and lead to emergence of gas bubbles, which create an undesirable aesthetic problem in coastal sawmill and pulp mill areas.

At the other end of the size spectrum of wood solids are the larger pieces of bark and wood, including large wood fragments, blocks of wood, and sunken logs (deadheads). This material can serve as a substrate for such invertebrates as sea anemones, snails, and various wood borers. Fish may utilize it for shelter, and, following colonization by various invertebrates, the colonizers may serve as a source of food. Because of the relatively small surface area-to-volume ratio, with the attack of bacteria being confined to the surfaces of these large pieces of wood, the impact on the aquatic ecosystem is considerably less than that from an equivalent amount of fiber. The depauperate fauna usually found in log-booming areas is generally due to gross modification of substrate by bark and wood fragments (McDaniel, 1973), and possibly also due to leaching of toxic substances from these materials. Some log-booming areas that are well flushed by river currents and tidal action, such as those found in the Fraser River estuary, however, are not seriously detrimental to juvenile salmon (Levy et al., 1982).

18.3. CASE STUDIES OF EFFECTS OF THE DISCHARGE OF WOOD SOLIDS INTO COASTAL WATERS OF BRITISH COLUMBIA

British Columbia has 25 pulp and paper mills, 11 of which are on the coast (Waldichuk, 1983). Some of these mills have created ecological problems over the course of time, most of

COLLOIDAL
SUSPENSION
OF FINE PARTICLES.
SETTLED PARTICLES
RAPIDLY DECOMPOSED
BY BACTERIA.
DEPENDING ON
CONCENTRATION OF
WOOD PARTICLES IN
SEDIMENTS, CONDITIONS
MAY BE TOXIC DUE TO
HYDROGEN SULFIDE
FOR INFAUNA.

FIBER-BED
DEPOSITION.
BACTERIOLOGICAL
DECOMPOSITION
GENERATES
METHANE AND
TOXIC HYDROGEN
SULFIDE. EPIFAUNA
SPARSE OR ABSENT.
INFAUNA ABSENT.

SUBSTRATE
ALTERATION WITH
BARK, WOOD CHIPS,
AND OTHER WOOD
DEBRIS. REDUCED
CONDITIONS IN
SEDIMENTS.
MACROINVERTEBRATES
REDUCED IN NUMBERS,
BUT MEIOFAUNA MAY
BE ABUNDANT.

LARGE PIECES
OF WOOD SERVE
AS SURFACES FOR
SETTLEMENT OF
LARVAE, AND AS
SHELTER AND
CONCEALMENT
OF FISH AND
INVERTEBRATES.
ENHANCEMENT OF
FISH AND INVERTE-
BRATE HABITATS
MAY OCCUR.

| 0.001 | 0.01 | 0.1 | 1.0 | 10.0 | 100 | 1,000 | 10,000 |

WOOD PARTICLE SIZE - MILLIMETERS

Figure 18.2. The general relationship of the ecological impact in the marine environment of solid wood waste to particle size of the wood.

which could be attributed to low dissolved oxygen (DO) in the receiving waters (Waldichuk, 1962). Oceanographic observations were made from 1954 to 1969 in waters receiving effluents from most coastal British Columbia pulp mills (e.g., Waldichuk et al., 1968a,b). In water adjacent to all coastal pulp mills, suspended solids were collected monthly during 1963–1965 (Werner, 1965), and gases in fiber beds were collected monthly during 1964–1966 (Werner, 1968). Two pulp mill areas in the province have been chosen as case studies to illustrate how fiber deposits have created environmental problems. One of them which is now closed, at Ocean Falls, had been recognized for a long time as a heavy polluter, introducing wood-pulp fibers into the head of Cousins Inlet. The second pulp mill area, Harmac, near Nanaimo, was selected because studies have been conducted there for a long time (Waldichuk, 1965), and, although the mill has been in operation since 1950, the thick fiber bed in Northumberland Channel is a comparatively recent phenomenon, noted since a deep outfall and diffuser were installed in 1976.

18.3.1. Cousins Inlet

The pulp mill at Ocean Falls, located at the head of Cousins Inlet, (Fig. 18.3) commenced operation in 1912 as a sulfite and newsprint mill for modest production (perhaps 200 t d⁻¹). Subsequently, the mill increased production and diversified with kraft pulp and speciality papers. The sulfite and kraft mills ceased production in 1967. The groundwood operation for newsprint production continued until 1980. The mill discharged its effluent into the tailrace from the hydroelectric plant that produced electrical power from Link River, which drains Link Lake into Cousins Inlet.

The river water flows out over the surface of Cousins Inlet, creating a vertically stratified system in both salinity and density (Fig. 18.4). At the time the survey was made, 19–21 September 1961, the surfacewater was still quite warm, resulting also in vertical temperature stratification. Cousins Inlet does not have a significant threshold sill at its entrance

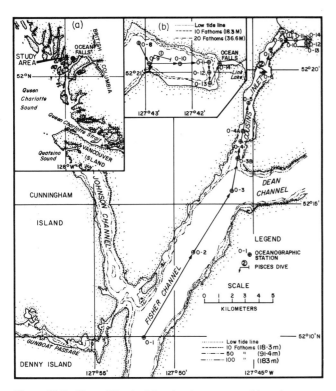

Figure 18.3. Chart of Cousins Inlet, showing oceanographic stations occupied during a survey, 19–21 September 1961, and transects of submersible dives, 20 October 1976 (Inset B).

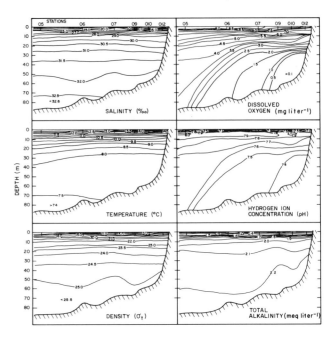

Figure 18.4. Longitudinal sections of Cousins Inlet, giving the vertical distributions of both the conservative properties (salinity, temperature, and density) and non-conservative properties (dissolved oxygen, pH, and alkalinity) during September 1961.

from Fisher Channel, so that considerable flushing of the deep water in Cousins Inlet occurs. The vertical DO distribution, with a pocket of low DO concentration in the bottom 30 m at the head of the inlet, shown in the upper right-hand panel of Fig. 18.4, was not likely a natural phenomenon in this inlet but was undoubtedly caused by the decomposition of fibers deposited on the bottom.

Bottom samples were difficult to obtain with a Dietz-LaFond clamshell-type grab in areas where the fibers were unconsolidated because the grab closes by a pressure-activated tripping arm that must hit solid bottom to trip and close the grab. When samples were obtained in the upper end of Cousins Inlet (stations 0-8 and 0-13), they exhibited high concentrations of hydrogen sulfide, judging by the extremely strong odor and by the blackening of metallic devices such as a nickel-plated current meter. There was no evidence of bottom-dwelling organisms living for about 2 km down the inlet.

Surveys conducted in Cousins Inlet during the 1970s were designed to examine benthic recolonization of the inlet, following anticipated closure of the 280-t d^{-1} groundwood mill in November 1972 (Fournier and Levings, 1982). However, the provincial government purchased the mill from private interests in April 1973 and continued to operate it until June 1980, when it was permanently closed. Four benthic sampling surveys were completed during the period July 1972–November 1975 with various bottom grabs (Van Veen, Shipek, Peterson, and Smith-McIntyre) (Fournier and Levings, 1982). The station numbers and locations are shown in Fig. 18.3. It is noteworthy that no organisms were found at stations 0-9 to 0-14, except for station 0-12 on 20 July 1972 and 3 December 1972, when there were fewer than five identifiable polychaete species, and station 0-9 on 3 December 1972, when sampling appears to have been off-station close to shore.

The number of polychaete species per station increased in each of the surveys with distance from the Ocean Falls pulp mill (Fig. 18.5). There is also some indication of increasing numbers of polychaete species from 1972 to 1974. An underwater survey conducted on 20 October 1976 with the submer-

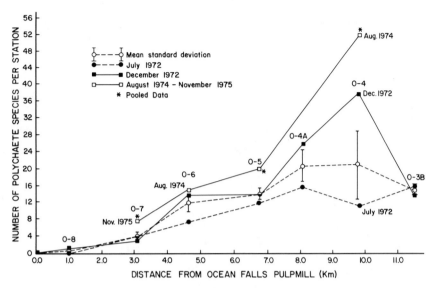

Figure 18.5. Numbers of polychaete species found at stations (see Fig. 18.6 for locations) in Cousins Inlet, during four surveys, conducted from July 1972 to November 1975 (from Fournier and Levings, 1982).

sible *Pisces IV* showed the continuing presence of the fiber bed and an opalescence in the water above it somewhat obscuring visibility.

A benthic survey, made by using a Smith-McIntyre grab, was conducted in Cousins Inlet again during 1–2 December 1981 (McGreer, 1984). Single samples were collected at each sampling location, and the abundance for all benthic invertebrate samples was expressed as number per 3-liter sample. Numbers of taxa were still low at sampling sites within 3 km of the former pulp mill outfall, as compared to sites further along the inlet. Polychaete worms continued to dominate the samples. The total abundance of individuals per sample was lowest (10) at the site sampled closest to the mill (~1 km from the former outfall). Another site nearby yielded 128 individuals, but 94 of these were nemertean worms. The total abundance of individuals per sample at sites ranging from 3 to 8 km from the Ocean Falls mill was variable, ranging from about 30 to 120. The organic content (total volatile residue) of the sediments ranged from 3.3% to 67%, and the metal concentrations in $\mu g\ g^{-1}$ were as follows: Cd, <0.3–8.0; Cr, 11–41; Cu, 35–157; Hg, 0.2–0.9; Mn, 66–619; Ni, 11–29; Pb, 9–71; and Zn, 69–764. Iron ranged in concentration from 0.7% to 3.3% (McGreer, 1984). The ranges of concentrations of some metals, for example, Zn and Cu, were unusually large, and the higher values in the ranges were abnormally high. The high Zn concentrations may have arisen from the use of zinc dithionite (ZnS_2O_4) as a brightening agent for

newsprint pulp. High Cd concentrations, as noted for the higher end of the range here, are typical of pulp mill areas; they pose problems for ocean disposal of dredged material under regulations of the Ocean Dumping Control Act when they exceed 0.6 $\mu g\ g^{-1}$ in the solid phase. Fournier and Levings (1982) suggested that the potential for benthic recolonization of the upper end of Cousins Inlet is poor, mainly as a result of low natural sedimentation; however, surveys have not been continued to follow the rate of recolonization.

18.3.2. Northumberland Channel

The Harmac full-bleach kraft pulp mill (Fig. 18.6) has been in operation since 1950, discharging its effluent into Northumberland Channel. The mill originally had a production of 500 t d^{-1} but expanded in 1963 to its present 1200 t d^{-1}. Effluent discharge is 1.61 × 10^5 liters min^{-1}. Loss of suspended solids averages 12.8 kg t^{-1} of pulp produced, or about 15 t daily. Originally, the mill discharged all of its effluents from the shore at the high-tide level. In January 1976, a submarine outfall and diffuser were installed to carry the effluent 1140 m offshore to a depth of 105 m (Fig. 18.6).

A series of oceanographic surveys, including observations of the currents, were conducted in Northumberland Channel from 1955 to 1965 (Waldichuk et al., 1968b). The surface current in Northumberland Channel flows almost continu-

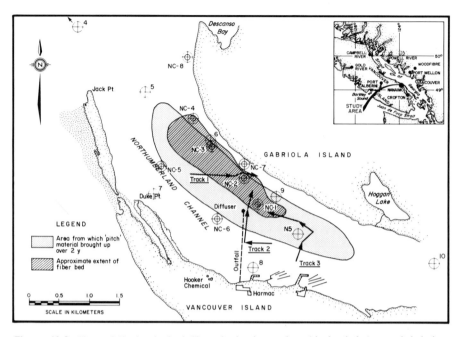

Figure 18.6. Chart of Northumberland Channel, showing stations (single circles) occupied during oceanographic surveys in July 1957 and July 1962, transects of submersible dives during 25–26 February 1981, stations (two concentric circles) for benthos during 9 October 1981, approximate distribution of "pitch" material brought up by fishermen during 1979–1980, and the approximate extent of the fiber bed observed from a submersible in February 1981.

ously on all stages of the tide to the southeast, toward Dodd Narrows; however, there is a net subsurface flow at a depth between 2 m and 10 m in the opposite direction to the northwest (Fig. 18.7). From observations of the currents over a 25-h period, the net current at depths between 15 and 30 m is also to the southeast. Northumberland Channel is vertically stratified in salinity the year round, and also in temperature during the summer, with the consequent stratification in density (Fig. 18.8). Because there is no direct inflow of a large volume of freshwater, however, the salinity and density stratifications are not as great in Northumberland Channel as in Cousins Inlet. Judging by the DO concentration in the deep water of Northumberland Channel, which generally exceeded 5.5 mg liter^{-1} in July 1962 (Fig. 18.9), the water in the channel below a 50-m depth undergoes regular renewal at least annually, corresponding to that in the Strait of Georgia (Waldichuk, 1957). The water in the upper 20 m is replaced much more frequently, about once per week (Waldichuk, 1965).

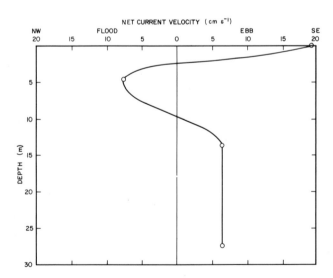

Figure 18.7. Net currents at different depths at station N-5 in Northumberland Channel (see Fig. 18.6 for location) during a 25-h period, 8–9 July 1957.

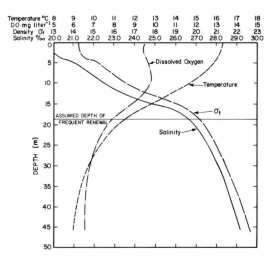

Figure 18.8. Profiles of salinity, temperature, density (σ_t), and dissolved oxygen at station N-5 in Northumberland Channel (see Fig. 18.6 for location), occupied on 6 July 1957.

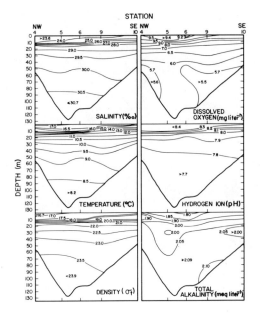

Figure 18.9. Distribution of properties in a vertical section along Northumberland Channel during the oceanographic survey of 17 July 1962.

During the 2-y period 1979–80, fishermen aboard shrimp trawlers reported finding clumps of material of unusual appearance over a large area of Northumberland Channel, with clumps ranging in size from 5 to 100 cm in diameter. The material was described as having a strong odor of hydrogen

sulfide and consisting of aggregates of wood debris, wood fibers, shell, and sand. In laboratory bioassays, these clumps appeared to be quite toxic to rainbow trout (*Salmo gairdneri*), with an LT_{50} (time to 50% mortality) of 20–24 h at 4.2% of unextracted sample (Petrie and Holman, 1983).

In order to investigate this material, three submersible dives were conducted with *Pisces IV* during 25–26 February 1981 (Petrie and Holman, 1983). While the materials reported by shrimp fishermen were not observed, an extensive fiber bed was noted at a depth of 100 m along the northeastern side of Northumberland Channel (Fig. 18.6). This mat was a considerable distance (70 m) from the Harmac pulp mill outfall, and, at first, it was difficult to associate the fiber bed with the pulp mill. The fiber accumulation was at least 1 m thick and appeared to be in the form of a very fluid slurry (Fig. 18.10) that behaved like a dense liquid, undulating at the surface when disturbed. Beneath the fiber bed were black reducing sediments. There were 20- to 50-cm diameter patches of fungus-like, whitish material on the fiber slurry, which were extremely difficult to sample from the submersible. No fish or benthic organisms were found in the fiber slurry, but shrimps, crabs, and ratfish (*Hydrolagus colliei*) were sometimes found swimming above the fiber-bed surface (Fig. 18.10). Deadheads and rocks protruding through the surface of the fiber bed provided a suitable substrate for attachment of sea anemones.

In the vicinity of the outfall at ~90-m depth, currents were ~25 cm s^{-1} setting to the southeast; they probably contributed to the scouring found under the outfall pipe. Near-bottom currents probably transported the fibers away from the outfall to the northeastern side of Northumberland Channel, where conditions were more quiescent and more suitable for settling the fibers. The aggregates reported by fishermen were probably formed by the "snowballing effect" on sticky bottom materials of shrimp trawls being dragged through the fiber bed (Petrie and Holman, 1983).

Bottom samples were taken in Northumberland Channel during 9 October 1981 for benthos enumeration (McGreer, 1984). Single samples were taken with a Smith-McIntyre grab at stations (two concentric circles) shown in Fig. 18.6. At the stations (NC-1) nearest the outfall (0.3 km), a total of 9 individual invertebrates and 7 taxa were identified. The highest total number of taxa (20) and individuals (64) were found at a sampling site (NC-6) 0.5 km from the pulp mill outfall. Then there was a sharp decrease in the number of taxa at all sites (NC-2, NC-7) at a distance from 0.5 to 1.0 km, followed by a second peak at stations NC-3 and NC-5 between 1.0 and 1.5 km from the outfall. The number of organisms per indi-

Figure 18.10. Photograph of the fiber bed in Northumberland Channel, with a fish swimming above it, observed from the submersible, *Pisces IV*, on 25 February 1981.

vidual sample (3–64) at all sites was one of the lowest reported for any British Columbia coastal pulpmill area. It has been suggested that the impoverished fauna might be due either to interaction of organic enrichment and effluent or to sediment toxicity (McGreer, 1984). The organic content (total volatile residue) of the sediments ranged from 0.8% to 4.7%, while the range of metal concentrations in $\mu g\ g^{-1}$ was Cd, <0.3–2.3; Cr, 35–53; Cu, 43–70; Hg, 0.2–0.4; Mn, 231–

394; Ni, 19–28; Pb, 7–26; and Zn, 49–96. Iron in the sediments ranged from 3.2% to 4.2% (McGreer, 1984). Except for Cd, which tended to be high at the upper end of its range, the metal concentrations did not appear to be unusual for coastal sediments.

Clearly, Northumberland Channel has been degraded by solid wood wastes as a benthic habitat for fish and invertebrates. It was at one time an area with a modest shrimp resource, and unfortunately, the deposition of wood fibers has likely rendered it unsuitable as a shrimp habitat. How much of the fiber on the bottom in Northumberland Channel was deposited prior to the installation of the deep outfall is uncertain, but its presence has come to light since the installation, and there seems to be little doubt that the problem has been exacerbated by the present outfall. The original discharge of pulp mill effluent at the surface, even though it was aesthetically offensive at times, with deep discoloration of surfacewater and occasional foam releases, allowed the surface currents to transport away and disperse rapidly the effluent and the solid particles contained in the effluent. The particulate matter in the discharge from the present deep outfall may be essentially trapped in the deep, quiescent water of the channel. This was obviously not foreseen by either the pulp mill company or the various government agencies responsible for reviewing and approving plans for disposal of effluent. The main concerns at the time of outfall design were the toxicity and the BOD of the liquid portion of the effluent.

18.4. COLONIZATION EXPERIMENT ON SEDIMENTS CONTAINING WOOD SOLIDS

Because of concerns regarding the impact of wood-rich dredged material on the marine benthic ecosystem, in connection with the administration of the Ocean Dumping Control Act, the Canadian Department of Fisheries and Oceans contracted a study to investigate the effects of different concentrations of solid wood materials on the colonization of sediment by benthic organisms. This was necessarily a short-term study, exposing the sediment containing different concentrations of wood fibers to settlement of macroinvertebrate larvae during an 11-week period in late summer and early autumn. Obviously, the long-term effects of wood-rich sediment could not be observed in the experimental design used, particularly with the relatively brief exposure allowed for the sediment. The experiment is summarized here; more detail is given by Kathman et al. (1984).

18.4.1. Source of Material

Solid wood wastes, typical of those deposited in the vicinity of coastal pulp mills in British Columbia, were collected from a loading dock area in the intertidal zone near the kraft pulp mill at Port Mellon on Howe Sound (Fig. 18.6 inset). This material was nearly pure wood fiber and small wood chips that had been leached and seasoned during the time that they had lain on the bottom. The species and their proportions represented in the fibrous material are unknown, but Douglas fir (*Pseudotsuga menziesii*), western hemlock (*Tsuga heterophylla*) and western red cedar (*Thuja plicata*) probably accounted for nearly all of the material. Marine sediment was procured by divers at a depth of 15–20 m in outer Burrard Inlet near the city of Vancouver (Fig. 18.6 inset). This sediment is comparatively clean, except for sedimentation from the Fraser River water that penetrates the area under certain tidal and wind conditions. The sediment was frozen at $-20°C$ for several days to kill existing fauna, then thawed, homogenized, and mixed with the wood waste in volumetrically determined proportions (v/v) of 0, 20, 50, or 100% wood waste.

18.4.2. Experimental Plots

The four different concentrations of wood waste–sediment mixture were placed in separate polyethylene sampling trays (30 cm × 30 cm × 10 cm) and frozen. Duplicate trays were prepared at each concentration. Each tray was bolted with plastic screws to an individual 60-cm × 60-cm plexiglass sheet as a base. A plastic cover was fitted to each tray, and the contents, still frozen, were lowered to the sea bottom by scuba divers. The base with the attached tray was anchored to the bottom at a ~25-m depth in outer Burrard Inlet, near the location where the sediment was procured for mixing in the wood fibers.

The trays were left in position for 11 weeks from 1 August to 20 October 1983. They were recovered by divers, and with each tray securely covered by a lid, brought to the surface, and transported to the laboratory within 2 h. Specially constructed divider grids with 16 compartments, each 7.5 cm × 7.5 cm, were inserted into each tray in the laboratory. To obviate possible edge effects that may have occurred in the outer subsections, only the four middle subsections were individually removed to provide a total of 8 subsamples from duplicate trays for each wood-waste concentration. Each subsample was preserved with 7–10% formalin in a labeled plastic bag and set aside for taxonomic analysis. The remaining sediment from one tray of each concentration of wood waste was used for physical and chemical analyses.

18.4.3. Methods of Analyses

18.4.3a. Taxonomic analysis

Each sample was washed in a 0.5-mm mesh sieve to remove excess formalin and fine sediment. The residue remaining on the sieve was placed in a plastic container, and enough water was added to just cover all material. Small aliquots of sample were examined microscopically in a gridded petri dish. All benthic invertebrates were enumerated by major taxonomic categories, generally class or order, and placed in 60% isopropanol. The process was continued until all organisms in the sample had been examined and enumerated, except when the sample was excessively large, in which case the sample was volumetrically divided into two portions: one for benthic invertebrate sorting and one for archiving. All organisms were identified to the lowest possible taxonomic level, consistent with the available literature.

18.4.3b. Physical and chemical analyses

Sediment samples from each concentration of wood waste were analyzed for particle size, total nitrogen, and total organic carbon. Particle-size analysis was conducted by the pipette method (Walton, 1978). Total nitrogen was determined colorimetrically on a sulfuric acid digest by using a modified micro-Kjeldahl procedure (McKeague, 1978). The Wakley-Black wet oxidation method was used for total organic carbon determination (McKeague, 1978). Sample analyses were generally done in duplicate.

18.4.4. Results

It was assumed that homogeneous invasion and distribution by invertebrates occurred within each tray and that treatment of the subsamples could be validly carried out as eight replicates for each concentration of wood waste. One of the two trays with 100% wood waste was lost, presumably by current action, so that only four replicates were available for this concentration.

The detailed statistical analyses of the data have been reported by Kathman et al. (1984). Only highlights of the results are given here. Three data matrices (M1, M2, and M3) were used for analyses. The original data matrix was M1 (28 samples × 81 taxa). It was visually inspected for rare or

incidental taxa. Deletion of taxa with recorded abundances of one or less in ~95% (26 of 28 samples) of the treatment samples (first edit) resulted in matrix M2. Deletion of taxa with recorded abundances of two or less in ~95% of the treatment samples (second edit) resulted in matrix M3.

As shown in Fig. 18.11, the total and mean number of taxa were significantly higher in the samples with 20% wood concentration than in the other concentrations. The total number of organisms was similar (i.e., not significantly different) in all treatments (Fig. 18.12). Significantly large variations occurred, however, for most of the major taxonomic groups, especially polychaetes and bivalve mollusks. The fewest species of polychaetes occurred in the samples with 100% wood fiber, but the number of individuals was nearly twice as high in the 100% wood fiber as that in the sample with next greatest abundance of polychaetes. This was nearly entirely due to large numbers of *Capitella capitata* and *Armandia brevis*, which are characteristic of organically polluted areas. The same pattern was followed with bivalves. A significant drop in diversity was noted in the 100% wood-

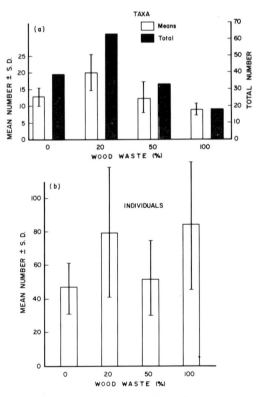

Figure 18.11. Numbers of taxa and individuals in original data matrix M1 (28 samples × 81 taxa).

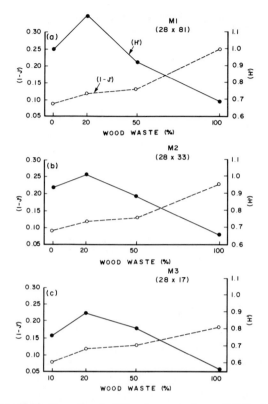

Figure 18.12. Mean diversity (H') and mean dominance (I-J') for the three data matrices M1, M2, and M3 (see text for explanation), analyzed for the four concentrations of wood fiber.

fiber concentration, compared to that for the 20% concentration, but a high number of individuals occurred, comparable to that found in the other concentrations of wood fiber. *Bankia setacea*, a wood borer, was highly dominant among the bivalves in the 100% wood fiber.

The Shannon-Weaver diversity index (H') and dominance (I-J') were calculated for the three data matrices M1, M2, and M3 for each of the four concentrations of wood fiber (Fig. 18.12). Species richness was moderate at 0% wood fiber, highest at 20%, and had a dramatic decline at 100% wood fiber. Diversity and evenness were moderate at 0 and 50% wood fiber, highest at 20%, and by far the lowest at 100%. Dominance, which is the reciprocal of evenness, suggests that there were no particular species dominant at 0, 20, and 50% wood-fiber concentrations and that only a few species represented the majority of individuals in the 100% wood-fiber concentrations.

Cluster analyses (Ward, 1963) were carried out on the data and showed that by species (or *R*-type) for the M3 data matrix, three main groups of species were differentiated (Fig. 18.13). Group A species were associated with small amounts of wood fiber, and group B species were sensitive to high concentrations of wood fiber. The one polychaete and four bivalves composing this group occurred in high abundance at 0 and 20% wood fiber, decreased at 50%, and were virtually absent at 100% wood fiber, with only the bivalve *Mysella*

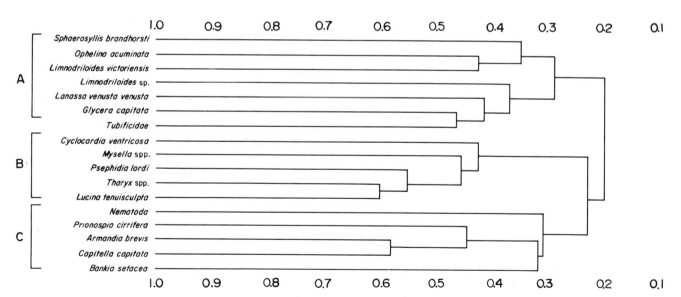

Figure 18.13. Species groupings from cluster analysis derived from the M3 (second edit) data matrix.

compressa being found there. Group C species favored wood-rich sediments. This group consisted of nematodes, three polychaete taxa, and the shipworm *Bankia setacea*. All species of this group increased substantially in numbers from the 0% to the 100% wood-fiber concentrations (Fig. 18.14). The large number of nematodes in the 20% wood-fiber samples contributed to the high number of individuals for this concentration in Group C.

The sediment samples with different concentrations of wood fiber were analyzed for particle size, nitrogen, and organic carbon (Table 18.1). Particle-size analysis, as described by Walton (1978), requires oxidation of the organic matter so that the organic components of the wood waste would have little or no effect on the results of particle-size analyses of samples. There was a general increase in the percentage of sand (0.063–2 mm) and a decrease in silt (0.004–0.063 mm) and clay (<0.004 mm) with an increase in wood fiber. Total nitrogen decreased with increasing concentration of wood fiber, and total carbon generally increased with the amount of wood fiber, although there was some inconsistency at the 50% wood-fiber concentration. Duplicate analyses were in agreement, but error could have arisen through faulty sampling. A correlation matrix incorporating the foregoing physical and chemical variables indicated that they did not contribute significantly to the distribution of

Table 18.1. Substrate Particle Size, Total Nitrogen, and Total Organic Carbon in Each Concentration of Wood Waste

Parameter	Concentration of Wood Waste			
	0%	20%	50%	100%
Particle size				
Sand (0.063–2 mm)	30.8	58.7	68.5	
Silt (0.004–0.063 mm)	35.3	18.7	13.4	
Clay (<0.004 mm)	33.9	22.6	16.1	
Total Nitrogen	0.14	0.06	0.04	0.02
Total Organic Carbon	4.21	7.58	6.70	46.20

species among the trays of sediment with different concentrations of wood waste.

18.5. DISCUSSION

The results of field observations in marine areas receiving solid wood waste from industries that process forest products clearly show adverse effects on the flora and fauna. Depending on the nature of solid wood-waste input and on the characteristics of the receiving water, the ecological effects can range from those that are hardly noticeable to total elimination of benthic flora and fauna. The effects of accumulation of fibers appear to be the most severe. This is largely related to adverse alteration of benthic habitat and decomposition of the fibers by bacteria, yielding noxious by-products (e.g., toxic hydrogen sulfide). These unfavorable effects do not become evident soon after solid wood-waste disposal is initiated, but rather appear in the long term after a few years of wood-waste input.

The short-term experiment described in this chapter on the effect of seasoned wood fibers and chips on colonization of sediments by invertebrates takes into account only the impact of the wood cellulose. There was little effect of leaching of toxic constituents present in fresh wood because the fibers originated from the adjacent pulp mill and had already been submerged for a long time. Most, if not all, of the soluble organic constituents had likely been either removed by the chemical pulping process or leached following disposal. The fibers in the sediments of the experimental containers were probably not exposed long enough, or the conditions were not quite right, for the effects of decomposing bacteria to be evident. Hence, it appears that the main effect of the fibers was alteration of the substrate and provision of a specialized

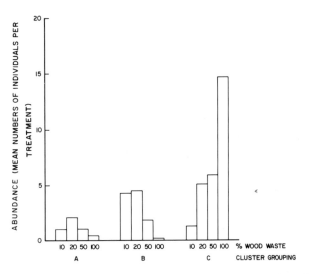

Figure 18.14. Mean number of individuals in different concentrations of wood waste for each cluster analysis species grouping. Data acquired from cluster analysis treatment groupings derived from M3 (second edit) data matrix.

substrate for opportunistic burrowing marine organisms (e.g., *Capitella capitata*) and such wood-boring organisms as *Bankia setacea*. From that point of view, wood waste does not appear to be too serious as a contaminant in the marine environment. In fact, one might conclude that benthic productivity, in terms of numbers of taxa and individuals, can be substantially enhanced, at least in the short term, with addition of wood fibers up to a concentration of 20%; however, the conditions set up in the experiment are seldom found in nature. The long-term effects of a continuing operation in which solid wood wastes are discharged into the marine environment cannot be simulated in a short-term experiment.

18.6. CONCLUSIONS

1. Solid wood wastes have an ecological impact in the marine environment, and this impact varies depending on the types and amount of wood solids discharged and on the physical characteristics (currents, tides, and wave action) of the receiving water.

2. The long-term effects of solid wood wastes are related to particle size, in that the surface area-to-volume ratio has an important bearing on the activity of decomposing bacteria. In that respect, accumulations of wood fibers can be far more serious ecologically than are sunken logs. Wood fibers not only degrade the benthic habitat but also lead to oxygen depletion and production of hydrogen sulfide in the sediment and overlying water. Logs and other large pieces of wood may serve as a substrate for attachment for such invertebrates as sea anemones and gastropods.

3. Fiber deposits in the vicinity of coastal pulp mills in British Columbia have not only eliminated the benthos but have also reduced DO concentrations in water overlying the fiber-contaminated sediment.

4. A colonization experiment utilizing four containers with different concentrations (0, 20, 50, and 100%) of seasoned wood fibers and chips (from the vicinity of the Port Mellon pulp mill), which were exposed to colonization by invertebrates at a depth of ~25 m in outer Burrard Inlet from 1 August to 20 October 1983, demonstrated that the highest total and mean numbers of taxa occurred in the sediments with 20% wood fiber. The total numbers of organisms were similar in sediments with 0 and 50% wood fiber and in sediments with 20 and 100% wood fiber. Although the total number of individuals was high in the container with 100% wood fiber, the species diversity was low, with the poly-

chaetes *Capitella capitata* and *Armanda brevis* and the shipworm *Bankia setacea* accounting for most of the individuals.

5. The colonization experiment measured only the short-term effects of wood cellulose and not effects of such processes as decomposition and leaching of soluble organic substances from the wood. The results of the experiment, therefore, should not be translated into permissible concentrations of wood waste in field situations.

6. Experiments are required to determine other variables affecting the impact of wood solids on marine ecology (e.g., age of wood fibers, thickness of fiber bed, and time dependence of effects). For long-term impacts, it may be necessary to monitor changes occurring in fiber accumulations over a period of several years.

ACKNOWLEDGMENTS

I thank N. Holman for making available underwater photographs taken from the submersible *Pisces IV* in Cousins Inlet and Northumberland Channel. E. R. McGreer was responsible for the design and the initiation of the experiment on the effects of wood waste on colonization of marine sediments by macroinvertebrates. R. D. Kathman coordinated the taxonomic work, and S. F. Cross carried out the statistical analyses.

REFERENCES

Edde, H. 1984. Environmental Control for Pulp and Paper Mills. Noyes Publications, Park Ridge, New Jersey, 179 pp.

Fournier, J. A., and C. D. Levings. 1982. Polychaetes Recorded near Two Pulp Mills on the Coast of Northern British Columbia: A Preliminary Taxonomic and Ecological Account. *Syllogeus* No. 40, National Museums of Natural Sciences, National Museums of Canada, Ottawa, 91 pp.

Hofsten, B. V., and N. Edberg. 1972. Estimating the rate of degradation of cellulose fibres in water. *Oikos*, **23**, 29–34.

Hourston, A. S., and R. H. Herlinveaux. 1957. A "mass mortality" of fish in Alberni Harbour, B.C. *Fisheries Research Board of Canada Progress Reports of the Pacific Coast Stations*, **109**, 3–6.

Iseki, K., R. W. Macdonald, and C. S. Wong. 1984. Effect of wood waste dumping on organic matter in seawater and surficial sediments of Alberni Inlet, British Columbia. *Journal of the Oceanographical Society of Japan*, **40**, 213–220.

Kathman, R. D., S. F. Cross, and M. Waldichuk. 1984. Effects of Wood Waste on the Recruitment Potential of Marine Benthic Communities. Canadian Technical Report of Fisheries and Aquatic Sciences No. 1284, Fisheries and Oceans Canada, West Vancouver, British Columbia, Canada, 50 pp.

Levings, C. D., E. P. Anderson, and G. W. O'Connell. 1985. Biological effects of dredged-material disposal in Alberni Inlet. *In*: Wastes in the

Ocean, Vol. 6: Nearshore Waste Disposal, B. Ketchum, J. Capuzzo, W. Burt, I. Duedall, P. Park, and D. Kester (Eds.). Wiley-Interscience, New York, pp. 131–155.

Levy, D. A., T. G. Northcote, and R. M. Barr. 1982. Effects of Estuarine Log Storage on Juvenile Salmon. Technical Report No. 26, Westwater Research Centre, The University of British Columbia, Vancouver, British Columbia, Canada, 101 pp.

McDaniel, N. G. 1973. A Survey of the Benthic Macroinvertebrate Fauna and Solid Pollutants in Howe Sound. Technical Report No. 385, Fisheries Research Board of Canada, Pacific Environment Institute, West Vancouver, British Columbia, Canada, 64 pp.

McGreer, E. R. 1984. Analysis of Marine Benthic Invertebrate Data from British Columbia Coastal Pulp Mills. Project EP-84-01, prepared by Coastline Environmental Services Ltd., Vancouver, British Columbia, submitted to the Environmental Protection Service, Environment Canada, West Vancouver, British Columbia, Canada, 45 pp.

McKeague, J. A. (Ed.). 1978. Manual of Soil Sampling and Methods of Analysis. Canadian Society of Soil Science, Ottawa, Ontario, Canada, 212 pp.

Pacific Northwest Pollution Control Council. 1971. Log Storage and Rafting in Public Waters. Task Force Report, approved by Pacific Northwest Pollution Control Council, Washington State Department of Ecology, Olympia, Washington, 56 pp.

Pearson, T. H., and R. Rosenberg. 1978. Macrobenthic succession in relation to organic enrichment and pollution of the marine environment. *Oceanography and Marine Biology*, **16**, 229–311.

Pease, B. C. 1973. Effects of Log Rafting and Dumping on the Marine Environment in Southeast Alaska. M.S. Thesis, University of Washington, Seattle, 68 pp.

Petrie, L., and N. Holman. 1983. *PISCES IV* Submersible Dives 1973–1982. Regional Programme Report 83-20, Environmental Protection Service, Department of the Environment, West Vancouver, British Columbia, Canada, 308 pp. + appendices I and II.

Poole, N. J., R. J. Parkes, and D. J. Wildish. 1977. Reaction of estuarine ecosystems to effluent from pulp and paper industry. *Helgoländer Wissenschaftliche Meeresuntersuchungen*, **30**, 622–632.

Poole, N. J., D. J. Wildish, and D. D. Kristmanson. 1978. The effects of the pulp and paper industry on the aquatic environment. *Critical Reviews in Environmental Control*, **8**, 153–195.

Stanley, S. O., T. H. Pearson, and C. M. Brown. 1978. Marine microbial ecosystem and the degradation of organic pollutants. *In*: The Oil Industry and Microbial Ecosystems, K. W. A. Chater and H. J. Somerville (Eds.). Heyden, London, pp. 60–79.

Vance, I. 1978. Bacterial Degradation of Cellulose in Marine Sediments. Ph.D. Dissertation, University of Dundee, Dundee, Scotland, 201 pp.

Vance, I., S. O. Stanley, and C. M. Brown. 1979. A microscopical investigation of the bacterial degradation of wood pulp in a simulated marine environment. *Journal of General Microbiology*, **114**, 69–74.

Waldichuk, M. 1957. Physical oceanography of the Strait of Georgia, British Columbia. *Journal of the Fisheries Research Board of Canada*, **14**, 321–486.

Waldichuk, M. 1962. Some water pollution problems connected with the disposal of pulp mill wastes. *Canadian Fish Culturist*, **31**, 3–34.

Waldichuk, M. 1965. Estimation of flushing rates from tide height and current data in an inshore marine channel of the Canadian Pacific Coast. *In*: Proceedings of the Second International Water Pollution Research Conference, Tokyo, 1964. Pergamon Press, New York, 133–165.

Waldichuk, M. 1983. Water pollution from pulpmill effluent in British Columbia: a general overview. *In*: Proceedings of Pulp Mill Effluent Monitoring: An Information Development Program Sponsored by the Environmental Protection Service, March 17 and 18, 1983, W.M. Pomeroy (Ed.). Regional Program Report No. 83-15, Environmental Protection Service, Department of the Environment, West Vancouver, British Columbia, Canada, pp. 1–60.

Waldichuk, M., J. H. Meikle, and J. R. Markert. 1968a. Physical and Chemical Oceanographic Data from the East Coast of Vancouver Island, 1954–1966. Vol. I: Discovery Passage–Duncan Bay and Baynes Sound–Comox Harbour. Manuscript Report No. 989, Fisheries Research Board of Canada, Nanaimo, British Columbia, Canada, 133 pp.

Waldichuk, M., J. H. Meikle, and J. R. Markert. 1968b. Physical and Chemical Oceanographic Data from the East Coast of Vancouver Island, 1954–1966. Vol. II: Northumberland Channel–Departure Bay, Stuart Channel–Osborn Bay, and Haro Strait–Juan de Fuca Strait. Manuscript Report No. 989, Fisheries Research Board of Canada, Nanaimo, British Columbia, Canada, 325 pp.

Walton, A. (Ed.). 1978. Methods for Sampling and Analysis of Marine Sediments and Dredged Materials. Ocean Dumping Report 1, Fisheries and Environment Canada, Fisheries and Marine Service, Ottawa, Canada, 74 pp.

Ward, J. H. 1963. Hierarchical grouping to optimize an objective function. *Journal of the American Statistical Association*, **58**, 236–244.

Werner, A. E. 1965. Suspended solids from mill effluents. *Canadian Pulp and Paper Industry*, April, 109–114.

Werner, A. E. 1968. Gases from sediments in polluted coastal waters. *Pulp and Paper Magazine of Canada*, **69**, 127–136.

PART V: CONTAMINANT STATUS IN COASTAL WATERS OF JAPAN AND CHINA

Chapter 19

Residence Times of Trace Metals and Nutrients in Tokyo Bay Water

Eiji Matsumoto

Geological Survey of Japan
Yatabe, Japan

Abstract	**211**
19.1. Introduction	**211**
19.2. Experimental Methods	**212**
19.2.1. General Features of Tokyo Bay	212
19.2.2. Sediment Sampling	212
19.2.3. Water Sampling	212
19.2.4. ^{210}Pb Measurement for Sediment Cores	212
19.2.5. Elemental Analysis of Sediments	213
19.2.6. Elemental Analysis of Water	214
19.3. Results	**214**
19.3.1. Accumulation Rates with ^{210}Pb	214
19.3.2. Elemental Concentrations in Surficial Sediments	215
19.3.3. Elemental Concentrations in Water	215
19.4. Discussion	**216**
19.4.1. Model for Calculation of Residence Time	216
19.4.2. Sedimentation and Flushing Rates of Trace Metals and Nutrients in Tokyo Bay	217
19.4.3. Residence Times of Trace Metals and Nutrients in Tokyo Bay Water	217
19.5. Conclusions	**217**
Acknowledgments	**217**
References	**217**

ABSTRACT

Tokyo Bay (Japan) is well suited for a study on the behavior of trace metals and nutrients in coastal marine systems because the bay is heavily contaminated as a result of human activities. Accurate information concerning individual inputs of trace metals and nutrients to Tokyo Bay is not available. In this study, steady-state conditions are assumed for Tokyo Bay, and the total input to the bay is estimated as the sum of outputs, which consist of sedimentation to the bay bottom and flushing from the bay mouth. The sedimentation rate was determined with ^{210}Pb and sediment analyses; the flushing rate was determined from hydrological observations and water analyses. Then, the residence time in the bay water was calculated to be 0.013 y for Pb, 0.051 y for Cu, 0.055 y for Cd, 0.083 y for Hg, 0.11 y for P, and 0.12 y for N. The residence times of trace metals were quite short relative to the water residence time of 0.13 y. By contrast, the residence times of nutrients were close to the water residence time. After the introduction of trace metals into coastal waters, a significant fraction of the metals was quickly taken up as particulate material and deposited on the bottom. Though nutrients are also taken up by organisms, nutrients are easily regenerated to the water and, finally, transported from the bay to the open ocean.

19.1. INTRODUCTION

A striking feature of Tokyo Bay (Japan) is that it is heavily contaminated as a result of human activities. Elevated concentrations of certain pollutants, such as trace metals and nutrients, are now strongly suspected of influencing the ecosystem in the bay. To evaluate the possible short- and long-range effects on the ecosystem of the disposal of trace metals and nutrients, accurate measurements of pollutants in water and sediments are needed along with an understanding of their transport and fate in the bay. The residence time of pollutants in water is one of the basically important factors representing the behavior of pollutants in marine systems. In order to evaluate the residence time of a pollutant in a body of water, it is essential to determine both the concentration of the pollutant in water and the rates of input of the pollutant to the water body. Potentially important sources of pollutants are sewers, rivers, rainfall, aerial fallout, vessel dumping, and oceanic water; but accurate information concerning these individual inputs is not yet available for Tokyo Bay. The total input to the bay, however, can be estimated as the sum of sedimentation on the bay bottom and flushing from the bay mouth, if a steady state is assumed.

The primary objectives of this investigation are to estimate, on the basis of sedimentation and flushing rates, the total inputs of selected trace metals and nutrients, and then to determine the residence times of those contaminants in Tokyo Bay water.

19.2. EXPERIMENTAL METHODS

19.2.1. General Features of Tokyo Bay

Tokyo Bay is located on the eastern side of Honshu Island, Japan, and is surrounded by a densely populated and industrialized area. The quantities of metal and nutrient inputs are very large, and the effects are sometimes dramatic and easily measured (Matsumoto, 1983).

Tokyo Bay is 1000 km² in area and has an average depth of 17 m (Fig. 19.1). The bay is connected with the North Pacific through the Uraga Channel. The water exchange between the bay and the North Pacific Ocean is restricted by the narrow mouth at the head of Uraga Channel, and the residence time of the bay water is estimated to be 0.13 y (Unoki and Kishino, 1977).

19.2.2. Sediment Sampling

Sediment cores were collected at stations located on a 4 × 2 km grid during September 1980 (G80 cruise) and August 1981 (G81 cruise) aboard the *R. V. Kaiko No. 5* (Fig. 19.1). The modified gravity corer consisted of an acrylic pipe of 11 cm inside diameter (ID), with a sediment catcher and a clear vent. With slow entry of this corer, sediment cores with nearly undisturbed sedimentary strata were obtained. Immediately after collection, the sediment cores were cut into 5-cm

sections for analyses. The sediment samples were sealed in plastic containers and stored in a refrigerator at 4°C.

The sediment samples were dried at 110°C, and the water content was recorded. The residue was pulverized to fine powder for dating and elemental analyses. The density of the solid phases present in the sediments was determined by measuring water displacement in a graduated specific-gravity bottle. The sea salt content in dried sediment samples was calculated on the basis of the water content and the salinity of the interstitial water. The measured concentrations for sediments were normalized to salt-free sediments.

19.2.3. Water Sampling

Seawater samples for trace-metal measurements were collected at four stations (station numbers 9, 20, 29, and 36) on the G81 cruise. While the vessel was traveling steadily upwind, surfacewater samples were obtained in a clean Teflon® (E.I. DuPont De Nemours, Wilmington, Delaware) bottle tied to the end of a fishing line >5 m away from the vessel. Subsurface water samples were obtained with a peristaltic pump and Teflon® tube. All trace-metal samples except Hg were stored in Teflon® bottles and acidified with ultra-pure HCl. Methods for cleaning of bottles and tubing and purification of reagents are described by Hirao et al. (1983). Samples for Hg determination were stored in clean glass bottles and acidified with H_2SO_4.

The seawater samples for N determination were collected at 7 stations (1, 2, 3, 5, 6, 8, and 9) from the *R.V. Tansei* in January 1980 (KT80-1 cruise) and September 1980 (KT80-16 cruise), shown in Fig. 19.1. The samples for P determination were collected at 5 stations (2, 3, 5, 6, and 8) in June 1983 (KT83-9 cruise).

19.2.4. ²¹⁰Pb Measurements for Sediment Cores

The radioactivity of ^{210}Pb was measured by counting either beta activity of its daughter nuclide, ^{210}Bi, or gamma activity of ^{210}Pb itself. For beta counting, ^{210}Pb was extracted from the sediments chemically, followed by counting with a Tracerlab Omni/Guard (ICN Tracerlab, Mechelen, Belgium) low-background counter (Matsumoto and Togashi, 1980). Lead-210 was also measured non-destructively by gamma

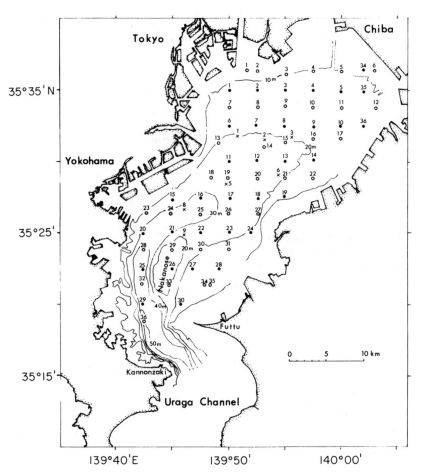

Figure 19.1. Sampling sites in Tokyo Bay, Japan: sampled September 1980 (G80, solid circle); sampled August 1981 (G81, open circle); sampled January and September 1980 and June 1983 (KT80 and KT 83, cross). Numbers above sites indicate core numbers.

spectrometry by using an ORTEC Gamma-X (EG&G OR-TEC, Oak Ridge, Tennessee) germanium detector equipped with a DAAS 7053 spectroanalyzer.

The excess ^{210}Pb was calculated by subtracting the supported ^{210}Pb from the total ^{210}Pb. The supported ^{210}Pb was determined from ^{210}Pb measurements at great depths in some cores and from ^{214}Pb measurements (by gamma spectrometry) in other cores.

19.2.5. Elemental Analysis of Sediments

Concentrated reagent-grade HNO_3 and HF (5 ml each) were added to a 0.5-g sediment sample in a Teflon® bottle. The airtight, capped bottle was heated at 100°C for 6 h, and then the mixture was dried in a fume hood. One milliliter of concentrated HNO_3 and 99 ml of H_2O were added to the bottle. The solution was analyzed for metals and P by direct aspiration into a Jobin Yvon JY48P (SA Jobin Yvon, Longjumeau, France) inductively coupled plasma emission spectrometer. Mercury determinations were performed by the cold-vapor technique by using a Nippon Jarrel Ash Model AA780 (Nippon Jarrel Ash Co., Kyoto, Japan) atomic absorption spectrophotometer (AAS). Nitrogen analysis was performed by dry combustion in oxygen at 800°C, followed by gasometric analysis of evolved N_2 by using a Yanako Model MT-500 (Yanako Ltd., Kyoto, Japan) nitrogen analyzer.

19.2.6. Elemental Analysis of Water

The concentrations of Pb, Cu, and Cd in water were determined by using an AAS under clean laboratory conditions (Hirao et al., 1983). For determinations of Pb, Cu, and Cd, the seawater samples were evaporated to dryness in storage bottles by using a hot plate and infrared irradiation. Nitric acid was added to the residue until a violent aqua regia reaction resulted, and then the samples were concentrated to salts. These procedures were performed in an ultra-clean Teflon® evaporation tank. The salts were redissolved in dilute HNO_3, and a dithizone extraction was performed. The Pb, Cu, and Cd were analyzed by using a Nippon Jarrel Ash AA8500 AAS equipped with an FLA-100 graphite furnace. The results obtained are defined as total metals in water.

Total Hg was analyzed after adding HNO_3 to the samples, which were stored in glass bottles, and heating to decompose

the particulate phases (Matsunaga et al., 1978). Mercury concentration was determined by the coldvapor technique by using an AAS as described in the Hg analysis for sediments.

Total nitrogen was obtained as the sum of dissolved and particulate nitrogen. The dissolved nitrogen was determined from analysis of ammonia by the Kjeldahl treatment of a sample filtered through a glass fiber filter (Bremner, 1960). The particulate nitrogen was determined from analysis of N_2 by dry combustion of the glass fiber filter by using a Yanako Model MT-3 nitrogen analyzer (Yanako Ltd., Kyoto, Japan).

Total phosphorus was determined from analysis of reactive phosphate by $K_2S_2O_8$ treatment of an unfiltered seawater sample (Menzel and Corwin, 1965).

19.3. RESULTS

19.3.1. Accumulation Rates with [210]Pb

Accumulation rates were determined from the excess ^{210}Pb profiles in sediment cores. Accumulation rates are expressed as mass per unit area per time to facilitate mass balance considerations and intercore comparisons. The log of excess ^{210}Pb was plotted against the cumulative weight of sediments, and the accumulation rate was determined from the slope (Matsumoto and Togashi, 1980).

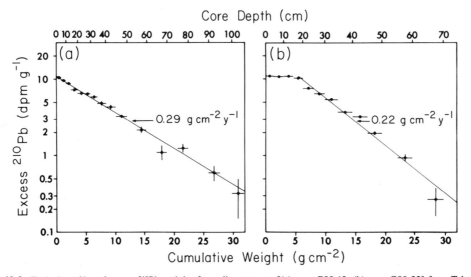

Figure 19.2. Typical profiles of excess ^{210}Pb activity for sediment cores [(a) core G80-12; (b) core G80-22] from Tokyo Bay.

Figure 19.2 illustrates typical ^{210}Pb profiles in the bay. The profile for G80-12 is characteristic of cores obtained from the bay, which generally have no mixed layer. The exception is in the vicinity of the Nakanose, where most cores have a surface mixed layer, as shown in the profile for G80-22. If accumulation and mixing are steady, an equal amount of freshly accumulated sediment is displaced below the region of active mixing, and ^{210}Pb in the displaced sediment decays radiometrically with its characteristic half-life. When a surface mixed layer was observed, an accumulation rate was determined from the logarithmic region below the mixed layer.

The distribution of accumulation rates for sediment in Tokyo Bay as measured by the ^{210}Pb technique is presented in Fig. 19.3. The accumulation rate generally decreased southward and eastward from the innermost bay. The region of the bay mouth is non-depositional and consists entirely of relict sand and Tertiary rock. The annual accumulation in the entire Tokyo Bay was calculated to be 1.2×10^6 metric tons (t).

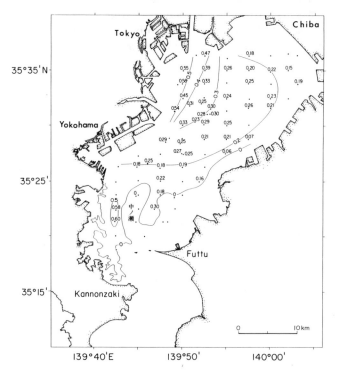

Figure 19.3. Recent accumulation rates (g cm^{-2} y^{-1}) in Tokyo Bay calculated from excess ^{210}Pb activity versus cumulative sediment weight.

19.3.2. Elemental Concentrations in Surficial Sediment

The top 5 cm of each sediment core collected on the G81 cruise was used for analysis for elements. Since the accumulation rates for sediment in Tokyo Bay are very fast, the top 5 cm of cores covers only the past several years. The surficial concentrations of elements (ranges and averages) are shown in Table 19.1. The pre-contamination values were determined from the measurements at depths deeper than 50 cm in cores. Fig. 19.4 illustrates the depth profiles for several elements in a representative sediment core from central Tokyo Bay. The concentrations of selected elements in surficial sediments are up to one order of magnitude higher than pre-contamination values (Table 19.1 and Fig. 19.4). The values reflect the extent of metal and nutrient enrichments in the recently deposited surficial sediment compared to those in deeper sediment accumulated before the advent of the industrial period.

Table 19.1. Elemental Concentrations in the Surficial Sediment Collected in 1981 from Tokyo Bay[a]

Element	Number of Samples	Concentration (µg g^{-1})		
		Range	Average	Background[b]
Pb	28	26–74	47	20
Cu	28	34–125	70	30
Cd	25	0.6–1.9	1.2	0.1
Hg	27	0.36–0.79	0.56	0.05
P	28	710–1000	840	600
N	29	2000–5500	3600	1500

[a]Values are on dry, salt-free weight basis.
[b]Background values were determined from the measurements at depths deeper than 50 cm in cores.

19.3.3. Elemental Concentrations in Water

The total trace-metal and nutrient concentrations in Tokyo Bay water (ranges and averages) are shown in Table 19.2. A more complete description of data may be found in publications by Hirao et al. (1983) for Pb, Cu, and Cd; Matsumoto et al. (1983) for Hg; and Hattori (1981) for N; and Sakamoto (1984) for P. These concentrations in Tokyo Bay water are several times higher than are those reported for surface waters of the North Pacific (Table 19.2) as a result of elemental inputs from the surrounding land.

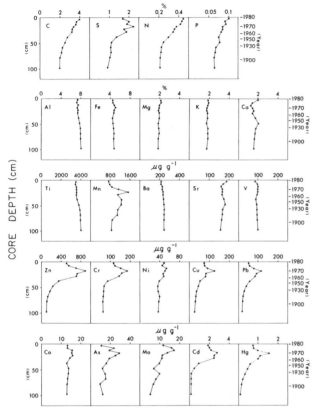

Figure 19.4. Profiles of elemental concentrations in a sediment core (G80-12) collected from the central Tokyo Bay as a function of depth or depositional age as calculated with the ^{210}Pb technique.

19.4. DISCUSSION

19.4.1. Model for Calculation of Residence Time

Assuming steady-state conditions for element inputs and outputs, the residence time of an element i in the bay water (τ_i) is given by

$$\tau_i = \frac{C_i V}{I_i} \qquad 1$$

where C_i is the concentration of element i in the bay water, V is the volume of the bay water, and I_i is the input rate of element i into the bay. Since accurate information concerning inputs is not generally available, the total input to the bay can be estimated as the sum of outputs (i.e., sedimentation and flushing); therefore, equation 1 is given by

$$\tau_i = \frac{C_i V}{S_i + C_i v} \qquad 2$$

where S_i is the sedimentation rate of element i on the bay bottom, and v is the flushing rate of the bay water from the bay mouth. The residence time of the bay water (τ_w) is simply represented to be V/v. The volume of the bay water is 16 km^3, and the value of τ_w is reported to be 0.13 y, based on the chlorine budget described by Unoki and Kishino (1977).

Table 19.2. Elemental Concentrations in Tokyo Bay Water

Element	Sampling Date	Number of Samples	Concentration (μg liter^{-1})		
			Range	Average	Open Ocean
Pb	1981	10	0.033–0.10	0.049	0.01[a]
Cu	1981	11	0.30–0.58	0.44	0.05[b]
Cd	1981	11	0.006–0.012	0.0083	0.001[b]
Hg	1981	11	0.0063–0.015	0.0097	0.005[c]
P	1983	30	50–119	59	4[d]
N	1980	71	280–1100	720	200[d]

[a]Schaule and Patterson (1981).
[b]Bruland (1980).
[c]Matsunaga et al. (1975).
[d]Hattori (1973).

19.4.2. Sedimentation and Flushing Rates of Trace Metals and Nutrients in Tokyo Bay

The sedimentation rate of an element on the bottom can be calculated by multiplying the average elemental concentration in surficial sediment (Table 19.1) by the average accumulation rate for sediment for the entire Tokyo Bay. The results are shown in Table 19.3.

The flushing rate of an element from the bay mouth can be calculated by multiplying the average elemental concentration in the bay water (Table 19.2) by the flushing rate of the bay water. The previously mentioned values were used for calculation, and the results are shown in Table 19.3.

19.4.3. Residence Times of Trace Metals and Nutrients in Tokyo Bay Water

By using the data above and equation 2, the residence times were calculated, and the results are shown in Table 19.3. The residence times for various elements increased as follows: Pb < Cu < Cd < Hg < P < N.

The residence times for the trace metals are quite short relative to the residence time of the bay water, 0.13 y. By contrast, the residence times for N and P are close to the water residence time. From the results obtained, it is possible to make certain generalizations. After the introduction of trace metals into the coastal water, most of the metals are quickly taken up by particulate material and then deposited on the bottom. Though nutrients are also taken up by organisms, they are easily regenerated to the water and finally transported from the coastal marine system into the open ocean.

Table 19.3. Budgets and Residence Times of Elements in Tokyo Bay

Element	Sedimentation Rate (t y^{-1})	Flushing Rate (t y^{-1})	Residence Time (y)
Pb	56	6.1	0.013
Cu	82	54	0.051
Cd	1.4	1.0	0.055
Hg	0.67	1.2	0.083
P	990	7,300	0.11
N	4,200	89,000	0.12
Cl			0.13[a]

[a]Unoki and Kishino (1977).

These findings agree with previous studies for N metabolism in Tokyo Bay (Hattori et al., 1983).

19.5. CONCLUSIONS

Tokyo Bay is surrounded by a densely populated and industrialized area that introduces large amounts of pollutants into the bay. The total input of trace elements and nutrients to the bay was estimated as the sum of the sedimentation on the bottom and the flushing from the bay mouth. On the basis of their budgets, the residence times of trace metals and nutrients in the water were calculated to be 0.013 y for Pb, 0.051 y for Cu, 0.055 y for Cd, 0.083 y for Hg, 0.11 y for P and 0.12 y for N. The residence times of trace metals are quite short relative to the water residence time of 0.13 y because of high rates of removal from the water column by sedimentation. The residence times of nutrients, however, are dominated by the water residence time. After introduction of trace metals into coastal marine waters, the trace metals are removed rapidly from the water and deposited on the bottom, but the nutrients are transported to the open ocean without significant net removal.

ACKOWLEDGMENTS

The author thanks A. Hattori and S. Sakamoto for the nutrient measurements and Dr. Y. Hirao for the trace-metal measurements. This work was supported by an environmental research grant from the Environmental Agency, Japan.

REFERENCES

Bremner, J. M. 1960. Determination of nitrogen in soil by the Kjeldahl method. *Journal of Agriculture Science,* **55,** 11–33.

Bruland, K. W. 1980. Oceanographic distributions of cadmium, zinc, nickel, and copper in the North Pacific. *Earth and Planetary Science Letters,* **47,** 176–198.

Hattori, A. 1973. Preliminary Report of the Hakuho Maru Cruise KH71-3. Ocean Research Institute, University of Tokyo, Tokyo 69 pp.

Hattori, A. 1981. Distribution and Fate of Pollutants in Coastal Environments: Data Record 1979–1980. Unpublished report prepared by the Special Research Project on Environmental Science, submitted to the Ministry of Education, Culture and Science, Japan, 87 pp.

Hattori, A., M. Ohtsu, and I. Koike. 1983. Distribution, metabolism and budgets of nitrogen in Tokyo Bay. *Chikyukagaku,* **17,** 32–41.

Hirao, Y., M. Koshikawa, H. Sugisaki, K. Fukumoto, K. Kimura, and E. Matsumoto. 1983. Lead, copper and cadmium concentrations in the seawater of Tokyo Bay. *Chikyukagaku,* **17,** 42–47.

Matsumoto, E. 1983. Environmental changes recorded in sediments of coastal marine zone closed by big city. *Memoirs of Geological Society of Japan,* **23**, 91–95.

Matsumoto, E., and S. Togashi. 1980. Sedimentation rates in Funka Bay, Hokkaido. *Journal of Oceanographic Society of Japan,* **35**, 261–267.

Matsumoto, E., K. Kato, and K. Matsunaga. 1983. Mercury geochemistry in the Tokyo Bay. *Chikyukagaku,* **17**, 48–52.

Matsunaga, K., M. Nishimura, and S. Konishi. 1975. Mercury in the Kuroshio and Oyashio regions and the Japan Sea. *Nature,* **258**, 224–225.

Matsunaga, K., H. Tsujioku, S. Fukasa, and K. Hasebe. 1978. On the behavior of mercury in some polluted seawater. *Bulletin of Chemical Society of Japan,* **51**, 3519–3521.

Menzel, D. W., and N. Corwin. 1965. The measurement of total phosphorus in seawater based on the liberation of organically bound fractions by persulfate oxydation. *Limnology and Oceanography,* **10**, 280–282.

Sakamoto, M. 1984. Phosphorous Cycle in Environments. Unpublished report prepared by Special Research Project on Environmental Science, submitted to Ministry of Education, Culture and Science, Japan, 227 pp.

Schaule, B. K., and C. C. Patterson. 1981. Lead concentrations in the Northeast Pacific: Evidence for global anthropogenic perturbations. *Earth and Planetary Science Letters,* **54**, 97–116.

Unoki, S., and M. Kishino. 1977. Oceanographic Conditions and Water Exchanges in Tokyo Bay. Technical report, Physical Oceanography Laboratory, Institute of Physical and Chemical Research, Japan, 89 pp.

Chapter 20

Manganese, Iron, Copper, and Zinc in Sediment Cores from Seasonally Stratified Beppu Bay, the Seto Inland Sea, Japan

Akira Hoshika and Takayuki Shiozawa

Government Industrial Research Institute, Chugoku
Kure, Hiroshima, Japan

Yasushi Kitano

Water Research Institute, Nagoya University
Chikusa-ku, Nagoya, Japan

Abstract	**219**
20.1. Introduction	**220**
20.2. Experimental Methods	**220**
20.2.1. Study Area	220
20.2.2. Sampling	220
20.2.3. Analysis	221
20.2.3a. Sedimentation rate	*221*
20.2.3b. Selective chemical leaching	*221*
20.2.3c. Sulfur in core sediment	*222*
20.2.3d. Manganese in interstitial water	*223*
20.2.3e. Organic carbon and nitrogen in core sediment	*223*
20.3. Results	**223**
20.3.1. Sedimentation Rate	223
20.3.2. Vertical Profiles of Heavy Metals in Core Sediment	223
20.3.3. Organic C, N, and S in Core Sediment	227
20.4. Discussion	**227**
20.4.1. Sedimentary Environment	227
20.4.2. Chemical Form of Mn in Core Sediment	228
20.4.3. Chemical Forms of Fe, Cu, and Zn in Core Sediment	229
20.4.4. Diagenetic Behavior of Mn in Core Sediment	229
20.5. Conclusions	**232**
Acknowledgment	**232**
References	**232**

ABSTRACT

Vertical profiles were determined for Mn and Fe in four sequentially separated fractions from sediment cores from two stations in Beppu Bay, a seasonally stratified basin in the Seto Inland Sea. The sediments were dated by the ^{210}Pb method. Since the mid-1960s, and coincident with urban development, the sedimentation rate in the innermost part of the bay has increased about threefold over the background rate. Since then, a seasonal oxidation–reduction cycle has appeared in the bottom water of the area, and the interstitial environment within the sediment has changed from oxic to anoxic. The depth distributions for Mn and other metals in sediment are discussed in the context of the oxic and anoxic conditions that prevail at the two stations. Under oxic conditions, Mn is deposited in the form of oxides and/or hydroxides, whereas under anoxic conditions, Mn is coprecipitated with stable iron sulfide.

20.1. INTRODUCTION

Because of the large amounts of organic and metal pollutants and nutrients discharged through human activities, coastal seawater and sediment in the Japanese islands have been seriously contaminated since the mid-1900s. In the inner coastal areas with weak tidal currents, reducing bottom water has appeared as a result of oxygen consumption by anthropogenic and authigenic organic materials and/or organic-rich sediment, compounded by minimal vertical mixing of water.

Manganese is one of the most mobile elements in the marine environment (Spencer and Brewer, 1971; Emerson et al., 1979). Manganese shows a characteristic behavior during the diagenetic process in sediment (Manheim, 1961; Li et al., 1969; Bonatti et al., 1972; Grill, 1978; Skei and Paus, 1979). Masuzawa and Kitano (1982), by using the results obtained from selective chemical leaching of sediment samples, described the coprecipitation of Mn with iron sulfide in the sediment core of a lake, which had changed from fresh to brackish water.

Beppu Bay is a seasonally stratified basin in a coastal area of the Seto Inland Sea (Shiozawa et al., 1977). In Beppu Bay, a very strong thermocline (temperature differences of 10°C) has been observed in the summer at depths between 50 and 60 m. High concentrations of dissolved and particulate Mn (for example, 930 and 120 μg liter^{-1}, respectively) have been observed both in the bottom water that contains hydrogen sulfide of 30 μg-atoms S liter^{-1} and also in the boundary-layer water of a few meters depth between the upper oxic and bottom anoxic waters. In winter Beppu Bay is unstratified (Shiozawa et al., 1977).

In the 1940s the bivalve mollusk *Lucinoma annulata* was found in the innermost and deeper part of this bay (Miyadi, 1941). In 1974 and 1975, however, this bivalve was not found in the deep areas of the bay, possibly due to a shift toward anoxic conditions in the sediments (Tamai, 1980).

We have studied the geochemical changes in the sediments of Beppu Bay by using ^{210}Pb dating techniques and selective chemical leaching techniques for Cu, Fe, Mn, and Zn.

20.2. EXPERIMENTAL METHODS

20.2.1. Study Area

Beppu Bay is located at the western part of the Seto Inland Sea, Japan (Fig. 20.1). The southwestern side of this bay is characterized by a steep slope from shore. The maximum depth of Beppu Bay is 73 m at the innermost part, whereas the depth at the mouth is usually <50 m. A weak counterclockwise circulation is observed in this bay, although the tidal currents are complicated (Ohita Fishery Research Laboratory, 1976). The tidal-current velocity near the bottom is not detectable by a current meter with a detection limit of 2 cm s^{-1} (Hoshika et al., 1978). In summer a very strong thermocline (>10°C temperature difference) at depths of 50 to 60 m prevents vertical mixing of top and bottom water. The concentration of dissolved oxygen was near zero in the bottom water; consequently, hydrogen sulfide was present (Fig. 20.2). High Mn concentrations (0.9 mg liter^{-1}) released from the sediment were observed in the bottom water. This dissolved Mn is oxidized as it comes into contact with more oxidized water, and it precipitates as particulate Mn, which is sharply concentrated above the oxygen–hydrogen sulfide interface (Shiozawa et al., 1977; Hoshika et al., 1978). The sediment of Beppu Bay is composed mainly of silty clay with a median grain size of >0.015 mm except in the area outside of the mouth (Inouchi, 1982). The surface sediment in the southwestern portion of the bay was characterized particularly by the presence of black, silty clay with a strong hydrogen sulfide smell, as contrasted with the gray, silty sediments (with a brownish oxic surface layer) found at the mouth of the bay.

20.2.2. Sampling

The sediment core samples used in the present study were collected in August 1981 with a 1-m box-type gravity corer (12 × 12 cm). One sample was from the innermost, seasonally stratified area (station 52), and the other was from the oxic mouth area (station 50) (Fig. 20.1). The upper 35 cm of the sediment core collected from station 52 was black and had a strong hydrogen sulfide smell, whereas the lower part was gray and had no hydrogen sulfide smell. No difference in sediment type was visible between the upper and lower portions of the sediment collected from station 50. After collection, the sediment cores were cut into 2- to 5-cm vertical sections and stored in polyethylene bottles. Water content was calcu-

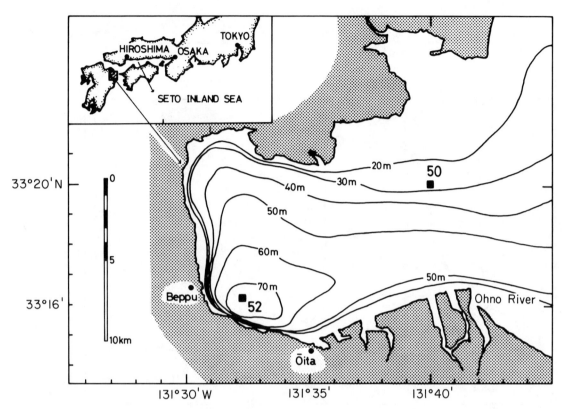

Figure 20.1. Study area and sampling stations (solid squares) in Beppu Bay. The inset shows the relationship between Beppu Bay and the Seto Inland Sea.

lated from the difference in weight between wet and dried (heated at 110°C) sediment.

20.2.3. Analysis

20.2.3a. Sedimentation rate

The sedimentation rate and age of the core sections were determined by the ^{210}Pb method. The amount of ^{210}Pb in the sediment was determined by counting the beta activity of its daughter, ^{210}Bi, in a flow-type beta counter with a low background of 0.5 cpm (ICN Tracerlab, Köln, Federal Republic of Germany) after HNO_3 digestion of the sediment sample (Matsumoto and Wong, 1977).

20.2.3b. Selective chemical leaching

The core sections were leached successively with four chemical reagents to produce four fractions of sediment components: (a) 10% acetic acid–soluble fraction (HAC); (b) 0.1 M hydrochloric acid–soluble fraction (HCl); (c) hydrogen peroxide–soluble fraction (H_2O_2); (d) HF-$HClO_4$-HNO_3 mixture–soluble fraction (HF).

About 0.5 g of dried sediment was digested successively in 25 ml of the first two leaching solutions, (a) and (b), by shaking for 2 h at room temperature. Acetic acid treatment leaches carbonates, amorphous Mn and Fe compounds, and ion-exchangeable sites (Loring, 1976; Skei and Paus, 1979), as well as unstable iron sulfides (Masuzawa and Kitano, 1982). Hydrochloric acid treatment was intended to leach

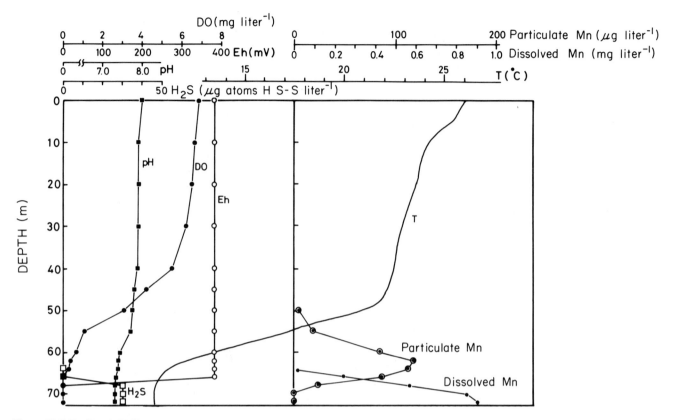

Figure 20.2 Profiles of pH, Eh, dissolved oxygen, hydrogen sulfide, temperature, and dissolved and particulate Mn in seawater (surface to sediment) at station 52, August 1981.

heavy metals in sulfides and carbonates and ion exchangeable and/or soluble forms in clay minerals (Jackson, 1968); however, stable pyrite (FeS_2) is not completely dissolved with this treatment (Kitano et al., 1981). Copper and Zn leached with 0.1 *M* HCl are regarded as coming from oxide and sulfide compounds (Kitano et al., 1981). The residue, after the above treatment, was digested in hydrogen peroxide solution (c) at ~80°C, which leaches heavy metals associated with organic materials and any pyrite (Kitano et al., 1981) that remains after the preceding treatments with (a) and (b). The residue was then decomposed overnight at 120°C with a solution made by mixing 10 ml HF, 5 ml $HClO_4$, and 10 ml HNO_3. Heavy metals bound in silicate could be leached with this treatment. A separate 0.5-g portion of original dried sediment was treated with a solution of 10% acetic acid and 1 *M* hydroxylamine hydrochloride (NH_2OH-HAC) to estimate the iron and manganese oxide phases in the sediment. Total

Cu, Fe, Mn, and Zn contents were described as the sum of contents of (a), (b), (c), and (d).

The Cu, Fe, Mn and Zn contents of each fraction were determined by atomic absorption spectrophotometry (AAS). Manganese contents of HAC and NH_2OH-HAC were corrected by subtracting the Mn content due to interstitial water, because water content of the sediment was high and the Mn content of the interstitial water was high, especially in the upper layers of the sediment. The metal content of the sediment was calculated on a salt-free dry basis, because the dried sediment contained up to 44% salt by weight.

20.2.3c. Sulfur in core sediment

About 0.3 g of dried sediment was shaken with ~20 ml of distilled water and then separated by centrifugation. The S content of the residue was determined by the method reported by Masuzawa and Kitano (1981). This method is an iodometrical titration, or a colorimetry with methylene blue, after decomposition of the sediment samples with bromine water and aqua regia, and reduction of sulfur to hydrogen sulfide with hydroiodic acid, acetic acid, and sodium hypophosphite mixed solution.

20.2.3d. Manganese in interstitial water

Interstitial water was extracted by centrifugation in the laboratory within a few hours after collection. The Mn concentration was determined by AAS (Japan Jarrell Ash, Tokyo) on the supernatant solution after filtration through a membrane filter (Millipore HA, 0.45-μm pore size).

20.2.3e. Organic carbon and nitrogen in core sediment

Organic C and N were determined by combustion at 880°C with a CN analyzer (Yanaco, Kyoto, Japan). Sediment samples were prepared in hydrochloric acid vapor for a few days to remove carbonate. Nitrogenous materials are assumed to be decomposed slightly in this treatment.

20.3. RESULTS

20.3.1. Sedimentation Rate

The ^{210}Pb profiles in the core sediment at stations 50 and 52 are shown in Fig. 20.3a and 20.3b. At station 50, the ^{210}Pb content of the upper 10-cm layer was nearly uniform with depth, and therefore the sedimentary strata are considered to have been disturbed, probably by benthic organisms. The sedimentation rate was obtained from the least-squares regression for the data below the surface-mixed layer of sediment (>10 cm). This rate was estimated to be 0.20 g cm^{-2} y^{-1}. At station 52, two different relationships between ^{210}Pb content and cumulative weight were observed. In the upper layer, the average sedimentation rate was 0.27 g cm^{-2} y^{-1} and in the lower layer 0.09 g cm^{-2} y^{-1}.

20.3.2. Vertical Profiles of Heavy Metals in Core Sediment

Figures 20.4 and 20.5 show the vertical profiles of Cu, Fe, Mn, and Zn in chemically separated fractions and their total contents in the sediments at stations 50 and 52, respectively.

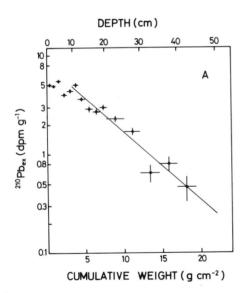

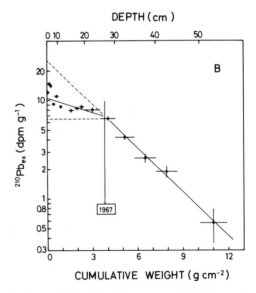

Figure 20.3. Profiles of excess ^{210}Pb in sediment cores plotted against cumulative weight of sediment. Vertical bars indicate standard deviation, and horizontal bars indicate the depth range of the sample. (A) Station 50, 0.20 g cm^{-2} y^{-1} sedimentation rate; (B) station 52, 0.27 g cm^{-2} y^{-1} sedimentation rate after 1967, and 0.09 g cm^{-2} y^{-1} rate prior to 1967.

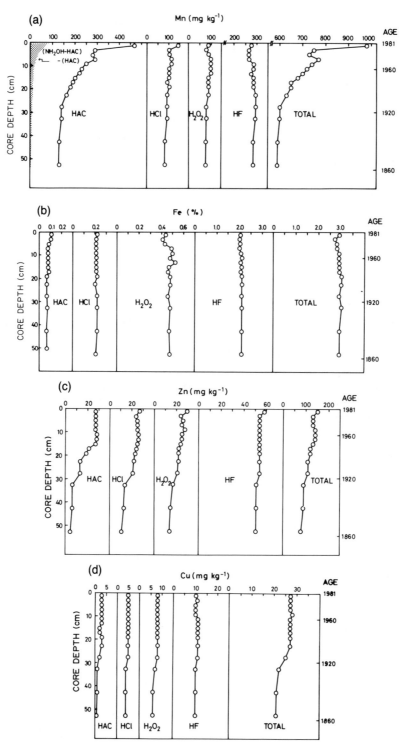

Figure 20.4. Profiles of (a) Mn (the stippled area represents the Mn concentrations in NH_2OH-HAC in excess of the concentration at the corresponding depth in HAC), (b) Fe, (c) Zn, and (d) Cu contents into 10% HAC-soluble fractions of the sediment core sample at station 50. Sediment age was determined by the Pb-210 method.

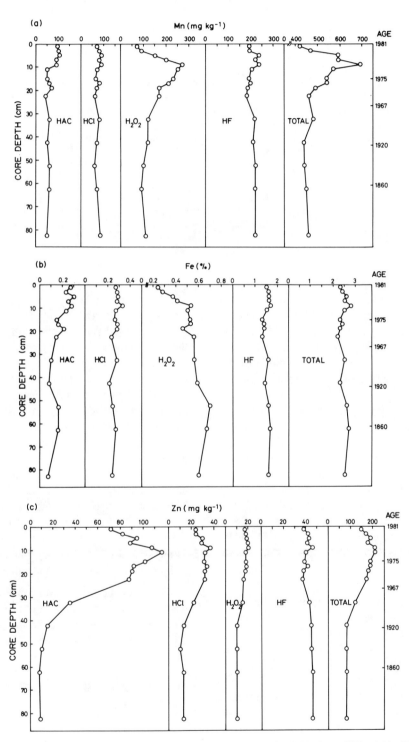

Figure 20.5. Profiles of (a) Mn, (b) Fe, (c) Zn, and on page 226 (d) Cu contents in 10% HAC-soluble, 0.1 *M* HCl-soluble, H₂O₂-soluble, and HF-soluble fraction of the sediment core sample at station 52.

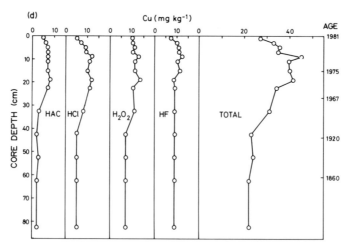

Figure 20.5. *(Continued)*

The Mn contents of the HCl, H_2O_2, and HF fractions at Station 50 were almost constant throughout the sediment core, whereas the Mn content of the HAC fraction showed a surface enrichment. The Mn content of the HAC fraction in the surface layer was 470 mg kg^{-1}, while a nearly constant value of 130 mg kg^{-1} was observed below 30 cm in depth. The Mn profile of the NH_2OH-HAC fraction was similar to that of the HAC fraction; however, the Mn content of the NH_2OH-HAC fraction was larger than that of the HAC fraction in the upper 30-cm layer and nearly equal in the lower layers. The difference in the content between the NH_2OH-HAC and the HAC fractions is shown by the dotted areas in Fig. 20.4a. The total Zn and Cu concentrations in the sediment increased upward from a depth of ~35 cm, but below this depth they were almost constant (Figs. 20.4c,d). The constant values of Zn and Cu at depth are 85 and 21 mg kg^{-1}, respectively; however, maximum values of 145 for Zn and 27 mg kg^{-1} for Cu were observed in the upper 20-cm layer.

The Mn contents of the HCl and HF fractions were nearly constant, while the Mn content of the H_2O_2 fraction varied significantly, with a maximum value of 270 mg kg^{-1} at a depth of about 10 cm at station 52 (Fig. 20.5a). The Mn content of the H_2O_2 fraction was 70 mg kg^{-1} in the topmost layer and a constant value of ~100 mg kg^{-1} below 30 cm in depth. The Mn content of the HAC fraction showed almost a constant value of 50 mg kg^{-1} below 10 cm in depth, but the content increased up to 100 mg kg^{-1} in the top 10 cm. The Mn content of the NH_2OH-HAC fraction was nearly equal to that of the HAC fraction throughout the sediment core.

The total Fe content was also almost constant at ~2.5% throughout the sediment core, as seen at station 50 (Fig. 20.5b). The Fe contents of the HAC and H_2O_2 fractions, however, varied significantly with depth. The Fe content of the HAC fraction decreased with depth from ~0.3% at the surface to ~0.1% at 25 cm, but the content of the H_2O_2 fraction increased from ~0.2% at the surface to ~0.5% at 10 cm (Fig. 20.5b). The total Zn aand Cu contents of the core sediment increased upward from the depth of ~45 cm. The Zn and Cu contents showed maximum values of 210 and 45 mg kg^{-1}, respectively, at the depth of 10 cm and 151 and 27 mg kg^{-1}, respectively, at the topmost layer (Fig. 20.5c,d). Below a depth of 45 cm, the Zn and Cu contents showed almost constant values of 78 and 22 mg kg^{-1}, respectively. The Zn content of the HAC fraction showed a significant change vertically, with the maximum value of 116 mg kg^{-1} at a depth of ~12 cm. The Zn content of the HAC fraction was 71 mg kg^{-1} at the topmost layer and showed a constant value of 10 mg kg^{-1} below 50 cm in depth.

The vertical profile of Mn concentration in the interstitial water at station 52 decreased exponentially from 1.2 mg liter^{-1} in the topmost layer to the nearly constant value of 0.05 mg liter^{-1} below 30 cm in depth (Fig. 20.6).

20.3.3. Organic C, N, and S in Core Sediment

As seen from Fig. 20.7, the organic C and N contents at station 52 decreased from 4.2 and 0.56%, respectively, in the

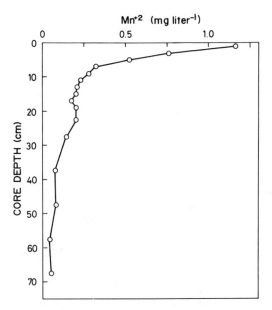

Figure 20.6. Profile of Mn^{2+} concentration in interstitial water of the sediment core at station 52.

topmost layer of the core to almost constant values of 2.4 and 0.31%, respectively, below 30 cm in depth. The S content at station 52 showed a nearly constant value of ~0.6% below 20 cm and decreased above 18 cm to ~0.2% in the surface layer (Fig. 20.7).

20.4. DISCUSSION

20.4.1. Sedimentary Environment

At station 52, two different sedimentation rates were observed (Fig. 20.3b). During the six-month summer season, a very strong thermocline forms in the innermost part of Beppu Bay. The water temperature drops from 23 to 10°C between a depth of 50 and 60 m, the oxygen content becomes zero, and hydrogen sulfide of 30 μg-atoms S liter^{-1} appears in the bottom water (Shiozawa et al., 1977; Hoshika et al., 1978); thus, the condition is too anoxic for macrobenthos to live. Tidal current velocity near the bottom of the basin is not

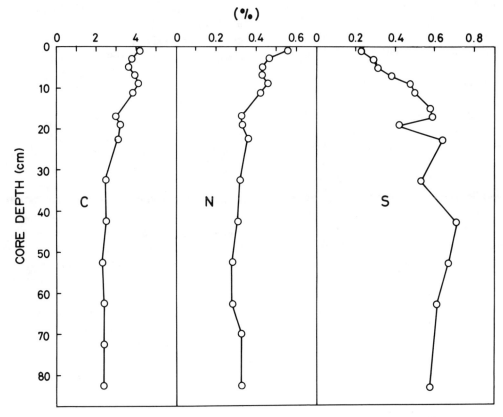

Figure 20.7. Profiles of S, N, and organic C contents in the sediment at station 52.

detectable by a current meter with a fixed detection limit of 2 cm s^{-1} (Hoshika et al., 1978). This velocity is considered to be too slight to disturb sedimentary strata in the innermost part of Beppu Bay. Thus, neither physical nor biological mixing is significant in the surface layer of the sediment; human activities or natural events are considered to have changed the sedimentation rate. By contrast, the uniform distribution of ^{210}Pb in the surficial sediment at station 50 indicated that sediment mixing occurred there, probably as a result of bioturbation.

High primary productivity, including increased frequency of red tide development with nutrification, has been associated with the inner part of the bay since the early 1960s (Ohita Fishery Research Laboratory, 1976). This biological activity, along with reclamation work (dredge and fill) along the southern and southwestern coasts since the mid-1960s, might have brought large amounts of particulate material to sediment in the western and the southern areas of this bay. It appears that the supply of particulate material since the mid-1960s has caused a threefold increase in sedimentation rate over the background rate in the innermost part of the bay.

Such a discharge of particulate material could have a significant effect on the formation of an anoxic environment with hydrogen sulfide in the bottom water during a summer stratification period. Miyadi (1941) collected *Lucinoma annulata* only in the innermost part of Beppu Bay in 1940. Miyadi pointed out that this bivalve can live in a low-oxygen environment only at low temperatures (<18°C); however, Tamai (1980) pointed out that it cannot live under the present anoxic conditions in the innermost part of the bay. We found shells of *Lucinoma annulata* in most layers between 35 and 90 cm in the sediment core, but no shells were found in the upper 35-cm layer, deposited since 1945. This may suggest that the bottom water of this bay changed from oxic to anoxic during a summer season due to the very significant discharge of pollutants and the formation of a strong summer thermocline (Shiozawa et al., 1977). Such a change in oxic and anoxic conditions would also have a significant influence on the diagenetic behavior of Mn in sediments.

20.4.2. Chemical Form of Mn in Core Sediment

The Mn profiles in the two sediment cores from oxic and anoxic environments are distinguished mainly by the Mn contents of the HAC and H$_2$O$_2$ fractions (Fig. 20.4a and 20.5a).

The vertical profile of the total Mn content with surface enrichment was mainly controlled by the vertical profile of the Mn content of the HAC fraction in the inner bay (station 50). The difference in the Mn content between the NH$_2$OH-HAC and the HAC fractions gradually increased toward the more oxic surface layer. Since loosely bonded manganese oxide and amorphous–hydrous Mn in the surface sediment are dissolved easily by dilute acetic acid (Loring, 1976; Skei and Paus, 1979), and manganese oxide in ferro-manganese nodules is dissolved by NH$_2$OH-HAC (Chester and Hughes, 1967), the large difference observed in the oxic surface layer may represent Mn in a high oxidation state. The Mn enrichment in the surface layer is considered to occur through its post-depositional mobilization under reducing conditions and subsequent precipitation in the oxygenated surficial sediments (Li et al., 1969; Bonatti et al., 1972; Skei and Paus, 1979).

The top sediment at station 52 is black, silty clay containing hydrogen sulfide. The profile of total Mn content is greatly controlled by the H$_2$O$_2$ fraction, in which Mn content changes significantly ~30 cm from the sediment surface (Fig. 20.5). This type of Mn profile has not been reported in common coastal sediments. It is very similar, however, to the profile reported in a sediment core from a historically meromictic lake (Masuzawa and Kitano, 1982). Manganese in the brackish lake sediment was reported to be associated with iron disulfide (FeS$_2$) included in the H$_2$O$_2$ fraction (Masuzawa and Kitano, 1982). If Mn is associated with organic material, it would be included in the Mn of the H$_2$O$_2$ fraction as with other metals. As seen from Figs. 20.5a and 20.7, however, there is no relation between Mn and organic material. In the H$_2$O$_2$ treatment, stable sulfides are decomposed (Kitano and Fujiyoshi, 1980; Kitano et al., 1981; Masuzawa and Kitano, 1982). Generally, manganese sulfide is seldom observed in sediment because of its high solubility (Krejci-Graf, 1975), except in the very special sediment in the Baltic Sea (Suess, 1979). If manganese sulfide exists in the upper anoxic layer at station 52, it will be leached in dilute HCl solution (Suess, 1979); however, the Mn content of HCl was relatively constant through the sediment core so that MnS was probably not present. The chemical form of the Mn dissolved with H$_2$O$_2$ solution remains unresolved. This will be discussed further in Section 20.4.4.

20.4.3. Chemical Forms of Fe, Cu, and Zn in Sediment

Iron associated with organic material will be leached by H_2O_2 (Kitano et al., 1980). As with Mn, there was no relation between the Fe and organic material content in the sediment at station 52. Figures 20.5b and 20.7 show a good relationship, however, between S and Fe content in the H_2O_2 fraction. The major part of the S is assumed to exist as stable iron sulfide (pyrite and FeS_2) because organic S content is negligible (Berner, 1970; Nissenbaum and Swaine, 1976; Kitano et al., (1981). Thus, the Fe content of the H_2O_2 fraction is considered to be related to stable pyrite (Gad and Le Riche, 1966; Kitano and Fujiyoshi, 1980; Kitano et al., 1981). As seen from Fig. 20.5b, stable iron disulfide (pyrite and FeS_2) was considered to exist in the layer below 10 cm in depth of this core because the average mole ratio of S and Fe was 1.8 in the lower layer as compared with 1.6 in the upper layer. The stable iron sulfide content of the upper 10-cm layer appeared to decrease significantly upward, whereas the Fe content of the HAC fraction increased. This suggests that the amount of unstable iron monosulfide (FeS), which is dissolved by acetic acid treatment, increases upward. It was reported that the Mn content of pyrite is larger than that of unstable FeS in some lake sediment (Masuzawa and Kitano, 1982). In this core sediment, the Mn content exhibited a maximum value at the 10-cm layer.

The initial increases in Cu and Zn contents correspond to about the early 1920s, as was seen from data from ^{210}Pb dating. The nearly constant contents of Cu and Zn in the lower layers seem to represent natural background levels before human activities (Matsumoto and Yokota, 1978; Hoshika et al., 1983; Hoshika and Shiozawa, 1984a,b); therefore, the increase in Cu and Zn contents in the upper layers of the sediment cores was considered to be caused by human activities. Contamination has decreased since the late 1970s, probably because of legal control of contaminant discharge. At station 50, the uniform distribution of Cu and Zn in the upper layers may be attributed to mixing of the sediment through physical and/or biological turbation. From the partitioning study, it is noted that at station 52 the most significant amount of Zn in the sediment was present in the HAC fraction. Most of the Zn in the polluted surface-sediment layer is associated with oxide or sulfide fractions, which are easily dissolved with diluted HCl solution (Kitano et al., 1981). Under anoxic conditions in contaminated sediment, sulfide is important for the fixation of Zn; therefore, the Zn dissolved with acetic acid

treatment is considered to represent unstable sulfides. In the present study the state of Cu was not clarified.

20.4.4. Diagenetic Behavior of Mn in Core Sediment

Stable pyrite formation appears to be favorable for Mn coprecipitation under anoxic sedimentary conditions (Masuzawa and Kitano; 1982). As seen from Fig. 20.6, dissolved Mn in interstitial water abruptly decreased downward from 1.17 mg liter^{-1} at the surface to 0.23 mg liter^{-1} in the 10-cm layer. We think that Mn diffuses downward and is removed from the interstitial water as a precipitate that dissolves with H_2O_2 treatment. The removal of Mn from the interstitial water occurred at 10-cm depth, where pyrite is precipitated actively; and Mn does not diffuse significantly to deeper layers. As described earlier, Mn is not generally associated with FeS or organic material. As reported by Masuzawa and Kitano (1982), however, the Mn in H_2O_2 is assumed to be associated with pyrite. The Mn content of H_2O_2 was high only in the subsurface layers to about 10-cm depths, although stable iron sulfide (pyrite) existed below 10 cm. The appearance of anoxic sedimentary conditions since the mid-1960s must have accelerated the formation of pyrite. Thus, during the process of rapid pyrite formation, mobile Mn is assumed to be coprecipitated with stable FeS_2. Figure 20.8a–d shows the horizontal distribution of Mn in individual fractions in the 0- to 2-cm surface sediment collected from Beppu Bay in November 1976. Since the sediment samples were collected with a Smith-McIntyre sampler, the surface layers of the sediment might have been lost. The total Mn content of sediment (Fig. 20.9) tended to show the largest values in the oxic areas outside the central basin. This distribution is controlled mainly by the Mn content of both the HAC and the HCl fraction. A high Mn content in the H_2O_2 fraction is observed in sediment in the area of the deep basin where the highest total sulfur contents are observed (Ohita Fishery Research Laboratory, 1976). The horizontal distribution of Mn, as well as the vertical distribution in sediment, shows the high accumulation of Mn in the anoxic region. Manganese redistribution within the sediment is explained generally as the result of reduction after burial, mobilization in interstitial water, and reprecipitation in oxidized sediment (Lynn and Bonatti, 1965; Li et al., 1969; Bonatti et al., 1972). As described in this chapter, however, the early diagenetic coprecipitation of Mn with iron sulfide occurred in the anoxic

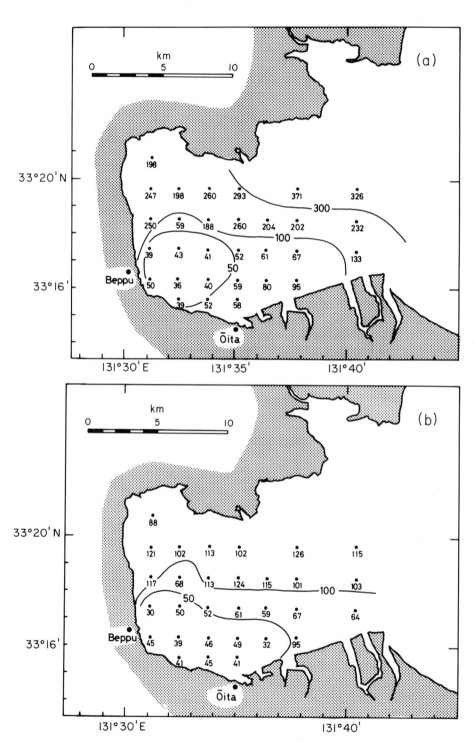

Figure 20.8 Horizontal distributions of Mn contents in (a) 10% HAC-soluble, (b) 0.1 *M* HCl-soluble, (c) H₂O₂-soluble, and (d) HF-soluble fractions of surface sediment samples (0–2 cm) from Beppu Bay.

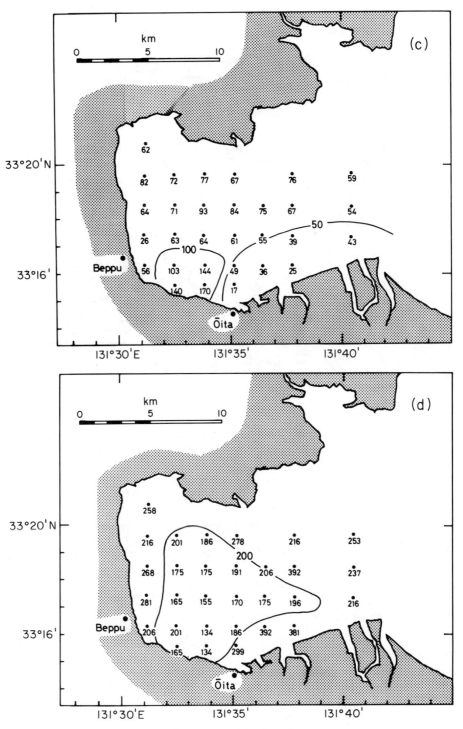

Figure 20.8. *(Continued)*

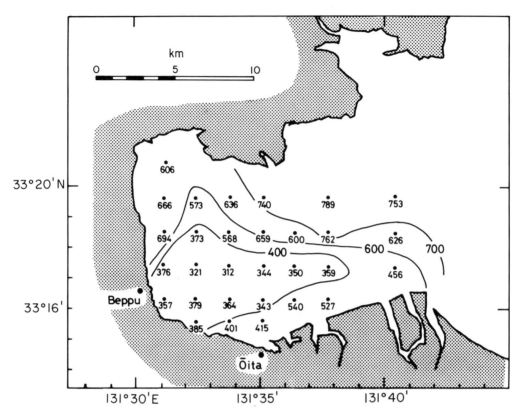

Figure 20.9 Horizontal distributions of total Mn content in surface sediment samples (0–2 cm) from Beppu Bay.

environment containing hydrogen sulfide in the sediment of inner Beppu Bay.

20.5. CONCLUSIONS

The results of ^{210}Pb dating suggest that the sedimentation rate in the innermost part of Beppu Bay has shown a threefold increase over the background rate since the mid-1960s. This increase in the discharge of particulate materials into the deeper sedimentation basin has lead to the formation of an anoxic environment with hydrogen sulfide in the bottom water during stratified periods in the summer.

The results of selective chemical leaching of core sediment show that the H_2O_2-leachable Mn content changed significantly in those sediment layers composed of black, silty clay and hydrogen sulfide. During the rapid formation of stable pyrite, FeS_2 in this anoxic environment, mobile Mn is presumed to be coprecipitated with the stable iron sulfide.

The high Cu and Zn contents in the upper sediment layers are explained by contamination due to human activities.

ACKNOWLEDGMENT

The authors thank T. Masuzawa of Nagoya University for teaching sulfur analysis and for giving helpful suggestions.

REFERENCES

Berner, R. A. 1970. Sedimentary pyrite formation. *American Journal of Science*, **268**, 1–23.

Bonatti, E., D. E. Fisher, O. Joensun, and H. R. Rydell. 1972. Postdepositional mobility of some transition elements, phosphorous, uranium and thorium in deep sediment. *Geochimica et Cosmochimica Acta*, **35**, 189–201.

Chester, R., and M. J. Hughes. 1967. A chemical technique for the separation of ferro-manganese minerals, carbonate minerals and adsorbed trace elements from pelagic sediments. *Chemical Geology*, **2**, 249–262.

Emerson, S., R. E. Cranston, and P. S. Liss. 1979. Redox species in a reducing fjord: equilibrium and kinetic considerations. *Deep-Sea Research*, **26A**, 859–878.

Gad, M. A., and H. H. Le Riche. 1966. A method for separating the detrital and non-detrital fractions of trace elements in reduced sediments. *Geochimica et Cosmochimica Acta*, **30**, 841–846.

Grill, E. V. 1978. The effect of sediment–water exchange on manganese deposition and nodule growth in Jervis Inlet, British Columbia. *Geochimica et Cosmochimica Acta*, **42**, 485–494.

Hoshika, A., and T. Shiozawa. 1984a. Sedimentation rates and heavy metal pollution of sediments in the Seto Inland Sea, Part 2: Hiroshima Bay. *Journal of the Oceanographical Society of Japan*, **40**, 115–123.

Hoshika, A., and T. Shiozawa. 1984b. Sedimentation rates and heavy metal pollution of sediments in the Seto Inland Sea, Part 3: Hiuchi-Nada. *Journal of the Oceanographical Society of Japan*, **40**, 334–342.

Hoshika, A., O. Takimura, and T. Shiozawa. 1978. Vertical distribution of particulate manganese and iron in the Beppu Bay. *Journal of the Oceanographical Society of Japan*, **34**, 261–264.

Hoshika, A., T. Shiozawa, and E. Matsumoto. 1983. Sedimentation rate and heavy metal pollution in sediments in Harima-Nada (Harima Sound), the Seto Inland Sea. *Journal of the Oceanographical Society of Japan*, **39**, 82–87 (in Japanese).

Inouchi, Y. 1982. Distribution of bottom sediments in the Seto Inland Sea— The influence of tidal currents on the distribution of the bottom sediments. *Journal of Geological Society of Japan*, **88**, 665–681.

Jackson, M. L. 1968. Soil Chemical Analysis Advanced Course, 2nd Ed. Department of Soil Science, University of Wisconsin, Madison, Wisconsin, 895 pp.

Kitano, Y., and R. Fujiyoshi. 1980a. Selective chemical leaching of cadmium, copper, manganese and iron in marine sediments. *Geochemical Journal*, **14**, 113–122.

Kitano, Y., M. Sakata, and E. Matsumoto. 1981. Partitioning of heavy metals into mineral and organic fractions in a sediment core sample from Osaka Bay. *Journal of the Oceanographical Society of Japan*, **37**, 259–266.

Krejci-Graf, K. 1975. Geochemical facies of sediments. *Soil Science*, **119**, 20–23.

Li, Y. H., J. G. Bischoff, and G. Mathieu. 1969. The migration of manganese in the arctic basin sediment. *Earth and Planetary Science Letters*, **7**, 265–270.

Loring, D. H. 1976. The distribution and partitioning of zinc, copper and lead in the sediments of the Saguenay fjord. *Canadian Journal of Earth Science*, **13**, 961–971.

Lynn, D. C., and E. Bonatti. 1965. Mobility of manganese in diagenesis of deep-sea sediments. *Marine Geology*, **3**, 457–474.

Manheim, F. T. 1961. A geochemical profile in the Baltic Sea. *Geochimica et Cosmochimica Acta*, **25**, 52–70.

Masuzawa, T., and Y. Kitano. 1981. Sulfate reduction and sulfur fixation in sediment of a historically meromictic lake, Lake Suigetsu, Japan. *Journal of the Oceanographical Society of Japan*, **38**, 21–27.

Masuzawa, T., and Y. Kitano. 1982. Diagenetic deposition of manganese in sediment of a historically meromictic lake, Lake Suigetsu, Japan. *Journal of the Oceanographical Society of Japan*, **38**, 73–80.

Matsumoto, E., and C. S. Wong. 1977. Heavy metal sedimentation measured with Pb-210 technique. *Journal of Geophysical Research*, **82**, 5477–5482.

Matsumoto, E., and S. Yokota. 1978. Accumulation rate and heavy metal pollution in Osaka Bay sediments. *Journal of the Oceanographical Society of Japan*, **34**, 108–115 (in Japanese).

Miyadi, D. 1941. Marine benthic communities of the Beppu-Wan. *Memoir of Imperial Maritime Observatory*, **7**, 483–502 (in Japanese).

Nissenbaum, A., and D. J. Swaine. 1976. Organic water–metal interaction in recent sediments: the role of humic substances. *Geochimica et Cosmochimica Acta*, **40**, 809–816.

Ohita Fishery Research Laboratory. 1976. Reports on Assessment of Fishery Environment—Data Book. Ohita Fishery Research Laboratory, Ohita, Japan, 96 pp. (in Japanese).

Shiozawa, T., K. Kawana, A. Hoshika, T. Tanimoto, and O. Takimura. 1977. Vertical distribution of heavy metals and their seasonal variations in Beppu Bay. *Journal of the Oceanographical Society of Japan*, **33**, 350–356 (in Japanese).

Skei, J., and P. E. Paus. 1979. Surface metal enrichment and partitioning of metals in a dated sediment core from a Norwegian fjord. *Geochimica et Cosmochimica Acta*, **43**, 239–246.

Spencer, D. W., and P. G. Brewer. 1971. Vertical advection diffusion and redox potentials as controls on the distribution of manganese and other trace metals dissolved in waters of the Black Sea. *Journal of Geophysical Research*, **76**, 5877–5892.

Suess, E. 1979. Mineral phases formed in anoxic sediments by microbial decomposition of organic matter. *Geochimica et Cosmochimica Acta*, **43**, 339–352.

Tamai, K. 1980. Distribution of two characteristic benthos, *Lucinoma annulata* (Bivalvia) and *Aricidea* sp. (Polychaeta) at the innermost and deeper part of Beppu Bay. *Bulletin Nansei Regional Fisheries Research Laboratory*, **12**, 105–114 (in Japanese).

Chapter 21

Identification of Pollution Sources of Heavy Metals in Marine Coastal Sediments from Patterns of Partitioning and Diagenetic Change

Hirozo Yoshimura, Takio Shiba, and Keizo Watanabe

Maritime Safety Agency Research Center
Kitanakadori, Yokohama-shi, Japan

Abstract	**235**
21.1. Introduction	**235**
21.2. Experimental Methods	**236**
21.2.1. Collection and Treatment of Sediment	236
21.2.2. Chemical Analyses	237
21.2.3. Selective Leaching of Sediment	237
21.3. Results and Discussion	**237**
21.3.1. Concentrations of Elements in Sediment	237
21.3.2. Chemical Analyses of Inorganic Industrial Waste Muds	238
21.3.3. Diagenetic Changes of Heavy Metals in Industrial Waste Mud	238
21.3.3a. Experiment 1: diagenesis of Cr, Cu, Sn, and Zn	*238*
21.3.3b. Experiment 2: diagenesis of Co, Cu, Ni, and Zn	*242*
21.3.3c. Diagenesis of Fe and Mn	*243*
21.4. Conclusions	**243**
Acknowledgments	**243**
References	**243**

ABSTRACT

Surface marine sediment from 15 Japanese coastal sites was analyzed for major and trace elements. The sediment from certain small, enclosed bays surrounded by factories contained higher concentrations of heavy metals than did that from more open water in highly industrialized areas. The ratios among metals in the sediment were compared to ratios in different types of industrial waste to gain insight on the origins of the metals in the environment. Laboratory experiments were conducted on the diagenesis of Co, Cr, Cu, Fe, Mn, Ni, Sn, and Zn in industrial waste muds discharged to coastal sediment. Metals were determined in different mineral and organic fractions of the sediment (ion-exchangeable, oxide, sulfide, organic, and silicate lattice fractions), by using selective chemical leaching techniques. The chemical forms of Cu, Ni, Sn, and Zn changed diametrically to insoluble compounds under the anaerobic conditions that were simulated in the experiments.

21.1. INTRODUCTION

About 2×10^6 metric tons (t) of inorganic industrial wastes are dumped annually into the marine environments of Japan. These wastes have been dumped mainly at two dumpsites authorized by governmental organizations, and located ~300 km southeast of the Japanese islands (Fig. 21.1). The seawater at these dumpsites has been monitored periodically after dumping. Organic C, N, S, and P from domestic sewage and some heavy metals (Cr, Cu, Pb, Ni, and Zn) from industrial sewage have been the principal pollutants in the past, but currently in Japan heavy-metal inputs are decreasing because liquid industrial waste is generally being treated to produce industrial sludges and waste muds.

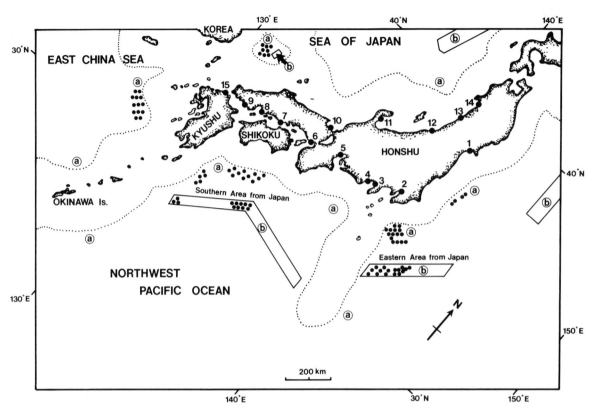

Figure 21.1. Ocean dumpsites and sampling locations around the Japanese Islands. The hatched areas are presently used for ocean dumping. The areas marked by (a) are authorized by the Japanese government for dumping, but insoluble waste muds are admitted only in the areas marked (b). Numbers in Japanese coastal regions refer to specific sampling locations as follows: (1) Matsushima Bay, (2) Tokyo Bay, (3) Tagonoura Harbour, (4) Shimizu Harbour, (5) Ise Bay, (6) Osaka Bay, (7) Mizushima Harbour, (8) Kure Harbour, (9) Tokuyama Bay, (10) Maizuru Bay, (11) Nanao Bay, (12), Niigata Harbour, (13) Sakata Harbour, (14) Akita Harbour, (15) Dokai Bay.

Before the legal control of pollutant discharges for environmental safety, the sewage from industrial factories was directly discharged into coastal areas. Since legal control was instituted, however, industrial waste materials in effluents have been treated through coprecipitation with ferric hydroxide, activated sludge treatment, centrifugal separation, and other treatment procedures. The waste muds are disposed into the ocean through dumping, or they are buried, either on land or in coastal areas being reclaimed by filling. Unauthorized dumping occurs occasionally in coastal areas, posing a serious problem in Japan and making it necessary to monitor these coastal areas to maintain and protect their environmental quality.

Knowledge of the chemical composition of inorganic industrial waste muds is an important requisite for identifying a pollution source. In this chapter, we describe techniques that may be useful for the location and identification of sources of

heavy-metal pollution through three types of experimental studies: (1) chemical analysis of the heavy-metal concentrations and forms in coastal sediments near urban industrial regions; (2) chemical analysis of the heavy metals in inorganic industrial waste muds; and (3) chemical investigations of the diagenetic changes of heavy metals in industrial waste muds discharged to coastal sediments, under aerobic and anaerobic conditions.

21.2. EXPERIMENTAL METHODS

21.2.1. Collection and Treatment of Sediment

Coastal sediment was sampled at 15 coastal stations (Fig. 21.1) by dredging with an Eckman dredge. The bottom sediment was collected to a depth of ~5 cm. Most of the sampling stations, located in harbors, bights, and the inner parts of bays (Fig. 21.1), are situated near coastal industrial regions. At most stations, two samples were collected (range 1–6) for a total of 39 samples.

Prior to chemical analyses, the sediment samples were sieved through a 2-mm pore-size screen and then centrifuged at 3000 rpm for 10 min to reduce the analytical correction for residual seawater in the sediment. After centrifugation, the sediment was dried at 110°C, and the dried sediment was used for chemical analyses.

21.2.2. Chemical Analyses

The content of organic C, N, S, and P in the sediment was determined. Total carbon was determined by the combustion method using a CHN analyzer (Yamaco model MT-3) at 950°C. Nitrogen content was determined by a standard micro-Kjeldahl method. Elemental sulfur and sulfur compounds in dried sediment were oxidized in a combustion tube at 950°C under flowing gaseous oxygen. The sulfur dioxide generated by this combustion was absorbed into 3% H_2O_2 (vol:vol) solution, and the sulfuric acid formed in the solution was titrated with standard KOH solution (Japanese Standards Association, 1980). Phosphorus was determined spectrophotometrically according to the method described by Murphy and Riley (1962) after decomposition of the sediment by HF-$HClO_4$ (5:1).

Major inorganic elements and minor heavy metals were determined after decomposition with HF-$HClO_4$. After initial decomposition of organic material in the samples by using HNO_3, the samples were heated with the HF-$HClO_4$ solution in platinum dishes to dryness, indicated by the extinction of $HClO_4$ fumes. The residuals were then redissolved by heating in HCl solution (Maritime Safety Agency Research Center, 1982, 1983, 1984).

Sodium and K were determined by flame photometry. The other metals (Al, Ba, Ca, Cd, Co, Cu, Fe, Mg, Mn, Mo, Ni, Pb, Sb, Sn, Sr, Ti, V, Y, Zn, and Zr) were determined by Inductive Coupled Plasma (ICP) spectrophotometry. The analytical results from ICP were sometimes confirmed, either by atomic absorption spectrophotometry (AAS) for Cu, Fe, Ni, Pb, and Zn or by a spectrophotometric method for Al, after extraction with organic solvents such as methyl-iso-butyl ketone (Corey and Jackson, 1953; Riley, 1958; Maritime Safety Agency Research Center, 1982, 1983, 1984). The

presence of major elements interfered with the ICP determination of Ag, As, and B.

As in our experiments, the decomposition of samples with HF-$HClO_4$ solution causes losses of volatile Cr compounds (Maritime Safety Agency Research Center, 1982). For the determination of Cr, alkali fusion with Na_2CO_3-$NaNO_3$ (20:1) was carried out after H_2SO_4-HF decomposition of the sample and analyzed by AAS after extraction with 3% (vol:vol) trioctylamine (TOA) butyl acetate (Japanese Standards Association, 1975).

Semiquantitative analyses of metals were performed by X-ray fluorescence spectrometry (Tanaka and Hashizume, 1975) on ~80 types of industrial waste muds collected from the liquid waste treatment sections of factories. Waste muds were dried at 110°C, and the dried samples were milled to powder. After dilution with cellulose powder, samples were compressed under 15 t cm^{-2} into pellets for analysis.

21.2.3. Selective Leaching of Sediment

The selective chemical leaching technique is based on the preferential dissolution of different mineral and organic fractions of sediment. A flow chart for the selective chemical leaching technique used here is shown in Fig. 21.2 (Kitano and Fujiyoshi, 1980). The various fractions obtained through the selective leaching process were analyzed for heavy metals by AAS.

21.3. RESULTS AND DISCUSSION

21.3.1. Concentrations of Elements in Sediment

Figure 21.3a,b shows the ranges in the contents of elements measured in Japanese coastal sediment. Extremely high contents of heavy metals and organic contaminants were observed in some samples.

The highest concentrations of Zn (>10 μg g^{-1}) occurred in the sediment of Dokai Bay, Tagonoura Harbour, and Akita Harbour. The Cr contents of sediment from Dokai Bay and sediment from Tagonoura Harbour exceeded 2×10^2 μg g^{-1}, while the Cr content was extremely high only in the inner district of Dokai Bay. These areas, where the most serious contamination by heavy metals was observed, are all small,

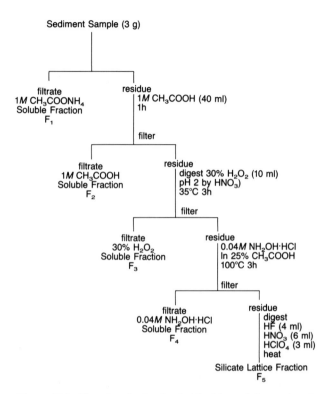

Figure 21.2. Flow chart for the chemical leaching techniques adopted to quantify the partitioning of heavy metals among different chemical forms: absorbed ion-exchangeable elements (F_1), hydroxides and carbonates (F_2), oxides (F_2–F_4), Sulfides (ordinarily F_3), organic compounds (mostly F_3), and the metals in clay or silicate lattices (F_5).

enclosed bays near districts crowded with factories. The sediment near the large industrial regions, such as Tokyo Bay, Osaka Bay, and Ise Bay areas, was less contaminated by heavy-metal pollutants than were those in the areas mentioned above.

21.3.2. Chemical Analyses of Inorganic Industrial Waste Muds

Some industrial waste muds, especially those from metal plating and electronics factories, contain many kinds of heavy metals, including large amounts of Cu and Ni, and significant amounts of Cr and Zn. Electronics industries also generate waste muds that may contain Cu, Fe, and either Cr or Ni, and sometimes Sn and Zn. The predominant metals generated by different industries are shown in Table 21.1.

Other than the elements shown in Table 21.1, S, P, alkaline metals, and Cl and Br (in waste muds from the photography industry) have been detected in waste muds in Japan. The bulk of the Cl, Na, and S arises through seawater treatment, where HCl, NaOH, and H_2SO_4 are used for neutralization.

Metals ratios may be useful for identifying future sources of contaminants in marine sediments. Figure 21.4 shows the relationship between (a) Cu and Zn and (b) Ni and Cu for different categories of waste muds and coastal sediment. Waste muds from metal plating and processing may promote higher sediment contamination by Cu (relative to Zn) in the future; however, electronics waste muds could produce the same trend for Cu contamination in the future. An increase in the Cu:Zn ratio in sediment would suggest, therefore, that the contamination source might be metal-plating, electronics, or certain metal-manufacturing waste mud. Similarly, if the Ni content of sediment is shifted upward relative to Cu (Fig. 21.4b), metal plating wastes would be the indicated contamination source.

21.3.3. Diagenetic Changes of Heavy Metals in Industrial Waste Mud

After the discharge of industrial waste mud to coastal sediment, heavy metals undergo diagenetic changes in the contaminated sediment. We expected that these diagenetic changes of heavy metals might be useful for identification of a contamination source, if enough basic information were available on the early diagenetic changes under aerobic and anaerobic conditions. Thus, in 1981, we began experiments on behavior of heavy metals in contaminated sediment under aerobic and anaerobic conditions.

Sediment samples were prepared by mixing a small amount of waste mud with coastal sediment in a 50-liter seawater tank. The chemical states of heavy metals in the contaminated sediment were determined over time by using the selective chemical leaching techniques described previously (Fig. 21.2). Similar experiments were carried out for two types of contaminated coastal sediment.

21.3.3a. Experiment 1: diagenesis of Cr, Cu, Sn, and Zn

The experimental mixture was prepared by mixing (1:13, dry wt) electronics industrial waste mud with coastal sediment,

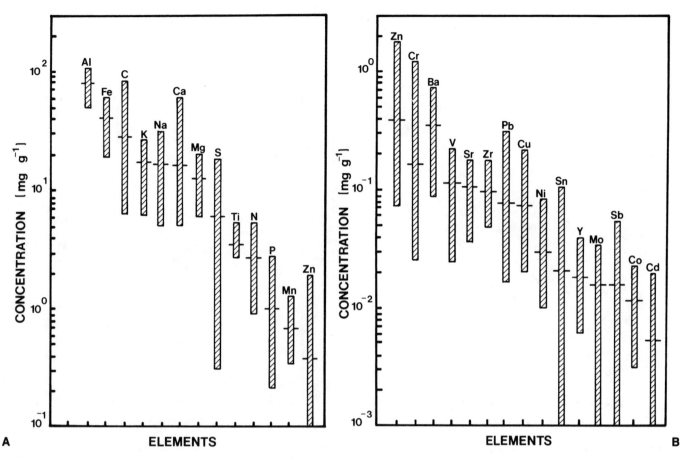

Figure 21.3. Concentrations of elements in coastal sediments of Japan. (a) Mean concentrations >3 mg g^{-1}, (b) Mean concentrations <3 mg g^{-1}. Hatched areas indicate maximum to minimum concentration while the crossbar indicates the average value.

Table 21.1. Outline of Elements Present in Ordinary Industrial Waste Muds

Industry	Number of Samples	Concentration Ranges[a]		
		<0.3%	0.3–0.02%	<0.02%
Metal plating	10	Ni, Cu, Fe, Sn, ((Mg))[b], ((Ca))	Zn, Cr, Co, Ba, Al, Si	Mn, Pb, Sb, As, ((Ag))
Electronics	5	Cu, Ni, Cr, Fe, (Zn)[c], (Sn)	Al, Co, B, (Ca), ((Y))	Mn
Steel washing and metal processing	16	Fe, ((Pb))	Cu, Zn, Al, Si, B, (Sn), (Ba)	(Mo)
Light metal processing	4	Al, B, (Fe)	Fe, Cu	Zn, Pb, (Cd)
Chemical	7	Al, Si, Fe, (Ca), (Mg)	Mg, Ca, (Pb), (Cr), (Ba), (Ti)	Ni, Zn, Cu, Mn, (Co)
Fine chemical	8	—	Al, Si, Fe, Cu, Ni, Zn, Ca	—
Photography	11	Al, Fe	Si, Cu, Zn, Ag, Ba	Ti, Mn, Ni, Sn, Pb
Medical factory	8	Al, Si, Fe, Ca, Mg, (Ba)	Ti, Zn	Mn, Cu, Ni
Food processing	15	Al, Si, Ca, Mg, (Fe)	Fe, Zn, Cu, Sr, ((Pb))	—

[a]Concentration ranges of detected elements on a dry-weight basis.
[b](( )) indicates rarely detected.
[c]( ) indicates occasionally detected.
[d]A dash indicates none detected.

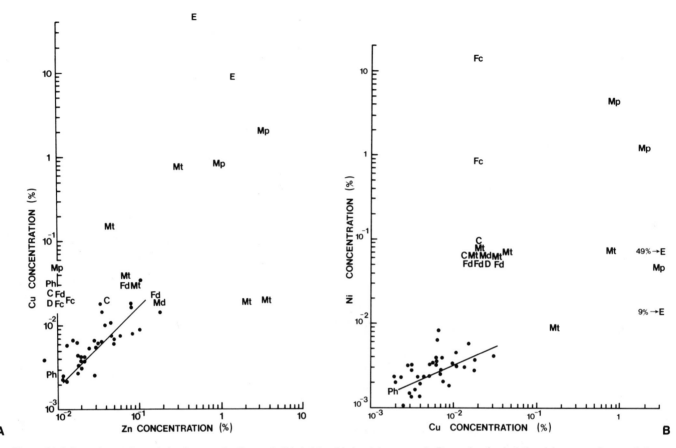

Figure 21.4. Inter-elemental correlation for coastal sediments (solid circle) and industrial waste muds. Data points for the industrial waste muds are coded as follows: Mp = Metal plating; E = Electronics; Mt = Steel washing and metal processing; C = Chemical industry; Fc = Fine chemical; Ph = Photography; Md = Medical factory; Fd = Food processing; D = Dye works. (a) Correlation between Cu and Zn contents, (b) correlation between Ni and Cu contents.

which had been collected previously from Mizushima Harbour and frozen for several months prior to the experiment. Dissolved oxygen (DO), pH, and Eh were measured periodically throughout the experiment. Content of heavy metals in the seawater were nearly at a trace level throughout the experiment. The concentrations of dissolved metals in the seawater during the first 11 d of the experiment were as follows: Cu and Zn, 1 μg g^{-1}; Cr and Sn, 0.2 μg g^{-1}; and Fe, 3–6 μg g^{-1}.

The sediment mixture was also used for selective leaching and chemical analysis. After 42 d, organic waste mud (1:20 of the experimental mixture) was added. This organic waste mud was a fermentation waste from the beer-brewing industry and was composed of 70% crude proteins, 28% polysaccharides, and small amounts of diatomaceous earth.

After the addition of the organic waste mud, the seawater

over the experimental mixture was not aerated, and the Eh of the sediment commonly changed to reducing conditions, with concomitant increases in the F$_3$ fraction (sulfides) for some heavy metals (Cr, Cu and Zn). The extent of reducing conditions was estimated by titration with 0.1 M KI-I$_2$ solution, along with measurements of DO, pH, and Eh.

Chromium in the sediment mixture occurred in the F$_2$, F$_3$, F$_4$, and F$_5$ fractions. Chromium was not observed in the F$_1$ fraction (ion-exchangeable), whereas Cu, Fe, Mn, and Zn all occurred in that fraction. The chemical form of Cr gradually changed to less soluble compounds with time. This change also reflected the change in oxidation–reduction potential.

Under aerobic conditions for 11 d, the partitioning of Cu among the different leachate solutions did not change (Fig. 21.5); however, after the addition of the organic waste mud (fermentation sludge), the partitioning of Cu was greatly

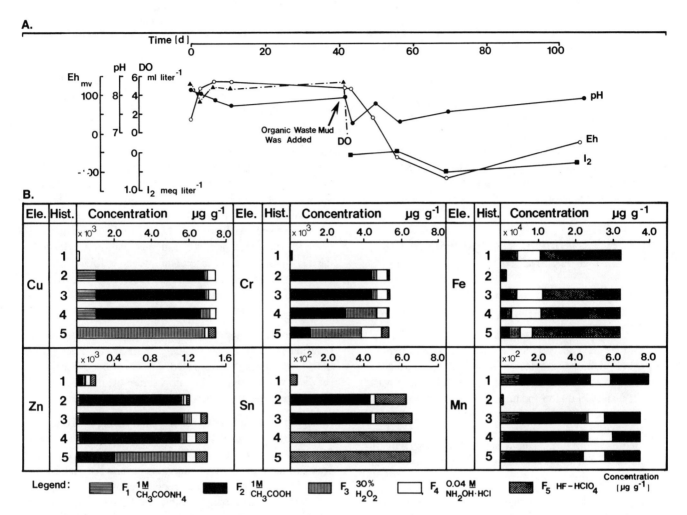

Figure 21.5. Experimental results on diagenesis of selected metals in a mixture of waste mud from the electronics industry and Mizushima Harbour sediments (Experiment 1). (a) The time course of Eh (hollow circle), pH (solid circle), DO (in ml liter^{-1}) (solid triangle), and I$_2$ consumed (meq liter^{-1}) in titration of bottom water (solid square). Organic waste was added on day 40. (b) Concentration (μg g^{-1}) of Cu, Cr, Fe, Mn, Sn, and Zn in the fractions (F$_1$–F$_5$) separated by selective chemical leaching of sediment samples from the diagenesis experiment. Samples are as follows: (1) Coastal sediment collected from Mizushima Harbour; (2) Electronics waste mud in seawater; (3) Sediment mixture immediately after mixing (calculated from (1) and (2)); (4) The sediment mixture 11 d after mixing (under aerobic conditions); and (5) The sediment mixture on day 107, 65 d after the addition (1:20) of organic waste mud (centrifuged fermentation sludge).

changed toward more insoluble fractions. The Cu content of the F$_3$ fraction (H$_2$O$_2$-soluble) increased greatly, with corresponding decreases in the 1 M-ammonium acetate-soluble fraction (F$_1$, ion-exchangeable) and the 1 M-acetic acid-soluble fraction (F$_2$, carbonate and hydroxide fractions). Copper of the F$_3$ fraction is regarded as associated mostly with organic material and partly with pyrite. The addition of organic materials would promote the activity of bacterial sulfate reduction, suggesting that the chemical form of Cu changed to copper sulfide after the addition of organic waste mud.

In the coastal sediment, Sn was found only in the insoluble fraction (F$_5$) soluble only with fluoric acid. This fraction is considered to be stable clay. In the electronics industry waste mud, however, the Sn content of the F$_2$ fraction (acetic acid-soluble) reached 5 × 10^2 μg g^{-1} on a dry-weight basis. The easily soluble stannous compound in fraction F$_2$ (probably stannous hydroxide) quickly changed to a very stable form in the sediment mixture, which was identified as iron–tin hydroxide [FeSn(OH)$_6$] by X-ray diffractometry.

Under aerobic conditions for 11 d, the Zn contents of the F$_1$

(ion-exchangeable) and F_2 (acetic acid-soluble) fractions remained almost constant (Fig. 21.5). The Zn contents of the F_4 and F_5 fractions were fairly constant throughout the aerobic and anaerobic periods.

After 65 d under anaerobic conditions, however, the Zn contents of the F_3 fraction (H_2O_2-soluble) increased dramatically, and the Zn content of the F_1 fraction disappeared. The increase in F_3 indicated that Zn became associated with sulfide. Zinc sulfide is also partially dissolved with acetic acid; therefore, the Zn content of the F_2 fraction (acetic acid soluble fraction) was high.

21.3.3b. Experiment 2: diagenesis of Co, Cu, Ni, and Zn

The experimental mixture was prepared by mixing (1:12.5, dry-weight basis) metal-plating waste mud with coastal sediment from Osaka Bay.

Dissolved oxygen, pH, and Eh were measured periodically for 120 d, and 4 samples (original Osaka Bay sediment; sediment mixture 1 d after mixing with metal-plating waste mud; 52 d and 119 d after the mix, still under aerobic conditions) were collected for selective leaching and chemical analysis. After 120 d, organic waste mud was added ($\sim$1:2.5 of the sediment mixture). This waste mud was from a distillery and consisted of $\sim$60% carbohydrate compounds and 16% crude proteins.

Forty days after the addition of the organic waste mud, the experimental mixture had become anaerobic, and the last sample was collected for selective leaching and chemical analysis. At this time, free sulfur occurred on the sediment surface due to the activity of sulfate-reducing bacteria and sulfur bacteria. Contents of heavy metals in the different components of the sediment mixture of Experiment 2 are shown in Table 21.2.

Before the addition of organic waste mud into the sediment sample, the Cu content in the H_2O_2-soluble fraction (F_3) was $\sim$3 $\times$ 10^2 μg g^{-1}, perhaps due to the reduced state of the Osaka Bay sediment. Thirty-five days after initial mixing of the sediment, the Eh in the bottom sediment had declined to -95 mv. At this point, aeration was initiated, and at 115 d, the Eh had returned to 30 mv, and the Cu in the F_3 fraction was $\sim$2 $\times$ 10^2 μg g^{-1}. Under the reducing conditions induced by the addition of organic waste mud into the sediment mixture, the Cu content of the F_3 fraction increased after 40 d to nearly 87% of the total. The anaerobic fermentation for 40 d reduced the oxidation–reduction potential to -170 mv.

The concentration of dissolved Cu in the upper layers of seawater from the experimental tank decreased from 40 μg liter^{-1} to 5 μg liter^{-1} after 158 d. The Cu of the experimental seawater was precipitated, mainly under the reducing conditions during the later phases of the experiment.

The diagenetic change for the partitioning of Co and Ni was similar to that of Cu. Cobalt sulfide (fraction F_3) was formed through anaerobic diagenetic processes in a manner very similar to the Cu behavior, more so than Ni. There was a large difference between the concentration of seawater-soluble Ni (or Co) and that of soluble Cu. Dissolved amounts of Co and Ni were significant, whereas the amount of dissolved

Table 21.2.   Contributions of Osaka Bay Sediment and Metal-Plating Waste Mud to the Sediment Mixture of Experiment 2[a]

| Element | Osaka Bay Sediment[b] | Metal-Plating Waste Mud | | Sediment Mixture | |
		Seawater Soluble[c]	Seawater Insoluble[d]	Sum[e]	Actual Analysis
Zn	3.8 $\times$ 10^2	10	5.3 $\times$ 10^2	9.2 $\times$ 10^2	8.8 $\times$ 10^2
Cu	70	1.4	4.8 $\times$ 10^2	5.51 $\times$ 10^2	5.5 $\times$ 10^2
Ni	25	7.5 $\times$ 10^2	2.0 $\times$ 10^3	2.78 $\times$ 10^3	2.8 $\times$ 10^3
Co	14	27	1.75 $\times$ 10^2	2.16 $\times$ 10^2	2.0 $\times$ 10^2
Fe	4.0 $\times$ 10^4	5.3	1.7 $\times$ 10^3	4.17 $\times$ 10^4	3.85 $\pm$ 10^4
Mn	4.3 $\times$ 10^2	10	17	4.57 $\times$ 10^2	4.05 $\times$ 10^2

[a]To facilitate comparison, all values are expressed in terms of μg g^{-1} (dry wt) of the resultant sediment mixture (12.5 parts sediment to 1 part waste mud).
[b]Estimated from direct analysis of dry sediment.
[c]From analysis of dissolved metals, normalized back to dry sediment.
[d]By difference between total (analyzed directly) and seawater-soluble metals.
[e]Sum of the first three columns.

Cu was negligible (Table 21.2). The concentration of seawater-soluble Co increased upon the addition of metal-plating waste mud, but the Co was subsequently precipitated, under aerobic conditions, after mixing with the coastal sediment. The seawater-soluble Ni fraction increased markedly upon the addition of metal-plating waste mud, but this fraction was not precipitated significantly under aerobic conditions. Seawater-soluble Ni compounds precipitated almost entirely, however, under reducing conditions.

The zinc sulfide content of the F_3 fraction (H_2O_2-soluble) in the original Osaka Bay sediment was $>2 \times 10^2$ μg g^{-1}, and remained about the same throughout the aerobic phase of the experiment. After the change to anaerobic conditions, zinc sulfide in the F_3 fraction reached 71% of the total Zn.

21.3.3c. Diagenesis of Fe and Mn

The partitioning of Mn in coastal sediment samples did not change throughout either experiment, whereas the Fe contents of the F_2, F_3, and F_4 fractions changed significantly. Under aerobic conditions, the iron sulfide (F_3) fraction gradually decreased, whereas this fraction increased under anaerobic conditions in both experiments (Fig. 21.5).

21.4. CONCLUSIONS

Changes in the chemical forms of heavy metals in coastal sediment have been studied by adding organic waste material to the sediment and then analyzing fractions obtained from selective chemical leaching techniques. Except for Sn, the chemical form of the heavy metals in inorganic waste muds that were added to coastal sediment did not change significantly under aerobic conditions. The soluble forms of Sn present in the waste muds were quickly converted to highly insoluble forms in the sediment mixture under aerobic conditions. Under anaerobic conditions, which ensued after the addition of organic waste material, the chemical forms of all heavy metals studied quickly changed to less soluble forms. For example, the chemical forms of Co and Cu changed nearly completely to sulfides.

These results provide useful insight on the chemical forms of heavy metals in waste mud and also on the diagenetic behaviors of heavy metals in coastal sediment. Some different industries generate wastes with different compositions of heavy metals. Heavy-metal ratios in coastal sediment may be useful in the identification of sources of heavy-metal pollution.

ACKNOWLEDGMENTS

We express our heartfelt thanks to Yasushi Kitano for his timely suggestion for the experiment and the preparation of this report. We also thank the other members of the Chemical Waste Identification Committee entrusted by the Maritime Safety Agency.

We give thanks to Y. Seto, M. Ishii, M. Koizumi, Y. Ukai, and the other cooperating members for their help in the laboratory work and field sampling.

This report was finished owing to the kindly suggestions and the alteration of construction by the editor; for this we express our deepest gratitude to Douglas A. Wolfe.

REFERENCES

Corey, R. B., and M. I. Jackson. 1953. Silicate analysis by a rapid semi-microchemical system. *Analytical Chemistry*, **25**, 624–628.

Japanese Standards Association. 1975. Methods for Determination of Chromium and Manganese in Stack Gas. Report No. JIS.K 0096, Japanese Standards Association, Tokyo, pp. 3–7 (in Japanese).

Japanese Standards Association. 1980. Testing Methods for Sulfur in Crude Oil and Petroleum Products. Report No. JIS.K 2541, Japanese Standards Association, Tokyo, pp. 20–24 (in Japanese).

Kitano, Y., and R. Fujiyoshi. 1980. Partitioning of cadmium, copper, manganese and iron into mineral and organic fractions in marine sediment. *Geochemical Journal*, **14**, 113–122.

Maritime Safety Agency Research Center. 1982. Experiment for the chemical identification of waste materials in coastal marine environments. *In*: Environmental Research in Japan. MSA Research Center report, Code No. 100, Environment Agency, Tokyo, pp. 8–17 (in Japanese).

Maritime Safety Agency Research Center. 1983. Experiment for the chemical identification of waste materials in coastal marine environments. *In*: Environmental Research in Japan. MSA Research Center report, Code No. 99, Environment Agency, Tokyo, pp. 6–8 (in Japanese).

Maritime Safety Agency Research Center. 1984. Experiment for the chemical identification of waste materials in coastal marine environments. *In*: Environmental Research in Japan. MSA Research Center report, Code No. 98, Environment Agency, Tokyo, pp. 4–7 (in Japanese).

Murphy, J., and J. P. Riley. 1962. A modified single solution method for the determination of phosphate in natural waters. *Analytica Chimica Acta*, **27**, 31–36.

Riley, J. P. 1958. The rapid analysis of silicate rocks and minerals. *Analytica Chimica Acta*, **19**, 413–428.

Tanaka, H., and G. Hashizume. 1975. The rapid determination of heavy metals in sediment by means of x-ray fluorescence analysis: Modification of the x-ray intensity using scattered radiation. *Bulletin of the Chemical Society of Japan*, **48** 1790–1794.

Chapter 22

The Pollution History of Jin Zhou Bay, Bohai Sea, China

Liu Guoxian, Yang Songlin, Zhou Yihua, and Wan Banghe

Institute of Marine Environmental Protection
State Oceanic Administration
Dalian, People's Republic of China

Abstract   245

22.1. Introduction   245

22.2. ^{210}Pb Geochronology of Jin Zhou Bay
      Sediments   246
  22.2.1. Dating Methods   246
  22.2.2. Results and Discussion   246

22.3. History of Heavy-Metal Pollution in
      Jin Zhou Bay   248
  22.3.1. Analysis of Heavy-Metal Profiles and
          Estimation of the Pollution Period   249
  22.3.2. Comparison of the Pollution
          Period (1941–1979) with
          the Pre-pollution Period   252
  22.3.3. Effects on Benthic Macrofauna   252

22.4. Conclusions   253

Acknowledgments   253

References   253

ABSTRACT

The history of pollution by heavy metals in Jin Zhou Bay, People's Republic of China, has been investigated, based on ^{210}Pb chronology and distributions of Cd, Cu, Pb, and Zn, in three cores from different sedimentary regimes of the bay. The mean sedimentation rates, calculated from ^{210}Pb-dating techniques, were 11 mm y^{-1} near the mouth of the Wuli River in the inner bay, 4 mm y^{-1} in the central bay, and 2.9 mm y^{-1} near the outer edge of the bay. From these sedimentation rates and the distribution of metals in the cores, we estimated the historical fluxes of the four metals in the different regions of the bay. The chronology of metals flux is discussed in relation to the history of waste discharge and the distributions and metal contents of macrobenthos in the area. Since the beginning of production of the nonferrous metal industries along the estuary of the Wuli River, heavy-metal pollutants have been discharged continuously into the bay, and the marine environmental quality has gradually deteriorated. Metals pollution became serious around 1951 and reached a peak in 1975. Since then the metal fluxes have decreased owing to the regulation and control of pollutant discharges, but concentrations of certain pollutants remained significant through 1979. Concentrations of Cd and Zn in some shellfish species, for example, have exceeded maximum permissible concentrations for human consumption. Continued control of pollutant discharges should result in further improvements of environmental quality within Jin Zhou Bay.

22.1. INTRODUCTION

In this chapter, the results of ^{210}Pb dating of sediment core chronology have been used to describe the pollution history of Jin Zhou Bay, an industrialized Chinese coastal embayment in the northern Bohai Sea. The sediment profiles of heavy metals were compared with the history of pollutant discharges and observations on macrobenthic fauna in this area.

Jin Zhou Bay is an open, shallow bay on the western side of Liaodong Bay on the northern Bohai Sea (Fig. 22.1). The coastal area along Jin Zhou Bay consists mainly of plains and the Liaoxi Rolling Hills, ~10–20 m above sea level. The

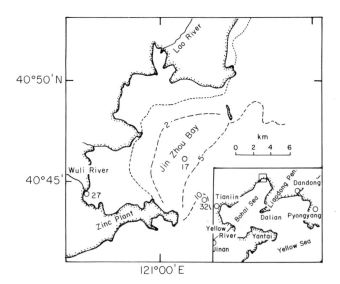

Figure 22.1. Location of sampling stations in Jin Zhou Bay, China.

submarine relief is also fairly flat, with a general slope from the northwest to the southeast. The mean depth of the water is 3.5 m in the bay and 5–6 m in the bay mouth. Wind-driven waves and some offshore swells enter the bay, generally from the south–southwest. The unequal semi-diurnal tide produces reversing currents in the bay mouth and cyclonic currents in the main part of the bay. The current velocity is 20–30 cm s^{-1}, and the residual flow is very weak. From south to north, the Wuli, Lianshan, Tashan, and Lao rivers enter the bay from the west (Fig. 22.1). These rivers are all small, however, ~20–30 km long, and significant run-off occurs only in the flood period (July–September).

Following the development of coastal industries in this region, various pollutants have been released continuously into the bay, leading to gradual deterioration of the environment. Pollution of Jin Zhou Bay is caused mainly by industrial discharges. The major source of heavy-metal pollutants in the bay is the waste discharge from the zinc smelter on the south shore of the Wuli River estuary (Fig. 22.1).

Studies were conducted during the period 1979–1982 to document the pollution history of Jin Zhou Bay and the evolution of the environment. We wanted to determine the vertical distribution of metals in the sediments of Jin Zhou Bay in relation to the chronology of sedimentation, in order to estimate the flux of metal pollutants entering the sediments. The results should aid in understanding the levels of pollu-

tants in marine organisms and foodstuffs, and, ultimately, in understanding the effects of pollutants on marine biota.

22.2. ^{210}Pb GEOCHRONOLOGY OF JIN ZHOU BAY SEDIMENTS

22.2.1. Dating Methods

Lead-210 is a member of the ^{238}U natural radioactive series. Its precursor (^{222}Rn) enters the ocean from runoff or atmospheric precipitation, and decays to ^{210}Pb, which is adsorbed onto particulate matter and removed to the marine sediments. The activity of unsupported (or excess) ^{210}Pb decreases logarithmically with depth in the sediment, so the accumulation rate can be calculated (Joshi and Ku, 1979):

$$S = \frac{gD}{\ln (C_o/C_D)}$$

where S is the accumulation rate of sediment (mm y^{-1}), g is the decay constant of ^{210}Pb (0.031 y^{-1}), and C_o and C_D are the specific activities [disintegrations per minute (dpm) g^{-1}] of unsupported ^{210}Pb at the surface and at depth D (mm) in the sediment, respectively. Since the half-life of ^{210}Pb is 22.3 y, this technique can be used to estimate the rates of sediment accumulation over the past 100–150 y.

A gravity core sampler (10-cm inside diameter, with inner liner) (Smith and Walton, 1980) was used to collect sediment from three stations in Jin Zhou Bay (Fig. 22.1). All three cores were >60 cm long. Each core was cut into successive horizontal segments 2 cm in length, and the density and water content of the sediments were determined at 10-cm intervals in the cores. The samples were dried at 110°C to determine the water content, then heated at 400°C to burn off the organic matter. Activities of ^{210}Pb were determined by alpha counting of ^{210}Po deposited on silver discs as previously described (Smith and Walton, 1980; Wan et al., 1983).

22.2.2. Results and Discussion

Results for ^{210}Pb measurements and sediment characteristics in the core sample from station 27 (Fig. 22.1) in the inner part of the bay are listed in Table 22.1. The surface layer of this core sample was red–brown arenaceous clay, with muddy silt in gray and blue–gray colors below. At a depth of 48–50 cm, the sediment consisted of silty sand with a greenish color. The

Table 22.1. Sediment Characteristics and ²¹⁰Pb in the Sediment Core from Inner Jin Zhou Bay, China (Station 27)

Depth (cm)	Lithology	Density (g cm⁻³)	Water Content (%)	Total ²¹⁰Pb (dpm g⁻¹)
0–2	Arenaceous clay (red–brown)	1.95	49	3.71[a]
9–11	Muddy silt (blue–gray)			4.18[a]
13–15	Muddy silt (blue–gray)			3.54[a]
18–20	Muddy silt (blue–gray)	2.2	28	4.51
22–24	Muddy silt (blue–gray)			3.72
26–28	Muddy silt (blue–gray)			2.77
30–32	Muddy silt (blue–gray)			3.08
34–36	Muddy silt (blue–gray)			3.36
48–50	Silty sand (gray–green)			1.77

[a]Not included in the calculation of sedimentation rates.

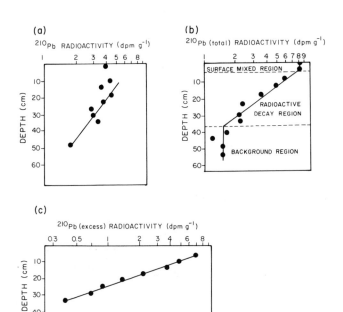

Figure 22.2. ²¹⁰Pb profiles of three stations in Jin Zhou Bay, China. (a) Excess ²¹⁰Pb in the sediment core of station 27 as a function of depth. The accumulation rate is 11.0 mm y⁻¹. (b) Total ²¹⁰Pb profile at station 17. The accumulation rate is 0.4 mm y⁻¹. (c) Excess ²¹⁰Pb in the sediment core of station 32 as a function of depth. The accumulation rate is 2.9 mm y⁻¹.

profile of ²¹⁰Pb (Fig. 22.2a) indicated that, excepting the upper layers where mixing occurred, the values of ²¹⁰Pb measurements decreased with depth over the range of 20–50 cm (correlation coefficient = −0.90). Since the accumulation rate in this area is high, no balance between ²²⁶Ra and ²¹⁰Pb was observed within the depth of this core. The estimated accumulation rate was 11 mm y⁻¹, and the sedimentary flux is calculated as 1.6 g cm⁻²y⁻¹.

Muddy silt predominated in the upper 31 cm of the core from station 17 in the central part of Jin Zhou Bay, whereas below 33 cm the core contained some shell and gritty sand (Table 22.2). Three regions were apparent in the ²¹⁰Pb profile (Fig. 22.2b). The surface mixed region, with a depth of 6 cm, was mixed by bioturbation, waves and currents. At depths between 6 and 38 cm, the activity of unsupported ²¹⁰Pb decreased logarithmically (correlation coefficient = −0.98) with depth, whereas below 38 cm, the unsupported ²¹⁰Pb had disintegrated to zero. In this background region, the radioactivity of ²¹⁰Pb is mainly due to ²²⁶Ra in the sediment and has a mean value of 1.46 dpm g⁻¹. The accumulation rate obtained through calculation is 4 mm y⁻¹, and the sediment flux is calculated as 0.56 g cm⁻²y⁻¹.

Just outside the mouth of Jin Zhou Bay (station 32; Table 22.3) the ²¹⁰Pb (excess) decreased logarithmically (correlation coefficient = −0.99) with depth (Fig. 22.2c). The calculated accumulation rate is 2.9 mm y⁻¹, and the calculated sediment flux is 0.39 g cm⁻²y⁻¹.

Two independent dating methods (x-ray study and the vertical distribution data of heavy-metal pollutants in sediment) were used to estimate accumulation rates for comparison with results of the ²¹⁰Pb-dating technique. The frozen core from station 27 was cut into vertical slabs of 2-cm thickness, and an x-ray photograph (Koide et al., 1972) was made. Between 30- and 40-cm depth, alternating light gray and deep-gray layers were evident. Figure 22.3, faded with time, illustrates these varve layers, which were very clearly visible in the radiograph in 1980 when it was made. The light-gray to white layers represent estuarine sedimentation over most months of the year, and the deep-gray layers represent the flood periods. These two layers together were assumed to represent the sedimentation of 1 y. The average annual sedimentation was estimated in this way at 9 mm y⁻¹. This result is basically in agreement with that of the ²¹⁰Pb method (11 mm y⁻¹) and that inferred from the vertical distribution of heavy-metal pollutants in the sediment (12 mm y⁻¹). Thus, we have added confidence in our values of accumulation rate obtained from the ²¹⁰Pb method.

Table 22.2. Sediment Characteristics and ^{210}Pb in the Sediment Core from Central Jin Zhou Bay, China (Station 17)

Depth (cm)	Lithology	Density (g cm^{-3})	Water Content (%)	Total ^{210}Pb (dpm g^{-1})	Excess ^{210}Pb (dpm g^{-1})
0–2	Muddy silt (gray and yellow–brown)		60	8.35	6.89
4–6	Muddy silt (blue–gray)	1.93	51	8.35	6.89
10–11	Muddy silt (blue–gray)	1.96		6.14	4.68
13–15	Muddy silt (blue–gray)		47	4.81	3.44
18–20	Muddy silt (blue–gray)	1.98	44	3.57	2.61
23–25	Muddy silt (blue–gray)		46	2.33	0.87
30–31	Muddy silt (blue–gray)	2.04	32	2.15	0.69
33–35	Shell grit (light gray)		29	2.20	0.74
40–41	Muddy grit (blue–gray)	2.05		1.64	
43–45	Muddy grit (blue–gray)			1.21	
48–50	Muddy grit (blue–gray)	2.18		1.48	
53–55	Muddy grit (blue–gray)			1.52	

Table 22.3. Sediment Characteristics and ^{210}Pb in the Sediment Core from Outside the Mouth of Jin Zhou Bay, China (Station 32)

Depth (cm)	Lithology	Density (g cm^{-3})	Water Content (%)	Total ^{210}Pb (dpm g^{-1})	Excess ^{210}Pb (dpm g^{-1})
0–2	Silty mud (gray–brown)			3.49	1.48
3–5	Silty mud (gray–brown)	1.90	50	3.68	1.68
6–8	Silty mud (gray–brown)			8.98	6.98
9–11	Gray silty mud	1.98	49	6.89	4.89
12–14	Gray silty mud			5.78	3.78
16–18	Gray silty mud			4.17	2.18
20–22	Gray silty mud		47	3.44	1.44
24–26	Gray silty mud			2.91	0.91
18–30	Gray silty mud	1.98	44	2.73	0.73
32–34	Gray silty mud			2.44	0.44
36–38	Muddy silt (dark gray)			1.98	
40–42	Gray silt	1.99	42		
48–52	Gray silt				
70–72	Gray silt				

Radiographs were not made for the cores from stations 17 and 32. Based on the general agreement between the varve thickness and ^{210}Pb results at station 27, we were confident that the ^{210}Pb method was applicable throughout the entire bay. This conclusion appears reasonable also from the sedimentology and comparative lithologies of the cores. We expected largely undisturbed cores at stations 17 and 32 because of the low wave energies predominant in the bay (mean wave height is ~0.4 m). Surge waves appear very infrequently over a short period, so the waves have little effect on station 17 (6-m water depth) and station 32 (14-m water depth). There is also little possibility of biological disturbance. Station 27 was the most polluted area, where there were no macroorganisms, while stations 17 and 32 were located in lightly polluted areas.

Burrowing organisms were few, and no burrows were found in any of the cores.

22.3. HISTORY OF HEAVY METAL POLLUTION IN JIN ZHOU BAY

After correction for weight differences due to compaction in the core, the chronology of the core was established from the sediment flux of ^{210}Pb. Combining the chronology with data on the content of metals in the sediment subsamples enabled us to calculate fluxes of Cd, Cu, Pb, and Zn to the sediments and to establish profiles for metals flux with depth (Chow et al., 1973; Goldberg et al., 1977).

Figure 22.3. X-ray photograph of a vertical section of the sediment core from station 27, showing the layering in the depth range of 30–40 cm.

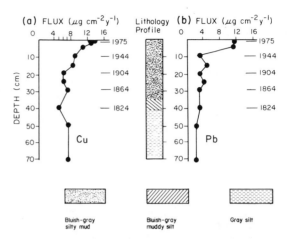

Figure 22.4. Depth profiles for the flux of (a) copper and (b) lead in the core sample from station 32, Jin Zhou Bay, China. The ^{210}Pb chronology and the lithology of the core are included for reference.

22.3.1. Analysis of Heavy-Metal Profiles and Estimation of the Pollution Period

The cores were extruded from the polyvinyl liner of the corer, and sediment samples were cut off with a piece of plexiglass for analysis of heavy metals. Cadmium, Cu, and Pb were measured by anodic stripping voltammetry, and Zn was measured by atomic absorption spectrophotometry.

Figure 22.4 shows the sediment-flux profiles for Cu and Pb in the relatively stable sedimentary area in the shallow sea just outside Jin Zhou Bay (station 32). Below a depth of ~20 cm, the flux of Cu was highly uniform at ~7 $\mu g\ cm^{-2}\ y^{-1}$. Above the 10-cm depth, the Cu flux abruptly increased upward, reaching a peak of ~14 $\mu g\ cm^{-2}\ y^{-1}$ in 1975 (Fig. 22.4a). The profile for the flux of Pb is similar, with nearly uniform values of ~4 $\mu g\ cm^{-2}\ y^{-1}$ below 10 cm, which rose

abruptly to almost 12 $\mu g\ cm^{-2}\ y^{-1}$ in the top 4 cm (Fig. 22.4). The formation year for the 10-cm layer was estimated as 1944. Since production began at the zinc plant on the southern side of the bay in 1941, the plant probably has been a major contributor of metals to the bay. There is strong justification, therefore, to regard the metal fluxes below 10 cm as natural, and those above 10 cm as anthropogenic.

Figure 22.5 shows the flux profiles for Cd, Cu, Pb, and Zn in the transitional sedimentary area in the middle of the mouth of Jin Zhou Bay (station 17). The lowest fluxes for all four metals occurred at depths of 50 cm or more. Moderate increases in flux were evident for Cd, Cu, and Pb from the 50-cm depth up to the 15-cm depth, corresponding to a period of ~1850–1942 (Fig. 22.5). Above 15 cm, concentrations of all four metals increased sharply. Three of the metals (Cu, Pb, and Zn) reached a maximum value in 1975, while Cd reached its maximum value in 1968; thereafter, all tended to decrease. The 15-cm layer in this core corresponded to 1942, again coinciding with the beginning of pollutant discharge from the zinc plant.

Figure 22.6 shows the profiles for the flux of metals at the relatively stable sedimentary area near the mouth of the river in the inner bay. Due to the high sedimentation rates at this station, the sediment depth corresponding to 1942 was at 40 cm. From 40 cm upward, the metal flux increased steadily, reaching exceptionally high values in the surface (0–5 cm) layers (Fig. 22.6). In addition to inputs from the zinc plant, one possible reason for the large increment could be that,

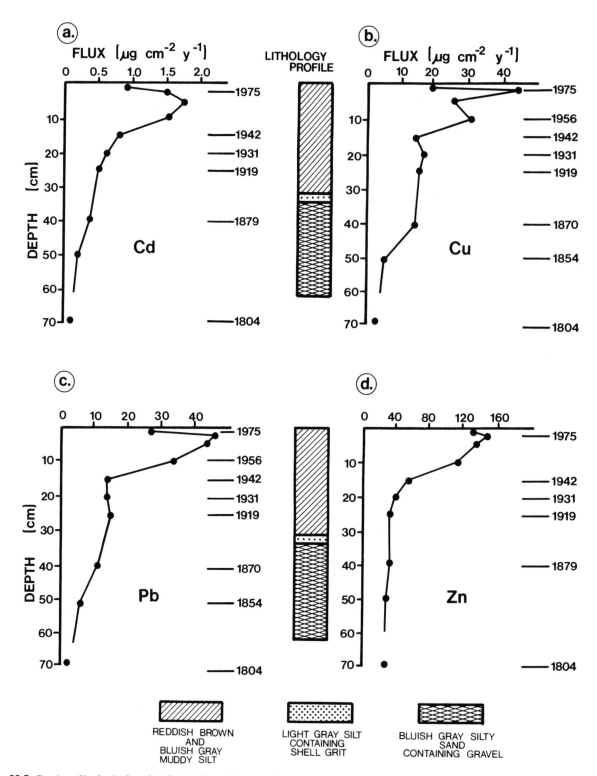

Figure 22.5. Depth profiles for the flux of (a) Cd, (b) Cu, (c) Pb, and (d) Zn in the core sample from station 17, Jin Zhou Bay, China. The ^{210}Pb chronology and the lithology of the core are included for reference.

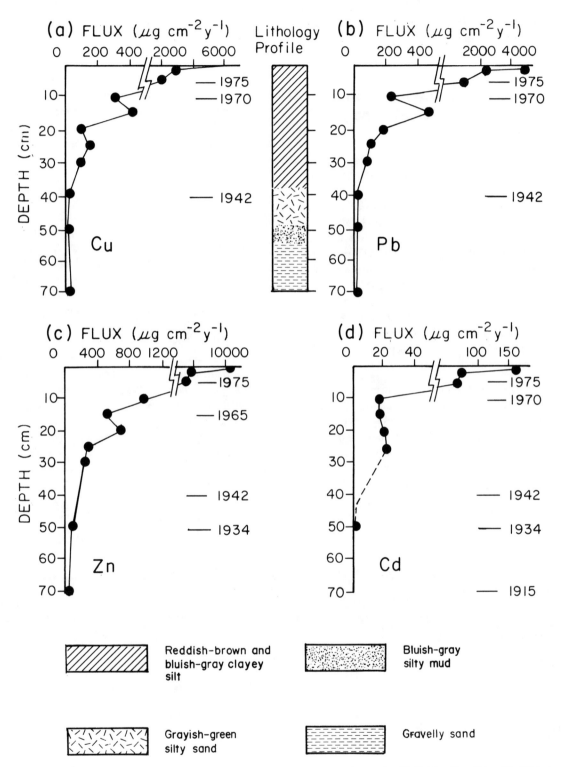

Figure 22.6. Depth profiles for the flux of (a) Cu, (b) Pb, (c) Zn, and (d) Cd in the core sample from station 27, Jin Zhou Bay, China. The ^{210}Pb chronology and the lithology of the core are included for reference.

since 1974, large mounds of dredged materials placed on the beach have been eroded into the sea.

22.3.2. Comparison of the Pollution Period (1941–1979) with the Pre-pollution Period

Prior to 1941, the metal profiles showed general features of stable and low value distribution, which indicates that the area was not significantly affected by industries before then; we refer to this as the pre-pollution period. The moderate increases observed in some profiles prior to 1940 (e.g., Figs. 22.4a and 22.5,b,c,d) could also have resulted from anthropogenic sources, but these are not well documented. For example, these changes could be related to inputs of domestic sewage or agricultural runoff from the upstream reaches of the Wuli River. During the years 1941–1979, the heavy-metal profiles showed rapidly increasing fluxes, indicating that this area was affected by industries during this period; we call this the pollution period.

The flux of metals of anthropogenic origin can be obtained by subtracting the amount supplied by nature before 1941 from the average value of metal fluxes during the pollution period. Comparison of the metal fluxes from anthropogenic and natural sources with those of other marine areas (Table 22.4) indicates that the anthropogenic metal flux is higher than natural rates by several to hundreds of times. The rates computed by Goldberg et al. (1977) for anthropogenic inputs to Narragansett Bay, Rhode Island, are intermediate between

those estimated in this chapter for stations 17 and 27 (Table 22.4).

In the northern part of Jin Zhou Bay, near the mouth of the Lao River, some 20 km from the zinc plant, the content of heavy metals in surficial sediment was low, generally corresponding to the pre-pollution levels in the southern portions of the bay. For example, the fluxes of Cu and Pb in the estuary of the Lao River were 13 and 16 $\mu g\ cm^{-2}\ y^{-1}$, respectively.

22.3.3. Effects on Benthic Macrofauna

Pollutants discharged into Jin Zhou Bay could affect benthic populations and change the ecosystem structure. Investigations of the intertidal benthic macrofauna of Jin Zhou Bay indicated that there were no intertidal macrobenthos in the mouth of the Wuli River, and there were only 8 species of intertidal macrobenthos along the whole southern coast. By contrast, the intertidal zone near the mouth of the Lao River in the northern bay had at least 20 species, including higher numbers of the crustaceans *Eriocheir sinensis* and *Helice tridens tientsinensis* and at least equal numbers of the fish *Acanthogobius hasta*. These observations suggest that the intertidal area in the mouth of the Lao River still maintains a natural ecological balance, but, in the southern areas, the structure of the ecosystem has been affected. While it is not clear that these differences are caused by heavy-metal pollution, it remains a distinct possibility, especially since concentrations of heavy metals were very high in the tissues of mollusks from the southern part of Jin Zhou Bay near the Wuli River (Table 22.5). At present many of these species

Table 22.4. Comparison of Heavy-Metal Fluxes of Sediment of Jin Zhou Bay, China, and Other Areas[a]

Metal		Jin Zhou Bay, Bohai Sea, China			Narragansett Bay U.S.A.[b]	Coastal Water, Santa Barbara U.S.A.[c]
		Station 32	Station 17	Station 27		
Cd	Anthropogenic		1.1	100	—[d]	—[d]
	Natural		0.2	3.2	—[d]	—[d]
Cu	Anthropogenic	4.7	22	3800	260	1.4
	Natural	6.7	7.6	29	3.3	2.6
Pb	Anthropogenic	6.1	31	1700	168	2.1
	Natural	2.5	5.4	22	3.0	1.0
Zn	Anthropogenic		99	6800	330	2.2
	Natural		31	22	16	9.7

[a]Units are $\mu g\ cm^{-2}y^{-1}$.
[b]From Goldberg et al. (1977).
[c]From Bruland et al. (1974).
[d]Dash indicates no data.

Table 22.5. Contents of Heavy Metals in Benthic Fauna in the Sea Area near the Mouth of the Wuli River, Jin Zhou Bay, China[a]

Metal		Oyster[b]	Clam[c]	Conch[d]
Pb	Detected range	0.98–0.05	0.58–0.02	0.36–0.10
	MPC[e]	1.5	1.5	1.5
Zn	Detected range	33.5–2.71	4.12–0.07	53.9–0.37
	MPC	40	40	40
Cd	Detected range	13.3–0.03	2.07–0.02	3.18–0.07
	MPC	0.03	0.03	0.03
Cu	Detected range	6.25–0.76	2.87–0.01	2.2–0.05
	MPC	—[f]	—	—

[a] Units are in $\mu g\ g^{-1}$.
[b] *Ostrea (Lopha) plicatula* Gmelin.
[c] *Seapharca subcrenata* (Lischke).
[d] *Neptunea cumingi* Crosse.
[e] MPC = maximum permissible concentration for foodstuffs consumed by humans.
[f] Dash indicates no MPC prescribed.

have lost their economic value because the metal concentrations exceed the maximum amount permitted under temporary standards developed by the Huanghai Institute of Fisheries, the Chinese Bureau of Fisheries, and the Academia Sinica Institute of Oceanography.

22.4. CONCLUSIONS

Sediment-accumulation rates have been measured with ^{210}Pb-dating methods for three cores from Jin Zhou Bay. The values obtained by the ^{210}Pb method were supported by observations on pollutant distributions and core stratigraphy. Fluxes of Cd, Cu, Pb, and Zn to the sediment in Jin Zhou Bay increased dramatically around 1941, coincident with the start-up of a zinc plant on the southern coast of the bay. The fluxes from anthropogenic sources after 1941 ranged up to about 100 times the natural fluxes that prevailed before then.

These fluxes peaked around 1975, when pollutant discharges were controlled, but they remained significant in 1979, which was the most recent year for which data are available. Populations of some benthic species may have disappeared in the affected area, and the amounts of heavy metals in the tissues of some remaining species were very high. Continued control of pollutant discharge should promote improvement of environmental quality in Jin Zhou Bay.

ACKNOWLEDGMENTS

The authors thank Shi Juemin and Zhang Peiran for supplying the vertical-distribution data of heavy-metal pollutants in sediment, and Jia Shulin and Wang Shufen for providing the data on heavy metals in the macrobenthos.

REFERENCES

Bruland, K. W., K. Bertine, M. Koide, and E. D. Goldberg. 1974. History of metal pollution in southern California coastal zone. *Environmental Science and Technology*, **8**, 425–432.

Chow, T. J., K. W. Bruland, K. Bertine, A. Soutar, M. Koide, and E. D. Goldberg. 1973. Lead pollution: records in southern California coastal sediments. *Science*, **181**, 551–552.

Goldberg, E. D., E. Gamble, J. J. Griffin, and M. Koide. 1977. Pollution history of Narragansett Bay as recorded in its sediments. *Estuarine and Coastal Marine Science*, **5**, 549–561.

Joshi, L. U., and T. L. Ku. 1979. Measurement of Pb-210 from a sediment core off the coast of California. *Journal of Radioanalytical Chemistry*, **52**, 329–334.

Koide, M., A. Soutar, and E. D. Goldberg. 1972. Marine geochemistry with Pb-210. *Earth Planetary Science Letter*, **14**, 442–446.

Smith, J. N., and A. Walton. 1980. Sediment accumulation rates and geochronologies measured in the Saguenay fjord using the Pb-210 dating method. *Geochimica et Cosmochimica Acta*, **44**, 225–240.

Wan, B. H., G. X. Liu, S. L. Yang, and Y. H. Zhou. 1983. ^{210}Pb geochronology method and its application in the study of the pollution history in Jin Zhou Bay, Bohai Sea. *Marine Science Bulletin* (China), **2**, 66–70.

SUBJECT INDEX

Acartia tonsa, 87
Acid-iron wastes, 80–89
Adaptation to contamination, 179–180
Adenylate energy charge (AEC), 139–140
Akita Harbour (Japan), 236–237
Aluminum (Al), 70–75, 215, 237, 239
American Smelting and Refining Company (ASARCO), 151, 158, 160, 171
Ampelisca abdita, 120–121, 137, 139, 143
Ampharete acutifrons, 173
Anoplopoma fimbria, 39
Anoxia, 91, 98–101, 171, 195, 220, 232–233, 242–243
Arctica islandica, 88
Armandia brevis, 204, 207
Arsenic (As), 24, 61, 149–150, 152, 158–161, 166, 215, 237, 239
Assimilative capacity, 3–10, 17, 92
  criteria of acceptability, 3, 6–8
  end-points, 3, 6–8
  scale problems, 8–10
  scale of effects, 6, 8–10
Atomic Absorption Spectrophotometry, 26, 69–70, 126, 213, 237
Avoidance response, to contaminants, 178
Azaarenes, 150

Bacteria, contamination of shellfish beds, 177
Bankia setacea, 205, 207
Benthos, 88, 141, 169, 171–173, 178, 193–196, 252–253
  colonization, 203–206
  community structure, 141, 171–173, 178, 197–199, 204–207
  effects of wood wastes, 193–207
  opportunism, 172–173, 185–186, 204–207
  recruitment, 194, 203–206
Benzo-a-pyrene, 163–164
  Beppu Bay (Japan), 219–233
Bioaccumulation (of contaminants)
  levels in tissue, 157–166
  tests, 125, 131–134, 139, 141–143
Bioassays
  acute toxicity, 103–112, 201
  chronic mortality, 120

sediment, 176–177
sublethal tests, 120–121
test comparisons, 109, 144
test precision, 109
Biochemical Oxygen Demand (BOD), 24, 93, 100, 170, 195, 203
Biomagnification (of contaminants), 161, 165
Birds
  contaminants in, 158–159, 162
  effects of contaminants, 175, 180
  population changes, 175
Black Rock Harbor (Connecticut), 119, 125, 138
Bohai Sea (China), 245–246
Boston Harbor (Massachusetts), 67–77
British Columbia (Canada), 193–207
Butadienes, chlorinated (CBD), 150, 153–154, 157, 163, 171

Cadmium (Cd), 23, 24, 131, 158–161
  dissolved, 70–75, 216
  in effluents, 24, 30, 61
  in organisms, 158–161, 253
  in sediments, 27, 29, 30, 131, 149–151, 159, 199, 202, 211, 215–216, 237, 239, 249–252
  in titanium dioxide waste, 81
Calcium (Ca), 215, 237, 239
California Bight, 4, 23, 34, 44, 49, 58, 177–179, 190
Cancer anthonyi, 39
Cancer gracilis, 178
Cancer irroratus, 177
Cancer magister, 178
Cancer productus, 178
Capitella capitata, 172–173, 177–180, 204–205, 207
Capitella spp., 185–190
Carbon
  dissolved organic, 93
  in sediments, 215, 223, 227–228, 237, 239
  particulate organic, 93, 96–97
  sewage loading, 99–101
Carcinogens, 166
Central Long Island Sound Disposal Site (CLIS), 118–119, 125–127
Centropages typicus, 87
Ceratium tripos, 92
Ceratium bloom, 91, 94, 100–101
Chesapeake Bay, 8, 9
Chlorinated hydrocarbons, see butadienes, DDT, polychlorinated biphenyl

Chromium (Cr), 23, 24, 131, 158–160
  in effluents, 24, 30, 61
  in industrial waste muds, 239
  in organisms, 159–160
  in sediments, 28, 30, 131, 159, 199, 202, 215, 237, 239, 241
  in titanium dioxide waste, 81
Citharichthys sordidus, 39
Clean Air Act, 4
Clean Water Act, 4–5, 7, 54
Cobalt (Co), 215, 237, 239, 242
Coliform bacteria, 43–47, 49–55
  California State Standard, 51–52
  dispersion, 43–47
  indicators of water quality, 49–55
  in effluents, 53
  monitoring, 49–55
  Most Probable Number (MPN) Index, 49, 51
Commencement Bay (Puget Sound), 157–166, 171–180
Comprehensive Environmental Response, Compensation and Liability Act (CERCLA), 4
Copepods, 87, 104–112
Copper (Cu), 23, 24, 25, 27, 131–132
  dissolved, 70–76, 216
  in effluents, 24, 30, 31
  in industrial waste muds, 239
  in organisms, 158–161, 253
  in sediments, 27–30, 76, 131–132, 149–151, 159, 199, 202, 211, 215, 219, 224–227, 235, 237, 239, 241, 249–252
  in titanium oxide waste, 81
  sources in Boston Harbor, 75–77
  toxicity, 75, 84
Coprecipitation, 220, 228–233
Cousins Inlet (British Columbia), 193, 197–199
Crassostrea gigas, 177–178
Cyanide, 61
Cyprinodon variegatus, 88, 104–112

DDD, 35
DDE, 35, 162, 167
DDT, 8, 23, 24, 33–40
  analysis, 26, 35
  effect on brown pelicans, 35
  in effluents, 24, 30, 36, 37, 40, 61
  in fishes, 36–40, 60, 62, 162–166
  in invertebrates, 38–40
  in sediments, 27, 30, 36, 60, 163
  in vertebrates, 174

Decision analysis, 11–13, 17, 118
  Alternatives, 11–13
  Environmental assessment, 3, 11–13
  Multimedia assessment, 3, 10–15, 17
  Outcomes, 10–15, 16
Deepwater Dumpsite-106 (DWD-106), 83, 92
Deepwater Industrial Waste Dumpsite, 79, 82–84
Diagenesis, 219, 231–233, 235, 238–243
Dinoflagellate blooms (see also *Ceratium*), 169, 177–178
Dispersion processes, 44–47, 68, 75–77, 85–86
Dissolved oxygen (DO), 98–99, 171, 179, 190, 193, 198, 200–201, 222, 240–242
Dokai Bay (Japan), 236–237
Dredged materials, 89, 115–145
  disposal site characterization, 118–119, 127–130
  effects, 137–144
  habitat destruction, 174
  hazard assessment, 115–145
  regulation of ocean disposal, 115–117
  upland disposal alternatives, 121–122
Dumpsites (ocean), 79, 81–84, 118–119, 236
  characterization, 118–119, 127–130
Dupont Acid Wastes Dumpsite, 79, 82–83

EC-50, 108
Elliott Bay (Puget Sound), 157–167, 171–173
Effluents, 23–24, 61
  chemical composition, 24, 36, 37, 53, 61
  industrial wastes, 23, 246
  mass emission rates (MERS), 24, 30, 36, 37, 53, 61, 68–69
  municipal wastes, 23–31, 36–38, 49–54, 68–69
  outfalls, 24, 34, 36, 44–45, 49–54, 68, 190, 199
  plume dispersion, 44–47, 68, 75–77, 85–86
  pulp-mill, 169–171, 193–208
  sewage, 23, 49–54, 68–69
Eh (Redox potential), 195, 219, 222, 240–243
Embiotoca jacksoni, 39
Engraulus mordax, 39
Eurytemora herdmani, 104, 106–109
Eutrophication, 92

Federal Insecticide, Fungicide and Rodenticide Act, 4
Field Verification Program (FVP), 118–122, 123–134, 137–144
Fin erosion in fish, 57–63, 175, 178
  prevalence, 61–62

Fish
  dietary composition, 168
  DDT, 36–40, 60, 62, 162–166
  epidermal tumors, 57–63, 88, 175
  fin erosion, 57–63, 175, 178
  gill impairment, 88
  histopathology, 173, 175–176
  kills, 92, 169–170, 177, 180, 194
  opportunism of predation, 185–190
  PCB, 37–40, 162–166
  population changes, 173–174
  prey selectivity, 188–189
  reproductive effects, 88
  toxicity of sludge, 108–112
Fisheries yields, 173–174
Flushing rate, 149, 211–212, 215–216
Food and Drug Administration (FDA)
  action levels, 166, 180

Gas-Liquid Chromatography, 26, 126
Genyonemus lineatus (white croaker), 34, 39, 164
Geochronology of contamination, 150–154, 215, 224–
    226, 248–252
Glyptocephalus zachirus (rex sole), 62, 185–190
Great Lakes (U.S.), 7, 8, 9

Haliotis cracherodii, 39
Hazard assessment, 115–145
  effects assessment, 119–120, 137–145
  exposure assessment, 119, 123–135
  monitoring, 121, 137–138
  site characterization, 118–119, 138
Hexachlorobenzene (HCB), 157, 163–167
Hinnites giganteus, 39
Histopathology, 140, 142, 173, 175–176
Hudson River, 93–94, 100–101, 162, 164
Hydrocarbons (see also Polynuclear aromatic
    hydrocarbons, PAH), 150, 152
Hydrogen sulfide, 193, 196, 207, 220, 227–229
Hydrolagus colliei, 201
Hyperion Sewage Treatment Plant, 49–55

Inductive coupled plasma spectrophotometry, 237
Industrial wastes, 79–86, 235–243, 245–246
Interstitial water, 223, 227
Iron (Fe), 70–75, 131, 199, 202, 214, 219–232, 235, 239,
    241

Jin Zhou Bay (China), 245–253

LC-50, 96-hour, 108–110, 120–121
LT-50, 201
Lead (Pb), 23, 24, 131
  dissolved, 70–75, 216
  in effluents, 24, 30, 61
  in industrial waste muds, 239
  in organisms, 158–161, 253
  in sediments, 27, 30, 131, 149–151, 159, 199, 202, 211,
      214, 237, 239, 249–252
  in titanium dioxide waste, 81
Lead-210, 211, 213–215, 221, 223, 245–247
Legislation, 4–5,
  Clean Air Act, 4
  Clean Water Act, 4–5, 7, 54
  Comprehensive Environmental Response, Compensation
      and Liability Act, 4
  Federal Insecticide, Fungicide and Rodenticide Act, 4
  London Dumping Convention, 4, 10, 194
  Marine Protection, Research, and Sanctuaries Act, 4–5,
      84, 92, 103, 115–116, 118
  National Pollutant Discharge Elimination System, 7
  Ocean Dumping Control Act (Canada), 194, 199, 203
  Resource Conservation and Recovery Act, 4–5
  Safe Drinking Water Act, 4–5
  Toxic Substance Control Act, 4
Leptocottus armatus, 178
Lipid
  basis for contaminant normalization, 161
  content in fish tissues, 161
Limanda limanda, 88
London Dumping Convention, 4, 10, 194
Los Angeles, California, 23, 34, 44, 49, 57, 164, 190
Los Angeles County Sanitation Districts, 23, 34, 44, 58
Lucinoma annulata, 220, 228

Macoma carlottensis, 178
Mammals, contaminants in, 159, 162, 174–175, 180
Magnesium (Mg), 215, 237, 239
Manganese (Mn), 70–75, 131, 199, 202, 215, 219–233,
    237, 239, 241
  chemical form in sediment, 220, 228–230, 240–242
Marine Protection, Research, and Sanctuaries Act, 4–5,
    84, 92, 103, 115–116, 118
Menidia beryllina, 104, 106, 109
Menidia menidia, 104, 106, 108
Mercury (Hg), 24, 61, 81, 149–151, 159–161, 166, 199,
    202, 211, 214–215

Metallic elements
  analysis, 26, 69–70, 212–213, 221–223, 237
  dissolved, 69–77, 149, 152, 223, 227
  flux to sediments, 252
  in effluents, 24, 30, 61
  in industrial waste muds, 238–239
  in interstitial water, 223, 227
  in invertebrates, 86, 131, 143, 158, 161, 253
  in sediments, 27–30, 74, 131, 149–152, 159–160, 211–
      212, 214–217, 219–233, 237–243, 249–252
  in suspended particulate matter, 71–75
  in titanium dioxide wastes, 81
  in vertebrates, 158–161
  in water, 69–77, 149, 152, 212–213, 215–216
  ratios in wastes, 238–240
  residence times in water, 149, 211, 216–217
  selective leaching, 221–222, 224–227, 230–231, 235,
      237–242
  sources in Boston Harbor, 75–77
  tidal effects, 70–77
Microgadus proximus, 178
Microstomus pacificus (Dover sole), 33–40, 57, 59–63,
      164, 178, 185–190
Microtox test, 104, 108
Middle Atlantic Bight, 79–84
Mizushima Harbour (Japan), 236, 240, 241
Models
  assessment, 117–118, 125
  ecosystem, 91, 93–95
  residence time, 216
  trophic, 185–186, 190
  water quality, 91–101
Molybdenum (Mo), 215, 237, 239
Monitoring, 3, 13, 15–16, 34, 121, 167, 235–236
  Compliance, 15, 51
  Design, 13, 137–138, 143–144, 167
  Hypothesis-testing, 15–16
  Objectives, 15
  Surveillance, 15
  Trend monitoring, 15, 51–55, 58–63, 167
Multimedia Environmental Assessment, 4–5, 10–15, 118,
      121–122
Mussels (*Mytilus*), 158, 160–162, 164, 167
Mysidopsis bahia, 104, 106–110, 120–121, 139, 143
Mytilus californianus, 33, 35, 37–39
Mytilus edulis, 125, 131–134, 139–144, 160–161, 164

Narragansett Bay (Rhode Island), 252
National Pollutant Discharge Elimination System, 7

Neanthes arenaceodentata, 139, 142
Neoplasia, 175–176
Nephtys incisa, 139–142
Neptunea cumingi, 253
Nereis virens, 139, 141–142
New Bedford Harbor (Massachusetts), 164
New York Bight, 4, 7, 11, 79–89, 91–101, 164, 177–178
New York Bight Acid Wastes Dumpsite, 81–83
Nickel (Ni), 23, 24, 30, 61, 70–75, 158–159, 199, 202,
      215, 237, 239–242
Nitrogen (N),
  ammonium, 24, 95, 99
  in sediments, 27, 30, 204, 206, 211, 215, 223, 227–
      228, 237, 239
  in water, 216
  nitrate, 95
  organic, 24, 25
Northumberland Channel (British Columbia), 199–203

Ocean Dumping, 79–84, 91–92, 115–122, 190, 235–236
  regulations, 4–5, 84, 103–104, 111, 115–117
Ocean Dumping Control Act (Canada), 194, 199, 203
Oil and grease, 24, 61
Opportunistic predation, 185–190
Opportunistic species, 172–173, 185–186, 196
Osaka Bay (Japan), 236, 242
Ostrea plicatula, 253
Oxygen
  consumption, 100, 195, 220
  depletion, 84, 91–93, 170–171, 179, 193, 196, 198, 207
  models, 91, 93–101

Palos Verdes Peninsula, California, 23, 24, 25, 34, 38,
      58–63, 164
Pandalus danae, 178
Panulirus interruptus, 39
Paralabrax clathratus, 39
Paralichthys dentatus (summer flounder), 164
Parophrys vetulus (English sole), 60, 158–161, 163–164,
      175–176, 178, 185–190
Perca fluviatilis, 88
Pb-210, 211, 213–215, 221, 223, 245–247
PCB, see polychlorinated biphenyl
pH effects, 84–85, 195, 198, 201, 222
Phenols, 61
Phosphorus (P), 211, 214–215, 237, 239
Phthalate esters, 162, 164
Phtoplankton, 86–87, 93–95, 97–98
Placopecten magellanicus, 86

Platichthys flesus, 88
Platichthys stellatus, 59, 178
Polychaete worms (see also *Capitella*), 198–199, 204–205
Polychlorinated biphenyl (PCB), 23, 24, 150
   Analysis, 26, 35, 126
   in birds, 162, 174
   in effluents, 24, 30, 36, 61
   in fishes, 37–40, 157, 162–167
   in invertebrates 37–40, 134, 143, 162
   in seals, 162, 174
   in sediments, 30, 36, 153, 163
   in water, 133
Polynuclear aromatic hydrocarbons (PAH), 150, 152–153
   from combustion (see also Benzo-a-pyrene), 152–153
Porphyra umbilicalis, 8
Port Valdez, Alaska, 7
Primary production, 97–100, 226
Pseudocalanus minutus, 104, 106, 108
Pseudocalanus sp., 87
Pseudopleuronectes americanus (winter flounder), 164
Public health, 166, 253
Puget Sound (Washington), 4, 149–154, 157–168, 169–183, 185–186
Pulpmill wastes, 193–208
   suspended solids content, 195

Red tide, 228
Redox potential (Eh), 195
REMOTS camera survey, 137, 139, 141–142
Residence times, 149, 211, 216–217
Resource Conservation and Recovery Act, 4–5,
Rhepoxynius abronius, 176, 178
Risk Analysis, 11, 166
   equity in, 5,
   human health, 166, 180, 253
Risk Perception, 5

Safe Drinking Water Act, 4–5
Salmo gairdneri, 201
Salvelinus namavcush, 8
Santa Barbara (California), 252
Santa Monica Bay (California), 24, 49–55
Sarde chilinesis, 39
Seattle, Washington, 151, 153, 170–172
Scope for growth, 139–142
Scorpaena guttata, 39
Sebastes dallii, 62
Sebastes paucispinis, 39

Sedimentation rates, 149, 211–214, 216–217, 219, 221, 223, 227, 232, 245–247
Sediments,
   age-dating, 211, 213–215, 221–227, 246–248
   bioassays, 176–177
   contamination history, 150–154, 215, 224–226, 248–252
   cores, 26, 150–154, 211–215, 219–233, 245–252
   diagenesis, 219, 231–232, 235, 238–243
   DDT in, 26, 30, 60, 153, 163
   metals in, 26–31, 150–152, 159, 211–216, 219–233, 235–243, 245–253
   organic content, 199, 202, 204, 206, 223, 227, 237
   particle size, 206, 220
   PCB in, 30, 153, 163
   selective chemical leaching, 219, 223–227, 230–231, 235, 237–242
   stratigraphy, 26, 27, 29, 150–154, 213–215, 223–228, 246–251
Selenium (Se), 24, 61, 215
Sellafield, England, 8
Seriphus politus, 39
Seto Inland Sea (Japan), 219–233
Sewage
   bacteriological contamination, 49–55, 177
   effect on dissolved oxygen, 93–101
   ocean dumping of sludge, 103–104, 235–236
   outfalls, 24, 34, 36, 44–45, 49–54, 68, 190
   toxicity of sludge, 103, 108–112
   treatment, 49–55, 68–69
Shannon-Weaver diversity index, 205
Shellfish, bacterial contamination, 177
Silver (Ag), 61, 149–151, 239
Sister chromatid exchange (SCE), 139–140, 142
Sludge
   industrial, 235, 238–242
   municipal, 103–112
Smelter wastes, 151, 158, 160, 171, 246, 252
Southern California Bight, 4, 23, 34, 44, 49, 58, 177–179, 190
Spectrophometry, 237
Stizostedion vitrium, 8
Stratigraphy, 26, 27, 29, 150–154, 213–215, 223–228, 246–251
Strongylocentrotus franciscanus, 39
Strontium (Sr), 215, 239
Sulfur (S), 215, 222–223, 227–233, 237, 239
Suspended Solids, 23, 24, 25, 81, 217
   emission rates, 24, 30

Suspended Solids (continued)
  residence times, 149
Tacoma, Washington, 151–152
Tagonoura Harbour (Japan), 236–237
Thalassiosira pseudonana, 86
Tin (Sn), 237, 239
Titanium (Ti), 215, 237, 239
Titanium dioxide wastes, 79–89
  composition, 81
  disposal sites, 82
  effects of disposal, 84–88
  quantities disposed, 82
Tokyo Bay (Japan), 99, 211–217, 236
Toxaphene, 8
Toxic Substance Control Act, 4
Toxicity
  of sewage sludges, 103, 108–112
  testing procedures, 105–107, 116
Tributyltin, 8
Tumors, in fish, 57–64, 175–176
  cause, 62–63, 176
  prevalence, 55–61
Turbidity, 96, 99, 190, 196

"Unreasonable Environmental Degradation", 14
Upwelling effects on dispersion, 43–48
Vanadium (V), 86, 215, 237, 239

Water Quality
  models, 91–101
  standards, 7
Windscale, 8
Wood fiber
  composition, 194–195
  degradation, 195
  ecological effects, 195–207
  particle size, 197, 206

X-Ray fluorescence, 237

Zinc (Zn), 23, 61, 81, 131, 158–160, 199, 202, 215, 245, 253
  dissolved, 70–75
  particulate, 70–75
  sediments, 131, 199, 202, 215, 219, 223–233, 237, 239–242, 248–253
Zooplankton, 87–88, 93

AUTHOR INDEX

ASTM, 107, *112**

Abel, K. H., 168*

Acton, A. B., 64*

Adams, A., 167*

Adelman, L., 13, *18**

Adler, D. M., 78*

Alexander, G. V., 160, 167

Allen, J., 144*

Allen, M. J., 186, 190, 191*

Allen, T. F. H., 9, 17*

Aller, R. C., 69, 77*

Alverson, D. L., 186, 191*

Amdurer, M., 78*

American Fisheries Society, Water Quality Section, 7, 18*

American Public Health Association, 51, 55*

American Public Health Association, 26, 32*, 51, 55*

American Society for Testing and Materials (ASTM) 104, 107, 112*

American Water Works Association, 55*

Anderson, A. R., 90*, 102*

Anderson, B.P., 40*

Anderson, D. E., 154*, 191*

Anderson, D. W., 35, 40*

Anderson, E.P., 207*

Anderson, Jr., C.O., 77*

Anderson, P. B., 34

Angell, C. L., 175

Angell, T., 180*

Anon, 92, 101*

Armstrong, J. W., 172, 173, 180*

Armstrong, P. B., 77*

Arndt, D. P., 174, 180*

Arnott, E. G., 182*

Arp, R. L., 167*

Arpke, B., 180*

Arthur, Jr., P. H., 40*

Arthur, Jr., R. H., 167*

Atkinson, D. E., 140, 144*

Ayers, J. C., 102*

Babinchak, J. A., 102*

Bagshow, J., 64*

Baird, R. B., 24, 26, 31, 32*, 41*

Bakalian, A., 14, 18*

Baker, E. T., 149, 150, 154*

Balcomb, K. C., 175, 180*

Bargmann, G. G. 173, 180*

Barnes, C. A., 154*

Barnes, C. R., 168*

Barnthouse, L. W., 19*

Barr, R. M., 208*

Barrick, R. C., 150, 153, 154*

Barvenik, F. W., 102*

Bascom, W., 170, 179, 180*

Bascom, W. J., 26, 32*

Basta, D. J., 19*

Bastian, R. K., 19*

Bates, T. S., 150, 152, 153, 154*

Bauer, R. R., 167*

Bayne, B. L., 141, 144*

Bean, D. J., 19*

Bebee, B. N., 183*

Becker, D. S., 186, 187, 190, 191*

Beckman Instrument, Inc., 107, 112*

Bedford, K. W., 126, 135*

Beezhold, F. L., 162, 168*

Behrens, W. E., 97, 101*

Bell, D. E., 13, 18*

Bell, J., 182*

Belton, T. J., 164, 167*

Bender, M., 77*

Bennett, J. T., 154*

Benninger, L. K., 77*

Berberian, G. A., 93, 99, 102*

Berman, C., 90*

Berner, R. A., 229, 232*

Berry, W., 113*

Bertine, K., 32*, 253

Beug, M., 168*

Bierman, V. J., 117, 122*

Birkholz, D. A., 182*

Biscaye, P. E., 86, 89*

Bischoff, J. G., 233*

Bisgaard, S., 191*

Bishop, D., 45, 48*

Black, D., 135*, 145*

Blasco, D., 48*

Blazevich, J. N., 167*

Bloom, N. S., 154*, 168*, 181*, 182*

Bloom, S. E., 144*

Blumfield, D. L., 32*

Boatman, C. D., 48*

Boesch, D. F., 13, 18*, 20*, 186, 191*

Bohlen, W. F., 126, 128, 130, 135*, 145*
Bohn, R., 180*
Bonatti, E., 220, 228, 229, 232*, 233*
Bonnet, J. C., 168*
Booth, G. D., 107, 112*
Borgmann, U., 77*
Borton, S. F., 191*
Bothner, M. H., 150, 154*, 158, 167*
Bowerman, B. L., 58, 64*
Bowman, K., 181*
Boyle, E. A., 74, 76, 77*
Brandt, C. C., 181*
Bratkovich, A. W., 46, 48*
Breitner, N. F., 167*
Bremner, J. M., 214, 217*
Breteler, R. T., 163, 168*
Brewer, C., 175, 181*
Brewer, P. G., 220, 233*
Brewer, S. D., 182*
Brink, K. H., 46, 48*
Broadus, J. M., 11, 19*
Brooks, N. H., 44, 48*
Brown, C. M., 208*
Brown, D., 19*
Brown, D. A., 41*
Brown, D. W., 167*, 168*, 182*
Brown, J. F., 90*
Bruland, K., 24, 32*, 69, 74, 77*, 216, 217*, 252, 253*
Brungs, W. A., 122*
Burnett, R., 34, 40*
Burrows, D. T., 167*
Cabelli, V. J., 53, 55*
Cairns, J., Jr., 118, 122*
Calabrese, A., 20*
Calambokidis, J., 159, 162, 165, 167*, 168*, 174, 175,
    178, 181*
Campana, S. E., 59, 60, 64*, 175, 181*
Canning, D. J., 175, 181*
Cannon, G. A., 154*
Cantillo, A., 101*
Capuzzo, J. M., 87, 89*
Cardwell, R. D., 176, 177, 178, 181*
Carey, A. G., 191*
Carpenter, R., 150, 151, 152, 154*, 163, 168*
Carr, M. I., 181*
Carrano, A. V., 140, 144*
Carroll, J. H., 182*
Carry, C. W., 34, 40*
Carter, S., 181*

Castle, W., 160, 168*
Chain, S. L., 168*
Chamberlain, C. E., 44, 48*
Champ, M. A., 4, 7, 11, 18*, 20*
Chan, S-L, 182*
Chapman, P. M., 173, 176, 179, 180, 181*, 182*
Chasan, D. J., 170, 181*
Chen, K. Y., 31, 32*, 76, 78*
Chervin, M. D., 102*
Chesapeake Executive Council, 8, 18*
Chesmore, A. P., 77*
Chester, R., 228, 232*
Chew, K. K., 172, 173, 180*, 183*
Cheyne, H., 171, 181*, 183*
Chow, T. J., 248, 253*
Christian, G., 168*
City of Los Angeles Bureau of Engineering, 50, 55*
City of New York, 110, 112*
Clark, R. C., Jr., 161, 162, 165, 167*
Clark, K. R., 144*
Clark, W. C., 9, 18*
Clayton, J. R., Jr., 154*, 165, 167*, 191*
Cline, J. D., 154*
Cochran, J. K., 77*
Cohn, M., 102*
Cole, F. A., 182*, 183*
Comiskey, C. A., 172, 173, 178, 180, 181*
Conley, D. J., 182*
Connolly, J. P., 93, 100, 101*
Connor, M. S., 13, 18*, 19*
Conti, M. A., 18*
Coomes, C. A., 154*
Corey, R. B., 237, 243*
Cornsby, B. W., 19*
Corwin, N., 97, 101*, 214, 218*
Couch, J. A., 57, 64*
County Sanitation Districts of Los Angeles County
    (CSDLAC) 58, 64*
Cox, J. M., 154*
Cranston, R. E., 233*
Crecelius, E. A., 149, 150, 151, 152, 154, 154*, 155*,
    168*, 170, 181*, 182*
Crill, P. M., 76, 77*
Cross, F. A., 13, 18*, 20*
Cross, J. N., 59, 60, 62, 64*
Cross, S. F., 207*
Csanady, G. T., 9, 18*
Cubbage, J., 181*
Cubbage, J. C., 167*

Cummins, J. M., 158, 167*
Cunningham, R., 177, 181*, 183*
Curl, H. C., Jr., 150, 152, 154*
Dames and Moore, 170, 172, 174, 175, 181*
Danielsson, L. G., 69, 77*
Davis, G. E., 141, 145*
Dawe, C. J., 63, 64*
Dawson, P., 181*
Day, D. S., 186, 191*
DeBen, W. A., 183*
DeLong, R. L., 34, 40*, 181*
Deacutis, C., 113*
Dethlefsen, V. 57, 63, 64*, 88, 89*
Devine, M., 92, 102*
Deweese, L. R., 40*
Dewling, R. T., 6, 7, 19*
Dexter, R. N., 150, 152, 154*, 181*, 182*, 186*, 191*
DiDonato, G., 173, 182*
DiToro, T. M., 93, 100, 101*
Dickson, K. L., 122*
Dillard, L., 182*
Ditsworth, G. R., 182*
Drager, B., 168*
Draxler, A., 102*
Drum, A. S., 168*
Dryden, F. D., 32*
Duce, R. A., 78*
Dudek, N., 78*
Dudley, S., 102*
Duedall, I. W., 19*
Dufour, A. P., 55*
Dugdale, R. C., 48*
Duke, T. W., 34, 40*
Dulmage, R., 78*
Duxbury, A. S., 18*
EG&G, 85, 89*
Eason, J. E., 23, 32*
Ebbesmeyer, C. C., 48*, 149, 154*, 182*
Edberg, N., 195, 207*
Edde, H., 195, 207*
Edgecomb, W. G., 40*
Edwards, C. J., 7, 19*
Eganhouse, R. P., 31, 32*
Elderfield, H., 76, 77*
Eldridge, E. F., 171, 181*
Elliott, D. G., 168*, 182*
Emerson, S., 220, 233*
Emery, K. O., 31, 32*
Engel, D. W., 84, 89*

Epstein, S. S., 140, 144*
Erdheim, E., 4, 14, 18*
Erickson, G. A., 181*, 182*
Eriksen, A., 183*
Esaias, W. E., 102*
Eustace, I. J., 160, 167*
Evans, C. E., 102*
Everitt, R. D., 181*
Fairbridge, R. W., 68, 77*
Fairbrother, A., 191*
Falke, E., 144*
Falkowski, P. G., 92, 100, 101*, 102*
Farmer, T. A., 181*
Farrell, M. A., 181*
Fava, J. A., 18*
Felton, J. S., 182*
Filip, S., 167*
Fink, R., 176, 181*
Finney, D. J., 107, 112*
Fischnaller, S., 48*
Fisher, D. E., 232*
Fisher, D. L., 167*
Fitzgerald, M. G., 68, 69, 74, 77*
Fitzner, R. E., 168*, 182*
Flegal, A. R., 167*
Fleischner, T., 181*
Folk, R. L., 187, 191*
Foncannon, P. R., 168*
Ford, W. L., 85, 89*
Forrester, C. R., 64*
Förstner, U., 151, 154*
Foster, R., 171, 181*
Fournier, J. A., 198, 199, 207*
Fowler, B. A., 89*
Franks, R. P., 74, 77*
Freeman A. M., III, 19*
Fresh, K. L., 182*
Friedman, A. J., 167*
Fujiyoshi, R., 228, 233*, 237, 244*
Fukasa, S., 218*
Fuller, R. H., 81, 89*
Furlong, E. T., 150, 151, 154*
Fye, P. M., 19*
GESAMP, 6, 10, 12, 18*
Gabriel, W. L., 187, 190, 191*
Gad, M. A., 229, 233*
Gahler, A. R., 158, 159, 160, 161, 162, 163, 164, 165, 166, 167*
Galloway, J. N., 24, 32*

Galt, J. A., 102*
Galvin, D. H., 160, 162, 164, 167*
Gamble, E., 253*
Gangmark, C. E., 167*
Gard, K. L., 32*, 41*
Gardner, R. H., 19*
Garrett, T. L., 4, 18*
Garside, C., 93, 95, 99, 101*, 102*
Gaudette, H. E., 77*
Gehrs, C. W., 19*
Gentile, J. H., 105, 112*, 122*, 139, 141, 143, 144*
Gentile, S. M., 112*
Gerlach, S. A., 187, 191*
Germano, J. D., 141, 142, 145*
Gift, J. J., 11, 13, 18*
Gilmartin, W. G., 40*
Glock, J., 180*
Glover, R. M., 182*
Goldberg, E. D., 6, 7, 8, 18*, 19*, 32*, 92, 101, 101*, 161, 167*, 248, 252, 253*
Goldstein, L. S., 154*, 191*
Goodman, L. R., 113*
Goodwin, M., 41*
Gorsline, D. S., 45, 48*
Gossett, L. R., 41*
Gossett, R. W., 38, 40*, 41*, 164, 167*
Graham, D. W., 78*
Grassle, J. F., 179, 181*, 186, 191*
Grassle, J. P., 179, 181*, 186, 191*
Great Lakes Water Quality Board, 9, 18*
Greenberg, A. E., 113*
Greig, R. A., 160, 166, 167*
Grice, G. D., 87, 89*, 90*
Griffin, J. J., 253*
Griggs, D. T., 191*
Grill, E. V., 220, 233*
Gronlund, W. D., 168*, 176, 181*, 182*
Gschwend, P. M., 152, 154*
Guard, H. E., 181*
Guillard, R. R., 105,, 113*
Guin, M. P., 191*
Gulbransen, T. C., 19*
Gunn, T., 155*, 168
Gurtisen, J. M., 154*, 168*, 182*
Gutjahr-Gobell, R., 135*, 144*
Hagerman, F. B., 59, 64*, 189, 191*
Halcrow, W., 160, 167*
Hamilton, P., 155*, 168*
Hamilton, S. E., 154*

Hammond, K. R., 13, 18*
Han, G., 94, 97, 98, 101*
Hancock, D., 190, 191*
Hansen, B. E., 32*
Hansen, D. J., 105, 113*
Hansen, D. L., 182*
Hansen, D. V., 101*
Hanson, A. K., Jr., 74, 77*
Harper-Owes, 162, 167*, 174, 176, 178, 181*
Harris, L., 36, 41*
Harris, W. H., 85, 86, 89*
Hart, J. L., 186, 191*
Harwell, C. C., 7, 18*
Hasebe, K., 218*
Hashizume, G., 237, 244*
Hattori, A., 102*, 215, 216, 217*
Haugen, E. M., 90*
Hauschildt-Lillge, D., 179, 181*
Haux, C., 90*
Haydock, C. I., 32*
Hayes, T. D., 31, 32*
Hedges, J. I., 154*
Heesen, T. C., 32*, 34, 35, 38, 41*, 64*, 168*
Heggie, D. T., 78*
Helseth, J. M., 154*
Heltshe, J., 135*, 145*
Heltshe, J. F., 112*
Hendricks, T. J., 28, 31, 32*
Herlinveaux, R. H., 194, 207*
Herman, S., 168*
Herman, S. G., 181*
Hershelman, G. P., 24, 32*, 64*
Heyward, A. A., 183*
Hieronymus, R., 180*
Hildebrand, S. G., 19*
Hinchey, L. R., 154*
Hines, M. E., 76, 77*
Hinsdill, R., 191*
Hirao, Y., 212, 214, 215, 217*
Hirsch, K. V., 183*
Hites, R. A., 152, 154*
Hittinger, R. C., 89*
Hoagland, E., 89*, 90*
Hodge, V., 167*
Hodgins, H. O., 167*, 168*, 182*
Hodson, P. V., 75, 76, 77*
Hoffman, G., 112*, 135*, 145*
Hoffman, G. L., 78*, 135*, 144*
Hofsten, B. V., 195, 207*

Hogue, E. W., 191*
Holling, C. S., 9, 12, 13, 15, 18*
Holman, N., 194, 201, 208*
Hom, W., 155*, 168*
Hood, D. W., 15, 18*
Hopkins, T. S., 101*, 102*
Hoshika, A., 220, 227, 228, 229, 233*
Hotchkiss, D. A., 41*
Houck, D. R., 167*
Houghton, J. P., 172, 183*
Hourston, A. S., 194, 207*
Howard, R. A., 11, 12, 13, 14, 15, 18*, 19*
Howe, S. O., 92, 93, 101*, 102*
Howells, H., 8, 18*
Hu, T. C. L., 35, 41*
Huested, S., 74, 77*
Hughes, C. F., 90*, 102*
Hughes, J. B., 178, 182*
Hughes, M. J., 228, 233*
Hullberg, L. W., 190, 191*
Hunt, C. D., 76, 77*
Huntamer, D., 168*
Hunter, W. G., 191*
Hurlburt, E., 180*
Huyer, A., 44, 46, 48*
Inouchi, Y., 220, 233*
International Joint Commission, Canada and the United
        States, 7, 8, 18*
International Maritime Organization (IMO), 4, 10, 18*
Iseki, K., 194, 207*
Iverson, R. L., 102*
Ivlev, V. S., 186, 191*
Jackson, A. L., 166, 167*
Jackson, M. I., 237, 243*
Jackson, M. L., 222, 233*
Jaeger, J., 191*
Jahnke, R. A., 154*
Jan, T. K., 32*, 41*, 64*
Japanese Standards Association, 237, 243*, 244*
Jehl, Jr., J. R., 40*
Jennings, C. D., 20*
Jeris, J. S., 90*, 102*
Jerome, W. C., Jr., 75, 77*
Jessup, P. S., 19*
Joensun, O., 232*
Johns, D. M., 134, 135*, 138, 139, 140, 142, 143, 144*
Johnson, A., 159, 163, 164, 167*, 180*
Jones, B. H., 44, 45, 48*
Jones, G. E., 77*

Jones, K. R., 182*
Jones, S. P., 77*
Joshi, L. U., 246, 253*
Kadeg, R. D., 7, 18*
Kalil, E. K., 32*
Kamlet, K. S., 19*
Kaplan, I. R., 24, 31, 32*
Kapp, R. H., 88, 89*
Kasper, R. G., 19*
Kathman, R. D., 181*, 203, 204, 207*
Kato, E., 218*
Katz, A., 24, 32*
Katz, C. H., 145*
Katz, M., 172, 183*
Kawana, K., 233*
Keeney, R. L., 11, 13, 14, 18*, 19*
Kelley, J. C., 48*
Kester, D. R., 84, 85, 89*, 102*
Ketchum, B. H., 68, 77*, 82, 89*, 92, 102*
Kettenring, K. N., 24, 32*
Kildow, J. T., 10, 19*
Kimball, K. D., 4, *19*
Kimura, D. K., 173, 181*
Kishino, M., 212, 216, 217, 218*
Kitano, Y., 220, 221, 222, 228, 229, 233*, 237, 243*
Kitsos, T. R., 10, 19*
Kjerfve, B., 9, 10, 20*
Klemas, V., 85, 90*
Kleppel, G. S. 190, 191*
Klinkhammer, G. P., 76, 78*
Knauer, G. A., 77*
Knudsen, E., 168*
Kocan, R. M., 154*, 177, 181*, 191*
Koh, R. C. Y., 44, 48*
Koide, M., 32*, 167*, 247; 253*
Koike, I., 217*
Konasewich, D. E., 182*
Konishi, S., 217*
Kowalski, B. R., 182*
Kram, D., 144*
Kranz, H., 64*
Kravitz, M. J., 189, 190, 191*
Krejci-Graf, K., 228, 233*
Kremer, J. G., 32*
Kristmanson, D. D., 208*
Kruger, D. M., 179, 181*
Ku, T. L., 246, 253*
Kuhn, M., 113*
Lahey, W. L., 7. 14, 19*

Lake, J., 129, 131, 133, 135*, 139, 141, 142, 144*
Lamberson, J. O., 183*
Lancaster, B. A., 87, 89*
Landolt, M., 154*, 191*
Landolt, M. L., 177, 181*
Larsson, A., 88, 90*
Latt, S. A., 140, 144*
Laughlin, R. B., Jr., 179, 181*
Lazoff, S., 183*
LeBlanc, P. J., 166, 167*
LeRiche, H. H., 229, 233*
Lear, D. W., 83, 90*
Lee, J. F., 20*
Lehtinen, K.-J., 88, 90*
Lehtonen, H., 88, 90*
Leon, H., 172, 182*
Leschine, T. M., 11, 13, 19*
Lesniak, J. H., 167*
Levin, M. A., 55*
Levin, S. A., 4, 19*
Levings, C. D., 194, 198, 199, 207*
Levy, D. A., 196, 208*
Li, Y. H., 220, 228, 229, 233*
Lindl, P. A., 144*
Liss, P. S., 233*
Litchfield, C. D., 20*, 102*
Liu, G. X., 253*
Livingston, R. J., 20*
Lockwood, K., 167*
Long, E. R., 173, 175, 176, 181*, 182*
Longwell, A. C., 88, 90*, 178, 182*
Loring, D. H., 221, 228, 233*
Lu, J. C. S., 31, 32*, 76, 78*
Luedtke, N., 77*
Lussier, S., 113*, 144*
Luthy, Jr., R. F., 32*
Lynn, D. C., 229, 233*
Lyons, W. B., 77*
MacGregor, J. S., 29, 32*
MacLeod, W. D., Jr., 164, 167*
Macdonald, R. W., 207*
Mackay, D. W., 167*
Madrid, A., 182*
Magnusson, B., 70, 77*, 78*
Mahoney, J. B., 102*
Mahoney, O., 78*
Maki, A. W., 122*
Malins, D. C., 157, 158, 159, 162, 164, 165, 167*, 168*, 170, 173, 174, 175, 176, 178, 182*

Malone, T. C., 92, 93, 94, 95, 96, 97, 98, 99, 100, 101*, 102*
Manheim, F. T., 220, 233*
Mann, D. C., 168*
Manning, D. C., 70, 78*
Manual, D. A., 183*
Marcy, M., 113*
Mardesich, J., 32*
Maritime Safety Agency Research Center, 237, 244*
Markert, J. R., 208*
Martens, C. S., 76, 77*
Martin, J. H., 77*, 167*
Martin, M., 160, 168*
Massoth, G., 154*
Masuzawa, T., 220, 221, 228, 229, 232, 233*
Mathematical Sciences Northwest, 173, 182*
Matheson, J. E., 11, 12, 15, 18*, 19*
Mathieu, G., 233*
Matsude, R., 182*
Matsumoto, E., 212, 214, 215, 218*, 221, 229, 233*
Matsunaga, K., 214, 216, 218*
Matte, A., 102*
Matthews, W. H., 5, 19*
Mattson, J. S., 19*
Mayer, B., 180*
Mayer, G. F., 92, 102*, 177, 178, 182*
McCabe, L. J., 55*
McCaffrey, R. J., 77*
McCain, B., 181*
McCain, B. B., 158, 162, 167*, 168*, 176, 182*, 191*
McCall, P. L., 191*
McDaniel, N. G., 194, 196, 208*
McDermott, D. J., 32*, 34, 41*
McDermott-Ehrlich, D., 41*, 63, 64*, 164, 168*
McGreer, E. R., 199, 201, 202, 208*
McGregor, J. S., 34, 41*
McIntyre, A. D., 7, 19*
McKeague, J. A., 204, 208*
McKee, J. E., 6, 19*
McNulty, J. K., 88, 90*
McRoy, C. P., 102*
Mearns, A. J., 19*, 24, 32*, 36, 40, 41*, 57, 63, 64*
Meikle, J. H., 208*
Melby, C. L., 182*
Menzel, D. W., 213, 218*
Merkhofer, M. W., 11
Meyer, J. H., 174, 182*
Meyers, M. S., 168*
Michael, A. D., 20*

Middaugh, D. P. 105, 113*
Miille, M. J., 41*
Miller, B. S., 180*, 186*, 191*
Miller, C., 183*
Miller, D. C., 90*, 104, 107, 113*, 122*
Millikan, A. R., 173, 181*
Mills, A. D., 183*
Mills, E. L., 186, 191*
Minkler, H. L., 144*
Mitchell, D., 181*
Mitchell, R., 44, 48*
Miyadi, D., 220, 233*
Möller, H., 57, 64*
Monk, D. C., 179, 182*
Montagne, D. E., 32*
Moore, D. G., 31, 32*
Moore, N. S., 168*
Morel, F. M. M., 24, 32*
Morgan, J., 181*
Morgan, J. J., 32*
Morgan, M. G., 16, 19*
Morse, M. N., 144*
Morton, R. W., 145*
Moshiri, M., 23, 29, 32*
Mowrer, J., 162, 168*
Mueller, C., 135*, 145*
Mueller, J. A., 83, 90*, 93, 94, 102*
Muench, R. D., 155*, 168*
Muir, W. C., 82, 90*
Muir, W. R., 19*
Mukherji, P., 89*
Munday, D. R., 181*
Munger, S. G., 183*
Munson, T., 41*
Murchelano, R. A., 57, 64*
Murdoch, W. M., 186, 191*
Murphy, J., 237, 243*
Murphy, L. S., 87, 90*
Murray, J., 168*
Murray, J. P., 19*
Murray, J. W., 76, 78*
Musgrove, N., 168*
Myers, E. P., 24, 32*
Myers, M., 181*
Myers, M. S., 182*, 168*
Myers, W., 175, 181*
Nairston, Jr., N., 112*
Nakatani, R. E., 182*

National Advisory Committee on Oceans and
    Atmospheres (NACOA), 4, 5, 19*, 54, 55*
Neff, J. M., 7, 19*, 163, 168*
Nelson, B., 163, 167*
Nelson, W. G., 134, 135*, 139, 141, 142, 145*
Nevissi, A., 150, 155*, 168*
New York City Department of Environmental Protection,
    11, 19*
Newendorp, P. D., 12, 19*
Nichols, F. H., 173, 182*
Nilsson, N. A., 186, 191*
Nishimura, M., 218*
Nissenbaum, A., 229, 233*
Nitkowski, M., 102*
Nolen, K., 191*
North, D. W., 11, 19*
Northcote, T. G., 208*
Norton, D., 167*
Norton, M. G., 19*
Nybakken, J. W., 191*
O'Connell, G. W., 207*
O'Connell, R. T., 58, 64*
O'Connor, J. M., 20*
O'Connor, J. S., 6, 7, 10, 12, 13, 15, 16, 19*, 20*
O'Connor, T. P., 9, 19*, 81, 82, 83, 87, 88, 90*
O'Malley, L. O., 168*
O'Malley, M. L., 90*
O'Melia, C. R., 32*
O'Neill, R. V., 11, 13, 19*
O'Reilly, J. E., 102*
Officer, C. B., 93, 102*
Ohita Fishery Research Laboratory, 220, 228, 229, 233*
Ohtsu, M., 217*
Oliver, J. S., 186, 190, 191*
Olsen, C. R., 86, 89*
Olsen, S., 168*
Olsen, S. J., 158, 168*
Olson, L. J., 191*
Orem, W. H., 77*
Orlob, G. T., 171, 181*
Pacific Northwest Pollution Control Council, 194, 208*
Palsson, W. A., 168*, 182*
Paquette, G. D., 145*
Park, P. K., 18*, 83, 90*, 102*
Parkes, R. J., 208*
Parrish, P. R., 113*
Parrish, R., 41*
Patterson, C. C., 216, 218*

Patton, J. S., 57, 64*
Paul, J. F., 122*
Paus, P. E., 220, 221, 228, 233*
Pavlou, S., 168*
Pavlou, S. P., 18*, 150, 154*, 155*, 167*, 191*
Pearce, J. B., 7, 19*, 84, 90*, 167*
Pearcy, W. G., 186, 187, 190, 191*
Peard, J. J., 181*
Peard, T., 167*
Pearre, S., 187, 191*
Pearson, T. H., 186, 191*, 196, 208*
Pease, B. C., 194, 208*
Pedersen, M. G., 173, 182*
Pence, G., 90*
Pesch, C. E., 135*, 145*
Pesch, G. G., 86, 90*, 134, 135*, 139, 140, 145*
Peterle, T. J., 179, 183*
Peters, N., 63, 64*
Peterson, D. R., 182*
Peterson, M. L., 154*
Petrie, L., 194, 201, 208*
Phelps, D. K., 135*, 143, 145*
Phillips, J. K., 183*
Philpot, W. D., 85, 90*
Phoel, W. C., 102*
Pickaver, A. H., 81, 84, 90*
Pierce, K. V., 191*
Pierson, K. B., 176, 182*
Pilson, M., 20*
Pine, R. E., 183*
Piper, D. Z., 158, 167*, 168*
Plugge, H., 18*
Poole, N. J., 194, 195, 208*
Poore, C. M., 64*
Pope, S. V. W., 167*
Port of Seattle, 172, 182*
Porter, W. P., 190, 191*
Poston, T. M., 7, 19*
Prahl, F. G., 163, 168*
Prohammer, L. A., 7, 19*
Prohaska, P. G., 167*
Pruter, A. T., 191*
Psuty, N. P., 88, 90*
Puffer, H. W., 40*, 167*
Pulak, R., 182*
Quinlan, E. A., 154*, 170, 171, 176, 178, 181*, 182*, 191*
Quinn, J. G., 74, 77*
Quinn, R. J., 11, 13, 19*

Raiffa, H., 11, 13, 14, 18*, 19*
Ramdahl, T., 165, 168*
Ramos, L. S., 167*
Rand, A. S., 186, 191*
Rand, M. C., 107, 113*
Rasmussen, L. F., 158, 168*
Redfield, A. C., 92, 102*
Redmond, M., 144*, 145*
Redner, J. A., 34, 40*
Reynolds, B., 90*, 145*
Rhoads, D. C., 141, 142, 145*, 168, 186, 191*
Rhodes, L. D., 168*, 182*
Rice, T. R., 8, 20*
Rieck, R. H., 167*
Riley, G. A., 127, 135*
Riley, J. P., 237, 244*
Riley, R. G., 154*, 158, 162, 163, 168, 175, 178, 181*, 182*
Risebrough, R. W., 34, 40, 41*
Robbins, J. A., 182*
Roberts, R. W., 150, 154*
Robertson W., IV, 19*
Robertson, A., 19*
Robertson, C. N., 102*
Roels, O. A., 101*
Roesijadi, G., 161, 168*
Rogerson, P., 90*
Rogerson, P. F., 125, 126, 131, 133, 135*, 139, 141, 143, 145*
Rohatgi, N., 31, 32*
Romberg, G. P., 149, 150, 151, 152, 153, 155*, 164, 166, 167*, 168*
Roney, J., 191*
Ronholt, L. L., 191*
Rose, C. D., 84, 87, 90*
Rosenberg, R., 186, 191*, 196, 208*
Ross, B. D., 182*
Roubal, W. T., 168*
Rowe, G. T., 90*, 102*
Rubin, B. L., 18*
Ruckelshaus, W. D., 7, 19*
Rue, W. J., 18*
Ruppel, B. E., 167*
Rydell, H. R., 232*
Ryder, R. A., 7, 19*
Ryther, J. H., 93, 102*, 105, 113*
Sakamoto, M., 215, 217*
Sakata, M., 233*
Salo, E. O., 182*

Samolloff, M. R., 177, 182*
Sample, T., 182*
Sanborn, E. W., 181*
Sanders, H. L., 141, 145*
Santschi, P. H., 76, 78*
Saunders, S., 177, 182*
Sawlan, J. J., 76, 78*
Sawyer, T. K., 177, 182*
Scanlon, J. A., 19*
Schafer, H. A., 32*, 61, 62, 64*
Schauer, P. S., 135*, 144*, 145*
Schaule, B. K., 216, 218*
Schell, W. R., 150, 155*, 158, 161, 168*
Schelske, C. L., 179, 182*
Schimmel, S. C., 109, 113*, 135*, 144*, 145*
Schmidt, W., 64*
Schmidt, W. B., 167*
Schneider, E., 144*
Schneider, E. D., 19*
Schoener, A., 18*
Schreck, R., 144*
Schroeder, R. A., 168*
Schuett-Hames, J., 181*
Schultz, D. W., 183*
Scott, J. T., 102*
Scott, K. J., 141, 144*, 145*
Segar, D. A., 18*, 19*, 93, 99, 102*
Seki, H., 102*
Sercu, K. A., 183*
Shea, G. B., 181*
Shear, H., 77*
Shelpuk, C., 167*
Sherwood, M. J., 40, 41*, 57, 63, 64*, 158, 162, 168*
Shiozawa, T., 220, 227, 228, 229, 233*
Shokes, R., 168*
Shokes, R. F., 155*, 168*
Shorfstein, B. F., 101*
Shuba, P. J., 176, 182*
Sick, L., 20*
Sidwell, V. D., 161, 168*
Silver, T. A., 182*
Simenstad, C. A., 170, 174, 182*
Simpson, J. G., 40*
Simpson, K. W., 168*
Sindermann, C. J., 57, 63, 64*, 92, 102*
Singer, R. E., 48*
Skei, J., 220, 221, 228, 233*
Skidmore, J., 181*
Slattery, P. N., 191*

Slavin, W., 70, 78*
Sloan, R. T., 162, 168*
Smith, D. L., 76, 77*
Smith, J. N., 246, 253*
Smokler, P. E., 24, 32*, 38, 41*
Smyth, M. E. B., 191*
Somayajulu, L. K., 154*
Sonzogni, W. C., 19*
Soutar, A., 253*
Sparks, A. K., 167*, 168*, 182*
Speich, S. M., 183*
Spencer, D. W., 220, 233*
Spencer, M. J., 77*
Spetzler, C., 12, *19*
Spies, R. B., 179, 182*
Spitzer, P. R., 7, 19*
Spyradakis, D., 168*, 183*
Stäel von Holstein, C. A. S., 12, 19*
Stamman, E., 18*
Stanley, S. O., 195, 208*
Starr, T. B., 9, 17*
State of California Department of Public Health, 50, 51, 55*
Stebbing, A. R. D., 179, 182*
Steiger, G. H., 167*, 181*
Steimle, F. W., 88, 90*, 102*
Stelle, Jr., W. W., 19*
Stepien, J. P., 102*
Stevens, B., 180*
Stevenson, R. E., 45, 48*
Steward, L. L., 145*
Stich, H., 64*
Stich, H. F., 57, 60, 64*
Stober, Q. J., 48*
Stoddard, A., 92, 93, 100, 102*
Stoermer, E. F., 182*
Storme, S. E., 18*
Stout, V. F., 162, 168*
Strickland, R. M., 154*, 177, 178, 183*, 191*
Stuart, D. W., 48*
Stubbs, H., 32*
Stull, J. K., 24, 26, 29, 31, 32*, 60
Suess, E., 228, 233*
Sunda, W. G., 89*
Suter, G. W., 19*
Sverdrup, H. V., 44, 48*
Swaine, D. J., 229, 233*
Swanson, R. L., 92, 102*, 128, 135*
Swartz, R C., 176, 183*

Sweeney, R. E., 24, 32*
Takimura, O., 233*
Takita, T., 105, 113*
Tamai, K., 220, 228, 233*
Tanaka, H., 237, 244*
Tanimoto, T., 233*
Taras, M. J., 113*
Tatum, H. E., 182*
Taylor, B., 181*
Taylor, P. A., 41*
Terry, R. D., 31, 32*
Tetra Tech, 160, 163, 164, 165, 168*, 176, 183, 186, 191*
Tettleback, S., 180*
Theis, T. L., 31, 32*
Thom, R. M., 172, 173, 180, 183*
Thomas, B. L., 154*, 168*, 181*, 182*
Thomas, J. P., 97, 98, 100, 102*
Thomas, N. A., 7, 8, 19*
Thompson, I., 88, 90*
Thompson, L. H., 144*
Thompson, W. R., 107, 113*
Thornton, I., 167*
Tice, R., 144*
Togashi, S., 212, 214, 217*
Tomlinson, R. D., 172, 173, 183*
Townsend, L. D., 171, 183*
Truesdale, V. W., 77*
Tsuji, T., 99, 102*
Tsujioku, H., 217*
U. S. Army Corps of Engineers, 175, 183*
U. S. Code, 4, 19*
U. S. Congress, 4, 14, *19*, 54, *55**, 116, 118, *122**
U. S. Court of Appeals, 92, 102*
U. S. District Court, 14, 19*, 54, 55*
U. S. Environmental Protection Agency (EPA), 7, 13*,
    19*, 26, 31, 32*, 81, 82, 83, 84, 85, 86, 88, 90*,
    92, 101, 102*, 104, 107, 113*, 116, 122*, 150, 166,
    168*
U. S. Environmental Protection Agency-U.S. Army Corps
    of Engineers, 116, 122*
U. S. Food and Drug Administration (FDA), 35, 38, 41*,
    161, 168*
U. S. Geological Survey, 127, 135*
U. S. National Academy of Sciences (NAS), 6, 11, 20*,
    34, 41*
U. S. National Oceanic and Atmospheric Administration,
    83, 90*
United Nations Environment Programme (UNEP), 170,
    183*

Unoki, S., 212, 216, 217, 218*
Vaccaro, R. F., 84, 85, 87, 88, 90*
Vaga, R. M., 19*
Valizahed-Alavi, H., 135*
Van Evra, R. E., 135*
Van Leer, J. C., 48*
Vance, I., 195, 208*
Vangilder, L. D., 179, 183*
Varanasi, U., 168*, 182*
Verber, J. L., 177, 183*
Vigers, G. A., 181*
Vinelli, J., 155*, 168*
Vogel, D. A., 174, 182*
Wahl, T. R., 175, 183*
Waldhauer, R., 102*
Waldichuk, M., 170, 183*, 196, 197, 199, 200, 207*,
    208*
Walford, L. A., 92, 102*
Wallace, G. T., 70, 78*
Walsh, J. J., 93, 94, 99, 100, 101*, 102*
Walton, A., 204, 208*, 246, 253*
Wan, B. H., 246, 253*
Ward, J. H., 205, 208*
Warren, C. E., 141, 145*
Waschitz, M., 85, 86, 89*
Washington Department of Ecology, 158
Washington State Department of Ecology (WDOE) 171,
    183*
Wate, S. O., 19*
Water Pollution Control Federation, 55*
Watermann, B., 63, 64*, 88, 89*
Waterstrat, P., 180*
Wattace, G. T., 69
Weaver, G., 164, 168*
Webber, H. H., 172, 183*
Webster, G. R. B., 182*
Weitkamp, D. E., 172, 183*
Wellings, J. R, 180*
Wenzloff, D. R., 167*
Werner, A. E., 196, 197, 208*
Westall, J. C., 32*
Westerlund, S., 70, 77*, 78*
White, H. H., 7, 20*
White, I. C., 88, 90*
White, R. J., 69, 74, 76, 78*
Whitfield, B., 144*
Whitledge, T. E., 45, 48*, 102*
Whitney, R. R., 183*
Widdows, J., 7, 20*

Wiebe, P. H., 87, 89*, 90*
Wildish, D. J., 208*
Williams, D. C., 158, 168*
Wilson, A. J., Jr., 34, 40*
Wilson, K. W., 88, 90*
Winant, C. D., 46, 48*
Wingert, R. C., 186, 191*
Winnick, K. B., 128, 130, 135*
Wirick, C. D., 102*
Wittmann, T. W., 151, 154*
Woelke, C. E., 181*
Wolf, H. W., 6, 19*
Wolfe, D. A., 6, 7, 8, 9, 10, 12, 13, 14, 15, 16, 19*, 20*
Wolff, S., 144*
Wong, C. S., 207*, 220, 233*
Woods, Jr., L. A., 40*
Word, J. Q., 24, 32*, 35, 41*, 47, 48, 191*
Yake, W., 167*
Yang, S. L., 253*

Yearsley, J. R., 167*
Yevich, C. A., 145*
Yevich, P. P., 139, 140, 142, 145*
Yingst, J. Y., 191*
Yokota, S., 229, 233*
Young, D. A., 167*
Young, D. K., 141, 145*
Young, D. R., 24, 29, 32*, 34, 35, 38, 40*, 41*, 60, 64*, 160, 167*, 168*
Young, J. S., 168*
Yuill, T., 191*
Zafiropoulos, D., 168*
Zaret, T. M., 186, 191*
Zaroogian, G. E., 134, 135*, 140, 142, 145*
Zeh, J. E., 172, 176, 183*
Zhou, Y. H., 253*
Ziebell, C. D., 176, 183*
Ziskowski, J., 57, 64*
von Bock, K., 97, 101*